AN ITALIAN SCANDAL

An Italian Scandal

CECIL CAMERON

Harper
North

HarperNorth
111 Piccadilly,
Manchester, M1 2HY

A division of
HarperCollins*Publishers*
1 London Bridge Street
London SE1 9GF

www.harpercollins.co.uk

HarperCollins*Publishers*
1st Floor, Watermarque Building, Ringsend Road
Dublin 4, Ireland

First published by HarperNorth in 2021

1 3 5 7 9 10 8 6 4 2

A catalogue record for this book
is available from the British Library

ISBN: 978-0-00-849399-8

Printed and bound in the UK using 100%
renewable electricity at CPI Group (UK) Ltd

MIX
Paper from
responsible sources
FSC FSC™ C007454
www.fsc.org

This book is produced from independently certified FSC™ paper
to ensure responsible forest management.

For more information visit: www.harpercollins.co.uk/green

GARIBALDI'S HYMN

Come join them. Come follow, o youth of our land!
Come fling out our banner, and marshal our band!
Come with cold steel, come with hot fire,
Come with the flame of Italia's desire
Begone from Italia, begone from us now!
Stranger begone, for this is our hour!

HISTORICAL NOTE

Before 1860, the Italian Peninsula was made up of separate states. Apart from the liberal kingdom of Piedmont, the Austrians occupied the north and the Spanish Bourbon king, Francis, ruled the kingdom of Naples and the Two Sicilies in the south. A campaign to liberate and unify Italy had been underway for decades, including the ill-fated revolution in Sicily of 1848. In May 1860, the scene was set for General Garibaldi, with his famous Redshirts, to sail from Genoa to Sicily and join the Sicilian patriots in a final attempt to free the nation from foreign occupation and oppression.

In Britain, Queen Victoria and her German consort, Prince Albert, reigned over a prosperous nation. The Industrial Revolution was at its height, creating wealth for a few and mass migration to the cities for many others. Society was divided between the very poor, the aristocracy and a new middle class who followed a strict code of etiquette and propriety.

PROLOGUE

PALERMO, SICILY 1849

'Sirocco! The sirocco is coming!'

The words spread through the streets and everywhere there was activity. Men scurried to and fro, clearing pavements and packing up goods on the open stalls. Boats in the harbour were secured and the great doors of the cathedral shut and bolted. By the time the sun reached its peak, the busy squares and boulevards of Palermo were deserted and the ancient capital still as a doomed city awaiting its fate.

The Devil's Wind, they called it, and it brought with it madness and despair. Moaning and whistling against shuttered windows, the sirocco rampaged in fury. Tiles were torn off roofs and rubbish tossed in the air. Barrels and crates were sent crashing against walls or spinning into the sea. Children cried while the old took to their beds and waited for the *tempesta* to pass.

Late in the afternoon, the sound of hooves on the cobbles brought a woman to her window. She made the sign against evil as a lone horseman passed below. Only the Devil would be abroad at such a time and the rider looked like Satan himself

1

going at such a pace. He was bent over the saddle, hat pulled down low, as he galloped down the narrow streets. On he went, past the naked statues of the Fountain of Shame until he reached the old quarter of the city where the alleys were narrow and steep. Flecks of lather flew from his horse's neck but he spurred it on until he came to a palace high above the city.

The horseman pulled up beside a barred gate. He dismounted and threw his hat and cloak across the saddle. Then he put his foot on the bar and hauled himself up. There was a gap at the top and he squeezed through, dropping down on the other side. For a moment he stood, his gaze scanning the front of the house. Then he began to walk. Every few paces he glanced up to the balustrade running along the floor above until he found what he was looking for. A window, left unlocked by a careless servant, had blown open, its lace curtain billowing in the wind. The interloper climbed branches of a wisteria, vaulted over the balustrade and slipped into the house.

Taking the scarf from his neck, he wiped the dust from his mouth. Hazy light caught his reflection in an old glass, revealing a face that was lean and hard. There was a deadly purpose in the blue eyes that looked back at him. He waited, listening intently. The only sound was the banging and rattling of shutters, and rugs on the floor muffled his footsteps as he walked to the door.

Prince Riccardo Scalia was dozing on his bed. He sensed, rather than heard, the turning of the door handle. Instinct, born of years of conspiracy, jolted him awake. Before the door was open, he was on his feet with a dagger in his hand. Seeing the tall man silhouetted in the entrance, his eyes narrowed. The raw look of vengeance was written on the intruder's face. How long could he hold him at bay? How long before someone heard them and sent for the guards?

'Ben Mavrone! My doormen have instructions not to allow revolutionaries into the house.'

'Your servants are asleep and I didn't wake them. We shall be left undisturbed.'

'May I enquire as to the nature of your visit?'

'You know why I'm here.'

'I know you were involved in the revolution. There remains a warrant for your arrest. However, I recall you ran off to Ireland or some such place to escape.'

'Yet you tried to capture me. You tried everything from spies to hired assassins. When you failed, you took my brother instead. You didn't care that he was innocent. You used him as bait to get me back to Sicily.'

As he spoke, Mavrone's hand moved to the hilt of his knife. He held it against the light, running his finger along the blade. Every move was calculated in the war of nerves between the two men. Prince Scalia placed his feet squarely apart. Mavrone was younger, but he was the one with the cooler head. He only had to reach his loaded pistol in the drawer.

'Come now! Your brother was tried and found guilty of treason. He would have been shot if King Ferdinand, in his mercy, hadn't spared his life. His death in prison was an accident. Although, had you returned earlier, I dare say it might have been prevented.'

Scalia accurately anticipated his opponent's reaction. As Mavrone sprang forward, he stepped aside so the strike glanced off his shoulder. Both knives were up. Scalia had the advantage with the light behind him. With one arm bent to shield his face, he began to edge sideways. Mavrone followed, step by step, as they circled the floor. As they neared the corner of the room, Scalia began to gain confidence. The drawer was half open – no more than an arm's length away. Then Mavrone made his move.

He was playing with him like a cat with a mouse and black fury rose in Prince Scalia. He hurled himself at Mavrone with his blade aimed for the heart. He expected the knife to penetrate flesh, but the weapon was sent spinning out of his hand. Mavrone hit him, whipping the side of his knife against his head and Scalia's knees gave way. He staggered and fell against a heavy screen, knocking it over and taking both men to the ground. Mavrone's weight came down on him, straddling his chest with his knife pressed hard under Scalia's chin.

'My God! What are you doing?' A woman's cry rang out.

Bianca! Prince Scalia had thought his wife was sleeping in her own rooms. She must have been woken by the noise. He prayed she was an angel signalling his reprieve, but Mavrone did not move.

'Leave us, Bianca,' he said, tersely.

'For mercy's sake, have you lost your senses?' Bianca was tugging at Mavrone's shoulder.

'Leave us, unless you want to see your husband killed before your eyes.'

'Why, in the name of heaven? What has he done?'

'Alex is dead. He was murdered in prison.'

Prince Scalia winced as the blade broke the surface of his skin. Blood trickled from his chin and he looked at Bianca. Why hadn't she the sense to call the guards? Why didn't she scream instead of standing there as if turned to stone? The stupid bitch! Couldn't she see there was no mercy in Ben Mavrone?

'I don't believe you! Riccardo told me his sentence had been reduced.'

'I assure you there is no mistake. I saw his body for myself. He was killed the day I returned to Sicily.'

'Dear God have mercy …'

Prince Scalia's gaze fixed on his wife's face and her voice was a whisper. 'Is it true?'

He gritted his teeth as Mavrone grabbed his hair and forced his head back.

'Tell her the truth,' Mavrone said.

'It's true.' A dry croak came from his lips. 'He was executed … on my orders.'

Bianca fell to her knees and caught hold of Mavrone's arm. For the first time he turned to look at her.

'Spare him, Benito. They will only kill you as well.'

'They've never succeeded before.'

'But this would be murder! Without a trial, it's a crime as evil as his. Don't you see?' Her fingers clutched frantically at his sleeve. 'Is this what Alex died for? Don't condemn your soul to eternal damnation. I beg you, if you still have any love for me.'

She was weeping and Scalia held his breath. Mavrone would never commit murder in front of Bianca! He thought he was saved until he saw Mavrone push her aside. In that instant, Riccardo Scalia knew the terror of death.

Mavrone hesitated no longer. He lifted his knife and cut the prince down one cheek and then the other. Blood spurted out, streaming down his neck and staining his shirt scarlet. Scalia screamed, clutching his face. His cries echoed around the room, diminishing along with his strength, until finally there was silence. Mavrone bent down and picked up a piece of torn tapestry. He cleaned the blood off his knife and dropped the fragment beside Scalia's unconscious body. Bianca buried her face in her hands as he touched her hair.

'I spared him for your sake, Bianca. I'll take this as a memento of your devotion.'

For a moment, he held her hair like a lover. Then he sliced off a curl and crushed it in the palm of his hand. When Bianca raised her head, Ben Mavrone was walking away. He did not look back. The door closed behind him and the wailing wind deadened his footsteps as he left the apartments of Prince Scalia as stealthily as he had come in.

CHAPTER ONE

LONDON, DECEMBER 1859

It was different now. Different from how it had been this morning when Oliver Temple's note arrived on her breakfast tray. The stiff white envelope was propped against the teapot with her name, Miss Carina Temple, scrawled in her uncle's hand. Carina waited until she was up and dressed before she opened the letter. There was no 'be so kind' or 'at your convenience', only a single line summoning her to attend upon him at three o'clock of the afternoon.

All the way there, Carina promised herself she would be civil. Her uncle, Oliver, was also her guardian with total control over her finances. Their dislike for each other was mutual, but on no account must she lose her temper. Oliver's brusque note had nothing to do with the other matter, she was sure.

The carriage turned the corner of Hyde Park and a recent conversation flooded her mind.

'What possible harm is there? Lord Danby's lonely with his wife tied up at Court,' Carina had argued with her aunt, Alice. 'We keep each other company, that's all. There's no impropriety in our friendship.'

'It is nothing to the purpose. Lord Danby is a married man.'

'He has always behaved impeccably.'

'That's not the point! My brother, Oliver, will come to hear of it and I will be held responsible. If you refuse to consider your own reputation, please have some consideration for mine!'

Alice had ended the conversation by getting up and going over to the piano. She was upset and played too fast, Carina recalled with a pang of guilt. She was happier when Aunt Alice was content, but she had continued to meet with Danby. Why shouldn't she? Her long period of mourning was finally at an end and she was starved of life. It was unnatural to be shut up, entombed in black crêpe and seeing no one. The gloomy ritual imposed by society couldn't bring back her father and, when it was over, Robert Danby had been the first person to take an interest in her. He was self-assured and worldly and she enjoyed his company – at least, that was so, until last week.

The weather had turned cold and Lord Danby escorted her to the picture gallery at Stafford House. He was knowledgeable, pointing out the best paintings and greeting various acquaintances with a nod of the head, not stopping to speak to them. Then, as they walked out of the front door, he slipped his arm around her waist and pulled her to him. Right there in the middle of St James's Street! Carina freed herself and glared at him.

'I'm only helping you down the steps, Miss Temple. We don't want you to slip and twist your pretty ankle, now do we?'

How easily he laughed it off, but Carina was appalled. Just imagine if anyone had seen them! It only took one person and rumour would spread like wildfire. They would be talked about in every salon and ballroom of London. Robert Danby had overstepped the mark, but he wouldn't be blamed. Oh no, the man was never guilty. His misdemeanour would be shrugged off and her character vilified.

She mustn't fear the worst, Carina decided as they arrived at the mansion in Belgrave Square. A footman ushered her into her uncle's study and Oliver Temple did not stand up. He sat behind his desk, indicating the chair opposite with a wave of his hand. Before Carina had time to arrange her skirts, he began.

'You know why I've sent for you?'

'I expect you wish to talk about my overdraft.'

'No, Carina, not this time. You're here to explain your conduct over these last weeks.'

Carina looked her uncle straight in the face. Oliver was a stocky man and had put on weight since she last saw him. Ginger side-whiskers could not hide the folds of his chin and his cheeks were as red as the claret he had consumed over lunch.

'I refer to your acquaintance with Lord Danby. What do you have to say for yourself?'

'Nothing. It is entirely my own affair.'

'There, you're mistaken.' Oliver leant forward and placed his hands on the desk. 'I had words with Lord Danby in White's club last night.'

He was bluffing, Carina thought. He must be! Robert Danby despised her uncle. He would go out of his way to avoid him. Her heart beat faster and Oliver continued.

'Rumour has it that you are intent on breaking up his marriage.'

'I'm surprised you take notice of such gossip.' Carina made an attempt to sound indifferent. 'Lord Danby is merely an acquaintance.'

'Merely an acquaintance? His wife is lady-in-waiting to Her Majesty, does that mean nothing to you?'

'As I've not been presented to the queen, I've not the slightest interest in either her or her courtiers.'

She had struck home, Carina saw by the way Oliver's mouth thinned and he shifted uncomfortably in his chair. Her uncle had no intention of arranging her presentation at Court. He was determined to keep that privilege for his own children.

Oliver picked a letter from his tray and read it through before he placed it face down on the blotter.

'Has Lord Danby been invited to your home?'

'No, he has not.'

'But you accompanied him to Lord Stafford's house last week, contrary to my sister Alice's prohibition?'

'Alice did not prohibit me. She knew nothing of it—'

'So you deceived your aunt in order to have an assignation with a married man?'

He gave her a hard stare, but Carina had herself in hand. She sat straight, a sea of blue velvet skirts around her, and kept her face blank. So they *had* been seen! And whoever recognised them, had gone straight to Oliver. *But why*, Carina wondered? She had no enemies as far as she knew. Who could have informed on her? Certainly not Alice or her friend, Harry Carstairs. They were the two people she trusted most in the world. It was possible Oliver might have had her followed. She wouldn't put anything past him and now he was speaking again.

'You're a great disappointment to me, Carina. Since your father's demise I've done everything in my power to take care of you. How do you repay me? By dragging the family's name through the mud!'

Carina's expression did not change, but her lips went white. She couldn't bear Oliver talking about her father. You pompous little man, she thought. Papa was worth a hundred of you. You're only my guardian because he died unexpectedly – not because he respected you. Hot words bubbled up and she forced them down for Alice's sake. Putting her hands on the arms of her chair, she made as if to rise.

'I will not remain here and be insulted, sir! Please would you order my carriage?'

'You will stay until I've finished and pay attention to what I have to say! News of your liaison with Danby is bandied about by every gossipmonger in London. So much so, I felt obliged to ask His Lordship if there was any truth in the allegations.'

He was trying to catch her out, Carina thought. She didn't believe him but a knot tightened in her stomach.

'Lord Danby claims you threw yourself at him and have pursued him relentlessly. He went so far as to describe you as an unscrupulous hussy. What he meant by *that*, I dread to imagine.'

Oliver was poisonous as a snake and hot colour washed Carina's cheeks. It was a preposterous allegation. How dare Danby say such a thing when she had ignored his overtures in the beginning and only accepted an invitation for luncheon when his wife was present? Admittedly, it had gone on from there but they both knew the rules. She had broken with Lord Danby immediately after the incident at Stafford House. Since then, his letters had been returned and his calling cards ignored. But none of this was Oliver's business. Let him think what he liked. She was under no obligation to justify herself.

'Well, do you deny it?'

Carina fixed her gaze at a point over Oliver's shoulder, looking at a landscape of cows in a field on the wall behind him.

'For shame, Carina! You're a disrespectful young woman!'

Oliver pushed back his chair and stood up. Walking over to the window, he opened the latch and let a stream of cold air into the room. Carina infuriated him and he blamed his brother for her unruly nature. Why John had married a foreigner in the first place, he didn't know. When Sonia died in childbirth, he had failed to find himself a suitable second English wife to discipline his only child. John may have taught Carina to ride and shoot as well as a man, but she had her way for the asking. As a consequence, she was as wild and wilful as the wind.

This was the age of the self-made man and Oliver Temple was not about to give way to a girl of eighteen. Unlike his older brother, he was the one who had worked, overseeing the cotton mills that provided prosperity for the Temple family. Apart from Melton, the family home, everything he owned had been gained by his own endeavour. Last year he had received a knighthood from the queen and was proud of his success. If Carina thought she could jeopardise all he had achieved on a whim, she was mistaken.

Oliver closed the window and gave himself a moment to study his niece. Carina was striking with her sloping eyes, so like her father's and sea green as a Russian cat. Her mouth was delicately curved and her copper hair pinned high above her collar to show off her slender neck. She was slim like her Sicilian mother, a small waist accentuated by the tight-fitting jacket. He could understand why a man like Danby might be attracted to her. On the surface, Carina appeared delicate as a spring flower, but he had seen the fire in her eyes moments before. Tempestuous blood ran in her veins and this time she had gone too far.

Carina wondered what Oliver was thinking. The muscles of her face were stiff from keeping still and she lowered her eyes as he returned to his chair.

'I've decided you're to go to Sicily until this unfortunate business has blown over.'

Carina's head came up, her chin lifting. For a brief moment the only sound in the room was the ticking of a clock. Then, hardly trusting herself to speak, she asked him to repeat what he had said.

'I dispatched a letter to your grandmother this morning, informing her you will arrive in Palermo early in the New Year.' Oliver paused, his voice dropping reverentially. 'Her Majesty is most concerned for Lady Danby's welfare and I'm charged with resolving the matter. A sojourn in Sicily is the obvious solution.'

'Damn the bloody queen and damn you, Oliver Temple! You've no right to order my life!'

As the words came out of her mouth, Carina leapt to her feet. In response, Oliver slammed his fist down on the desk.

'You'll not speak of our beloved sovereign with such disrespect! You're a spoiled and ungrateful child. I can think of nowhere to suit you better than a barbaric island like Sicily!'

'I'm not going to be sent away!'

'Then I shall cut your allowance with immediate effect.' Oliver collected himself swiftly. 'Not only will you be penniless but homeless as well.'

As if he expected her to jump across the desk and attack him, Oliver reached for the hand bell and rang it loudly. The door opened and the footman marched in carrying her cloak. Her uncle had manipulated the interview from the beginning, Carina thought, and the man had probably been standing by the door throughout.

'Your Aunt Alice will travel out with you as your chaperone.' Oliver stood up. 'Your passage is booked for the first week of January. That's all I have to say to you.'

Carina snatched her cloak from the footman and slung it over her arm. Without another word, she marched out of the room, her footsteps clattering on the marble stairway as she went down. She heard the footman hurrying after her, but did not stop. The front door was open and she ran through the hall and down the steps to where the brougham was waiting.

The lamplighters were already at work and, once inside, Carina took off her bonnet and threw it on to the seat. She wrapped her cloak tightly about her. Her heart was beating so hard in her chest it hurt. Oliver was a liar. Care for her indeed! When her father died, he couldn't wait to get his hands on Melton, the home where she had lived all her life. The house in Mount Street had been acquired with undue haste and she and Alice packed off to London within a month of her father's accident. For that alone she would never forgive him.

Tears pricked the back of her eyes and Carina squeezed them shut. She hadn't cried since leaving Melton and she would not now. Anger drove out pain and she flexed her fingers until the joints cracked. The conversation with Oliver had been a charade! He knew the dalliance with Danby wasn't serious – only a diversion to pass the time, easily begun and as easily ended. Her uncle had been looking for an excuse to send her away and Lord Danby had handed him one on a plate.

Carina was seized suddenly by panic. What was she going to say to Alice? It was all a pack of lies, but her aunt would be mortified. Fresh anger struck her. Robert Danby had behaved despicably and Oliver was ruthless – but they wouldn't get away with this! 'I won't let them bully me,' she swore under her breath. 'I'll think of a way to stop them before I talk to Alice.'

CHAPTER TWO

Carina entered the house quietly and crept past the drawing room where Alice was playing the piano. Her maid, Rose, was waiting in the bedroom and she undressed and climbed into the bathtub. She lay soaking in the warm water and by the time she returned to the bedroom it was six o'clock. Without much interest, she picked out a gown of blue crêpe and stood while Rose fixed the lacing on her corset. Then she went to sit at the dressing table.

Rose brushed her hair with long, smooth strokes as thoughts went tearing round her head. Oliver had said Alice was to travel with her as chaperone and Carina was swept by resentment on her aunt's behalf. Why should poor Alice have to journey half-way across the continent at his behest? What did Oliver think would happen to her if the house were closed?

'Your aunt's given up so much to care for you. She's still a young woman. I hope she finds happiness for herself one day.'

Carina recalled the words of her friend, Harry Carstairs. For sure he was referring to Sir Anthony Farne, a widower from Northumberland. He had become a frequent visitor to Mount

Street and, for the first time in her life, Alice was in love. Harry's understanding of human nature was uncluttered by experience, but, for once, Carina agreed with him. If their courtship foundered, then she would be to blame.

How had it all gone so wrong? She should have listened to Alice, but it was too late now. She had to think herself out of this mess and an idea took shape in her mind. She would ask Harry to speak to Robert Danby. They belonged to the same club and he might be able to extract an apology. Oliver wouldn't be able to send her away then. What was it Danby had called her? An unscrupulous hussy? Carina shook her head hopelessly. Lord Danby's priority was to save his own skin and he would never back down.

Two oval miniatures stood on the table and Carina picked up the one of her father and held it to her lips. It brought back to her the grief she suffered when he died. She had wanted to run with the pain and coped in the only way she knew how. She was young, her spirit of survival strong, and she had pursued everything and anything that filled the void inside. Living on the bright edge of life, nothing mattered so much that it could hurt her again – and this was the result.

Carina put the miniature down and studied the portrait of her mother. Sonia Temple had the expression of a woman who knew her own mind. How would she advise her daughter, she wondered? Would her mother tell her to submit to Oliver?

You will go to Sicily. The knowledge came to Carina with an absolute certainty she had experienced before. For as long as she could remember, she had been susceptible to a sixth sense – a voice in her head telling her what would happen. Her premonitions were rarely wrong and she drew a surprised breath.

'Are you feeling unwell, ma'am?'

'I'm fine, thank you.' Carina saw Rose's worried face in the glass and forced a smile. 'I will write my journal and ring when I'm ready.'

Rose left the room and Carina pressed her hands to her cheeks. It was so unfair, but life was unfair and self-pity never helped anyone. Alice had been both sister and mother to her. She was the most important person in her life and, if the outcome of this afternoon couldn't be undone, then she must come first.

So, why not go to Sicily? Her grandmother – the Contessa Denuzio – was eighty and a visit long overdue. Once Carina was safely in Palermo, Alice could return to England while she stayed on under the contessa's protection. There was one condition. She would let it be known this was her decision and had nothing to do with Lord Danby or Oliver Temple. A winter in the Mediterranean was hardly a life sentence, after all. Hadn't Byron and Shelley taken refuge in warmer, friendlier climes when society turned against them?

Lord knew, she was weary of London. Hot houses smelled sweet, but they suffocated you if you stayed in them too long. Alice was her closest companion and Carina had few girlfriends. Young women of her age were mostly concerned with the pursuit of a wealthy husband while her ambition was to be a poet. She read every piece of verse she could lay her hands on and knew most of the Romantics by heart. Carina wasn't sure that she was any good, but Alice had always encouraged her.

There was time before dinner and she went over to the bureau and took a small bound volume from the drawer. She held it under her nose, smelling the soft leather, before she began to turn the pages. Along with a first edition of Byron's *Childe Harold*, her journal was her most treasured possession. Quotations were interspersed with scatterings of verse and she skipped to the first blank page. Picking up a pen, she stroked the feathered end against her cheek. Then she dipped the nib in the inkwell and began to write.

If I am to trace the footsteps of my hero on his Pilgrimage—

Here, she broke off and neatly scored through the line. She thought for a moment and then wrote beneath:

Remember thee, remember thee!
When exiled far in Sicily,
O false uncle, doubt thee not
A fiend like thee is best forgot!

Her mood brightened for the first time that day. Writing stilled the clamour in her head and she felt calmer. She blew on the ink and closed the journal, returning it to the drawer before she rang the bell for Rose. It was time to finish dressing and go down for dinner.

CHAPTER THREE

She was going to be late, Carina thought as she hurried downstairs the next morning. Harry Carstairs had sent a note saying he would call at noon and she dozed off after breakfast so they had to rush. Rose was flustered and kept dropping hairpins. Then Carina couldn't decide what to wear. She dithered, picking one outfit after another and finally settled on a tarlatan promenade dress. Its hem was high enough to show off her new Moroccan boots and the crinoline so wide her skirts brushed both sides of the staircase as she went down.

The tall-case clock in the hall was chiming twelve as she walked into the morning room and went to stand by the fire. She loved this room with its red wallpaper and brocade curtains. She would miss it while she was away, she thought. She would miss Alice and Harry too and she wondered how she could have been so confident the night before.

Sir Anthony Farne was just leaving when she went down and, once he had gone, she told Alice about the meeting with Oliver.

'Oh dear, oh dear!' Her aunt's hands fluttered like two white birds in her lap. 'I'll call on him first thing tomorrow and persuade him to change his mind.'

'It won't do any good. You know Oliver! He would hang rather than incur Her Majesty's displeasure.'

'I can but try—'

'Please don't! I've quite made up my mind to go.'

Sitting across the hearth, Carina was sharper than she intended. Alice was twelve years older than her and as refined as her brother was coarse. She looked pretty in a plush velvet dress with a wide collar that complemented her china-blue eyes. Her auburn hair was pinned under a trimmed tulle cap and, for all her concern, there was colour in her cheeks. Carina felt comforted in her presence. She hadn't meant to snap at her.

'I'm sorry you're obliged to travel with me. I promise to make sure you return to England just as soon as I'm settled.'

'Hush now, dearest. I'm delighted to accompany you. I was very fond of your mother. It will be good to see something of her home.' Alice smiled and smoothed the scalloped trim of her cuffs. 'By chance, Anthony and I were talking about Sicily earlier. He reminded me that Miss Parsons is cousin to the British Consul in Palermo and intends to visit him in January. Do you think we might travel out with her?'

Recalling the small, energetic spinster who was Alice's friend, Carina's heart sank. There was nothing to dislike about Miss Parsons except that she talked a good deal and mostly about politics. Last month she persuaded them to spend a whole morning in a draughty hall in Kensington, tasked with sorting clothes for veterans of the Crimea. Carina had longed to be out riding in Rotten Row. The smell of camphor clung to her for days afterwards and when Harry suggested she continue the good work, she told him smartly he could go in her place.

There was a knock at the door and Thomas, the footman, showed Harry into the room. Carina held her hands out to the blond young man who came towards her.

'Harry, what a pleasure.'

Carina led Harry to the sofa and patted the seat next to her. She studied him as he sat down, noting the smart cut of his coat and buff trousers. Every detail of his dress, from his embroidered waistcoat to the ruby solitaire nestling in the folds of his cravat, was up to the mark. Harry had become quite the man about town and was good-looking with his thick moustache and hazel eyes. Although he denied it, she knew of several young ladies in London who were in love with him.

'As well as can be expected under the circumstances.' Harry rubbed his hands on his knees. 'It's all over London this morning, you know.'

'What's all over London, the Great Stink of last summer?'

'Don't be frivolous, Carrie. It ain't one of your railway novels. This is real life, where actions have consequences.'

Real life? Oh yes, she knew what that meant for women – staying at home with a brood of children while your husband was free as air. Well, it wasn't the life she wanted. She had tried to explain this to Harry so often. Why couldn't he understand? He was forever pulling her up and Carina hoped he hadn't come to give her a lecture for she wasn't sure she had the patience to endure it.

'How many times did I tell you Lord Danby was untrustworthy?' Harry asked.

'So many that I don't recall a time when we spoke of anything else. You said I would lose my reputation and now I have. Are you satisfied?'

'Of course I'm not satisfied! I bumped into Sir Oliver in White's last night and he told me he'd spoken to you. Is it true that you're banished to Sicily?'

Carina stood up and walked to the centre of the room. Picking up a newspaper, she opened it to hide her face. The idea of Harry talking to Oliver behind her back made her furious. He professed himself her champion but, when it came to it, members of the gentlemen's clubs of St James's stuck together like clams. And to think she had almost asked him to appeal to Robert Danby!

A stinging retort was on her lips, but Carina caught herself. There had been too many arguments lately and, afraid of saying something she might regret, she skimmed through the paper instead. A leading article caught her eye. She glanced over it and then read aloud: 'Our correspondent writes from Sicily that revolution is in the air and Palermo is a hotbed of intrigue and conspiracy.'

Carina lowered the broadsheet and looked across the room at Harry. 'Do you hear that? Palermo sounds almost as bad as London.'

Before she had finished, Harry rose to his feet and walked over to the hearth. His brow was furrowed and his shoulders hunched. There was a bruised look in his eyes and Carina's irritation left her.

'I'm only teasing, Harry! I don't mean it.'

'Don't you? Difficult to know what you mean these days. You're like a stranger most of the time.'

'I should have taken your advice and I'm sorry I did not. Now, please will you stop being cross?'

Carina went to stand beside Harry as he flicked through the invitation cards stacked on the mantelpiece. She had said she was sorry. What more did he want? Harry was still frowning and when he took the fob watch from his waistcoat and snapped it open, she laid a hand on his arm.

'I've finished with Robert Danby. It's over and done with.'

'But the scandal's not over. It's the talk of the town.'

'Next week someone else will behave outrageously. Then you'll talk about them instead.'

Harry covered her hand with his. He was beginning to weaken, Carina thought, but his grip tightened.

'It's no good, Carrie. Can you imagine, my father's forbidden me to call on you? I shouldn't be here now, in truth.'

The Carstairs had been her family's closest neighbours in Yorkshire and Carina was shocked. Mr Carstairs had been her father's best man. How could he take Robert Danby's side against her? The betrayal cut deep and she withdrew her hand as Harry ploughed on.

'Too many people heard Danby talking to your uncle. You can't imagine some of the things he said. They were beyond the pale—'

'Are you here to tell me you're no longer my friend?' Carina cut in.

'Of course I'm your friend.'

'Then you should trust me! I never encouraged Lord Danby. He lied to my uncle—'

'So why are you being sent away?'

Oliver had been at work and the damage was done. What a time they must have had of it, Carina thought – all those so-called gentlemen listening to the salacious gossip! She waited until coolness came back and then lifted her shoulders in a dismissive shrug.

'You can tell your friends that the trip to Palermo is entirely my own idea. I've always wanted to visit my mother's family.'

'But you don't know your maternal relations!' Harry stated as if it was good reason never to do so. 'Sicily's a wild and unciv-ilised place. I don't like the sound of it. Don't like it at all.'

'My grandmother's lived in Palermo all her life. It's not the least uncivilised …' Carina trailed off, uncertain of what Harry was thinking. He ran his hand through his hair and there was a taut look on his face.

'Listen to me, Carrie. It's crucial that you regain your good name. You must promise me your conduct will be irreproachable while you're away!'

'I thought you said my reputation was damaged beyond repair—'

'People will forget once you've gone. If you behave impeccably, Sir Oliver will relent. Then I'll be damned if I don't come to Sicily and fetch you home myself!'

Harry's tone was vibrant, his expression so full of hope that goose bumps pricked the back of Carina's neck. She enjoyed other men's admiration, but Harry was her oldest friend. He had switched from disapproval to passionate intensity so fast and she didn't know how to answer. If it had been anyone else, she might almost have mistaken the pleading look in his eyes for something quite different. The world had turned topsy-turvy in the last twenty-four hours and she was desperate to return to normality.

'That is most gallant of you, sir. Pray tell me, what would your father say *then*?'

Carina spoke lightly but Harry's head went down. He slipped the fob back into his waistcoat as the door opened and Alice walked in. 'I'm sorry. I didn't know you were visiting, Mr Carstairs. What a pity, for I am just on my way out.'

Carina did not hear Harry's reply. She was wondering why Alice was dressed in funeral clothes. How she hated those scratchy dresses and heavy veils! Her weeds had been burnt months ago and she thought Alice had done the same.

'I'm due at a service of remembrance at one o'clock.' Alice answered her unspoken question. 'I would offer you a ride, Mr

Carstairs, but I'm already late. No doubt you'll be glad of a breath of fresh air.'

'Indeed, Miss Alice. I am going to White's. The walk will do me good.'

'And what do you have planned for this afternoon, dearest?' Alice turned to Carina.

'I'll finish my shopping and then write to my grandmother. I know she will take my word for the truth – unlike some other people I know.'

When Alice left the room and Harry followed without saying goodbye, Carina could have bitten off her tongue. Harry brings out the worst in me, she thought. What does he mean I'm like a stranger? He's the one who has changed, not me. One minute he's scolding me and the next ... And the next ... he's looking at me like a lovesick schoolboy.

The workings of a man's mind were an enigma to Carina. Too often they said one thing when they meant another. How could anyone know what they were really thinking? She had spent so much of her childhood alone, there were times she felt ill equipped in her dealings with people and her confidence wavered. Could she have everything the wrong way around? Was it possible she had unwittingly given Robert Danby a false impression? No, it wasn't so! Danby had made all the running. She had never led him on – not to the slightest degree!

Carina dismissed the idea and went over to the window, looking down to the street as Harry helped Alice into the brougham. She tapped on the glass pane, but Harry strode off without a backward glance. His cane made a spotted pattern in the snow on the pavement and she watched until he disappeared round the corner.

As she turned back into the room, a chill touched her. Harry and Alice were the bedrock of her life. She would never intentionally hurt either of them. The strain of yesterday was playing on her mind and she had read too much into Harry's words. He was only trying to cheer her up and she must write at once and apologise for her asperity. Thomas could take her letter this afternoon so he had it when he came home and by tomorrow they would be friends again. There was no need to be afraid.

CHAPTER FOUR

The Burlington Arcade was filled with Christmas shoppers and the crush of people made it difficult to move. Despite Alice's instruction to take Rose with her, Carina was alone. Footmen, their arms stacked high with parcels, followed customers to their carriages, while her purchases would be delivered to the house the next day. The arcade was sparkling with Christmas decorations and she was content to make her way slowly towards Piccadilly where a queue of people were waiting for Hackney cabs.

The thin gauze veil of her bonnet fluttered against her cheek as she searched for one that was free. It might be quicker to walk, but she was without a chaperone and the pavements were wet with snow. It would be a shame to ruin her new boots. As she deliberated, a familiar voice spoke from behind her.

'Miss Temple! This is a fortunate coincidence.'

A hand dropped on her shoulder and she was spun round to find herself facing Robert Danby. Carina saw at once he looked dreadful. He was unshaven and leaning heavily on his cane.

'I've been trying to call all week.'

'I have been greatly occupied.'

'Too occupied to read my letters? They've all been returned, don't you know.'

'I cannot delay, sir. My aunt is waiting for me—'

'How very strange.' Danby's expression darkened. 'My cousin, Mrs Vere, told me she was accompanying your aunt to a remembrance service this afternoon. I believe she invited her for tea afterwards.'

'You may believe whatever you like! I don't want to talk to you or to stand here all afternoon.'

'Dear girl, I've no intention of keeping you here. My carriage is at the north entrance and I will drive you home.'

'I told you my aunt is expecting me—'

'And you, Miss Temple, are a very poor liar.'

Robert Danby released her shoulder and tucked her hand under his arm. Carina was obliged to walk with him back up the arcade. He elbowed his way through the crowd and she noticed people turning their heads and whispering behind their hands. She could imagine what they were saying and kept her head low until they came to the north entrance. The landau, drawn by the famous Danby matching greys, stood waiting and group of young men in greatcoats were admiring the equipage.

Their encounter was no accident, Carina thought with a twist of alarm. Robert Danby had followed her to the arcade and had been waiting to catch her on the way out. His subterfuge infuriated her. She wanted to shout at him and throw off his arm, but didn't dare risk a scene. If she wasn't careful, news of this latest debacle would wing its way across London and Alice would come to hear of it.

The monkey boy unfolded the steps and she had no choice but to let Robert Danby escort her to the carriage. He gave instructions to the coachman and Carina lifted the side of her cloak to cover her face as she climbed in. The distance to Mount Street was no more than ten minutes' drive and she could handle Lord Danby. She would tell him exactly what she thought of him and that would be the end of it.

When he joined her, Danby sat down clumsily, ignoring the fact he was crushing her skirts. He knocked on the roof with his cane and then slumped back and stretched out his legs. He was staring into the middle distance and Carina stole a glance in his direction.

Grey light from the window fell on his face and the dark stubble on his chin. He had taken off his gloves and her gaze was drawn to the thick hairs on the back of his wrists. Robert Danby was a big man and everything about him displayed the arrogance of inherited wealth. He wore the best clothes, owned the best horses and gambled his money away. Looking at him now with his florid complexion and full red lips, Carina couldn't think how she ever thought him attractive. Then Danby turned his head. His gaze swept boldly over her as it had the first time they met. Recalling that occasion and her own unaccountable reaction, her heart missed a beat.

'I believe you owe me an explanation, ma'am.'

'And you, sir, owe me an apology.'

'Do I now? And why is that?'

'Because you are no gentleman! You lied to my uncle and defamed my name! Is it true you told him that I pursued you shamelessly?'

'I don't deny it. And I'll lay a hundred to one it was that upstart uncle of yours who stopped you seeing me.'

'Your behaviour is contemptible, sir. You have caused myself and my family the greatest distress.'

'Well, there's a thing! You never cared tuppence for your

family before.' Robert Danby's mouth twisted in a smile that did not reach his eyes. 'What's your game, Miss Temple? Do you have ambitions to become the second Countess Danby? Are you playing fast and loose in order to ensnare me?'

Carina was struck dumb by the question. She could smell brandy on his breath. Danby was drunk and she stiffened as he shifted closer.

'I hoped our relationship might be different. But one way or another, I will have you.'

There was a gale blowing through her head and Carina struggled to keep calm. Robert Danby had discarded his air of sophistication and she sensed violence beneath the surface. Any provocation might be dangerous. She was terrified she might laugh – the shocked, hysterical laughter that comes with panic. Her pulse raced so fast it was difficult to breathe and she pressed her hand to her heart to slow its frantic pace.

'It was never my intention to mislead or encourage you, sir.' Her voice was husky with nerves. 'If I have led you to believe otherwise, then I apologise most sincerely.'

She hoped to pacify him, but Danby did not answer. He was looking out of the window and, following the direction of his gaze, Carina saw they were in Berkeley Square. Thank heavens, she was almost home. Then, just as she expected the landau to swing left into Mount Street, it swerved in the opposite direction. She was thrown back against the cushions and, by the time she leant forward, exclaiming that the coachman had missed the turn, they were increasing speed.

'I'm not taking you home yet.' Robert Danby leant across her and pulled down the blind. 'You and I shall enjoy ourselves first.'

'Turn around at once, do you hear! You—'

She was silenced as Robert Danby's hand went for the ribbons of her bonnet. He undid them roughly and tossed it to the floor. One arm went around her shoulders and she let out a cry as his hand grasped her chin. His fingers squeezed her jaw and his mouth smothered her lips. As Carina clawed wildly at his face, she felt herself being bent over backwards. Her cloak was caught beneath her and Danby's weight bent the hoops of her crinoline until they snapped.

'I know this is what you want ...'

Danby began combing his fingers through her hair, mumbling wild, incoherent sentences until he bent his head again. This time his kiss was indescribably worse. His wet mouth traced a path across her cheek and his tongue pressed her lips apart. He had broken the frogging of her jacket and reached inside for her bodice. Carina grabbed a handful of his hair and pulled, hard. Danby groaned, but did not lift his head. She pummelled at his shoulders and arms. She would kill him rather than let him do this! She would kick and bite until he was forced to let her go, but Danby was too strong and she could not get free.

Her arm thrashed outwards. If she could reach the strap, she might pull herself up and get to the door. Her hand touched the cane lying on the floor. She tried to get hold of it, but Danby caught her arm and trapped it by her side. He attempted to kiss her again and Carina sank her teeth into the side of his cheek. As his neck jerked backwards, she flung out her hand. Fumbling along the floor, her fingers closed around the cane. She raised it above his head and, using all her strength, brought it down across the back of his skull.

Carina hit him so hard that the cane cracked in two. A look of astonishment crossed Danby's face, but, for a moment, the blow seemed to have no effect. Then the pupils of his eyes rolled upward and he slumped forward. His body was a dead weight on top of her and Carina struggled to get from underneath him. She pushed with her hands and knees until a final shove sent him to the floor.

Lord Danby lay so still she thought he was dead. Violence had answered violence and she had killed him! Carina was close to hysteria, half laughing and half crying until she saw the fingers of one hand twitch. Not only was he alive, Danby was already regaining consciousness! There was no time to lose and she scrambled over his legs and banged on the front partition with her fists. They were travelling at such a speed no one could hear, so she picked up the broken cane and hammered on the roof. At last, there came a shout from above and the landau began to slow down.

Carina found the catch and swung the door open. Hanging onto the straps, she glanced back. Robert Danby lay sprawled on the carriage floor but his eyes were open, the glassy look in them changing from bewilderment to rage as his gaze came into focus. He moved his hand in a feeble attempt to grab her skirts and, before the carriage came to a halt, Carina jumped.

She landed awkwardly, falling onto her knees in the snow. The monkey boy leapt down and tried to help her up, but she shouted at him and pushed him away. Seconds later, she was on her feet and sprinting down the street. She had no idea where she was going, no thought but to get away. Her hair fell across her eyes, half blinding her, and when her petticoats caught between her legs, Carina hitched her skirts above her knees and ran on.

Danby would come after her and she could hear a carriage travelling fast behind. Carina pressed back against a wall, terror squeezing her heart until the vehicle went past. It was only a Clarence cab, but she had to dig her fingers into the palms of her hands to control her panic. For a long time she stood motionless. Then she plucked up her courage and looked back.

Dense fog thickened the night and there was no sight or sound of the Danby landau. Gas lamps spread soft pools of light onto the pavement and at the far end of the street she made out the skeleton of trees. Was it her imagination or were they the trees of Berkeley Square? By some miracle, had her flight led her in the right direction?

Coming closer, Carina recognised the houses that led into Mount Street. She was safe, but the cramp in her side made her bend double. As fear and revulsion gave way to shock, she began to shake so violently she had to cling to the iron railings for support. She kept her neck bent until the nausea and faintness passed. Then she straightened up. Her jacket was torn and there was no sign of her bonnet. She must have left it in the carriage or dropped it along the way. With trembling hands she looped her hair into a knot at the back of her head before she turned her attention to her dress. There was nothing to be done about the broken frogging of her jacket. The snapped bones of her crinoline stuck through her skirts like knitting needles – but now her only thought was of Alice.

Her aunt must never discover what had happened! Carina had lost all track of time. Alice might not yet be home. If she was lucky, she might get upstairs before her aunt returned. She would enter by the basement door and swear Thomas and Rose to secrecy. She would say she had been attacked by pickpockets and Carina didn't care that she lied. She would do anything to prevent Alice finding out what a narrow escape it had been.

You damned fool, she swore under her breath. You stupid, stupid fool! Why, for once, couldn't you do as Alice asked? It was madness not to take Rose with you this afternoon. Flirtation is not a game and you brought this on yourself! Incensed by her own folly, blood coursed through her veins and strength returned. She could see the house and light from downstairs rooms shining onto the street. There would be time for self-re-crimination later. The only thing that mattered was to reach her bedroom without meeting Alice. Cold flakes touched her cheeks and Carina realised it was snowing. Pulling her hood over her head, she picked up her skirts and broke into a run.

CHAPTER FIVE

SICILY, JANUARY 1860

Carina stood on deck as the steamer that brought them from London approached Palermo harbour. The city nestled beneath a crown of gold-topped mountains and she could see palm trees and rose-coloured domes. As they came into the shelter of the bay, the light was so dazzling she tipped the rim of her bonnet down to shade her eyes.

There was time before disembarkation and her mind went back to that fateful afternoon. Whenever she thought of Danby's assault, Carina felt sick to the pit of her stomach. There was no one she could tell and she dared not report him to the police – for who would take her word against a peer of the realm? Alice was still out when she had reached home and Rose the only person who witnessed the state that she was in. Rose had come from Yorkshire with her and Carina trusted her completely.

'If you want my opinion, miss,' she had remarked as she inspected the jacket. 'Good thing I be coming with thee to Sicily. Folk in those parts wouldn't put up with this kind of thing.'

There had been no further letters or calling cards from Lord Danby and a week later Carina read in the Court Circular he had been received by the queen at Buckingham Palace. No matter how badly he had behaved, Danby was welcome back in the fold. The hypocrisy of the court disgusted her and, from that day on, she couldn't wait to get away.

It had been raining on the day of their departure and Harry Carstairs drove with them to the docks. She had looked back from the ship to his tall figure standing under an umbrella and thought: Harry is a good man and I will always disappoint him.

'Born with a devil in your heart.' The words of Paddy O'Brien, the head groom at Melton, came into her head. 'Let's hope your guardian angel catches him quick. Then you'll be a saint!'

It was strange to think of Paddy after so many years – but she would never be a saint. Carina understood herself too well for that. She was aware of her faults – her quick temper and impulsive nature that led her into trouble. She had wasted four years in mourning and then made a fool of herself. How could she have been so naive? Don't look back, she told herself. There's no room for bitterness or regret. You're eighteen years old with your whole life in front of you. You made a mistake and have learned your lesson. Now you've been given a second chance. Think only of the future.

Ahead lay an exotic city that filled Carina with hope. After two weeks cooped up on board, how she longed to be ashore! The passage through the Bay of Biscay had been rough. Alice, and Jane Parsons, suffered from seasickness and stayed in their cabins until past the Straits of Gibraltar while Carina walked on deck every day. She had never left England before and loved the adventure of a sea voyage, the spray in her face and taste of salt on her tongue. When the weather improved, she found a sheltered spot close to the bridge. There, Jane Parsons discovered her one morning reading *Childe Harold*.

'Could any man have written with such feeling without experiencing *life*?' Jane's tone was passionate. She was dressed in the same corduroy jacket and skirt she wore every day with her hair scraped back beneath a poke bonnet. She might have been considered drab were it not for her bright brown eyes and eager expression.

> *What is there wanting to set thee free,*
> *To show thy beauty in its fullest light?*
> *Make the Alps impassable; and we,*
> *Your sons, for Italy – Unite!*

'Lord Byron believed Italy must become one nation. He was a prophet as well as a poet. On the Continent he is admired above all others!'

Of all people in the world, Carina would never have guessed Jane Parsons shared her love of Byron. Her opinion of her changed in that instant. Jane wasn't the dull woman she had thought in London and they would surely be friends! Carina wanted to learn about Sicily and the closer they came to their destination, the more animated Jane became. Walking on deck or taking supper in their cabin, she spoke of the island's troubled past.

'The revolution in Sicily of '48 was suppressed with dreadful brutality. Hundreds of people were executed or imprisoned and many more forced into exile. You cannot imagine the suffering the patriots have endured. Mind you, my cousin, the consul, says it's only a matter of time before the Sicilian people rise up and cast off the Bourbon yoke!'

Carina thought of the newspaper article she had read to Harry in London. The idea of revolution had seemed far away then, but Jane's words last night had sent a shiver down her spine.

'You promise to call on me at the consulate as soon as you are settled?' Jane's voice beside her now made Carina start. She had come up on deck with Alice and was leaning over the rail, pointing to the beach. 'Our baggage will be taken to the Passport Office. Make your way there and wait for whoever the contessa has sent to meet you.'

They left the steamer in groups, clambering down steep steps to the long boats that were to row them ashore. Alice hung on to Carina's arm and sat close to her on the narrow bench with Rose hemming her in on the other side. They were packed so tightly together her new turquoise dress would be ruined. She should have worn a travelling habit like Alice, Carina thought, but she wanted to make a good first impression on her mother's family and she was too excited to care.

Arriving on the beach, the women were surrounded by men eager to offer them assistance. Carina had learned Italian, but they spoke in a dialect she couldn't understand. Somehow they had become separated from Jane, and Alice was pale with anxiety. Carina stood on her tiptoes, searching over the heads of the crowd for the Passport Office but the beach was so crowded it was impossible to see beyond the shoreline. She was wondering what to do when someone called her name and she turned so quickly she almost knocked into the young man who had come up behind them.

'Carina, it is you! I knew the minute I saw your dress. What a sensational colour! I'm your cousin, Paulo Denuzio.'

He bent over her hand, brushing it with a kiss and as he looked up Carina's gaze met a pair of laughing brown eyes.

Paulo was about her age with dark curling hair. There was a becoming droopiness to the corners of his eyes and his smile was that of a mischievous boy.

'Well, are you going to present me to your aunt?' he asked.

'I'm very pleased to make your acquaintance. How very kind of you to come.'

Alice's response was heartfelt and Carina was delighted to meet her cousin. She was aware her mother's brother was married with children, but believed they lived in Naples.

'Gabriella is with me. She's waiting in the carriage.' Taking for granted they knew who he meant, Paulo offered both Carina and Alice an arm. 'Gino will take your maid to identify your luggage and drive her home. Please be so kind as to come with me.'

A coachman in livery stepped forward and Carina was relieved to let Paulo guide them through the melee. The energy in the air was exhilarating and she did not mind the chaos and noise. The sun was warm and the sky bluer than any sky she had ever seen before. It was a world away from dismal, grey London. I'm going to be happy here, she thought with a thrill of pleasure. I'm not going to miss England one little bit.

They came to the road where a landau stood open in the mild air and a girl of about sixteen was peering over the side. Gabriella was pretty with large dark eyes. Her hair was coiled in thick plaits around her head and she wore a plain linen smock. Carina hoped her turquoise dress, with its low décolletage and petticoats peeping beneath the skirts, wasn't too risqué. At least a fur-trimmed mantle covered her arms and no one could disapprove of her bonnet. With its cream silk lining and wide ribbon tied under her chin, it was modest enough. She smiled at Gabriella and her cousin's cheeks dimpled shyly.

'Behind us is Mount Pellegrino, and there's the marina.'

Paulo pointed out the sights as they set off and came to a street lined with elegant houses. 'This is the Toledo. When the nobility lived here it was considered the finest boulevard in Sicily. Now the houses are all religious establishments and it's gone to the dogs—'

'Paulo, don't you talk so!' Gabriella spoke for first time.

'It's perfectly true. They were built for pleasure – and what have they become? Convents for celibates!'

Paulo went on to tell them about his family. He was a student of Law at the University of Perugia while Gabriella was being educated at a convent in Naples. They were in Palermo on vacation and their parents due to arrive the following week.

'My sister's going to be a nun,' he explained. 'Unless, that is, she's rescued from the religious life by one of my bachelor friends.'

At that moment, as if on cue, a young man on horseback rode up beside the carriage. He removed his hat and made a sweeping bow as Paulo introduced him.

'May I present Enrico Fola? Enrico belongs to one of the noblest families in Sicily, yet, for all that, he's a rogue! Do you know our friend is in danger of becoming a Liberal?'

The words had an edge to them that made Carina look at Enrico Fola more closely. Apart from his wide-brimmed hat and long hair, he didn't appear very different from Paulo. With his pale face and deep-set eyes, he was handsome in a romantic way and she noticed how Gabriella blushed when he spoke to her.

'And that,' Paulo declared after Enrico Fola took his leave, 'is the reason my little sister will not become a nun. She's been in love with Enrico all her life.'

Gabriella shot him a look that would have silenced most people, but Paulo was irrepressible. 'There's no use denying it, Ella. The whole world knows it's true.'

'Be sure we won't take notice of him,' Alice intervened mildly. 'Brothers always love to tease.'

Her aunt was more relaxed already and Carina was impressed by Palermo with its fine churches and statues in pretty squares. The citizens were smartly dressed, their carriages drawn by horses in harnesses adorned with plumed feathers. Painted donkey carts drove alongside stylish phaetons and on every corner were flower stalls and women selling fruit. At Paulo's insistence they stopped for iced sherbet brought to them in the carriage before setting off again.

The open boulevards were left behind and the streets became narrow and dark. Lines of washing were strung from one side to the other, blocking out the sun. Instead of the scent of flowers, the air was close and fetid and Carina sensed hostility in the silent stares of the women and children who crowded in doorways. Barefoot urchins ran after the carriage calling out for money and when an old man spat under the wheels, the coachman cracked his whip. No one spoke until the slums were left behind and they came out above the city and trotted across a piazza with a church. As they rumbled through a barrel-vaulted entrance, she glimpsed the Denuzio coat of arms and Carina knew they had arrived.

Her first impression of the palazzo was of a large honey-coloured house with shuttered windows. They alighted in the inner courtyard and Paulo and Gabriella escorted them up a flight of steps to enter on the first floor.

'This is the *piano nobile*,' Paulo explained. 'It's where we meet, eat and entertain. The bedrooms are above, rather less *nobile* but a good deal more comfortable.'

Carina glimpsed a series of rooms, leading from one to another, before they ascended a second staircase. Alice was shown into her suite and then Gabriella led Carina down the passage. She beckoned her into a bedroom with a balcony over-looking the city, where Rose was already surrounded by boxes and giving orders in uncompromising English to the young girl helping her to unpack.

A note awaited her from her grandmother saying she was looking forward to welcoming her once she was settled. An hour later, Carina set out to find her. Her hand gripped the banister rail as she went down. What would they make of each other, she wondered? If only she knew what Oliver had said in his letter! He was bound to have written a damning indictment. How would she answer if her grandmother asked about Robert Danby? She must tell her the truth, she decided as she reached the gallery.

A footman was waiting and there was no chance to think further. Carina followed him downstairs, through an arched doorway and along a dark corridor with shadowy portraits gazing down from the walls. Presently, they arrived at her grandmother's apartments and Contessa Denuzio rose stiffly from her chair and held out her arms.

'My beloved child, welcome home.'

Carina had a miniature of her grandmother as a young woman and took in every detail of her appearance. She was small and, apart from a lace cap, dressed entirely in black. Nonna was thin as a sparrow – Carina felt her shoulder bones as she embraced her – but her grasp was strong as she led her over to sit by the window. Her skin was like parchment and Carina had a strange urge to run her hands over her face. This was the closest she had ever come to her mother and all she could think was: Sonia was hardly older than me when she left Sicily. I should have come before. Why did I leave it so long? Tears filled her eyes and her grandmother held onto her hand so she couldn't reach her handkerchief. Too overcome to speak, the two women sat in silence until there was a tap at the door and a maid entered with a tray of refreshments.

Carina sipped her lemonade and then, prompted by her grandmother, began to talk about her childhood. She was hesitant at first, gradually becoming more confident. She told her of Melton and the Yorkshire dales, how she loved horses and her passion for reading and poetry. As she was speaking, she had the sensation she was describing someone she hardly recognised or remembered. There was a vital, undiscovered part of her in this room and she longed to ask about her mother. Do I remind you of her? What was she like? Would she have approved of me?

Her grandmother's sharp old eyes never left her face. It would be too painful for her to speak of Sonia now, she thought, and her questions must wait. She was trying to think of something else to say when Nonna asked about her life in London.

Carina took a quick breath before she answered. 'I believe my uncle wrote to you regarding the circumstances of my visit.'

'Oliver Temple's correspondence was private.' Nonna put up her hand, waving the question away. 'I'm grateful he decided to make an old woman happy, but your mother didn't care for him. I weighed his words accordingly.'

So that was it. She had read Oliver's version of events and had no wish to talk about it. The topic Carina dreaded the most was dismissed and Nonna continued briskly, 'I'm delighted your Aunt Alice is to stay with us for a few weeks. Sonia wrote of her with great affection and I look forward to meeting her. Now, let me tell you what I have planned for you …'

She went on, speaking of picnics in the gardens of La Favorita and visits to the Teatro Santa Cecilia. The Princess del Monti had invited them to her box at the opera the following week, thus ensuring her entrée into Palermo society, and Paulo promised to escort them around.

'We're not as sophisticated as you are in London, but Sicily is never dull. I'm sure you'll be happy here, my dear.'

Carina felt a glow of warmth radiate through her. How could one not respond to such a welcome? She already felt more at home than she ever had in London. There was an immediate understanding with her Sicilian relations. The sense of kinship buoyed her up, and when she came downstairs later she was pleased to find Paulo waiting in the salon.

He poured out two glasses of chilled wine, handing one to her, and raised a toast. 'To my beautiful cousin, who has come to set Sicily alight! The whole of Palermo is asking about you. "Will Miss Temple be allowed out of the house?" "When may we be presented?" I've never been so popular in my life.'

'Why so, I cannot imagine.' Carina looked at him questioningly.

'Don't say you thought to arrive in Palermo and not find your reputation gone before you?'

There was mischief in his eyes and Carina dropped her gaze. She shouldn't mind, but her grandmother had made her feel all the unpleasantness was left behind. She hadn't expected this of Paulo and answered coolly. 'Does our grandmother listen to the same gossip as you?'

'Nonna would never hear a word against you.'

'So what's your opinion of my reputation?'

'Should I denounce a scandal if you don't yourself?'

Carina did not answer and Paulo went over to the side table to refill his glass. He continued without looking round. 'It's really of no significance. Papa thought it advisable to apprise us of certain rumours, that's all.'

To be sure, he was an impudent young man! What did he expect her to say? Did Paulo think she'd admit or deny anything to him? If so, he was a fool as well as a prattler. She had liked him so much that morning and was now disappointed. When he came and sat down beside her, she turned her back and picked up a small enamel box from the table.

'Are you annoyed with me?'

'Not in the slightest,' she said shortly.

'Yes you are. Of course indiscretions are only acceptable as long as they remain discreet.'

Carina imagined Paulo smiling at his own wit and turned the box over in her hand. A hint of vulnerability usually did the trick and she sighed.

'I'm sorry you choose to think badly of me. I hoped we might be friends.'

'Of course we're friends. Why ever not? And I don't think badly of you. I'm full of admiration!'

Before she could think of a suitable retort, he slipped off the sofa and knelt on the floor with his arms across his chest. 'I didn't mean to offend you. Please will you forgive me?'

He was being ridiculous and Carina refused to answer.

'Tell me what I can do to appease you? I'll challenge anyone who casts doubt on your honour. Pistols at dawn – whatever you demand! I will risk life and limb to prove my allegiance.'

It was all an act, but Paulo was hard to resist. His antics made her want to laugh and Carina struggled to keep a straight face.

'How you behave is up to you. Now, will you please get up?'

If her attempt at coolness worried him, Paulo did not show it. He was back on his feet, a smile lifting the corners of his mouth even as he tried to prevent it.

'You'll never refer to my life in London again. Is that understood?

'Upon my honour, I swear to be your most loyal champion. However ...'

Just then a footman entered carrying a tray of olives, which he placed on the table. The setting sun threw beams of light across the room, turning the walls from gold to pink and through the open door came a murmur of voices. Alice and Gabriella were talking as they approached, their silk skirts rustling on the marble floor as they came down the gallery.

'Silence is my bond, dear cousin.' Paulo placed his hand over his heart. 'But know this: in Sicily a scandal attached to one's name is a greater asset than a fortune. If it turns out that you have neither, you'll be considered a nonentity!'

CHAPTER SIX

In the days that followed, Paulo was good as his word. When they were not admiring sights in the city, they drove into the countryside and Alice painted watercolours while they explored local villages and markets. Carina admired the jewellery and fine silks from Catania and bought a quantity of both, watching intrigued as Paulo haggled with the merchants. Nothing seemed too much trouble for him, even when she ordered a case of coral to be sent on approval and he had to arrange a substantial deposit. He obliged her every whim and Carina was as captivated by her cousin as she was by her mother's childhood home.

Apart from the universal ringing of church bells, there were as many different aspects to Palermo as mosaics in the cathedral. It was a city of light and shade where delicate arabesque arches stood beside baroque churches and solid Norman buildings. There were twisted trees and donkeys in straw hats. Grand palaces were hidden behind doors in filthy streets and puppet shows performed next to the outright macabre. Despite Paulo telling her it wasn't to his taste, Carina insisted they visit the famous Cadaveri. Alice declined to join them and Carina was appalled when she saw the mummified bodies dressed in clothes and hung up in alcoves. In Sicily, it seemed, people were in love with death as much as with life and Palermo was mysterious, shabby and magnificent.

They had arranged to call on Jane Parsons and Carina was in the best of spirits as they set out. The sun was shining and her new bonnet with its long ribbons was a sensation. She couldn't help noticing how many young men turned their heads to look as they drove by.

'Do you like my flirtation ribbons?' she asked Paulo.

Paulo smiled, but gave no reply. He had business in town and would drop them off on the way. He had been quiet all morning and Carina was content to absorb the atmosphere. It was a festival day and broughams and phaetons jostled for space with speedy *caleffini* to the sound of pipes and drums. Families were gathered on balconies, the men smoking cigars on the first floor while women stood above, waving to their friends, and children pressed forward to get a better view.

'There was a great rumpus at the opera last night,' Paulo announced as they turned into the Toledo, pausing until Carina and Alice gave him their full attention before he continued. 'A demonstration broke out during the overture. The police dragged out the culprits, but the entire performance was cancelled. The teatro is closed until further notice.'

'But we're invited for tomorrow night! Who was responsible?' Carina and Alice spoke simultaneously.

'The usual troublemakers – so-called patriots and rebels.'

'Why at the opera, of all places?' Alice enquired.

'The composer of *La Traviata* is a supporter of Italian Unity. His name's their slogan. V.E.R.D.I. for Victor Emmanuel Re D'Italia.'

'But I don't understand. You already have a king in Naples.'

'Oh, they want rid of *him*. Their ambition is to create a united Italy with the king of Piedmont as figurehead.'

'I see …' Alice began, and then trailed off.

'What will happen now?' Carina asked, a small frown creasing between her eyebrows.

'The police are taking no chances. The theatre will remain closed until all those responsible are behind bars. I'm afraid your entrée into Palermo society must be postponed.'

Carina remembered Jane Parsons telling them about the chief of police. Jane said Count Maniscalco ran a system of spies, using torture to extract false confessions and that he was the most hated man in all of Sicily.

'What a pity. We were so looking forward to the evening,' Alice remarked. '*La Traviata* caused a furore when it opened in London, albeit for different reasons.'

Alice did not elaborate as they swung through the gates of the British Consulate and the carriage pulled up in front of a white stucco house. A Union Jack hung above the portico and they were greeted by an official who took them up a wide flight of stairs. Sheffield sconces adorned the walls and Carina noticed all the furniture was English. When they reached the drawing room, a large portrait of Queen Victoria met her eyes. It was so vast it dominated the room and she thought: how ridiculous when everyone knew the queen was tiny.

Beneath the painting stood Jane Parsons, who hurried forward to greet them. The consul was instantly recognisable in white tie and morning coat with his wife beside him. She had a hesitant way of moving, peering short-sightedly in front of her as she approached. There was another gentleman with them. He had intelligent eyes and a distinguished air, Carina thought, as Jane presented Baron Riso.

'It is a great pleasure to meet you, Miss Temple.' The baron spoke English in an attractively stilted fashion. 'Miss Parsons tells me you're the daughter of Sonia Denuzio. I'm glad you have returned to her homeland.'

'Did you know my mother?' Carina asked in Italian.

'I met her on several occasions. She was a beautiful and clever woman.'

The baron's words made Carina's heart swell. Her father had been too heartbroken to ever speak of her mother and Alice was the only person who had told her about her. There's so much I don't know, she thought. Until now, I've been afraid of letting myself think too much about her. Why do I feel such a sense of loss for someone I never met?

They went outside to sit on the terrace and Baron Riso was placed between Alice and Carina. The baron paid her great attention, asking her opinion on a number of things and listening attentively to her answers. Carina found him charming and was sorry when Alice announced it was time to leave. Paulo was collecting them on his way home, she explained. On the way down, Baron Riso offered her his arm and complimented her on her bonnet.

'I'm pleased you approve.' Carina bestowed on him a dazzling smile. 'My family consider it a little *de trop*.'

'Nothing is ever too much in Sicily. We are a nation in love with excess.'

They walked through the front door into the sunlight and Carina caught sight of Paulo standing beside the carriage.

'Please come here, Paulo!' she called to him. 'I would like to present you to our friends.'

Paulo walked over slowly, even reluctantly, it seemed to Carina, and when he shook Baron Riso's hand did not look him in the eye.

'My wife and I are hosting a ball at our home next week. It would give us great pleasure to extend an invitation to you. We would be honoured by your attendance.'

'Most civil of you, sir, but I'm afraid we can't accept,' Paulo interjected.

'We'd be delighted to receive your invitation.' Aggrieved by Paulo's interference, Carina immediately contradicted him. 'Would you be kind enough to write to my grandmother?'

'I will send a card to the Contessa Denuzio today.' Baron Riso smiled and bowed. 'It's been a pleasure to make your acquaintance, Miss Temple. Good day to you all.'

The baron strode off and they took their leave. They were barely out of the gates before Paulo rounded on her.

'Do you always accept invitations from *anyone* who asks you anywhere?'

'The British Consul and Baron Riso aren't just *anyone*! What's wrong with you today? I've never been so mortified in my life. Don't you agree, Alice?'

Alice would not be drawn in and the two cousins glared at each other in silence, neither of them prepared to give way until Paulo said in a superior tone of voice. 'The demonstration at the opera wasn't a random event. It was planned by certain rebels, including your new friend, Baron Riso.'

'I don't believe you! If so, then why hasn't he been arrested?'

'Because the police don't have enough evidence against him—'

'I'm sure because there is none!'

'Saints have mercy, do you have to be so stubborn?' Paulo leant forward, lowering his voice. 'Baron Riso has powerful friends and the authorities don't dare touch him. However, I'm convinced this soirée is cover for a secret meeting. He's done it before, you know, using the rank of society to camouflage a conspiracy.'

'Really, that's too much!' Alice responded so sharply that Carina stared at her. 'Respectable people such as the British Consul would never—'

'Respectable?' Paulo did not let her finish. 'That's *not* how Mr Goodwin is perceived in Palermo. His sympathies are well known. General opinion is that the British should keep their nose out of what doesn't concern them.'

In the split second that followed, Carina thought Alice might lose her temper. Two bright spots of colour appeared on her cheeks, but she remained silent.

'Unlike my parents, I've no affection for our current leaders.' Paulo continued undaunted. 'But these people are fanatics. Given half a chance, they would stir up another revolution.'

'Is your friend, Enrico Fola, one of them?'

'Enrico's a dreamer. He may support their ideals, but he would never act against the king.'

'So why is he permitted to call on your sister?'

'My parents are old friends of his family. I've known Enrico all my life – but sometimes despair of Gabriella's crush on him. If he's not careful, she'll be left with a broken heart.'

Most likely, Paulo suspected Enrico's involvement in last night's events, Carina thought. Why, only yesterday Gabriella let slip that Enrico declared the inspection of private houses for weapons unlawful! Her cousin believed everything Enrico said and had made Carina promise not to tell for fear of getting him into trouble.

They travelled on and, as they entered the old quarter, the landau was brought to a halt. There was a commotion in the street ahead and, leaning out, Carina saw a phaeton tipped on its side blocking the way. The horses were uncoupled and men were pushing from behind while others hauled with ropes from the front. A crowd had gathered and everyone was shouting different instructions.

Then an old woman, eyes bright with malaria fever, stepped forward. Her bony hands clutched the carriage door. '*Poveretta – more di fame! Fata la carita. O boni servi di Dio, facite la carita!*'

Paulo had instructed them never to carry money and neither Alice nor Carina had a purse. Alice sat with her hands clasped, her spine not touching the back of the seat and Paulo took out his watch and started fiddling with the mechanism. Carina glanced to the other side of the street and her gaze locked with that of a young woman standing in a doorway. She had the hollow-cheeked look of starvation and held a small, motionless bundle to her breast. Looking straight at Carina, she began to unwrap the blanket. A tiny, dark head emerged, but the baby lay so still there was no way of telling whether it was dead or alive.

Seconds passed. Carina was terrified the girl meant to give her the baby. Then a man's voice barked from within and she pulled the blanket back over the child. Not taking her eyes off Carina, she drew one finger across her throat before she turned and went inside.

There was no mistaking the gesture and Carina blushed scarlet. She wanted to snatch off her new bonnet and throw it after her. It would sell for good money – but the girl was too proud – and most likely it would end up on the fire. The only other thing she had was a new coral brooch and she twisted her neck to look past Alice. The old woman was still hanging onto the door and while Paulo talked to the coachman, Carina grappled with the pin on her corsage. With a wrench she had it off and passed it to Alice, indicating to the woman with her eyes. As soon as the brooch was handed over, she was gone. At the same time there was a loud cheer and the phaeton was pulled free.

They were on their way and Carina's head was spinning. How could such misery exist in the heart of the city? And why had Paulo instructed them never to give alms? There was great poverty in London too, but they didn't have to drive through slums every time they went out. Their carriage and fine clothes felt like an insult in the face of such misery. Whether Paulo approved or not, she would take her purse with her in future. Anything would be better than what had just happened!

Her enjoyment of the visit to the consulate evaporated and Carina felt depressed. She didn't like to see Paulo in a bad mood. It wouldn't do to end the morning on a sour note, so she smiled at him.

'We don't wish to compromise you, Paulo. Alice and I are happy to go Baron Riso's ball on our own.'

'That would be extremely unwise.'

'I've brought my best ball gowns from London and not had a single occasion to wear them,' Carina paused. Paulo would probably think she was being reckless, but she was tired of constraint and added, 'I'm sure it will be a splendid adventure.'

'The kind that ends up in the Vacaria prison?'

'One can't be arrested for dancing a waltz.'

'Carina's right,' Alice put in graciously 'You've been very kind to us. The last thing we want is to place you in a difficult situation.'

Paulo did not answer immediately. He leant back with his arms behind his head and then, when they were crossing the piazza, remarked as if the thought had only just occurred to him,

'I expect you'll sweet-talk Nonna into giving you permission, Carina. For my part, I'll wait until my parents arrive tomorrow and let them decide. No doubt, I'll be obliged to escort you just to keep you out of trouble.'

Paulo wasn't as reluctant as he made out, Carina thought. His tone was too languid and artificial and he was dying to go. Suddenly she longed to dance and for the music and gaiety of a party. Which dress should she wear? There were a dozen to choose from, but the white organza was her favourite. Her gloom was forgotten and she was excited, looking forward to the evening already. If Baron Riso were a man of his word, which she was sure he was, the invitation should arrive this afternoon and she would speak to her grandmother just as soon as she was home.

CHAPTER SEVEN

If sweetly you love me and deeply you care
When Autumn is falling and Winter is bare;
If you are constant in Spring's rushing tide
When Summer is calling, you stay by my side,
In all seasons true, our life will we share;
For sweetly I love you and deeply I care.

She had thought of the first line on the day she left England and the poem found its voice today. Carina had spent all afternoon finishing the draft. A handful of women were celebrated poets in England. Would anyone consider her verse worthy of circulation, she wondered? It wasn't enough to rhyme and scan. Poetry should express true emotion. What was it like to experience true passion? I don't want to die a spinster, she thought. One day I will fall in love – and then poetry will flow from my pen like water.

Stiff from sitting so long, Carina stretched her arms above her head. Dogs were barking and she could hear a flurry of activity downstairs. Her uncle and aunt must have arrived from

Naples. She would go down with Alice later, she decided. It would be easier to meet them when everyone was gathered together before dinner.

The door to the grand salon stood open and Gabriella was playing the piano as Carina and Alice walked down the gallery. She stopped as they entered and put away her music. Before Carina could speak to her, the door at the far end opened and her uncle and aunt entered, followed by Paulo.

Her mother's brother, Carlo Denuzio was of medium height with dark hair thinning on the crown. His expression was difficult to read behind thick-rimmed spectacles, while his wife Anna Maria was friendly and vivacious. She had a pretty, round face and bombarded Carina with questions about the latest fashion news from Paris.

During dinner, talk was livelier at her aunt's end of the table but Carina did her best to pay attention to her uncle. Surreptitiously observing her cousins as he droned on at her, she was glad to see Paulo had recovered his spirits. Gabriella, on the other hand, was subdued. She barely touched her food and, when they withdrew to the salon, went to sit by herself in a corner, taking no part in the conversation.

As soon as the others retired and the three of them were alone, Paulo was on to her.

'What's the matter, Ella? The cat got your tongue this evening?'

'Don't pretend you don't know.' Gabriella looked at him, her black eyes glistening. 'You were there and you heard Papa. He has no right to speak so, denouncing all patriots as criminals and traitors to the king.'

'Papa's entitled to his opinions – as we are to ours. How else would Enrico Fola be allowed in this house?'

Carina watched as Gabriella stood up and walked over to

her brother. She was tiny beside him, the top of her head barely reaching his shoulder, and there was a quiver in her voice.

'Don't you dare bring Enrico into this! At least he has principles – which is more than anyone can say about you.'

'Well, I'm glad he wasn't caught up in last night's shenanigans.' Paulo put a hand across his mouth to stifle a yawn. 'All words and no deeds with Enrico. Let's hope it stays that way.'

'Are you blind as well as partisan? Do cruelty and injustice mean nothing to you?'

'Dear Ella, I may be blind but I'm certainly *not* partisan. We're to entertain Prince Scalia for lunch on Friday and I'm dragooned into attending. To top that off, I must then escort Carina to a ball at the Palazzo Riso next week. There are no greater political extremes in the kingdom. I don't know which I dread most. On balance, I dare say Prince Scalia's probably the worse of two evils.'

Carina ignored the slight on Baron Riso for she was interested in the lunch party. Paulo had spoken to her of Riccardo Scalia, Duke of Pallestro. The prince was a friend of his parents and a powerful member of the Bourbon court. He was also in charge of law and order in Sicily and Paulo did not like him.

'Is Prince Scalia really the monster that you say he is?'

'Scalia's an agent of the Devil,' Gabriella exclaimed.

'I wouldn't trust him as far as I can spit,' Paulo grimaced, wrinkling his nose. 'I hope you're not squeamish, for Mama's bound to place you next to him. His face is scarred as a butcher's block.'

'Why? What happened to him?'

Paulo looked mysterious and made no answer. He would string her along for his own amusement, Carina thought. She would ask Gabriella later. As she returned to her chair, Paulo announced he was going out. Without giving them a chance to ask where he was going, the door closed behind him.

'Paulo's studying Law – but he doesn't understand the meaning of justice,' Gabriella stated flatly.

'I'm sure he cares more than he admits.'

'I'm afraid he does *not*! Many of his friends are liberals but he refuses to get involved. Enrico's given him evidence of illegal executions and he takes no notice ...'

Gabriella dropped her crochet needle on the floor and knelt down to search for it. When she had it, she stood up, her face flushed as her sentences tumbled over each other. 'Papa's even worse! He has the ear of the king and yet denies the atrocities committed in his name. He knows Scalia and Maniscalco are acting outside the law, but he's too weak to denounce them! I'm ashamed to be a member of this family and that's the truth!'

Gabriella was so upset Carina was afraid she might burst into tears. Her cousin was blinded by her love for Enrico, she thought, while Paulo was a cynic and she didn't know which one of them to believe.

'Sicily's a rich island, but the people aren't permitted to grow enough food to feed themselves.' Gabriella went on, anger running in her voice.' The government hope to break our spirit, but they'll never succeed!'

The girl and baby came into Carina's mind and she said nothing. Gabriella possessed a quality she admired. Her cousin would always do what she believed to be right. And then there was Jane Parsons. Why should a sensible woman like Jane make similar allegations if they were untrue?

'I'm sure Paulo's going to the ball on the orders of Prince Scalia!' Gabriella announced suddenly.

'Why on earth? He detests the man ...'

'Promise me you won't let him out of your sight. He will try to gather evidence against Baron Riso and you must stop him.'

Carina was too tired to argue. As they made their way upstairs, she took her cousin's hand.

'The idea of Prince Scalia makes me quite nervous. You will stay by my side at this lunch on Friday, won't you?'

'I've volunteered to keep Nonna company. She doesn't care for the prince either, although she speaks well of his wife. She says it's a shame Bianca married him. Something happened a long time ago but Nonna's never really explained. I'm sure you could find out. You're good at winkling things out of people.'

On the morning of the lunch party Carina woke up early. Through the open window came the cries of street vendors and she could hear footsteps on the stairs. The household was up and yet she was no wiser about Princess Scalia. When she questioned her grandmother, her only comment was that Isabella del Angelo had been a friend and she knew her daughter, Bianca, as a child.

Anna Maria was in charge of preparations and the palazzo had been turned upside down. Rugs were hung out of windows to be beaten, the best table linen pressed and the courtyard scrubbed until the cobbles shone like marble. They were to eat in the blue salon and footmen had been hurrying up and down all of yesterday, bringing the best wine and gold plate from the cellars. Extra staff had been drafted in to help and blocks of ice and flowers had been arriving since dawn.

Carina had wanted to show off her latest creation from Mr Worth, the finest dress designer in London, but Alice insisted she wore a less flamboyant outfit and suggested the green bombazine. It was too bad, Carina thought as she studied her reflection in the Venetian glass. Her hair was parted down the middle in a severe style and the dress buttoned to the chin with a starched white collar that scratched her neck. It made her look positively dowdy. Why not the turquoise silk with its pretty neckline and scalloped hem? Alice wouldn't even be there – she was confined to bed with a chest infection. Carina was tempted – but she had promised to obey Alice in future and couldn't go back on her word so soon.

To make matters worse, when she went downstairs, Carina found everyone else decked out in their finery. Anna Maria's friend Donna Marcella was encased in gold satin with rows of pearls draped over her bosom and her aunt bright as a peacock in blue crêpe. Even the bishop was arrayed in a riot of episcopal purple. She wanted to run upstairs to and change, but there was no time for the guests of honour had arrived.

As she curtsied to the princess, Carina took in her fair hair and soft blue eyes. Bianca Scalia was dressed to the height of fashion. Her silk skirts seemed to float in the air, her mantle trimmed with agate, and on her head sat the prettiest veil pinned over a comb in the Spanish style. Never again, even if Alice were on her deathbed, would she heed her fashion advice, Carina vowed; and then, before she was quite ready, she was being presented to the prince.

'*Molto piacere*,' Prince Scalia murmured as he lifted her hand to his lips.

The prince was of a slight build with a narrow face and hooded eyes. He was impeccably dressed in a cutaway coat and crossover cravat. His scars were partially concealed by a trimmed beard, but they were impossible to ignore. From beneath each earlobe, a ridge ran down his cheek to the corner of his mouth so that when he smiled his upper lip lifted in a sneer. The prince held her hand longer than was necessary and

Carina pretended not to notice. Determined not to stare, she kept her eyes down until Anna Maria fetched her over to talk to the princess by the window.

With her high cheekbones and flawless complexion, Bianca Scalia was undeniably beautiful. Was this her first visit to Sicily, she asked Carina? And how long did she plan to stay? Carina answered vaguely, distracted by the constant movement of the princess's hands. She fiddled with everything she touched, her fingers plucking the lace of her cuffs or straying to the heart-shaped locket that she wore around her neck. She would hold it for a moment and then let it drop, clasping her hands on her lap. A few moments later she would start again. It was a disconcerting habit in a woman so outwardly sophisticated and a relief when the party moved through for lunch.

The blue salon had been transformed. Winter light filtered through the windows so the stamped wallpaper shimmered like seawater and the table was weighed down with gold plate and glass. A liveried footman was posted behind each chair and Carina was placed next to Prince Scalia. They stood with heads bowed as the bishop said Grace and, when they sat down, the prince turned to her first.

His manners were as polished as his conversation, but Carina didn't remember afterwards what they talked about. His unblinking gaze stayed on her face and she was increasingly aware of his dark eyes lingering on her lips. Prince Scalia was old – at least forty – and she was the only single woman present. His unabashed flirting embarrassed her. When she dropped her napkin, the prince waved the footman away and picked it up himself. His hand brushed against her arm and Carina withdrew it hastily.

'I hope you'll come to visit us at the Villa Pallestro.' The prince was undeterred by her awkwardness. 'It will be a pleasure to show you our country estate. Rarely are Sicily's shores graced with such grace and beauty as your own.'

It was a flowery speech with a nuance that Carina recognised. It made her think of Robert Danby. Despite Scalia's exquisite manners, she sensed a predatory, ruthless personality and gave him a cold look before she turned to talk to Paulo. She had already noticed how often her cousin beckoned the footman to refill his glass. Carina saw the devil-may-care look in his eyes and prayed he would behave himself. Surely Paulo wouldn't dare stir up trouble in such elevated company? Then, as Anna Maria was about to rise from the table, he made a remark that was like a small explosion. 'I'm told Captain Mavrone has been seen in Palermo.'

The statement was directed at no one in particular, but Paulo might have danced a jig on the table for the effect it had. There was an audible intake of breath followed by a tense silence and, for no reason at all, Carina looked at Bianca Scalia. She was staring at her husband, her features frozen in shock before she had time to compose herself. What had Paulo said to provoke such a response? Carina dared not enquire. Time seemed to stand still until Prince Scalia spoke from beside her.

'Paulo is obviously au fait with all the gossip in Palermo. Where does he pick up such tittle-tattle, I wonder?' The prince's tone was quietly malevolent. 'I hope he doesn't frequent the establishments of ill-repute where conspiracy and treason are rife in our city. I advise you to keep a closer eye on your son's proclivities in future, Carlo.'

The prince looked around the table, his gaze resting briefly on each of them before it settled on her uncle. Carina saw Carlo Denuzio's cheek twitch and a film of sweat break out on his forehead. He lifted his napkin, dabbing his lips, and Anna Maria signalled to the butler. Chairs were pulled back, scraping the parquet floor as the ladies rose and withdrew to the gallery. Her aunt was visibly flustered, using her fan with vigour, and Donna Marcella began talking about a sculpture exhibition in Naples. Bianca Scalia pretended to show an interest, occasionally inclining her head, but conversation was stilted, and, when the men joined them, Paulo was not with them.

It was not until later that Carina saw him again. She had been with her grandmother and was taking a stroll in the garden. Following a path between hedges of myrtle to the fountain with a satyr dribbling green water from its mouth, she came across Paulo and Enrico Fola.

'By the saints, the roasting I've just had! Their Excellences were hardly out of the house before my father let fly!' Paulo rolled his eyes dramatically. 'If Enrico hadn't arrived, it would have been the rack and thumbscrews.'

'I gather Paulo's been shooting off his mouth again.' Enrico fell into step beside Carina. 'He can't resist taunting Prince Scalia, but should have more sense than to do so in his own home.'

'He certainly set the cat among the pigeons! And I was the only one there with no idea what it was about.' Carina directed her tone of accusation at Paulo. 'Who is this Captain Mavrone, anyway?'

'Enrico can tell you. The captain is one of his comrades.' Paulo kicked a pebble off the path. His tone was sulky, bringing a swift retort from his friend.

'Mavrone and I may share the same views on the future of our country, but we have little else in common.'

'Don't be a humbug!' Paulo laughed in his friend's face. 'What you mean is the man isn't the same rank as yourself.'

'Who is he?' Carina persisted. When Enrico didn't answer, she turned to Paulo and repeated the question. He was silent and she stood in front of him until he gave a hitch of his shoulders.

'Ben Mavrone is Riccardo Scalia's arch-enemy. There's been a deadly vendetta between them for years.' Paulo's eyes lit up at Carina's astonished expression. 'After the '48 revolution, Scalia put a price on his head. Mavrone escaped from Sicily so the prince incarcerated his brother, using him as bait to make Mavrone return.'

Carina gazed at him. Was he making it up? One never knew with Paulo, but he was getting into his stride and she was too curious to stop him.

'The brother met with an accident and died in prison. Scalia then disappeared from Palermo, supposedly on a political mission to France. When he returned, the surgery had been performed on his face. You're free to draw your own conclusions.'

'Do you mean they fought a duel?'

'I doubt it was so honourable. The odd thing is why, when Mavrone had him at his mercy, didn't he finish him off? A life for a life and all that?'

'Because there's no greater humiliation for a man like Prince Scalia than to owe his life to his enemy,' Enrico offered.

'Maybe, but there's another theory.' Paulo dug his hands into his pockets and strolled onward. 'It's rumoured Captain Mavrone was, and possibly still is, Bianca Scalia's lover.'

'Really, that's outrageous!' Enrico Fola interjected forcibly. 'There's no foundation—'

'And no smoke without fire. You have to admit, my friend, being a rebel has a dangerous attraction for the ladies.'

Carina saw Enrico scowl and Paulo changed the subject. The story of murder and revenge was the stuff of Gothic novels, she thought; yet Prince Scalia exercised a sinister power that was hard to throw off. They had all heard the menace in his voice and Paulo had better watch himself. He shared her own impulsive nature and the prince would make a dangerous enemy.

Carina walked on, lifting her skirts high and unconsciously showing off her ankles as she climbed the stairs to the veranda. She thought Paulo and Enrico were behind her, but when she looked back there was no sign of them. Paulo must have taken his friend off to apologise – and so he should! She didn't believe half of what he said. The idea of the nervous creature at lunch having a liaison with an outlaw was beyond credibility.

'A rebel has a dangerous attraction for the ladies.' The sentence echoed in her mind. It was a mild evening, but a shadowy feeling touched Carina. Something strange had happened at lunch, something she didn't understand. She was accustomed to premonitions, but this was different. Until just now she had no idea about the vendetta. So what was it that impelled her to search out the princess when Paulo mentioned Captain Mavrone? And why, in that briefest of moments, had she been convinced the look she saw on Bianca Scalia's face was one of unguarded terror?

CHAPTER EIGHT

It was past seven o'clock when their carriage drew up outside the Palazzo Riso. Lights blazed from the upper windows and they could hear music as they waited in line in the street. The courtyard was packed with vehicles dropping off their guests and by the time Alice, with Carina and Paulo, reached the reception, the party was in full swing.

Liveried footmen met them at the door and ushered them upstairs. Carina was both excited and apprehensive. Paulo had said news of the scandal in London had reached Palermo. If so, would she be lionised or cut dead? She was longing to dance, but she wouldn't tolerate being snubbed. If that seemed likely, she would plead a headache and ask Paulo to take her home. At any rate, no one could criticise her appearance. Her hair was pinned up in a chignon, threaded with ribbons, and her dress cut wide across the shoulders with a daringly low neckline. Her arms were bare and her waist tiny above skirts that billowed out in a cascade of flounces.

They waited in line behind a group of chattering girls and Carina fidgeted with her fan. Through the doorway was a room full of people and the hum of conversation. At last her name was announced. As she stepped over the threshold, there was a sudden hush. Carina was aware everyone was looking at her and gripped her fan hard between her fingers. Then, with a lift of her chin, she extended her hand first to his wife and then to Baron Riso.

Baroness Riso was a handsome woman with a warm smile and grey hair. Carina would have liked to talk to her, but others followed behind. Paulo had disappeared and she stood with Alice by the door until the baron offered them both an arm. As he led them to the centre of the room, the hubbub of voices started up again. Within moments, they were surrounded by young men pressing for introductions. Baron Riso returned to his post by the door and Carina was pestered by suitors until every polka, mazurka and waltz was taken and her dance card was full.

'I reserved the first dance for you. And the supper dance.' Carina waved her programme at Paulo as he made his way through the crowd to her side.

'I thought it was polite for a lady to wait until she was asked?'

'You'd have been too late so I filled them in myself.' Carina turned to Alice. 'Why did you refuse every dance? We're at a ball, don't you know?'

'I've been waiting for you.' Jane Parsons came over before Alice could answer. 'We've secured a table over there. Do please join our party.'

Jane indicated to where Mr and Mrs Goodwin were sitting with another couple. Alice nodded and smiled at Carina and Paulo. 'You two go off and dance. I'm more than happy in the company of my friends. We shall meet for supper.'

'Come on, Paulo. It's time to do your duty!'

With Alice settled, Carina hurried Paulo towards the dance floor. Chairs and sofas were arranged for sitting out and in one

corner men were playing rouge et noir with ivory chips. Paulo
suggested they might join them, but she dragged him on, too
eager to admire the pictures and fine Florentine tapestries until
they came to the ballroom. Beneath the candle-lit chandeliers,
couples swept by in a fast, spinning waltz. Paulo led her onto
the floor and bowed as she dropped a curtsy. Her cousin was an
accomplished dancer and after him came a stream of others
until Carina was breathless and begged to sit down.

Her latest partner, a young man with soft brown eyes, went
in search of refreshments and Carina looked around. The ballroom was gold and white with a carved ceiling and mirrors
reflecting the swing of the men's swallow-tailed coats and the
girls' dresses as they danced by. Heavy chignons were balanced
on the girls' shoulders and fans tied to velvet ribbons dangled
from their wrists. The men were elegant although there was
hardly a uniform to be seen – no epaulettes, sashes and shining
boots. Carina missed the bright colours of the military – but
she was at a ball, the first she had been to for months. Her heart
thrilled to the sound of music, her foot tapping in time as
Enrico Fola appeared beside her.

'Your curiosity about Captain Mavrone is about to be satisfied. He's over there. A warrant for his arrest and he shows
himself openly in public. I believe he does it deliberately to
provoke the authorities. Word will be all over Palermo by
tomorrow.'

The music stopped and Carina looked in the direction Enrico
indicated. A group of men stood talking at the far side of the
room and her attention was drawn to a tall man with his back
to her. Dark hair curled over the top of his collar, and, unlike
other guests in tailcoats, he wore a jacket and breeches. As he
turned to greet a fellow guest, his eyes caught her inquisitive
gaze. They were a startling blue against his tanned skin and his

regard was bold. The captain was clean-shaven, the lines of his mouth finely shaped and there was cool recklessness in his handsome face. He was the kind of man who would break a woman's heart and walk away unscathed, Carina thought as her dancing partner returned.

She presented him to Enrico, and, when she looked again, Mavrone was still watching her. Carina opened her fan, peeping over the top, and saw him turn to one of his companions. Then he looked back and smiled, the invitation in his eyes as clear as if he had spoken the words out loud.

He was flirting with her, but not in the way practised in London. She was familiar with the tricks for attracting a man – the sideways glance and fluttering eyelashes – but she sensed Captain Mavrone had no time for frivolity. He appeared relaxed, but there was a tension in his pose that reminded her of a soldier away from his regiment in time of war.

Warning bells rang in her head. Look away now. Don't encourage him! Oh, but he was so good-looking … His gaze was magnetic and Carina couldn't help herself. She lowered her fan and their eyes locked again. Mavrone bowed his head and raised his glass. Was he toasting her health or admitting defeat? There was no way of knowing, for a naval officer stood in front of her to claim the next dance. By the time it was over, both Baron Riso and Captain Mavrone had left the ballroom.

'Enrico tells me you spotted the infamous captain,' Paulo commented as he led her in to supper. 'Were you bowled over like every other woman in Palermo?'

'In my opinion he's a rogue with too high an opinion of himself.'

At the far end were tables laden with dishes of meats and salads and her cousin declared he was famished. He filled their plates before they went to find Alice with Jane and the

Goodwins. They sat down at their table and conversation picked up from where it had left off. When she had finished, Carina emptied her glass of wine and smiled at Paulo.

'So, are you enjoying yourself? I hope you've dispensed with your reservations?'

'It's a grand affair, but there's more to it than meets the eye. Don't you find it odd Captain Mavrone attends a ball where he's in danger of arrest for the sake of a few waltzes?'

'Enrico says he does it to taunt Maniscalco and Prince Scalia.'

'Enrico's my oldest friend, but he's not always right. And I've seen other disreputable characters who don't normally attend occasions like this.'

'Why shouldn't they be here if they're friends of our host?'

'Then tell me where they've all gone! Before the last dance I walked through the reception rooms and didn't see any of them. Baron Riso doesn't appear to be mingling with his guests.'

That much was true. Every table was occupied and Baroness Riso sat close by, surrounded by a large party. But her husband was not with her and Captain Mavrone nowhere in sight.

'So where do you think they are? Making bombs in the basement or hatching a plot upstairs?' Carina was glib.

'I wouldn't be surprised if they were doing both.'

Paulo placed his hands on the arms of his chair and Carina gave him a suspicious look. 'I hope you're not planning a reconnaissance?'

'The idea never entered my head, sweet cousin.' Paulo smiled disingenuously. 'It's warm in here and I need some fresh air.'

Paulo stood up, excusing himself to Alice, and Carina watched as he made his way through the oncoming tide of guests. Waiters brought puddings to their table and Jane announced that the small pink mounds were shaped like breasts in honour of the martyrdom of St Agatha.

'How utterly awful!' Alice declared, and put down her spoon.

'They're made by the nuns in the Convent of Santa Maria and are quite delicious. Do please try some.'

Carina did not hear her aunt's response. She was wondering where Paulo had gone. Gabriella said he was capable of espionage and perhaps he was, after all. She imagined him creeping around, taking notes on his host's activities to report back to his father. Coffee was served and he should be back by now. It was exactly as Gabriella had feared. Paulo was searching the house and she must find him before it was too late! Looking down at her programme, Carina said the first thing that came into her head.

'Forgive me, but I'm engaged for the next mazurka. When Paulo returns, please tell him I'm on the dance floor?'

As she left the table, Carina realised the mazurka was over. The orchestra was playing a polonaise and she hoped Alice and Jane were too occupied by the pudding to notice. The dance was underway and it was easy to slip unnoticed into the next room. The sound of laughter came from an alcove where a couple was sitting but most of the guests were at supper and when she reached the landing the hall was deserted. Where was Paulo? It was far too chilly for him to have stayed outside all this time. Had he gone to search the upper floors or was he down in the cellars?

Carina peered cautiously over the bannister. The hall below was empty and she made up her mind and started up the stairs. She prayed she wouldn't run into Baron Riso or anyone else. What possible reason could she give for coming up here? She was doing nothing wrong, she told herself. If she were caught, she would think of some excuse. The wine she had drunk with supper gave her courage and when she reached the upper floor she stopped and listened.

She could hear the orchestra playing far off, but all around her was quiet. A passage leading off the stairwell disappeared into a void of blackness and the stillness made her apprehensive. Perhaps she should return to the anteroom and wait for Paulo there? But before she did, she must make certain he wasn't up here. She would take a quick look along the passage and then go back downstairs.

Running her hand along the panelled wall, Carina walked down the corridor. There were no illuminations and every few paces she peered over her shoulder to the stairwell. On one side, the windows were draped with heavy curtains and there were doors on the other. The bedrooms must be on this floor, she thought, and all their occupants downstairs. Soon maids and valets would come to tend the fires. She was about to retreat when she glimpsed a crack of light beneath a doorway ahead.

Carina crept forward, her shoulder pressed against the wall. She heard voices and held her breath as she tried to make out what they were saying. The name 'Denuzio' was enunciated in a slow, distinctive drawl and anxiety flashed through her. Had Paulo been caught? Was he inside the room being interrogated?

As she concentrated, trying to distinguish her cousin's voice from the others, she began to catch the drift of the discussion. Count Maniscalco's name came up and then another she recognised, Francesco Crispi. Where had she heard that name before? Jane had spoken of him, she remembered. Francesco Crispi was a Sicilian exile in London and an outspoken advocate of revolution! Carina felt the hairs stand up on the back of her neck.

'Why wait?' someone asked.

'Because we're not ready.' Baron Riso's voice was unmistakable. 'We need Francesco Crispi to rally the support of our countrymen. Without him the revolution will fail.'

There was no doubt that he was in charge and Carina clasped her hand over her mouth. She had done exactly what she suspected of Paulo and spied on Baron Riso! She couldn't bear to hear another word and, flattening the sides of her skirts with her hands, sped back along the passage. She was in sight of the landing when she heard the click of a door and the soft tread of footsteps. Someone had left the meeting early. Whoever it was, they would see her the moment she came into the light of the stairwell! She must find somewhere to hide, and, as her arm brushed against fabric, Carina remembered the concealed windows.

She slipped behind a heavy curtain, heart skittering as the footsteps came nearer. Please don't let them stop! Don't stop! As she willed the footsteps to go on past, she noticed the hem of her skirt was caught beneath the curtain fringe. She bent down to pull it back out of sight, then let out a yelp of fright as a hand grasped her wrist and the curtains parted to reveal the unsmiling face of Ben Mavrone.

'So what have we here? A mouse skulking in a corner or a new recruit for Count Maniscalco?'

His eyes went over her and Carina's mouth turned dry.

'Has complicity deprived you of the power of speech, Miss Temple?'

'I lost my way. I'm looking for my cousin. He's … he's unwell …' she stammered. 'I believe he came up here to lie down in the library.'

'And you expected to find the library up here? Surely you passed through it downstairs?' Mavrone's grasp tightened.

'I meant Baron Riso's private library.'

She was improvising wildly and Mavrone took a step forward. The curtains closed behind him and Carina was acutely aware of the proximity of his body in the cramped space. Her chest rose and fell in rapid breaths but, apart from the way he held her, Mavrone seemed relaxed.

'Did you come up here to spy on Baron Riso or to meet a lover for a secret tryst?' he asked, studying her with faint curiosity.

'I told you I was looking for my cousin.'

'I don't believe you, ma'am. Please will you try again?'

'I heard nothing, I tell you!'

He hoped to force an admission from her and Carina responded in a fierce whisper, 'I've told you the truth. Now let go of me!'

'You don't really expect me to do that, do you? Perhaps you'd rather tell Baron Riso why you were eavesdropping on his private party?'

'Take me to the baron if you wish. I know he will believe me. I *know* him to be a gentleman and not an ill-mannered bully!'

When Mavrone released her, Carina experienced a moment of triumph. She had made him back down. If she were prepared to explain herself to Baron Riso, then he could detain her no longer. She would tell the baron just what she told him. Unless they had found Paulo, she was in the clear. So why didn't he move out of her way?

'Are you in such a hurry to leave?'

The question was an enticement, echoing the silent exchange of earlier and Carina could barely breathe. There was danger here, a dark enchantment to which she was susceptible and she swallowed hard.

'Will you please let me pass?'

Mavrone nodded, but did not move. Only the bulk of her petticoats kept the lower half of her body from touching his as Carina began to edge past him. Later, when she dissected the manoeuvre in detail, she couldn't think why, when she had to move sideways, she did not turn her back. It was awkward in any case and made more difficult by the width of her skirts. One of his buttons snagged the ribbon of her corsage. Carina felt his hand brush against her breast as he broke the thread to release it.

Captain Mavrone was testing her to the limit and waited until the last moment. As Carina's hand reached for the curtain, his arm went round her waist. He pulled her back and Carina did not resist or cry out. Moonlight turned the colour of his eyes metallic and she gazed at him, spellbound. He ran his fingers lightly down the side of her cheek and then his mouth came down on her lips.

The memory of Robert Danby ripped across her mind and vanished. Mavrone's kiss induced a different sensation altogether. She could feel the warmth of his body beneath his jacket as he kissed her deeply and passionately. Her eyes closed and her head fell back against his arm. Mavrone's hand tangled in her hair, the other caressing her neck and Carina melted into his embrace. Wrapped in the dark night, she was aware only of the exquisite feel of his lips and the touch of his fingers. When he stood back, she swayed unsteadily against him. He placed his hands on her shoulders to look down into her face.

'By God, ma'am, you're certainly worthy of your reputation.'

As his words penetrated her trance-like state, rage and humiliation flowed through Carina and she drew back her hand and slapped him hard across the cheek. She would have hit him again but Mavrone caught hold of her wrists. Maddened by the way he held her, she shouted at him.

'Damn you to hell! Damn you, let me go!'

'I believe you came up here looking for me and I'm flattered.' In contrast to her own, Mavrone's voice was level. 'It's been a pleasure to make your acquaintance. When you're ready, I shall escort you back downstairs.'

Carina's hands shook as she straightened the line of her bertha. Unable to think of an insult crushing enough, she pushed past him and stepped into the passage. The hem of her skirt caught and she jerked the fabric so hard a panel of organza split from hem to waist. She couldn't go back to the party looking like this! She must tidy her hair and find someone with a needle and thread to repair her dress. There would be a retiring room, most likely on the ground floor, and she walked swiftly to the landing.

Gathering up her skirts, she heard Mavrone's footsteps behind her as she ran down the stairs, fury bursting within her, until she was halted by the sight of Paulo in the hall. Her cousin was staring at her as if she had fallen out of the sky; he appeared so surprised that at first he didn't notice who followed.

'Angels defend us, where have you been?'

'The young lady was looking for you upstairs,' Mavrone answered before Carina could utter a word. 'Miss Temple was concerned for your welfare. So much so, in fact, she was oblivious to the compromising situation in which she placed herself. She was searching the bedrooms. You can imagine my surprise when she entered mine.'

Paulo's mouth dropped open and Carina's gaze swung from him to Mavrone. What the devil was he talking about? Was the captain afraid she might tell Paulo of the conversation she had overheard? Mavrone wanted to ensure her silence and didn't care if he traduced her – but what could she say in defence? To admit she'd been upstairs was bad enough, but the sight of her hair and torn dress was explicit condemnation. If she gave the conspirators away, he would surely let it be known she had been in his bedroom. Gossip was the meat on which the appetites of

Palermo fed and the look in his eyes implied the story would be embellished in the telling.

Left speechless by his audacity, Carina turned her back on the men. She heard Paulo answer, his voice tight with the effort of controlling himself. 'My cousin's not feeling herself tonight. I'll find her aunt and take her home immediately. We would be grateful if you'd keep this unfortunate incident to yourself, sir.'

'That would certainly be best for all concerned.' Mavrone's easy tone was deceptive. 'However, my discretion comes at a price. I will only remain silent if the bargain is kept by all three of us.'

'You have my word upon it.'

'And that of Miss Temple?'

'Miss Temple will gladly forget she ever made your acquaintance,' Paulo answered firmly. 'As far we're concerned, we didn't see you here this evening, Captain Mavrone.'

Without giving her a chance to gainsay him, Paulo took Carina by the arm, his fingers pinching above the elbow as he marched her across the hall to the front door and called for a man to bring their cloaks.

'Stay here and don't speak to him again, do you understand!' he hissed in her ear. 'I will go and fetch Miss Alice.'

When a footman brought her cloak and placed it over her shoulders, Carina did not take the trouble to thank him. Seething with rage, she waited in the cold draught for Paulo to return with Alice. Their carriage was summoned and, once hidden in the dark interior, she looked in the direction of the hall and saw Mavrone had gone.

Oblivious to the frost between the cousins, Alice chatted happily on the way home while Carina huddled in a corner. She wondered how an evening that began with such high hopes could end so badly. If Paulo hadn't gone wandering off, the encounter with Mavrone would have been avoided. And what was he doing in the hall when she came down? He should never have given in to the captain's blackmail! If he believed in her virtue, then he should have followed her example and kept quiet. She would talk to him in the morning, she decided, but, when they arrived back and Alice went upstairs, Paulo caught her before she could escape. 'What, in the name of heaven, do you think you were up to?'

'I was looking for you. I bumped into Captain Mavrone. He accused me of trespassing and we had a brush.'

'A brush! A brush?' Paulo looked at her as if she had lost her wits. 'Is that what you call it – when you turn up looking for all the world as if you've been rolling in the hay with a farm boy?'

'It wasn't my fault! You were away so long I was worried about you.'

'Enrico and I played a few hands of piquet. When I came back, I was told you were on the dance floor.'

Paulo would never admit he was guilty and maybe he wasn't – but he had an alibi, which was more than she could say for herself. If she alienated him further, he might go to his father and that would be a catastrophe. She would be locked in a nunnery or worse. An apology was in order.

'I'm truly sorry, Paulo. I beg you not to say a word, please! There was no harm done. I swear I'll die if you betray me.'

'I'm beginning to understand why you were banished from London.' Paulo searched her face to assess how much sincerity was in her words. 'We've standards in Sicily, too, you know. It's a grave mistake to ignore them.'

'Oh, Paulo, you told me all those things and they went to my head. If it were the other way round, I would never give you away. I would stand by you, even on pain of death.'

Carina hung her head as she stood in front of Paulo, trying

to look ashamed, and finally he touched the back of his hand to her cheek. She kissed him goodnight and, halfway up the stairs, stopped to look down. There was a gleam of amusement in Paulo's eyes. He had a fair idea of what had happened, she thought, but her cousin wouldn't betray her. They were two of a kind and she could trust him.

Rose was waiting in the bedroom to help her out of her dress and untwine the ribbons from her hair. The delicate watch-spring steel of her new crinoline had survived and when Rose left, her arms full of organza and stiff petticoats, Carina went to sit by the hearth.

She closed her eyes and felt again the pressure of Mavrone's arms around her and the taste of his lips. The memory of his kiss sent tremours down her nerves. She would like to think he had taken advantage of her, but she couldn't deceive herself. The moment their eyes met, a charge of electricity had leapt between them. For the first time in her life, she had experienced a physical response that was beyond her power to control. Yet equal to the fire she had felt, was the heat of her indignation. Mavrone was a hardened soldier – but to throw her reputation in her face was contemptible. How could she have let him kiss her?

She needed fresh air and Carina slung her shawl about her shoulders. Opening the shutters, she stepped out on to the balcony. Palermo was spread out below, its slender spires silhouetted against an indigo sky and lights bobbing in the harbour as fishing boats set out for the early catch. Down there, men like Ben Mavrone and Baron Riso were plotting revolution. She had learnt their secret. Did that make her an accomplice to the crime? There was no real evidence. She had only overheard a few words. Besides, if Gabriella was right, then Baron Riso was on the side of the angels. And for all she knew, she was too …

It was time for bed and Carina turned back towards her bedroom. Her thoughts returned to Ben Mavrone and it struck her then that the whole of the conversation upstairs had been in English. Mavrone was Sicilian, but when they were alone he had spoken in her native tongue and she hadn't noticed until now because his accent was perfect, his use of the language as fluent and natural as her own.

CHAPTER NINE

PALERMO, FEBRUARY 1860

The noise of rain, coming in a sudden downpour, made Carina look up from the letter she was writing. She went over to the window and stood with her fingers absently tracing the pattern of raindrops on the glass. It was on days such as this that she missed Alice most. The morning her aunt left for England, she hadn't gone to see her off. Alice said it would be too upsetting, so Anna Maria went in her place. When they had said goodbye at the house they had both wept. Then, yesterday, a letter arrived from Alice announcing her engagement to Sir Anthony Farne.

Alice wrote that a small wedding was planned in March and there was no need for her to come home.

'The timing is most propitious now that you're settled, dearest. We are to live in Northumberland, but Anthony appreciates the close bond between us. When you return I will travel south to be with you in London. The house in Mount Street will remain open and everything just as it was before ...'

No, it would not! How could it be? Last night Carina had hardly slept. She paced her bedroom until dawn. Alice hadn't abandoned her, she told herself over and over again. It was only because she was lonely that she was upset. She loved Alice and this was what she wanted for her.

'I am delighted to receive your wonderful news.' She began her reply. *'I know that you and Anthony will find true happiness together. My only sadness is that I will miss your wedding ... I'm not sure when Oliver expects my sojourn in Sicily to come to an end – but my grandmother has asked me to stay for as long as I want. I have no desire to return to London, at present, and expect to remain in Palermo until after the summer.'*

How she wished Paulo and Gabriella were still here. They had returned to their studies a week after Baron Riso's ball. Paulo did not mention the evening again, but he hadn't forgotten, Carina was sure. She tried not to think about him, but Ben Mavrone was constantly on her mind. Where had he gone? Which part of Sicily was his home? How could she find out more about him? He had become an obsession and she couldn't get him out of her head.

She was too much alone, Carina decided, and sent a card to Jane Parsons. A note came back informing her Miss Parsons was in Rome. Palermo was deserted and her only consolation was the time she spent with her grandmother. They talked about her mother and Nonna gave her Sonia's letters to read. Her mother wrote with verve. She was outspoken and confident, in love with her husband and looking forward to the birth of her first child. That part brought tears to Carina's eyes and Nonna patted her hand.

'Sonia would be very proud of you, Carina. You're like her in so many ways. Once she decided on a course of action, she never wavered from it.'

One evening, to give her granddaughter some younger company, the contessa invited a group of Paulo's friends, including Enrico Fola, to dinner. Carina bit her tongue through the social niceties until she could venture the one question she wanted to ask: if there was news of Captain Mavrone.

'He's not in Palermo. No one knows if he's even in Sicily.'

It was obvious Enrico didn't want to talk about Mavrone and Carina wondered if Paulo had said anything. She would kill him if he had, but she was not to be put off. She could have no peace until she tracked him down and placed her hopes in her budding friendship with Bianca Scalia. The princess had come for tea and invited her to stay at their country villa. She had also spoken of her mother.

'When I was growing up, Sonia was the person I admired most in the world. She was both beautiful and kind. It was so romantic when a dashing naval officer swept her off to England! All of us girls swooned with envy.'

The sound of a dog barking broke into her thoughts and Carina went back to the bureau. She had wasted half the morning dreaming and would finish her letter to Alice this afternoon. There was just time before lunch to dash a line off to Harry. She had told him of the vendetta between Prince Scalia and Captain Mavrone, mentioning in passing she had met them both.

Harry's response was typical.

'Do take care, Carrie. Remember your promise and leave this matter well alone.'

Carina reached for a fresh piece of paper. Harry was right not to trust her, she thought as she wrote in a fast, sloping hand.

I have been invited to stay at the Villa Pallestro by Bianca Scalia. The visit is a timely diversion, although I doubt I will discover the truth. Have no fear, dear Harry. I shall act decorously and with the utmost discretion.

'There is the Villa Pallestro!'

Bianca Scalia leant forward, pointing out of the carriage window. They were bowling along the coast road towards the village of Bagara and Carina saw a large house standing on a hill. The ride from Palermo had taken less than two hours and as Carina straightened her gloves, smoothing the soft leather between her fingers she realised Bianca had asked her a question.

'I'm sorry. My mind was far away.'

'I was wondering if you miss your family and friends in England?'

'I miss my aunt, but Palermo is more agreeable than London at this time of year. The *carnivale* was a delight and I enjoyed the ball given by Baron and Baroness Riso.'

'May I ask you a favour, Miss Temple?' Bianca hesitated. Then looked at her squarely. 'Please would you refrain from mentioning that evening to my husband? He is no friend of Baron Riso.'

It was the opening Carina needed, but there was no chance to take the conversation further. The carriage rattled through iron gates and up a cypress-lined avenue, coming to a halt in front of a large villa with a columned facade. Two lines of servants bowed and curtsied as they entered and Bianca led the way through salons scented with flowering lilies to the drawing room.

Wherever her eye alighted, Carina saw the Scalia emblem of a dragon entwined in the Bourbon fleur-de-lys. It was carved into marble, engraved on brass and every inch of plaster on the walls was painted with frescoes. There were animals and birds, gods and goddesses reclining on celestial clouds, and a ceiling painted blue with a scattering of gold stars. The villa was far grander than she had expected, and when the butler took Bianca aside, Carina wandered over to the window to look out.

The garden was laid out in the classical style, with topiary and statues. Beyond it, the road to Palermo stretched like a ribbon through green fields.

'I'm afraid there's been a delay,' Bianca said, coming up behind her. 'Your maid and luggage have only just arrived. They left Palermo before us and I don't understand.'

'I am more than happy to wait—'

'Riccardo never said anything! I'm so sorry.'

'Please don't worry on my account. I will refresh myself later.'

'Are you sure?'

Bianca's restless gaze scanned the road to Palermo and Carina had no idea why she was so concerned. After a light lunch, she was shown to her room and lay down on a chaise longue, listening to Rose's mutterings as she hung up her dresses.

'I've never known such a palaver! You'd have thought Old Nick was under the seat the way the soldiers carried on. Gino told them we were on our way to the Villa Pallestro, but they took not a blind bit of notice!'

'What do you suppose they were looking for?'

'Revolutionaries and such like.' Rose held up a skirt, assessing it for creases, her tone as matter of fact as if she were discussing the traffic in Piccadilly. 'Gino says the authorities discovered a hornets' nest in Palermo. The military are rounding suspects up from here to Messina, but they're wasting their time. The rebels are far too slippery to be caught by a bunch of idiots! He told me so – right in front of the soldiers.'

And that, no doubt, was why the Denuzio carriage had been held at the side of the road for most of the morning, Carina concluded. A nervous frisson ran through her. Was it also the reason Bianca was so agitated? Thoughts and questions darted through her mind; she had to speak to Bianca before Prince Scalia arrived.

With this in mind, Carina changed for dinner early, but when she arrived downstairs it was Prince Scalia and not his wife who awaited her in the drawing room. A footman served champagne on a silver salver and the prince took a flute and handed it to her. The bubbles tickled her nose and she made an attempt to be gracious.

'You're most indulgent, Your Excellency. Champagne is quite my favourite of all the French wines.'

'I'm delighted to hear it. We don't stand on formality at the villa. I hope you will consider yourself on intimate terms with us.' Prince Scalia twisted the stem of his glass between his thumb and fingers. 'I've arranged to take you riding in the morning. It will be a pleasure to show you our estate. Bianca is happy to provide you with the suitable attire and will lend you her mare.'

Carina might have prevaricated, but just then the door opened and Bianca came in, accompanied by a black-frocked priest. Father Domenico had soft, plump hands and she caught a whiff of rosewater as he was introduced. He embarked on a long story about her uncle and Carina saw the prince greet Bianca with a kiss on the cheek before he gave her his arm and led them into the dining room.

Dinner was a sumptuous meal of pasta followed by fish and then meat. The moment Carina finished one course, her plate was whisked away to be replaced by another and she lost count of how many times her glass was refilled. She felt light-headed as she listened to Prince Scalia and Father Domenico discussing local matters. There was no mention of roadblocks and when the footmen withdrew, she remarked casually, 'My maid tells me they were held up on the road due to trouble in Palermo.'

Carina folded her hands together as Prince Scalia took a cigar from the box and held it under his nose. She was surprised he didn't wait for the ladies to withdraw, but customs were different in Sicily. He struck a match and inhaled until the end glowed.

'I apologise for any inconvenience, but we're obliged to enforce extra measures of security.'

'Not more arrests, Your Excellency?' Father Domenico asked.

'The action we take is not of our choosing, Padre. If the rebels continue their subversion, then we use all our powers to destroy them.'

'What extra measures, precisely?' Bianca's hand reached for the heart-shaped locket. Her fingers clasped it briefly.

'Every man of working age will be questioned and anyone who can't provide evidence of employment or lodging taken to Palermo for investigation. Not a single traitor will slip through our net this time.'

For a time no one spoke. The atmosphere in the room seemed to close in and Carina glanced at Bianca. She was completely still, not even her hands moved, and her eyes were veiled by lowered eyelashes.

'It's been a successful exercise,' the prince continued. 'Once we get the prisoners to Palermo, we have the means to make them confess. I'm confident we will extract all the evidence necessary to condemn them.'

In the first instance, Carina was not sure she had heard him right. For Prince Scalia to confirm the allegations made against him so complacently outraged her. She couldn't let him get away with it! She meant to speak calmly but anger sharpened her voice.

'Surely you don't have authority to arrest innocent men when no crime has been committed?'

'If the security of the State is threatened, all men are guilty until proved innocent. Those who speak against the king must answer for their opinions – even if they expound only hot air.'

Prince Scalia dropped a column of ash into a dish and inclined his head towards her.

'The more prominent the rebels are, the greater danger they present. Liberals like Baron Riso believe they live a charmed existence, but they're not beyond our reach. Take your friend, Enrico Fola. His family enjoy the trust of our beloved monarch and yet he belongs to a secret society bent on treachery.'

'I've never heard Enrico Fola speak against the king!'

'We've placed Baron Riso and Enrico Fola under close surveillance.' Scalia ignored her intervention. 'It's only a question of time before they become careless and then we'll have them.'

So the prince had been informed of her visit to the Palazzo Riso. Was he also aware Ben Mavrone had been there that evening? Carina could feel Bianca's gaze across the table, willing her to stay silent, but caution was swallowed by indignation.

'My grandmother gave me permission to attend the reception. Am I to infer you've also placed her under surveillance?'

'I believe the Contessa Denuzio was misled as to the nature of Baron Riso's invitation. I shall write and advise her to put an end to your association with such people – and the sooner the better.'

'I'm not given to jumping at shadows, Your Excellency. There were no traitors in Baron Riso's home—'

'My husband isn't implying you did anything wrong, Carina. He's only concerned for your safety.'

'Well said, Bianca.' The prince looked approvingly at his wife. 'Miss Temple doesn't appreciate having her friends chosen for her. Indeed, we're privileged that she honours us with her presence.'

'We live in difficult times, Miss Temple. It's hard to know who one can trust.' Father Domenico sounded flustered.

'Thank you, Padre, but I'm quite capable of looking out for myself.'

'Of course, you're a woman of the world and should be respected as such.'

The bite of malice in Scalia's words was not lost on Carina. The wine had made her rash, but as they went through to the salon, she saw his expression change. No longer supercilious, the prince's regard was hard and intense and it seemed he was attracted by her defiance. He said goodnight at the bottom of the stairs and she followed Bianca down the corridor to her bedroom.

Rose helped her undress and Carina sat down to brush her hair. Prince Scalia is a calculating, clever man. I must keep him at arm's length, she thought. I will be aloof but not unfriendly. I will simply ask him why Paulo dislikes Captain Mavrone. That should be enough to provoke a reaction. It won't get Paulo into trouble – and by this time tomorrow, I will have learnt something.

CHAPTER TEN

Rose drew back the curtains and, as she had every morning that Carina could remember, gave a succinct account of the weather.

'It will be fine today, ma'am, but sharp, mind you.'

It couldn't be seven o'clock already! Carina had drunk too much wine and her head ached, but it was too late to change her mind. She downed two cups of strong coffee before Rose helped her into Bianca's riding habit.

The jacket was on the small side and she held onto the bedpost as Rose tugged the lacing of her corset until it was tight enough to fasten. The skirt was a little short, but the hat was pretty, with a veil and streamers, and the boots a perfect fit. Carina's footsteps resounded on the marble as she went down to the hall where Prince Scalia was waiting.

His gaze travelled from her neck down to the tip of her black boots and then returned to her face.

'My wife's habit fits you like a glove, my dear. The outfit is most becoming.'

What he meant was that it was rather too tight, Carina thought irritably. Her mood improved when the horses were led up to the front door. Bianca's mare, Pabla, was pure Arab and pranced delightfully. It took two grooms to hold her head as Carina mounted. She arranged her skirt over the saddle horn and Prince Scalia offered her a riding crop, with a vicious-thong attached to the end.

'I don't need a whip. The mare is raring to go.'

'Take it, all the same.'

Prince Scalia thrust the crop into her hand and they set off, trotting down the drive and out through the gates. Pabla's narrow neck arched as she danced sideways and when they had turned off the road, Scalia called to her,

'Give her head! I'll catch you up …'

She loosened the reins and the mare leapt forward, flattening her neck to reach full stride. Carina experienced a thrill of exhilaration. This was what she had missed, the wind in her face and the fluid movement of a horse beneath her. The Arab's speed was breath-taking and she did not slow down until Pabla began to blow. They drew up near a ravine, where wild flowers peeped between rocks. Prince Scalia was a long way behind, keeping the bay at a steady canter. She might have lost him altogether, Carina thought, but the gallop had dispelled the stagnation of drawing rooms and her mind was clear.

She was aware her cheeks were flushed as Prince Scalia drew level. 'Did Pabla bolt with you?'

'I wanted to try her paces and she responded magnificently.'

'And you were in control all the time? I'm impressed by your horsemanship.' The prince nudged his horse closer and leant over to brush a straggling hair off her face. 'You're an unconventional young woman, Miss Temple. Do you approach everything in life with such abandon?'

'It depends on what I want to achieve.'

'Were you trying to get away from me?'

'No, of course I wasn't … I knew you would catch up. Your horse has more staying power.'

'A quality I greatly admire.'

His knuckle was hard beneath his glove and there was hot, keen look in his eyes. This was her chance. The question was on the tip of her tongue, pressing against her lips, when a burst of gunfire exploded above their heads. Pabla shied so violently Carina was almost thrown off and Prince Scalia dug his spurs into the bay's flanks.

'Some fool's shooting rabbits! Follow me!'

Carina followed close behind as they climbed a steep bank. The ground was littered with stones so the horses stumbled and slipped until they came out of the gully on to a high plateau. Thorns stuck out their spiky heads between scattered boulders and she saw a circle of army tents positioned on a slope to the left. The sun was in her eyes and when she looked more closely, Carina realised what she had taken for rocks were prisoners in chains. There were hundreds of them, sprawled over the wasteland like an army in disarray. A chill ran through her but she was determined not to show Scalia that she was shocked.

'Quite a catch, don't you think?' The prince touched his thumb to his nose.

'I offer you my commiserations. There can't be many loyal Sicilians left at liberty.'

'Come now, Miss Temple.' Scalia gave her a stern look. 'This is not the time nor place to propagate your liberal opinions.'

'You misjudge me, Your Excellency. I'm merely commenting on statistics. How can you suspect so many men are a threat to the state?'

'Because every Sicilian peasant is born with treachery in his soul. Discipline is the only way they learn it's not worth their lives to support the rebels.'

Scalia meant to reprimand her, and Carina did not answer. Her gaze passed over those prisoners close to the roadside. They were a pitiful lot, with manacles on their wrists and ankles, and she felt sorry for them. Watching her face, Scalia's mouth twisted in a distorted smile.

'I must speak to the commandant. If our methods of law enforcement offend your sensibilities, you had better wait here.'

The words were thrown over his shoulder as he touched his whip to the bay's neck and Carina watched him go with simmering resentment. There was a guard post along the road and a soldier stepped forward to challenge him. Prince Scalia leant down. She hoped he was giving instructions for her safety, but the soldier returned to his companions without so much as a glance in her direction.

The guards were a damned sight too complacent, Carina thought. She could easily ride away, but Scalia would take any form of retreat as weakness. So she stayed where she was, speaking softly to the mare to calm her. Wild fowl hooted in the distance and she could hear a low murmur of voices behind her. The prisoners seemed to be closer than before and sensing the stealthy approach to her rear, Pabla struck the ground with her front hooves. Now, Carina clearly made out the clanking of leg-irons and shuffling footsteps on the track. Her hand tightened around the riding crop and when a stone was kicked carelessly, rolling along the ground under the horse's hooves, she could bear the suspense no longer.

'If you come any closer, I'll set the guards on you!'

'We only want to pay our respects, lady.'

The answer came in a guttural voice, and was followed at once by another. 'So *you're* Scalia's new favourite – and not ashamed to be seen out riding with him.'

Carina wouldn't be intimidated. If she ignored them, they

would tire of their jibes and leave her alone. Then, from the corner of her eye, she saw one of the prisoners step forward. She had the impression he was taller than the others and, despite his chains, moved with agility.

'Why don't you get off your horse, Miss Temple?'

She heard the words before she saw him, but Carina would have recognised the voice anywhere. It was the same drawl that had mocked her before and her breath caught in her throat as Ben Mavrone moved to Pabla's head. With a quick movement he took hold of the bridle.

'We have met, or don't you remember?'

A thick layer of dust covered his face and there was blood on his wrists. Mavrone was as filthy as his companions, his appearance so far removed from the picture in her mind, Carina wouldn't have known him apart from his voice and the colour of his eyes. His regard passed over her as if he could see through her riding habit and her heart jerked unsteadily.

'Yes, I remember,' she said, finally finding her voice. 'I don't know why you're here – but I'd be grateful if you would let go of my horse.'

'I'm sure you understand the circumstances under which I'm detained.' Mavrone did not release Pabla's bridle. His hand slid along the rein close to her own. 'It's a pity I wasn't aware you were an intimate of Prince Scalia when we last met.'

'I'm not ...'

Carina faltered. Mavrone's eyes were like the sea on a bright day, only colder, and the contempt in them undisguised. He thought she had betrayed their conspiracy and seeing her with Scalia confirmed his suspicions. He would never accept she was innocent and a combination of shock and nerves kept her silent.

'You find us in desperate circumstances. I hoped you might offer us some assistance.'

Refusing to answer, Carina fixed her gaze on a point between Pabla's ears.

'What's the delay, Capitano?'

One of the men came to stand beside Mavrone and Carina remembered the others. Three of them had formed a semicircle in front of Pabla. She saw the way they watched Mavrone, waiting for his command. The captain had instigated the manoeuvre. Did he plan to steal the horse and make his escape? Surely, he couldn't ride in shackles? No one could – yet he would manage somehow, she thought. He would haul himself over the mare's back and gallop off, leaving her to the mercy of his companions.

Carina let her gaze roam over the men. They were close enough for her to smell the stench of stale sweat and she wrinkled her nose.

'Miss Temple doesn't like the scent of patriots, Ruffo.'

'Get your men out of my way or I'll use the whip on you,' she commanded in a low voice.

'Will you indeed? Has Prince Scalia initiated you already?'

Carina ignored the question. With a flick of her wrist, she uncoiled the leather thong to its full length. Her heart was tight in her chest as she waited for Mavrone to step out of the way, but he did not move.

'I order you to release my horse!'

'I don't take orders from Prince Scalia's—'

What happened next was like a nightmare. As she lifted the leather thong above her head, Mavrone forced Pabla's head round towards him. He grabbed the heel of her boot and wrenched her foot out of the stirrup. In a panic of terror, Carina lashed out. The whip caught Mavrone across the face. She saw blood on his forehead, but still he hung on. Then someone yanked the whip from her hand in a grasp that almost broke her wrist and Mavrone's arm went around her waist. He was dragging her from the saddle and, knowing she was about to fall, Carina screamed.

Terrified by the commotion, Pabla reared up on her hind legs. Then her hooves touched the earth and she jumped forward, whinnying with fright as she bolted. The reins snapped, flapping uselessly, and Carina clung on to the mane as they careered along the track. There was a crack of rifle fire and she bent down, her arms around the horse's neck. Bullets whistled overhead and the saddle horn pressed painfully into her stomach but she hung on until Pabla lost her footing. The horse's head went down and Carina was thrown from the saddle.

She landed so hard the air was knocked out of her body. Carina lay still, gasping for air until the feeling of suffocation lessened, then checked the movement of her arms and legs. Nothing was broken and she opened her eyes to find Pabla standing over her. They had reached the army encampment and she staggered to her feet. She leant against the horse as a soldier marched towards her. He demanded identification. Carina shook her head and he turned on his heel and began shouting orders. Suddenly there were soldiers running in all directions. The flap of the nearest tent lifted and Prince Scalia emerged. He stood for a moment, and then strode to her side.

'Did the mare run away with you? Are you hurt?'

'You're guilty of gross negligence, sir!'

'But the guards?'

'Your guards are blind and incompetent! They were shooting at me, for heaven's sake!'

'My dear girl, you're concussed. Come and lie down until you are recovered.'

'Don't be a fool! I've fallen off a horse before,' she replied in a harsh whisper. 'What was your purpose, sir? Did you mean to punish me for my political views?'

Prince Scalia's face went taut until every feature was rigid and Carina turned her back on him.

'Miss Temple believes her accident was due to the actions of your guards, Falcone.' He spoke loudly so that she would hear. 'If she can identify the culprits, you will ensure they're severely punished.'

The broken rein lay across her palm and Carina turned round slowly.

'I wish to return to the villa at once. I take it those responsible will be reprimanded?'

'Certainly, ma'am. My officers are down there already.'

'There's only one way to deal with them, Falcone. Single out the ruffians and send them ahead to Palermo. Count Maniscalco will deal with them personally. You know the procedure.'

Was he talking about the prisoners or guards? Carina did not know. The prince's face was hard and his tone chilling. 'And get me a fresh mount. Miss Temple will ride my horse. I'll send a groom to collect the mare this afternoon.'

Prince Scalia took hold of her arm as if he expected her to resist, but Carina was too shaken to respond. She waited while the side saddle was put on the bay and the prince gave her a leg up. As they left the camp she was beyond feeling anything except fiery hatred for both men. Scalia was a sadistic monster and Ben Mavrone a rough and abusive criminal. The image that possessed her had been an illusion and she should have known better. The cold wind went through her and Carina shivered. She hadn't given them away, but the guards would blame the prisoners and it wouldn't take them long to identify Mavrone. Once Scalia discovered he was among the captives, his fate would be sealed. She would never see him again.

CHAPTER ELEVEN

Carina leant back against the cushions as the Scalia carriage sped along the road back to Palermo. She had managed to escape a day early and the rest of the visit had been torture. By this morning she had reached breaking point.

She made sure she was never alone with Prince Scalia, but felt his eyes on her wherever she went. Her remarks to him were caustic and ill-tempered; yet the more she repudiated his advances, the more cloying he became. The prince made no attempt to conceal his interest and Bianca spent most of the time in her private apartments. On the few occasions she joined the party, she was nervous and distracted. Carina had hoped they might be friends, but understood her no better the day she left than when she arrived.

Was Bianca slightly unbalanced, Carina wondered? She was beginning to think she was losing her mind herself. A string of sleepless nights had left her nerves shattered. Now anger had faded, she was tormented by guilt. Every time she thought of the encounter with Ben Mavrone she felt ashamed. She had beaten a man in chains. How could she have acted with such violence? She wasn't a bad person, Carina told herself. She was proud of her courage and Mavrone had frightened her – but she should never have breathed a word to Scalia. If she only she'd said Pabla bolted and she fell off, he might have escaped.

A tear slipped from her lashes and slid down her cheek. She wished she had never gone to the villa. And never set eyes on Captain Mavrone. Prince Scalia had received an urgent summons and departed for Palermo last night. Carina was terrified of what it might mean. She must warn Enrico and Baron Riso! Whatever she felt for Mavrone, she hated Prince Scalia more. If she could save her patriot friends, then at least one good thing would come out of the visit.

Worn out by the conflict of her emotions, she fell asleep, not waking until they reached the outskirts of Palermo. The storm that had threatened all day broke over the city and a battery of rain hammered on the roof. Torrents of water gushed down the streets so it took forever to reach her grandmother's house. When they drove into the courtyard, Carina didn't wait for the coachman to bring an umbrella. She was out the minute the steps were down, running to the porch with her face turned up so rain fell on her cheeks.

She could see Pietro, her grandmother's footman, reading a newspaper as she tugged the bell rope. He swung the door open and Carina dumped her bonnet and cape on a chair and set off down the passage. The curtains were drawn in the sitting room and Nonna was installed by the fire with game of patience laid out on a table in front of her. She looked up in surprise.

'My dear! I wasn't expecting you until tomorrow. Why, you're wet through!'

'It's only a drop of rain. I thought you'd be pleased to have me home.'

'I'm delighted to see you.' The contessa paused, studying Carina's face, as she rang the bell. 'First, you must have something to eat. Then you can tell me everything.'

Pietro was dispatched to the kitchen and Carina stood warming her hands in front of the fire. Nonna picked up the cards, shuffling the pack, and then set it down with a slap.

'Scalia has the habits of a tomcat. I hope he didn't misbehave in any way?'

Pietro came in with a tray, which he placed on the table, and Nonna waited until he had gone before she continued, 'I expected him to act properly with his wife in residence but one should never underestimate Riccardo Scalia. He's a strange, unpredictable man. Carlo says it's because his parents showed him no affection and he was bullied at school. In my opinion, he was born devious and your uncle is a little afraid of him.'

'It wasn't because of *the prince* I left early. There was an odd atmosphere about the place, Nonna. I couldn't make head or tail of Bianca. She was like a different person there ...'

Her grandmother began to lay her cards down on the table, turning them over slowly. The fire crackled in the grate and Carina took a glass of wine from the tray and drank it. The wine warmed her and she crossed her ankles, looking at the toes of her boots glowing in the firelight.

'They're an ill-matched couple. I can't understand why Bianca married him. She must have had a hundred suitors.'

'It wasn't a love match, if that's what you mean. Isabella del Angelo was a good woman, but not wise. She regarded the proposal as a golden opportunity for her daughter. On the surface, Prince Scalia offered everything – wealth and a high position in society – everything except happiness. The child was only seventeen, how could she know better?' The question was rhetorical. 'Bianca was also very susceptible at the time. She was recovering from a broken heart.'

'So she married Prince Scalia after her engagement to Captain Mavrone was broken off?'

'What makes you think that?'

'Paulo told me. Well, he didn't say they were engaged exactly. He implied they were ...'

Carina couldn't get the word out and Nonna answered without looking up. 'I'm sure Paulo puffed a lot of nonsense! Bianca was never *engaged* to Mavrone. It was a childhood attachment and brought to an end the moment her mother found out. The Mavrone boys were sent abroad and within months she was married to the snake.'

'And Mavrone never forgave Prince Scalia. Was that the beginning of the vendetta?'

'No one knows. Mavrone was a wild young man, but he respected Donna Isabella. He and his brother were orphans and she brought them up out of the kindness of her heart. Her only mistake was to allow Bianca to spend her holidays with them. Can you imagine, the daughter of Count del Angelo falling for the son of a peasant?'

At once everything became clear – Bianca's strange behaviour and her relationship with her husband. Theirs was an arranged marriage embittered by the memory of her first love. And Bianca must have known Ben Mavrone was near the Villa Pallestro! That was why she had been distressed about the road-blocks. It was the only possible explanation. Mavrone had come to meet with her and been captured, quite by accident, along with the others.

A quiver of jealousy darted through Carina. Ben Mavrone was Bianca's responsibility – so let her save him! Bianca wouldn't have the nerve, she thought. Then a new idea occurred to her.

Bianca might appear fragile, but there was resilience beneath her fragility. There must be, and cunning, too, to carry on with her lover under her husband's nose.

Suddenly Carina was furious. Furious with herself and furious with all of them. Her infatuation had been madness, a stupid girlish fantasy, and thank God it was over! She didn't care what happened to Mavrone. She wanted nothing more to do with the whole wretched business. And yet, she must speak to Enrico and warn him. She would ask Nonna to send a card, requesting he call upon her at his earliest convenience.

Refreshed by a good night's sleep, Carina felt better as she waited for Enrico in the garden. The storm had passed and the sun was out, warming her as she sat on the stone bench. She wanted to speak to Enrico outside so they wouldn't be over-heard. Should she say she had seen Ben Mavrone? Only if absolutely necessary, Carina decided. She didn't want to think about him and Enrico was in enough trouble already.

A bird was nesting in the viburnum bush close by, darting in and out and Carina looked up to see Enrico walking down the path. How attractive he was with his pale face and limpid eyes, she thought. No wonder Gabriella was in love with him. Enrico was far nobler than the man who branded him a traitor.

What's so urgent that I'm summoned here post-haste?' Enrico sat down beside her.

'A matter of the greatest importance. It concerns Prince Scalia. He claims you're a member of a secret society and a traitor to the king!'

'Does he really?'

The look in Enrico's eyes was guarded and his stiffness made Carina feel awkward. Did he think this meeting was a contrivance on her part to entrap him? Why, the very idea was absurd! She caught her lower lip between her teeth and waited a minute before she spoke.

'The authorities discovered a plot involving Baron Riso. You're suspected of treason and are under surveillance. You could be arrested at any time!'

A smudge of yellow pollen fell on Enrico's sleeve and he blew it off, his tone indifferent. 'I'm sure Scalia was keen to impress you, but they have no evidence.'

'They don't need evidence, you know that! Please listen to me, Enrico! You must consider your safety and that of your family. Think of Gabriella.'

'Gabriella would want me to stay.'

Lord, he was being difficult! If she'd known he'd be so stubborn she might not have bothered. Carina twisted her hands to contain her frustration.

'How does it serve your cause if you are imprisoned?'

'It testifies to the world there are men in Sicily prepared to sacrifice themselves for their country. It gives the people hope.'

'Fiddlesticks! The people don't want martyrs – they want food! The revolution failed last time. How can you prevail against the might of the Bourbon army?'

'In '48 we were alone. If we demonstrate the courage to rise up ourselves in the name of unity and freedom, Garibaldi will come …'

As if he had said too much, Enrico gazed up to the palm fronds swaying in the breeze. Carina had read about Garibaldi in the newspapers. He was a charismatic leader whose aim was to unite Italy. Enrico's no dreamy idealist, she thought suddenly. He's in far deeper than any of us ever imagined. Heaven protect him, does he have any idea of the risk he is taking?

'Not even Garibaldi can perform miracles. Whatever it is

you're planning, you must postpone until circumstances are more fortuitous. It would be folly to act now.'

'If we delay, every free-thinking man in Sicily will be silenced.'

'And if the revolution fails, you'll achieve the opposite of what you hope. The injustice and suffering will only be worse—'

'Forgive my impertinence, but you've only been in Sicily a month.' Enrico lowered his head to look her in the face. 'What do you know of injustice and suffering?'

'I know you cannot fight suffering and injustice with the sword. They are only be defeated by endurance, using pain as your weapon and courage your strength.'

Enrico looked at her curiously, but said nothing. He was impatient to be gone, Carina could tell. She had failed to convince him and must play her last card.

'Captain Mavrone has been arrested,' she said in a low voice. 'I saw him with other prisoners on the Scalia estate. He's on his way to be interrogated in Palermo.'

There was a moment of silence and then Enrico swung round. 'Are you sure it was him?'

'I'm absolutely sure. And if they have Mavrone, they'll soon arrest you. You must leave Palermo before it's too late!'

He stood up and Carina followed suit, disconcerted by the shift in his reaction.

'Please forgive my lack of civility earlier.' Enrico extended his hand. 'We dare trust nobody – not even our own families. You're a true friend and I thank you.'

'Will you warn Baron Riso?'

'I'll warn Francesco, but we cannot run away. It's our patriotic duty to win Sicily her freedom.'

For all his fine words, Carina would have done anything to stop him. Tears welled up in her eyes and Enrico dipped his head beneath her bonnet and kissed her cheek. Then he stood back.

'Don't lose faith in us, Carina. And stay away from Prince Scalia. That man would move heaven and earth to have you in his power.'

Enrico's resolve was unbreakable. Did Paulo have any idea of his friend's commitment, Carina wondered? More importantly, was Gabriella aware of the danger he was in? Her cousin would be proud of him, she thought. And what of herself? Enrico's passion stirred her heart. The patriots had right on their side, but revolution was a bloody business and the odds stacked against them. They must be certain, she thought as she watched his slim figure disappear towards the house. They must be sure that their sacrifice is not in vain.

CHAPTER TWELVE

Dearest Alice
Palermo is a different city without you and my cousins. I miss you
and am less confident now than when we first arrived. Sicily has a
cruel and savage side that is hard to understand. I would like to
speak to Jane, but she is in Rome and I dare not visit the consulate
on my own. I wonder if I truly belong here? Please write soon. My
grandmother is in good health and sends you her blessing on your
marriage.

A little over a fortnight later, Carina received an answer.

Our separation is a bitter pang, dearest. I understand you are
lonely without the company of Paulo and Gabriella – but please
don't be too downhearted or discouraged. These weeks of winter
will pass and when your cousins return for Easter, your spirits will
revive. I have never seen you so happy as in the company of your
mother's family. Sicily is in your blood and will never leave you …

Alice understood her better than anyone and Carina was reassured. Still, Enrico's remark about Scalia troubled her. Was he referring to her in particular, or anyone acquainted with Baron Riso? She was safe under her uncle's protection and it was Enrico who was in danger. Where was he now?

A wall of silence surrounded the palazzo and she was desperate for news. Anna Maria had returned to Palermo and called twice at the Palazzo Scalia already. She must have learned something, but Carina could not question her in front of her grandmother. It was impossible to discover anything until, out of the blue, Anna Maria suggested she accompany her on a pilgrimage to the monastery of Santa Fiore in the mountains.

When Nonna expressed reservations, her aunt brushed them aside. Prince Scalia had assured her that the roads were safe, she declared; and even been so kind as to offer a mounted escort.

'It's only for our peace of mind. Count Maniscalco's been busy all winter. The brigands who caused us so much trouble are all under lock and key.'

So it was settled. Nonna gave way and Carina rose early on the morning of the excursion. Anna Maria had stipulated nothing too ostentatious, so she chose a dress of dove-grey crêpe without a crinoline. Despite Rose's admonitions, she refused to wear a corset. Tightly laced stays were unnecessary on a pilgrimage, she argued. Besides, it would be cold in the mountains and flannel pantalets were warmer than petticoats.

Carina's arrival in the courtyard preceded that of her aunt by a few seconds. Anna Maria was rigged out like a ship in full sail, with a gold crucifix pinned to her chest and clasping a jewel-encrusted prayer book. Observing her difficulty in negotiating the narrow doorway into the carriage, Carina wondered if they would both fit inside. Once she was in, Anna Maria gathered as many folds of her skirt about her as she could and Carina squeezed in opposite her. A sea of black taffeta filled the space between so she could hardly breathe, but when they reached the city gates the horses were whipped up and a breeze came in through the window bringing relief.

Scalia's two outriders, with their distinctive cockaded hats, were with them and Anna Maria announced she was going to say her prayers. Her lips moved silently as the beads passed through her fingers and the smell of wild herbs by the roadside made Carina think of Melton. Alice had told her how Sonia instructed the gardeners to pick sweetly perfumed leaves, laying them out in trays to dry before they were brought into the house. The custom had carried on after her death but it only occurred to her now that it came from Sicily.

'What are you dreaming about? Some young man perhaps?' Anna Maria put away her beads as the landau jolted over a bad patch of road.

'I was thinking about the brigands who've been arrested. What will happen to them?'

'If they're found guilty, they'll be sentenced accordingly. Now let me see, where are we?'

'Will any of them be executed?'

Anna Maria was gazing out of the window and turned her head, her face crumpled with disapproval.

'You forget we're on a pilgrimage, Carina! Such morbid fascination does not become you. You make me feel faint with such talk. Now, where are my smelling salts?'

Anna Maria searched in her pouch for a bottle and waved it under her nose. Then she leant back and shut her eyes. She didn't look faint, but it was an effective way to put an end to questions. She must wait for the return journey, Carina decided. Then she would pester and cajole Anna Maria until she extracted every morsel of information she had to offer.

They had come to the foothills and were lumbering up a narrow road between rocky escarpments. Judging from the position of the sun, it must be almost midday. If her calculations were correct, they would arrive at the convent of Santa Fiore within the hour. The thought of shady cloisters and the fresh mountain air made Carina drowsy. She was half asleep when a loud noise jolted her awake. For a confused moment she thought she was dreaming. Then she heard shouts and a rattle of gunfire. The horses plunged forward and the landau lurched, tilting precariously. As it came to a shuddering halt, both women were thrown to the floor.

The carriage was tipped on its side, making it difficult to move, but Carina managed to heave herself up on to the seat. As she leant down to help Anna Maria, a high-pitched keening came from outside. It was a spine-chilling sound and silenced by a gunshot. One of the horses must have broken a leg! They had shot one of the horses! As Carina tried to get to the door, Anna Maria clutched her skirts. 'We've been attacked! *Madre de Dio*, we've been ambushed!'

'We've had an accident. I expect a wheel's broken off. I'm going to open the door. You stay here.'

Anna Maria began to intone a prayer and Carina grasped the door handle. Where was Gino, the coachman? He should be here by now. The door was jammed fast and after a couple of attempts she gave up. Reaching for the blind, she undid the catch. Then she hauled herself up, resting her elbows on the rim as she looked out.

They had crashed at a point where the road was only wide enough for a single vehicle to pass. Just as she had thought, one of the wheels had sheared off. Carina could see the coachmen gathered in a group ahead. One of them – she thought it was Gino – was giving orders and waving his arms. Squinting her eyes, she counted the men. There were too many figures! Then, with a lurch of her stomach, she looked up and saw others standing at the top of the bank.

Anna Maria was right – they had been ambushed. Carina stared in horror at the bandits. Cartridge belts were slung over their jerkins and they carried knives with wide blades that caught the sun as they scrambled down the escarpment. The man she had mistaken for Gino was herding the coachmen to the side of the road. He prodded them onto their knees with the butt of his gun as they were tied up and made to lie face down on the ground.

Where was Scalia's escort, for God's sake? Carina twisted her neck and searched back along the road. Two bodies were sprawled on the ground and one lay close to the carriage. He had been trampled under its wheels and his hat, bearing Prince Scalia's cockade, was soaked in blood by his head. Nausea rose in her throat and Carina let go of the window ledge and sank back onto the seat.

'Holy Mary protect us!' Anna Maria raised her head. 'Santa Rosalia, come to our aid. Jesus save us—'

Carina was brought to her senses by her aunt's wailing. 'We must give them money if they come for us. How much do you have?'

'I don't know. It's in my purse …'

Anna Maria fumbled in her skirts and Carina saw the purse first. It had fallen out and was lying on the floor. She picked it up and spilled the contents on to her lap. Among the bottles and handkerchiefs were a few coins and a roll of banknotes tied to a large white piece of parchment.

'What's this?'

'A letter from Prince Scalia—'

'Well, we won't have need of that.'

Carina detached the notes and stuffed the letter into her pocket. She squeezed the banknotes in her palm as footsteps approached. The handle of the door was shaken and then the whole panel wrenched off its hinges. The gaping hole was filled by the shadow of a man who caught her by the shoulders and dragged her out.

She landed on her feet, a knife held beneath her chin so her head was forced back. The brigand's arm was tight beneath her ribs and a strangled sound came from her throat. The pressure eased and Carina breathed in air as the bandits crowded around her.

'What brings you to Santa Fiore with a mounted bodyguard?'

'We're on our way to the monastery. We'll give you money.'

'Sure you will – but maybe we want a bit more.' One of the men made an obscene gesture with his hips. 'Shall we have us some sport, my friends?'

'You forget our purpose, Paco. Where's the money, lady?'

Carina's arms were pinioned to her sides and the one called Paco took her hand and opened her fist. With a yell of triumph, he waved the bankroll in the air before digging into the pockets of her skirt.

'What's this?' He held up the letter from Prince Scalia.

'Tell us what it says!' one of them shouted.

Paco dropped the paper to the ground and the bandits laughed.

'Didn't you go to school, Paco? Can't you read?'

They had discarded the document and Carina saw greedy delight on their faces as the money was distributed. The knife beneath her chin was removed as the man who held her took his share. She momentarily forgot about Anna Maria until, like a signal from hell, Carina heard a scream as two bandits lifted her aunt out of the landau. The crucifix had been torn from her dress and tears streamed down her face. She tripped over her long skirts and a rough hand sent her to the ground.

'Time to say your prayers, you old cow!'

'Let's hear you beg for your life—'

'Leave her alone! Stop it! Stop it at once!'

Carina shouted at them, but she was forced to listen as the bandits goaded Anna Maria. Her aunt was on all fours, her vast crinoline billowing behind her. She was weeping and pleading until suddenly her sobbing ceased. She had seen Prince Scalia's letter and Carina's blood slowed in her veins. No, she wouldn't be so stupid! Even Anna Maria couldn't be such a fool! As she willed her to ignore it, Carina saw her fingers stretch out for the roll of parchment.

'Come on! Kiss my boots and I might let you live.'

'Never!' Anna Maria waved the letter in the air. 'We're under Prince Scalia's protection. This is—'

She was silenced as Paco hit her across the face. Blood dripped from her mouth and when his arm went up to strike her again, Anna Maria fainted at his feet. Paco reached down and snatched the letter from her limp fingers.

'Do you know who they are? They're Scalia's friends. It was in her possession, Ruffo! She knows what it says. Make her read it!'

He strode over and thrust the document in front of her face. Carina was turned about so she was staring at her captor. Above the thunder in her ears, she heard him say her name. 'Miss Temple, if I am not mistaken?'

Shifting his gaze from her, he looked over her head to the others. 'Leave the woman to me. Keep the letter, Paco. I know someone who'll have use of it. Search the carriage and search well. Make sure no more of Prince Scalia's spies are hiding inside.'

The orders were given and darkness swirled in Carina's brain. The brigand who held her was the same man she had seen with Mavrone near the Villa Pallestro. Anna Maria had placed them in mortal danger and such terror seized her. Carina cried out as Ruffo pushed her back against the broken wheel. Her aunt lying unconscious on the ground; her neck was bent sideways and her eyes closed. A lizard scuttled by, its tail touching her hand and her fingers twitched. Thank God she was alive – but what had they done with Gino and the others?

Scalia's men lay dead on the road but Carina couldn't see Gino. Where was he – and how could she save any of them? She must try to bargain with the bandits. Apart from Ruffo, they were swarming over the landau, ripping up seats and tearing off brass fittings and she twisted round to look at him.

'We're on a pilgrimage. It would be sacrilege to do us injury.'

'Sacrilege, do you say? Isn't whipping innocent men sacrilege?'

What was he talking about? Carina stared at him blankly. The rim of the wheel bruised her spine and she winced as Paco emerged from the carriage, grinning toothlessly.

'Is she too much for you, Ruffo?'

'Get the weapons on the horses and hurry up! You can keep the money – but the woman is mine.'

'What do you want to take her for? Get on with it here. Save yourself the trouble.'

They spoke in dialect, but Carina understood enough. The bandits were desperate and there was no hope of bargaining with them. She must escape and ride for help. With a suddenness that caught Ruffo off guard, she threw her body sideways and ducked under his arm. Her long legs streaked out as she sprinted towards the uncoupled horses. When she reached the first, she grabbed hold of its mane and had one leg over the withers before Ruffo caught her and threw her to the ground. Paco held her down as a foul-smelling wedge of material was stuffed in her mouth and her wrists bound with rope.

Ruffo slung her over the horse so her head hung below its flanks. When he mounted, he pulled her up to ride astride in front of him and Carina looked around in panic. Anna Maria was on her knees, clinging to the broken axle and Ruffo shouted over to her.

'Tell Prince Scalia we have his whore! If he wants her back he'll have to pay! Otherwise, she's dead!'

Her skirts were hitched up and Carina kicked her heels at the horse's shoulders. Her boot caught in the reins and she yanked the bit, trying to bring the animal over backwards. The next instant a hard object slammed into the side of her head. There was a blinding flash before everything went black and the last thing she heard was Anna Maria's voice, fading, calling out her name.

CHAPTER THIRTEEN

The horse stumbled and Carina groaned as consciousness forced itself upon her. Her head ached and she was astride a horse, slumped against a man's chest. Her hands were tied but the gag had been removed and the air she breathed was cool. It was almost dark, but she made out a column of riders ahead and the serrated edge of a mountaintop. How long had she been unconscious? Too weary to search for answers, her eyelids dropped and closed.

Occasionally in the hours that followed, she heard Ruffo talking and, when they stopped, the sound of running water. A stream gushed down the hillside and the bandits dismounted and waded in alongside their horses, scooping water into their mouths. Ruffo remained in the saddle while one of the men filled a skin and handed it up to him. He took long gulps and finished with a grunt. Then Carina's head was pulled back and he prised her mouth open, pouring water down her throat.

Paco's hand slid up her leg, pinching her calf through the thin material of her pantalets.

'Keep your filthy hands off her. She's mine,' Ruffo growled.

He pulled up the horse's head and took the lead, following a path no wider than a sheep track. Carina felt lather from the horse's flanks, hot and sticky on the inside of her legs. Her head throbbed as she forced herself to think. They had been on the move for half a day and were far away from Santa Fiore. The bandits intended to use her as a hostage and would do her no harm, she told herself. She tried to be brave, but her teeth chattered. Where were they taking her?

Ruffo guided the horse carefully and when they reached a small clearing he reined in and dismounted. Reaching up, he grasped Carina around the waist and lifted her down. Her legs were cramped and he gripped her arm, steadying her.

'Stay close to me – if you try to run, I'll let Paco have you,' he muttered.

She hated this man with his thick body and bull-like strength, but she feared Paco more. As she followed Ruffo, loose shale made her stumble and he squatted down beside her. Not knowing what he meant to do, Carina drew her legs up away from him.

'No need for fancy shoes where you're going.'

Her boots were pulled off and Ruffo helped her to her feet. With his hand heavy on her shoulder, they passed through a thicket of thorns. When they came out the other side, she glimpsed the outline of tumbledown shacks. A fire had been lit and Ruffo cupped his hands to his mouth and gave a long, warbling whistle. There was no responding signal and he swore.

'*Merda!* He's a suspicious devil. Stay here.'

'I'll take care of her.' Paco's arm encircled her waist and Carina fixed her gaze on Ruffo. She saw a man standing by the fire and Ruffo raise his arms as he came into the light. Then he turned to point in their direction.

'So, lady-whore, it's time to get you ready.' Paco's fingers pulled her hair loose and moved to her collar.

'Behave yourself, Paco! You heard what he said,' one of the others whispered.

'Ruffo's a fool if he thinks he can keep her for himself.'

She would scream if he touched her again, but Paco let her go for Ruffo was coming back. With his fist in the small of her back, he pushed Carina ahead of him and when they reached the campfire, took her by the shoulders and turned her round.

'Here she is, my friend. A worthy prize, eh?'

Ice fingers of shock reached down inside her as Carina stared at Ben Mavrone. She must be delirious, she thought. He was being interrogated in Palermo. How could he be here? Then hope leapt in her heart. Mavrone was a friend of Baron Riso. He wasn't a murderer and would come to her rescue! There was a distant look in his eyes as they went to her face. Didn't he recognise her? How different she must look in dirty, torn clothes with her hair hanging loose – but surely he would save her? Then Carina thought of their last encounter and all certainty vanished.

'I told you how we captured the horses. She was in the carriage,' Ruffo said. 'She's the one we saw with Scalia! He'll pay good money for her!'

Mavrone turned to Ruffo without speaking to her and Carina watched as the other men come forward. They shook his hand, greeting him in turn, and she sensed his authority. He only had to tell them to free her and they would do so. What was he waiting for? A bottle was passed from one to the other but her attention was only on Mavrone as she strained to hear what he was saying.

'You've money and horses enough. Tomorrow, when you're rested, you'll make your way to Marsala.'

'What about the woman?' The question came from Paco.

'She's the property of myself and my friend,' Ruffo answered. 'That's right, isn't it, Capitano? It was on Miss Temple's orders you and I were picked out for punishment.'

That's *not true!* Carina shouted inside her head. This couldn't be happening. She felt her grip on reality slipping and at any moment might become hysterical.

'Read this, Capitano! Tell us if she's a Bourbon spy.'

Paco stepped forward with Scalia's letter and gave it to Mavrone. He looked at it, frowning as he scanned the page, then held it up and read aloud.

I, Prince Riccardo Scalia, Duke of Pallestro, authorise Contessa Denuzio and Miss Carina Temple to travel to the Convent of Santa Fiore. If anyone impedes their progress or causes them unnecessary delay, they will be reported to the Office of Justice and prosecuted accordingly.

'There you are! The whore was doing penance for her sins.'

'She's a spy!'

'What ransom will Scalia pay for her?'

A cacophony of voices rose around them and Mavrone crumpled the paper and dropped it in the fire. The bottle was handed to him and he tipped it to his mouth, draining it to the last drop before he sent it crashing against the rocks. The violence of his action brought silence and he walked over to Carina. For the first time, he spoke to her.

'So, will your lover pay good money for your return?'

'I was with my aunt. We were on a pilgrimage—'

'I don't care what you were doing. I want to know how much you're worth to Prince Scalia.'

A small animal ran across the earth, scurrying between them. There was a squeal as a boot struck it aside. The sound skimmed the surface of Carina's mind as Mavrone took hold of the front of her dress. He drew her towards him until she was pressed against the length of his body. His hand went to her neck and he felt the rapid beat of the pulse beneath his fingers.

'Are you frightened, Miss Temple? Do you think you'll get your just desserts?'

Mavrone hoped to make her beg for mercy, but she would rather die than give him satisfaction. Carina raised her head, her voice cold and clear.

'I despise you, Captain Mavrone. But I wasn't the one responsible for your punishment. It was the guards I condemned to Scalia. If you were punished, then you brought it on yourselves by your actions.'

Mavrone towered over her and Carina raised her eyes to his shadowed face. When he spoke, his command was so quiet she barely heard it.

'Hold her still, will you?'

Ruffo held her by the arms and Mavrone moved behind her. The ropes binding her wrists became tight and Carina stifled a cry before she realised he was cutting her loose. Someone threw wood on the fire so the flames were high and Ruffo held her so she couldn't move. Mavrone lifted his knife to the side of her face. As the blade touched her cheek, her eyes glazed. She felt it trace a path down her neck to her throat. Then the knife was withdrawn and she heard his voice.

'The hostage is an Englishwoman, comrades. If we want the support of her country we must be circumspect.'

'I told Ruffo it was unlucky to bring her with us,' Paco's whiny voice joined in. 'What shall we do with her? She's seen too much.'

'If we don't return her, we'll get no help from England. If we free her, she'll go to Scalia and endanger all we've worked for.'

'So what do you propose? Make her disappear into thin air?'
Ruffo was belligerent.

'I'll have to try and get her to Monteleone.' Mavrone's tone
brooked no opposition. 'Scalia's men don't dare travel beyond
Castelvano. It won't be easy but there's no other way.'

As the discussion moved from one to the other, Carina
thought she discerned grudging acceptance. Where did he say
he was taking her? Supposing, she thought wildly, he meant to
deceive the bandits and set her free?

'I won't help you again, Ruffo. Next time you get up to your
old tricks, leave the damned women behind.'

'May we enjoy her for tonight?' Paco asked.

'Let the capitano have her,' Ruffo answered gruffly. 'There's
plenty of women for us in Marsala. If we made a mistake with
this one, we made plenty of money too – and I'll drink to that.'

The men began to move away to sit by the fire and Carina's
façade of courage splintered. Her legs gave way and, as she
sank to the ground, Mavrone scooped her up in his arms. He
carried her with his arm under her knees and her cheek pressed
against the rough leather of his jerkin. Coming to the first hut,
he bent his head under the lintel and kicked the door shut
behind him before he put her down.

It was pitch black inside and reeked of sheep. Carina heard
the bolt being drawn and Mavrone moving around. He struck
a match and a small flame flickered into life. As he placed the
candle on a table, she edged into the corner, backing away until
her spine was pressed against the damp wall. Her hands were
slippery with sweat and her voice hoarse.

'Tell me how much you want. I'll get it for you.'

'I don't want your money.'

Mavrone took paper and tobacco, rolling them together. He
bent his dark head above the candle and she noticed he had

shaved off his beard. It helped to stay sane by concentrating on small details and she must keep him talking.

'Are you going to set me free?'

'Not at this precise moment.'

'Then when?'

'When the time's right. You're lucky those scoundrels handed you over.'

'Are you saying you didn't plan this? It wasn't your idea?'

'I knew nothing about it.'

'But they're your men. I heard you give them orders.'

'They're outlaws, Miss Temple. I have no authority over them.'

'So why was he, you know … the man with you the day—'

'It so happened that Ruffo and I were detained at the same time. If I'd known what he planned today, I'd have stopped him and saved myself a lot of trouble.'

'You could have left well alone.'

'Don't play the innocent, Miss Temple. You know the men would rape you. The *banditti* are rather less fastidious than myself.'

Of all the abuse she had received, this last was the worst. How could he say that word in front of her? No gentleman spoke of such things. But Mavrone wasn't a gentleman! He was as cruel and coarse as the others. The insult was more than Carina could bear, unhinging the last part of her mind under control.

'You're not fastidious, Captain Mavrone. You're afraid you'll compare poorly with Riccardo Scalia!'

Mavrone dropped his unfinished cigarette and crushed the stub under his boot. When he reached Carina, he pushed her so hard against the wall she was lifted off her feet. One elbow rested above her head, his mouth above her lips and his breath rasping down her throat. The blazing light in his eyes terrified her. With an agonised cry, Carina twisted her head away and he let go of her so suddenly she almost fell.

'By God, ma'am, you deserve a bringing down.'

His voice cracked across the room and someone shouted from outside.

'Hey, Capitano! Hurry up! We're waiting for you!'

'*Pazienza!* I'm coming.'

The door slammed shut and Carina slid slowly to the floor. What had she done? Dear God, who would help her now? The candle spluttered and went out but the cold kept her alert. She heard the scraping of footsteps outside and was on her feet before Mavrone came back through the door. He relit the candle, its glow spreading to his face as he turned towards her.

'Don't look so frightened. I'm not going to hurt you.'

Carina did not hear his words. There was a rushing sound in her ears and the space between them lost focus. Her arms went out, flaying empty air, and Mavrone caught her as she fell. He laid her down on a pile of sheepskins and she felt his hand at the back of her head.

'Drink this …'

A flagon was pushed against her lips and into her mouth. Raw spirit scorched her throat and Carina gagged. She tried to spit it out but he held the bottle in her mouth until she swallowed. As her head fell back, liquid trickled from the side of her mouth and she thought she would be sick.

The brandy seeped into her bloodstream, dulling her senses. Her limbs felt too heavy to move, her mind too tired to think. She was dimly aware of Mavrone locking the bolt and snuffing out the candle before he lay down beside her. His arm dropped on her stomach and Carina rolled over on her side. She stared sightlessly into the dark but Mavrone did not stir. His breathing became light and, finally defeated by trauma and exhaustion, she fell asleep with his arm a dead weight across her waist.

Carina heard the creak of a door and could not think where she was. Her brain was befuddled by a sense of foreboding. She was lying on hard ground and every muscle in her body ached. Then she remembered the events of the day before. She prayed she was dreaming, but she was awake and the horror was real.

What devil made her taunt Mavrone with Scalia's name? She had alienated the one person who might have helped her. The ordeal must have shattered her wits, Carina thought with rising panic. There was no one she could turn to now. Her only hope was to escape. But how? She recalled the bushes near the entrance and the place where they had left the horses. Now that she was rested, she could run faster. If she could get to the horses, she might have a chance.

Carina opened her eyes. The only window was a small opening in the wall where stones had been removed and she saw Mavrone standing by the door. He had his back to her and his hunting knife lay on the table. He thought she was asleep and had left it unguarded. *Now,* she thought. *Now!* In one movement Carina came to her feet and grabbed the knife off the table, brandishing it in the air as Mavrone wheeled round.

'Unlock the door!' She ordered in a hoarse voice.

'I'm surprised you're so keen to join Ruffo and his friends.'

'Unlock the door. Then get out of my way.'

Carina jabbed the blade at Mavrone and he stood aside, but without slipping the bolt. He hoped to unnerve her, but she was the one with the weapon! She waved it at him again and he moved further away. Carina stepped cautiously towards the door. The iron bolt was stiff so she had to lift one hand off the hilt to open it. Glancing over her shoulder, she saw Mavrone watching her with an expression of absorbed interest. He thought she wouldn't make it but she was too desperate to contemplate failure. She opened the door a crack and looked out.

A couple of bandits were sitting around the fire while others were still asleep and she estimated the distance she had to run. If she kept behind the buildings she could get more than half-way before she had to break cover. Barefoot she wouldn't make a sound and Carina shoved the door wide open. Ruffo was kneeling by the fire poking it with a stick and she took a deep breath.

'*Figlio de puttante*, bring some coffee over here!'

Carina heard Mavrone's shout and spun about. He moved like lightning across the room and she went for him with the knife. The blade slashed through his shirt. Holding the hilt with both hands, she lunged at him again. Mavrone took a step side-ways and his fist slammed down hard, knocking the knife out of her hands. It fell to the floor, sliding under the table beyond her reach. In a frenzy of rage, Carina threw herself at him, punching his chest until he hooked a foot behind her knees and kicked her legs from under her.

'Am I interrupting anything?' Ruffo walked through the door. Together they bound Carina and pushed her up against the wall.

'So she cut you, my friend.' He pointed to the thin red line of blood on Mavrone's shirt. His lips drew back in a smile that showed his yellow teeth. 'The knife – now that was careless.'

He had brought coffee and bread, which he placed on the table and Mavrone dipped a cloth in water.

'I've always been susceptible to feminine charms and this one's no exception,' he remarked as he cleaned his wound. 'It's only a scratch but she'd kill us all if she could.'

Carina sobbed in desperation and fury. If only she *had* killed him! Mavrone was treating her like an animal and she wanted him dead. For pity's sake, what was happening to her? Why hadn't she tried to negotiate with him? There was a chance she could have persuaded him to let her go. In less than twenty-four hours she had become as barbaric as her tormentors. Pain spliced her neck from the temple and she wondered if the blow to her head had affected her brain.

The smell of coffee made her stomach cramp with hunger. How long was it since she had last eaten? Not since yesterday morning but when Ruffo waved a mug at her, Carina shook her head. Mavrone dipped a hunk of bread in his coffee and brought it over and she clamped her mouth shut.

'You will eat, even if I have to force food down you. Don't fight me, Miss Temple. It won't do you any good.'

There was a hard look in his eyes as he pushed the crust into her mouth and Carina dared not spit it out. The bread had been softened by coffee and she swallowed it whole. Mavrone filled a mug with water and held it to her lips and she took a small amount.

'Make sure Prince Scalia pays a good price for her.' Ruffo leant down beside Carina, breathing sour liquor into her face. 'Behave yourself if you want to stay alive.'

'She'll soon learn. Now help make sure she doesn't escape.'

Everything Mavrone had said last night was a lie! Ruffo and the other bandits were under Mavrone's command. Why bother to deny it? As they dragged her over and looped a rope around her and the table leg, Carina shouted at them, heedless of the emotion in her voice.

'You won't get away with this! Never! Not even when you're dead and damned in Hell!'

'Maybe so.' Mavrone hunkered down and tied her ankles together. 'But until then it would be easier on us both if you were more amenable. Are you going to be quiet?'

Carina wanted to spit in his face but she saw the dirty cloth in Ruffo's hand. The idea of the filthy rag in her mouth made tears sting her eyes and she looked away so that Mavrone wouldn't see. There was no need for a gag. She could shout and scream all she liked, but no one would hear and he seemed to understand.

'Leave her be; only wolves pass this way.'

Mavrone retrieved his knife from under the table and wiped it clean before he tucked it into his belt. Ruffo was already outside, calling to his companions to hurry up, as Mavrone slung a knapsack over his shoulder and walked to the door. He stopped to look back and Carina dropped her head.

'I'll be away for a few hours and will return this evening. Be kind enough to wait for me until then.'

CHAPTER FOURTEEN

A fly settled on her nose and Carina tossed her head to get rid of it. Despair smashed into her like a battering ram. Where had Mavrone gone? How long before he would return? What if he never came back? To keep terror at bay, she concentrated on her discomfort; the cramp in her legs and the rope chafing her wrists. As the hours passed she recited lines from Byron and focussed her mind on thoughts of rescue.

Anna Maria must have been found and word sent to Palermo. The Scalia household would be alerted. No matter that she disliked him, the prince would do everything in his power to find her. He had troops at his disposal. His men would be searching the region of Santa Fiore by now. They could have picked up her trail already. It might take time, but they would come.

How could anyone find her in this godforsaken place? Reality forced its way in and tears filled Carina's eyes. They streamed down her cheeks and she wept until her heart was empty. Afterwards, she must have slept for when she awoke the light had dimmed. There was a snap of twigs underfoot and the door opened, letting a welcome draught into the stuffy atmosphere.

From her position on the floor, Mavrone looked taller and more imposing than ever. Walking over to the table he lifted the flap of the knapsack and took out her boots.

'I imagine these are yours?'

Mavrone tossed them onto the floor and went on unpacking. A bottle of wine with bread and strong-smelling cheese was laid out above her head. He took the pitcher outside and fetched fresh water. Then, without a word of explanation, he bent down and cut her loose. Not knowing what else to do, Carina stayed where she was, rubbing her chafed wrists.

'I don't need my boots. I'm not going anywhere.'

'Don't pin your hopes on Prince Scalia, Miss Temple. Ruffo backtracked to lay the search party off the scent. They won't find you here. No one will.'

'So what are you going to do with me?'

Mavrone took the bottle of wine and dug out the cork with the point of his knife before he cut a slice of bread.

'I'm not abandoning you, nor am I letting you go. Are you hungry?'

A hunk of bread was held in front of her. Carina turned away and he ate it himself. He did not offer her wine, but filled a mug with water and gave it to her.

'You should eat. We've a long journey ahead of us.'

When she shook her head, he replaced the cork in the bottle and returned the remainder of the food to the knapsack. Then he walked over to the sheepskins and lay down with his arms folded behind his head.

'I'm going to have a rest. Go outside and get some air.'

'Is it a habit of yours to abduct innocent women, Captain Mavrone?' Carina snapped at him. 'Do you do it for pleasure or for money?'

'On this occasion, neither. Now, if you don't mind, I'd like some peace and quiet.'

Carina walked out of the door and made her way to the fire. She looked up at the sky, scattered with white stars, and it seemed unbelievable that, only two nights before, she had stood on her balcony and gazed at the same sky. Her entire world had been swept away and everything familiar taken from her. There was no use trying to escape now. It was dark and she didn't even know if they had a horse between them. Hunger pains gnawed at her stomach and she should have eaten. The rational part of her brain told her it was stupid to refuse but resistance to Mavrone was the only way to hold on to her identity. If she gave in to him she was lost.

Carina knelt down by the fire, blowing the hot embers into life and thought of her grandmother. Poor Nonna would be distraught. She dare not think about her. What did Mavrone really want? Why was he being more lenient? Was he going to help her after all? She couldn't read his mind any more than she could anticipate his next move and her brain was tired from trying. When he emerged from the hut it was almost a relief.

Mavrone had her boots in his hand and he dropped them on the ground beside her before he went to the other side of the fire.

'There are a few things I want to set straight.' He spoke slowly as if she were hard of hearing. 'Firstly, we are both in a situation neither of us anticipated—'

'That's not true.'

'Secondly, I am in your debt.'

Carina's head came up, her eyes wide and uncertain. The glow of flames cast light on Mavrone's face and his expression was serious.

'After you alerted Enrico Fola of my capture, Baron Riso sent his men to free me. I'm sure it wasn't your intention to facilitate my release, but that's the fact of it.'

So Enrico had gone to the baron when he left her and Baron Riso had saved Mavrone. They were all in this together. The patriots shared the same ideals but Enrico would never associate with criminals like Ruffo. He would be horrified if he knew what had happened to her. Carina tucked her feet under her skirt and did not answer.

'In Sicily, every debt must be repaid in kind,' Mavrone went on. 'I owe you my life, or at least my present good health. I will negotiate your return to Palermo once we reach my home, Monteleone.'

'And where's that, may I ask?'

'On the west coast, not far from Marsala.'

'Why not nearer to here? Baron Riso can make arrangements for my return.'

'Sicilians are suspicious of strangers. There's not a village this side of Palermo that would offer you safe refuge. Now, will you put on your boots?'

He expected her to obey and Carina kicked the boots aside. It was a futile gesture, but she wasn't satisfied with his explanation. Why did he have to take her to his home? He could escort her back to the sanctuary of Santa Fiore, for heaven's sake! There was something Mavrone wasn't telling her.

He put her boots in the knapsack and stamped out the fire, then took hold of her hands, running his thumbs over raw patches of skin.

'I'd rather not tie you up again. Are you going to walk?'

'What happened to the horses?'

'I gave them to Ruffo in exchange for you. Not a good bargain on my part.'

She could take it or leave it, Carina thought. There was no way she could survive up here and Mavrone gave her no choice. She tracked his footsteps and they left the camp in silence. Passing through the thorn bushes, branches sprang back, scratching her arms and Mavrone was waiting on the other side. He set off at a brisk pace, his tall figure silhouetted against the skyline as they climbed and Carina struggled to keep up. She was weak from lack of food and perspiration poured off her neck, running down her arms and back. Then, as they neared the summit, she turned her ankle and fell, tumbling backward until she crashed against a rock.

'Breathe slowly. Slowly—'

Darkness hovered and Carina was aware of Mavrone lifting her up. He wiped the dirt off her face and brushed her hair out of her eyes. When the faintness passed, he probed the ligaments of her shoulders. Then he took hold of her knee and manoeuvred it upwards.

'Try to move your feet and wriggle your toes. If there's a fracture I'll have to splint your leg.'

Putting her weight on her hands, Carina straightened her legs and moved her toes.

'That's better. You've only sprained your ankle. A few hours' rest and you'll be fine.'

Mavrone wouldn't care if she broke every bone in her body! He was without pity and Carina turned on him like an angry cat.

'Why don't you just kill me while you're about it?'

'I don't want you dead. There's shelter in the trees up ahead. Come on, I'll help you.'

He bent down, reaching for her hand, and Carina gritted her teeth. She hung onto his arm, hopping on one foot until they reached a copse of trees bent sideways by the wind. There,

Mavrone let her rest but it seemed she had only just fallen asleep when his hand nudged her shoulder. A lark was singing and a thin coil of smoke drifted up through the trees. Carina stood up and an arrow of pain shot up her calf. Mavrone was busy with the fire so she crawled over to him on her hands and knees.

He poured black coffee into a mug and passed her bread with a chunk of salted meat. Carina took the food without a word. The meat made her jaws ache but the hot, sweet coffee revived her. She noticed his shirt was spread out on the grass; Mavrone had been swimming. His hair was wet and his hands cold as he examined her swollen ankle. She tried not to look at his bare chest but the pressure of his fingers made her groan.

'I can't walk! You'll have to find alternative transport.'

Mavrone reclined back on his elbows and his air of wellbeing infuriated her. 'So what will you do, Captain Mavrone? Are you going to carry me all the way to the west coast?'

'Once I've bandaged the ankle, your boots will give you enough support. There's a stream over there if you want to wash.'

Kindness had no truck here and Carina hobbled painfully to the stream. She longed to be home and a lump rose in her throat. I mustn't give up, she thought desperately. I must keep fighting. 'Pain your weapon and courage your strength.' It seemed a lifetime ago she had said those words to Enrico.

'Pain my weapon and courage my strength,' she murmured as she dipped her head and arms in the water, scrubbing off dirt that caked her skin and hair. She used her skirt to dry off and when she finished, Mavrone was packing up. He emptied the billycan on to the fire and folded the blanket, everything he did executed in the same methodical way. By the time she limped back, all traces of the camp had gone. Mavrone told her to sit down and Carina braced herself as he knelt in front of her.

As he bandaged her ankle, she found herself looking over his shoulder and saw a pattern of weals across his back. They were deep cuts and some not yet healed. The sight of them sickened her. The brutality of Scalia's punishment was not her fault, she told herself, but still she felt guilty.

'Not a bad effort on the part of Colonel Falcone,' Mavrone remarked as he laced her into her boots. Then he stood up and put on his shirt. 'I'm surprised you didn't stay to watch.'

'Abduction is a capital crime, Captain Mavrone.' Carina's eyes slanted up at him. 'It's not a whipping I'll come to next time – but a public execution.'

'Would it make you happy to see me shot?'

A smile lifted the corners of his mouth and Carina remembered the first time she had seen him. How bold and handsome she thought he was at Baron Riso's reception. She'd imagined he was some kind of hero and how wrong she had been.

'You were a good deal more friendly when first we met. It's a shame our amicable relationship was so short-lived.'

The sudden flash of attraction between them brought Carina to her feet. The magnetism that drew her to Mavrone upset and confused her. Never again, she had sworn. Never. Not ever again. The alert look in his eyes made her nervous and she knotted her fingers as he dropped on his haunches.

'I'm going to shorten your dress so you'll not trip again. Hold still, will you?'

Mavrone cut a wide strip off the bottom her skirt. His hand brushed her legs and when Carina flinched, he laughed softly.

'There's no cause for embarrassment, Miss Temple. The shorter length is perfectly acceptable under the circumstances.'

Before she could think of a stinging retort, there was a rustling sound and a large hare hopped into the clearing. It froze, long ears switching forward, then turned and disappeared into the undergrowth. To her surprise, Carina saw Mavrone had drawn a gun and watched as he unloaded it, dropping the bullets into his pocket and then put it in the knapsack. Her father had taught her to use just such a pistol and she was a good shot. If only she could get hold of the gun. The bullets would be more difficult to retrieve, but there was bound to be extra ammunition in the knapsack. Somehow, she would steal the pistol! Mavrone wouldn't laugh at her then, she thought, but he was already walking away.

The trek was long and hard across a barren, windswept landscape and followed no trail that Carina could discern. When they made camp at nightfall Mavrone did not light a fire. He threw the blanket on the ground and lay down. Exhausted, and with no other option, she lay next to him with her back turned. She shivered with cold so he drew her into his arms and she lay rigid until he was asleep.

The next morning they rose at dawn and walked until the sun was high. When they were thirsty they drank from streams that tasted of snow and all her energy was spent in keeping up. Her only thoughts were not to fall behind, the ache in her ankle and blisters on her feet. Hunger and fatigue alternated with the heat of day and cold of night and Carina could not get to the gun. Mavrone kept the knapsack strapped to his back as he walked and beneath his head at night and gradually the idea of trying to escape retreated to the back of her mind.

Weariness curbed her spirit and Mavrone became less abrasive. He allowed her to rest when she was tired and gave her more than her fair share of the food. Days and nights passed without sense of time but there was never a moment Carina was not aware of him, her eyes on his back as he strode ahead and his arms around her at night. He stayed close to her and when one morning she awoke to find herself alone the thought he had abandoned her filled her with panic.

They had spent the night in the hollowed-out trunk of a vast tree and she stumbled into the sunlight and saw him coming up the hill with a basket on his arm.

'I went to find us some breakfast. There's a farmhouse below and the owner gave me food. Let's have ourselves a feast.'

Mavrone tipped the food onto the grass and the smell of fresh bread and cheese made her mouth water. Sitting cross-legged on the ground, Carina ate until her stomach was full. She finished with an orange, sucking the juice from inside.

'You can see Castelvano from here.'

Almond trees blossomed in puffs of white smoke across the valley and he pointed to a walled town on top of a hill. A road snaked up the mountainside and Carina made out figures setting off for the fields. It was the first sign of human habitation she had seen since leaving Palermo and her gaze sharpened as a cavalcade of horsemen came into sight.

'*Perfidio!*' Mavrone swore under his breath. 'The Compagni d'Armi are garrisoned in town. Don't raise your hopes, sweetheart. They're not here for you.'

Had he seen the flare of excitement in her eyes? At once, Carina's exhaustion left her. Whatever Mavrone said, the cavalcade was a patrol searching for her, she was sure. Drawing a breath she remarked in a breezy tone of voice.

'You may leave me in the custody of the Compagni in Castelvano. My family will arrange an escort to take me back to Palermo.'

'How do I know you won't betray me?'

'I'll give you my word of honour.'

'Honour? There's no such thing in Sicily these days.'

His tone made her smart, but the stakes were high. Carina held her temper and tried to sound persuasive.

'You'll be rewarded generously for my safe deliverance. I have friends who will see to it.'

'Such as?'

Mavrone's expression was inscrutable. She couldn't tell if he was considering the proposal or had already cast it aside. Carina searched for an answer. When it came to her, she didn't know how she hadn't thought of it before.

'Enrico Fola will act for us. We both know we can trust him.'

She spoke with just the right amount of insouciance and Mavrone studied her in silence. Why was he looking at her with that gleam in his eyes? It was a perfectly reasonable proposition. Carina tried to assume an attitude of indifference, but she couldn't keep it up and her fingers plucked nervously at her skirt.

'As I told you before, I don't want your money.'

Damn him! Damn him to hell and back! He had led her on for the pleasure of setting her down and her eyes were bright with anger. His next words inflamed her further.

'You're very desirable when you're in a temper. I'm sorry to disappoint you, but your proposal is absurd.'

'So you won't consider it?'

'I'm afraid not. I enjoy your company too much. No amount of gold would compensate for being deprived of it.'

His gaze sought her lips and Carina made up her mind. If one tactic failed then she would try another. Scalia's men were garrisoned in town and would return this evening. If she could delay near the road, they would rescue her. Mavrone said there was no such thing as honour and she could be as dishonest and devious as he was. Sensing his desire, her mouth curved provoc- atively. 'I'm flattered by the compliment. I thought you would be glad to be rid of me.'

Carina held his gaze and Mavrone moved to lie on the grass beside her. Now what was she supposed to do? He was waiting for her to make the first move and she was at a loss. He was older and more experienced. Would he be able to tell she was a novice? She hesitated before putting her hand on his arm and he took her by the shoulders, turning her to face him.

Looking into his blue eyes, Carina saw none of the coldness she was used to. His regard was appreciative and warm. Worn and dirty as she was, Mavrone wanted to kiss her and she wouldn't stop him. It was the only way to get him to lower his guard and, before his steady gaze, her eyes fell.

He leant over and took her in his arms, one hand resting casually on her bodice. He cupped her chin with the other and kissed her slowly with warm, dry lips. She felt heat pulse in her veins as a surge of longing swept through her. All thought of subterfuge vanished. It no longer mattered who he was or what he had done. Carina's arms went round his neck and she began kissing him back, her tongue darting inside his mouth, until he rolled her over to lie on top of him. Mavrone's hand pressed her down and she felt the hard muscles of his thighs beneath her. Her arms were flung on either side of his head and her whole body trembling.

Then the cool breeze touched her face and sanity returned.

'Not like this, please. I want to be clean.' Her voice sounded small and unnatural. 'Can we wait until we reach Castelvano? How long will it take us?'

'A couple of hours at the most. We'll walk up this evening. I agree, you could do with a good wash.'

'Speak for yourself! You smell as bad as me!'

'No doubt much worse.' He grinned and his hands slid up her arms. 'What will my friends in Castelvano make of you, Carina? They're not used to finding a beautiful woman as my accomplice.'

It was the first time he had called her by her given name and Carina shifted her body to lie close to him. She raised herself up on her elbows and studied his face. There was mischief in his eyes and it gave her a glimpse of the boy he had once been. Remorse stirred her conscience. She had deliberately led him on and her surrender meant more to him than she realised. Everything was mixed up in her head. Mavrone spoke of her as his accomplice and suddenly she wished she were. If only it was always like this! The absurd idea of telling him her plan popped into her head. Instead, she heard herself say,

'Promise never to speak of this to anyone? My family could not bear the dishonour.'

'I promise to return you to Palermo with your reputation intact. When we get to Monteleone I'll send word to your family that you're safe. It may take some time. Are you happy to stay with me until then?'

Carina nodded and it meant nothing she deceived him, she told herself in the hours that followed. Mavrone slept and she positioned herself against the tree with his head on her lap. What was wrong with her? She had nearly gone too far and pulled back just in the nick of time. It was unnatural for a woman to experience such feelings. Carina had read about courtesans in books. Their motive was money while her reaction had been spontaneous, driven by a madness that she didn't understand.

Looking down at Mavrone her troubled gaze took in his tousled dark hair and long lashes. She wanted to remember him like this. He would never force himself on her. The danger came from within and her body's treacherous response went against all she had been brought up to believe was right. Love outside marriage was a sin and if she gave herself to him she would be ruined.

'The Compagni will not travel beyond Castelvano.' Carina remembered his words on the night of her abduction. She had been granted a God-given opportunity. Her ankle had recovered and when the patrol came by she would make a run for it. How did she know Mavrone would ever set her free? She must get away before it was too late.

CHAPTER FIFTEEN

She must have dozed, for Carina opened her eyes to find Mavrone ready to go. He had packed up and now helped her to her feet.

'We'll stay in Castelvano long enough to give you a chance to rest. It's time I took better care of you.'

He looked into her tense face and Carina felt her cheeks redden. He doesn't mean it, she told herself. He's only being nice because I let him kiss me.

'I won't thank you for being so hard on me before,' she said, trying to sound indignant.

'So you're never going to forgive me?'

'It depends on your future behaviour. How far is Castelvano to your home?'

'Four days' walk to Monteleone.'

'Monteleone ...' Carina repeated the name, rolling the vowels on her tongue.

'I've a hunch you'll be happy there – so much so, you may never want to leave.'

Why did she have to notice then how the grooves on either side of his mouth deepened as he smiled? For a brief moment

Carina longed for him to take her in his arms and kiss her again. Am I mad? she thought feverishly. I cannot change my mind. I know what will happen.

He was teasing her but Carina was so tense, she felt her nails cutting into the skin of her clenched hands and Mavrone bent down to pick up the knapsack.

'Don't worry, sweetheart. However much I may want to, I'm not going to kidnap you.'

Clouds gathered over the mountain peaks as they made their way down the hill and, afraid they were too early for the patrol, Carina affected a limp. Mavrone slowed his pace but did not stop until they were down in the valley. Donkey carts and mule wagons were making their way home and a girl in a red shawl, who was singing, sat perched on the one at the rear. Carina's nervous gaze searched down the hill. There was no sight of the Compagni. Why were they so late? In half an hour it would be nightfall.

Mavrone took her hand and spoke quietly. 'We'll keep off the road but cannot delay. If we enter after curfew we'll be taken in for questioning.'

'I must rest a while, please. My ankle's so painful.'

'Then wait for me here. I'll try to find a wagon.'

Had he put his hand to her neck, he would have felt the fast beating of her pulse, but Mavrone did not touch her and Carina watched as he moved stealthily from tree to tree. It was dusk already. The Compagni must come soon! She sat down, twisting her hair with her fingers until at last she heard the sound she was waiting for. The distant rhythm of hoof beats was faint at first, growing louder as they approached, and the cavalcade was travelling at speed.

Carina leapt up, ducking under low branches as she ran through the olive grove. She was clear of the trees and on open ground when a blur of horsemen came around the corner with their cloaks flying out behind them. A cloud of dust rose from under the horses' hooves and she shouted and waved her arms. The officer at the front lifted his arm to bring the troop to a halt. Carina was close enough to see his face before a shadow hurtled from behind and tackled her to the ground.

Mavrone fell with his full weight on top of her and his hand over her mouth. Her ear pressed to the ground and she heard muffled orders and bridles jingling as horses were reined in. A grassy bank rose above their heads and she began to struggle. She hunched her back, beating her feet on the ground and he threw his leg across her thighs. He was squeezing her jaw and she sank her teeth into the palm of his hand, hanging on as fiercely as a terrier at the neck of a rat. Her cries were muffled and she bent and twisted beneath him until she thought her heart would burst. Then she heard the command: '*Avanti!*'

In her mind's eye, Carina saw the officer wave his troop forward. They were so close. One of the men must look over the bank and see them! Then someone shouted to leave the lovers undisturbed and the drumming of hooves faded into the distance. Mavrone took his hand from her mouth and rolled off her. His fingers dug into her shoulders, he pulled her up and guided her back to where he had left her before. He thrust her down on her knees and she felt the bite of rope as he tied her hands. Then he put his hand under her chin and forced her head up. His face was black with fury and Carina thought he might break her neck.

'You didn't believe me! You knew all the time!' she cried out. 'You left me alone as a test!'

'The most dangerous part of our journey is ahead. I needed to be sure of you. My friends are bringing a cart. I trust your ankle's better?'

How could she have thought she had deceived him? The rope chafed her wrists, but Carina was too miserable to feel pain. She had taken a gamble and lost. Her mind was empty of anything except bitter disappointment. A shrinking feeling inside numbed her as she knelt on the ground until Mavrone was alerted by a birdlike call. He left her and when he came back two strangers were with him. Speaking to them in dialect, he threw a cloak around her shoulders and the small group made their way to the road.

A donkey cart was waiting and Mavrone pushed her up the bank and dumped her in the back like a piece of baggage. Carina lay with the side of her face on rough wooden boards as he climbed in beside her. Sacking was thrown over them and his breath touched her neck.

'If you make a sound I'll kill you. After your little performance, it would give me no pain to cut your throat.'

Bags of grain were added and the smell of corn filled her nostrils as the cart moved forward. They jolted and bumped along and when they halted they were at the gates. Voices rang with authority as they snapped questions to the driver and heavy footsteps marched to the back of the cart. A hard object prodded her side but Carina did not make a sound and the order to pass was given. When they stopped again, they were inside the town. The heavy bags were taken off and Mavrone lifted her out and stood her on her feet. There was a rumble of thunder and slow rain began to fall as the cart was led away.

With one arm beneath her ribs and the knife at her neck, Mavrone marched her through a maze of alleys and up a steep flight of stone steps. Reaching the top, he pulled her into the shadowed entrance of a church. Opposite was a bar with tallow burning in the windows. The door opened and a soldier in uniform of the Compagni stepped out into the rain. He stood with his legs apart, hand resting on the hilt of his sword. He seemed to be looking straight at them and Mavrone's blade touched her throat. Then the soldier belched and set off unsteadily down the street.

Mavrone let out a low whistle. 'You attract the Compagni like a bitch on heat! Let's move before other dogs catch your scent.'

They skirted the piazza and he lengthened his stride so Carina was forced into a run. Dogs were howling and she glimpsed a man with a snuff-coloured nose huddled against a wall but Mavrone ignored the beggars and strays of Castelvano. He made her go on until they came to a stairway leading off the street. An invisible hand opened the door and a boy's pale face emerged from the shadows.

Once inside, Mavrone took a candle bracket from the wall and gave it to the boy whose dark eyes gazed at Carina. He cut the rope loose and his hand closed around her arm in a grip hard as iron. The boy led the way along a subterranean passage with wet patches on the walls and places where the ceiling was so low that they had to bend double. And then, quite suddenly, they came out into a room filled with people.

Carina blinked in the bright light as an old woman came forward. She reached up to touch Mavrone on the forehead and a little girl tugged at his arm. Everyone was staring at her and she dropped her head so her hair fell over face. Mavrone leant down to speak to the child and then a man with an oil lamp ushered them down another passage to a stone cellar. He walked in and placed the light on the table. Carina saw an iron bed with a mattress and bed clothing rolled in a bundle and stood frozen in the doorway until Mavrone pushed her inside.

'These will be your lodgings. I've ordered you a bath.'

Two young men appeared with a wooden hip tub, which they dragged across the floor to the centre of the room. They returned with buckets of water, accompanied by a blue-eyed girl carrying a towel and clothes, which she put on the bed. The girl looked dubiously at Mavrone. He did not respond and she tossed her head so her black hair bounced on her shoulders and followed the boys out.

'Take off your clothes.'

As the door closed, the tension of the last few hours hit Carina all at once. Terror travelled down her veins so fast she thought she might faint. Her hands were shaking so she had to break the thread to get the buttons undone. She bent down to remove her boots and, wearing only her camisole and pantalets, walked towards the tub.

'I'm sure this isn't the first time you've undressed for a man. Take everything off.'

Carina tried to protest but her voice failed. If she disobeyed him, Mavrone would likely strip her naked himself. She turned her back, removing her underclothes and climbed into the bath, banging her hip on the side in her haste. He threw her a cake of black soap and she lathered herself all over, rubbing her legs and arms until the water was grey.

'That's enough. I want you clean – not scrubbed raw.'

Mavrone came to stand by the tub. His gaze raked over her and shame scorched her cheeks, spreading down her neck to her chest. He hauled her out and sat on the bed, pinioning her between his knees. Looping the towel behind her, he dried her before dropping it on the floor.

'You've only yourself to blame if I take up your invitation of this morning.'

'I wanted to get home.' Carina bit her lip to hold back tears. 'I wasn't going to betray you.'

'Well you made a damned good show if that's the case. It so happens I don't want you tonight. When I do, I take it you're willing to render me the service you offer your other lovers. Do you understand?'

Carina fixed her gaze on a spider crawling up the wall. There was a lump, like a small stone, stuck in her gullet and she did not answer.

'Do you understand?' he repeated.

Carina refused to submit, but a tiny sob escaped her lips. Her cheeks were wet and she buried her face in her hands as Mavrone collected up his belongings,

'Cover yourself before the lads come back,' he said tersely. 'They're honest fellows. I don't want them corrupted by your easy charms.'

They departed from Castelvano three days later and in that time Carina did not see Mavrone again. The black-haired girl brought her food, but she ate little. She was given clean clothes, a pair of loose trousers and a linen shirt, and allowed to rest undisturbed. When she was not asleep she listened to the rain pouring down outside. There were times she wanted to bang her head on the wall and bite her knuckles until they were raw. Mavrone punished me because I tried to trick him but I will never let him break me, she swore. I'll fight him to the end. One day I'll repay him for his treatment of me.

Late one evening two men came to the cellar. They had a quiet, professional manner and, with one on either side, Carina was taken from the cellar to the high-vaulted room she remembered from the night they arrived. An old man was smoking a clay pipe near the stove while children lay asleep on blankets on the floor. The women stood back and the girl with blue eyes stared her as she was led through their midst to the underground tunnel.

Mavrone was standing at the end and the light extinguished before they went out. When they reached the street, he walked so close behind her that his legs knocked into the back of her knees. With his hand on her shoulder, they made their way in silence to the guardhouse at the town gates. Beacons burnt inside and Carina saw soldiers sitting at a table with cocked hats tilted back on their heads.

'The duty officer will open the gate for us. When I tell you to walk, do just that.' Mavrone turned to the others. 'Stay back and cover us.'

The pale moonlight was as spectral as the fear that gripped Carina as the door of the guardhouse opened. One of the soldiers came out. He glanced furtively in their direction. Then he walked to the gate and unlocked a small door. Propelled by Mavrone, she stepped through and heard the bolt being drawn behind them. They were out of Castelvano, heading downhill, and she noticed that instead of the pistol he carried a rifle. When they halted, he lifted the muzzle to her cheek.

'I've better range with this and the aim is more accurate. Don't try to run away ...'

I will shoot you if you do ... The last sentence was unspoken, but Mavrone made her walk so hard and fast that night if an entire army had passed them by, Carina wouldn't have had the strength to run or the voice to call out. The pace he kept up was relentless. When they stopped she slept where she had fallen. The temperature dropped and it was bitterly cold but Mavrone no longer lay beside her. As she lay shivering on the ground, she knew he was not asleep and was watching her.

Making their way westward through forests freshened by spring rain, Mavrone avoided even the smallest hamlets. He rarely spoke and Carina kept her mind on the immediate future. When would she be able to rest? How long before the next bite of food or drink of water? They fed on stale bread and berries gathered from the bushes. One evening he shot a rabbit and roasted it on a wooden spit – she devoured the meat, tearing the flesh off with her teeth, and picking the bones clean. That night, for the first time since leaving Castelvano, she slept without the pain of hunger in her stomach.

They set off early next morning and now the streams they splashed across turned into fast-flowing rivers. Swollen by melted snow, they were increasingly perilous to cross. Carina came up behind Mavrone as he stood looking into a deep ravine where a waterfall crashed down with such force spray was thrown up into their faces. He deliberated for a moment before he unfastened his cartridge belt and laid the rifle on the grass.

'Give me your boots and I'll take them across.'

Carina sat down and took off her boots. She gave them to him and watched as he waded into the river. The water came up to his waist and he lifted the gun and rucksack above his head. A curtain of spray hid him and she craned forward until he emerged on the other side. He deposited his burden and then started back for her.

Too worn down to think of escape, she slithered down the bank and stepped into the river. Mavrone had his arm round her waist as they went forward together. Freezing water broke over their heads and the current whipped her heels. Carina lost her footing and clutched Mavrone's arm so that he staggered. Then her feet touched solid ground and he pulled her up the bank on the other side.

'Strip off and we'll dry out in the sun.'

They were in a glade of dappled sunlight and Carina was aware her wet clothes clung to her body. She took off her shirt and Mavrone waited until she removed her trousers. He went over to a tree stump and spread them out to dry in the sun. She kept on her vest and drawers while he undressed to his breeches, wringing the water from his shirt, before he stretched out beside her.

A bird was chirping, its range of notes bright and tuneful, and Carina sat with her knees hugged to her chest. Twisting her neck to ease the ligaments, she glanced at Mavrone. His eyes were closed and she studied him with vague curiosity, noting the firm muscles of his stomach and his long legs. It was strange that the sight of his body didn't shock her. All vestiges of civilised behaviour had been stripped away, she thought, and they were little better than savages.

There was a buzzing in her ears like the hum of a mosquito and a dull ache in her temples. Carina longed to sleep – but she could not rest with Mavrone half-naked beside her. To stay awake she picked up a pebble and sent it spinning into the water below.

'What makes you so restless? Do you want to make love?'

Carina took a shuddering breath. This was the moment she dreaded. I won't let him touch me, she thought. If he lays a hand on me, I'll throw myself in the river. She stood up and looked down at him, her face hard and taut.

'I despise you – or have you forgotten?'

'Sure you do – but it doesn't mean you don't want me.' The expression in his eyes belied the easy tone. 'Do you despise Prince Scalia as well?'

Mavrone had made her cry in Castelvano – but he would never find her so susceptible again. She knew how to hurt him and her voice filled with venom.

'Prince Scalia is a gentleman. No doubt that's why Bianca chose him for a husband and not—'

Mavrone was on his feet before she could finish with his fist raised above his head. Carina braced herself for the blow, but his arm stopped in mid-air.

'You'll keep Bianca Scalia's name out of your conversation or else—'

'Or else what? Will you beat me?' Her blood was up and Carina threw back her head. 'I dare say you enjoy assaulting defenceless women.'

Mavrone strode over to the tree stump and put on his shirt and boots. He turned around, letting his hand drop on her shirt and Carina experienced a rush of intoxicating energy. He was baiting her like a hunter with a trap and she began to walk towards him, her eyes on her shirt and the hand toying with the buttons. She was almost within reach when his voice checked her.

'So tell me about Prince Scalia. Does he make love to you like a gentleman?'

'He doesn't—'

Her answer ended in a rasping cough. A searing pain tore through her chest and Carina felt the strength drain out of her as fast as it had come. Her shoulders sagged and her arms were so heavy they felt glued to her sides. Thoughts formed and then broke off, drifting away. She tried to remember what she meant to say but the only thing lodged fast in her mind was the look on Mavrone's face when she spoke of Bianca Scalia.

With a bad-tempered gesture he threw the shirt at her feet and tossed her trousers over afterwards. He reached for his rifle, ready to go. Her clothes felt damp as Carina put her shirt over her head and pulled on her trousers. She followed at a distance and by the time they reached the coastal plain, Mavrone was well ahead. No longer wary of strangers, he greeted fellow travellers as they went by in their brightly coloured wagons. Children shouted as they hung out the back. When the same carts drove past her, Carina kept her head down.

Dirt was thrown up from under their wheels and she tasted grit in her mouth. The glare of light hurt her eyes and she stopped to wipe a hand across her face. In the far distance, she saw a ribbon of blue. It was the sea – they had reached the west coast but she was too sick to make anything of it.

She took a few steps and then halted again. Mavrone's figure was a shimmering mirage and Carina tried to call to him. Her voice came out as a wheezy rattle. She was shivering with cold and burning with fever at the same time. Every breath was agony, lacerating her lungs. Her vision was hazy as though someone had put a veil over her eyes and she imagined the sun spiralling through the sky towards her. The next moment she was incinerated in its heat and she pitched forward, falling headlong onto the dusty road.

CHAPTER SIXTEEN

'Signorina, you must wake up.'

The words were accompanied by a nudge and Carina felt herself being drawn out of deep slumber. She was lying on a feather mattress with her face pressed against sweet-smelling linen. The hand touched her again and she opened her eyes to see a woman with white hair looking down at her.

'Who are you?'

'I'm Selida. I've been nursing you. You have slept for two days.'

Selida brought over a tray and sat down by the side of the bed. She helped Carina to sit up and wrapped a napkin round her neck.

'The fever has broken, but you're still weak. Let me help you.'

Selida ladled a spoonful of broth into her mouth and a frown creased Carina's brow.

'I don't understand. Where am I?'

'You're at Monteleone,' Selida explained gently. 'Your carriage broke down. You were obliged to travel the last few miles on horseback. Benito is concerned for your welfare and asked me to take care of you. You must rest now and I will return later.'

When she left the room, Carina lay back on the pillows. Her carriage? Benito? Did she mean Mavrone? She had thought Selida was a housekeeper, but her quiet dignity suggested a more elevated position. Carina tried to recollect what happened after she collapsed. She had a dim memory of faces peering down at her and Mavrone lifting her onto a horse. After that nothing, until he carried her into this room – she recognised it now – and laid her down on the bed. Monteleone was Ben Mavrone's home and he had dragged her halfway across Sicily to bring her here.

Carina closed her eyes and slept until Selida returned. She followed her into a small room with a basin and a bathtub filled with water. Declining her offer of assistance, Carina poured water from the jug into the bowl and washed her face. Looking into the glass, there was no beauty in her hollow cheeks and her face was as pinched as a street urchin. She climbed into the bath and lay in the comfort of the warm water before washing her hair. When she returned to the bedroom, a young girl was with Selida.

'May I present Bella Campi? She's your maid. I will come to see you every day.'

Bella gave her an impudent look as she bobbed a curtsy. They left and Carina was relieved to be alone. The windows were open and she heard the sound of waves and a rake scraping on gravel. There were voices beneath her window and, looking down, she saw a courtyard smothered in blue wisteria. Mavrone was speaking to a small, well-dressed woman whose face was hidden by the wide brim of her hat.

Too tired to wonder who she might be, Carina spent the rest of the day in bed. She ate supper by the fire, wearing the wrapper given to her by Selida. Bella attended to her and Carina let her go as soon as she was finished. As the door shut, a draught made the candles flicker and she went over to close the window. Black night shut her in. Monteleone was a prison, she thought, as dark and forbidding as its owner. Her illness had left her weak and she hoped Mavrone would keep away as he had at Castelvano. She needed time to bolster her defences. And then, as if she had summoned him up, his voice came from behind her.

'I'm glad you're recovering. Take care not to catch another chill.'

Mavrone was standing by the door with a decanter of wine and two glasses in his hand. She walked slowly back and sat down, pressing her knuckles until the joints cracked. It will be different here, she told herself. There are people like Selida at Monteleone. Mavrone will have to behave himself.

He took the chair next to her – close enough for Carina to see nicks in his skin, where he had cut himself shaving, and smell his cologne. He poured wine into the goblets and gave one to her. The wine warmed her and she waited for him to go on.

'Are you feeling better?'

'Who was the woman with you outside today?'

'Greta Mazzini. She's an old friend and cousin to Italy's greatest political philosopher, Giuseppe Mazzini.'

Mazzini was an exile in London, Carina remembered, a radical intellectual whom Jane Parsons admired. Had Mavrone told Signora Mazzini she was here, she wondered? What reason might he have given for her presence?

'Greta has kindly agreed to write to your family – to inform them you're safe and no ransom is demanded. You will be returned to Palermo as soon as possible.'

'And when might that be?'

'When I can make the appropriate arrangements. Your disappearance caused quite a stir and Scalia's agents are still scouring the island. You've caused my fellow patriots a good deal of trouble.'

'That's hardly my fault!'

'And I wasn't the one responsible for your abduction.' Mavrone's glance swept her face. 'You're free to go as you please in the house and garden but no one leaves Monteleone without my consent. I advise a little patience. You never know, you may come to enjoy it here in time.'

His hand dropped over hers, stilling the restless movement of her fingers, and Carina snatched it free coming to her feet so fast she knocked over her glass.

'I've been with you long enough to be sure I will not!'

Mavrone picked up the goblet and used his handkerchief to mop up the spilled wine. Then he leant back in his chair and looked up at her.

'I've only one question for you. We were betrayed soon after the evening at the Palazzo Riso. Did you pass on any information you overheard to Prince Scalia?'

'I didn't betray Baron Riso.'

Carina shook her head. Mavrone must know she hadn't betrayed them. Why else would she have warned Enrico? She had used Scalia as a weapon against him – and what good had it done her? She was too sick at heart for another battle, too tired to go on fighting. The only thing she wanted was for him to go away.

'I'm not Prince Scalia's accomplice – nor am I his mistress. I loathe the man.'

'Do you really expect me to believe that?'

'I don't expect anything.'

'Are you saying your relationship with him was innocent? Riccardo Scalia doesn't know the meaning of the word.'

Carina fixed her gaze on the intricate carving of the mantel-piece. A nerve beneath her eye began to jump and she put a hand up to stop it. There was a bitter taste, like lemon pith, in her mouth and she swallowed.

'I've told you the truth.'

'And the scandal in London, do you deny that as well?'

'Is it beyond you to imagine I might have retained my virtue?'

Mavrone was on his feet and, meeting his incredulous gaze, Carina reached for the arm of her chair and sank down. There was no way of knowing what he made of her admission for he had turned his back on her. Reaching for the poker, he stirred the logs in the grate and stood for a long time looking into the fire.

Carina listened to the hiss of flames until he moved away from the hearth. Her eyes followed him as he took off his jacket and hung it over the back the chair. He went round the room extinguishing candles and then sat down to tug off his boots. The first one came off and dropped onto the floor.

'What are you doing?'

The question was superfluous, for it was quite obvious he was undressing. Mavrone, occupied with the other boot, looked up, for a moment uncomprehending. Then he pulled it off and stood up.

'It's late and I'm preparing to retire for the night.'

'You're not going to sleep here. This is my room.'

She broke off as Mavrone divested himself of his shirt. Firelight cast shadows on his chest and her heart began to race. She pressed her hands together, clenching and unclenching her fingers. Surely, tonight he could mean her no harm? A shiver ran down her spine as he moved his chair opposite her. He sat down and leant forward with his elbows on his knees.

'If what you say about you and Scalia is true, why didn't you tell me before?'

Carina kept her head low, taking care not to meet his eyes.

'I wanted to annoy you – and make sure you kept your distance.'

'And well I might have, had you not encouraged me otherwise.'

'So why didn't you let me escape?'

'Because if you betrayed us, the Compagni would have arrested every man of fighting age in Castelvano. We're preparing for war and cannot lose a single patriot. Nevertheless, I apologise for my behaviour and retract what I said about your virtue. You're under no obligation to me.'

So that was his answer. It was nothing personal. No matter he had hurt and degraded her. Words cost him nothing and Carina was silent.

'I treated you badly and I'm very sorry,' Ben added slowly, after a pause. 'I hate to be deceived and lost any sense of decency. Please look at me, Carina.'

He unpeeled her fists from the arms of the chair and took her hands in his own. Carina tried to pull back, but he held her fast. Unwillingly, she raised her gaze to his face. There was regret in his eyes and something else she had seen before. Ben said he was sorry, but that wouldn't stop him trying to seduce her. I swore never to let him come near me, she reminded herself. Let that be his punishment.

'If you want me to leave, I'll go immediately. The choice is yours.'

'Have you no principles, Captain Mavrone, no morality at all?'

'None whatsoever. I wanted you from the first moment I set eyes on you. I haven't forgotten our meeting in the Palazzo Riso.'

Ben lived outside the laws of society as he lived outside those of the state. With his good looks and silver tongue he expected her to yield, Carina thought. Beyond here lay the scorched wasteland of the fallen woman, ostracised by society and a disgrace to her family – but what did he care? Ben took any opportunity that came his way. It was the same as ever; his determination against hers, mind against body. Why did he have to torment her?

'Do you honestly think I'll let you ruin me?'

'If I ask you to marry me, would it make a difference?'

What was he talking about? He had no intention of marrying her! Carina would never know why she didn't challenge him then. She felt possessed by a devil, lurking in the shadows, waiting until this moment to claim her. Suddenly she was overcome by a sense of inevitability. Hadn't she known from the beginning her fate was bound up with his? Ben Mavrone had infiltrated her soul and she had neither the will nor strength to send him away.

Let it be … Let it be … Her head fell back and Ben knelt on the ground in front of her. He drew his finger from her chin down to the collar of her wrapper and planted a kiss at the base of her neck. Then he took the garment by the sleeves and pulled it down to reveal her bare shoulders. His hand made its way up her arm, returning to her elbow, brushing upwards again and across her collarbone to close over her heart.

'So what's it to be, sweetheart? Shall I go or stay?'

Tell him to leave now. Don't let him do this … The instructions hammered in her head but Carina ignored them. She longed for the comfort of his arms and warmth of his body. Fear and shame died away and Ben undid the sash of her gown and laid his head on her breast. She looked down at his hair, so dark against the whiteness of her skin, and pressed her lips to the top of his head.

'Stay.'

The conflict was over and Ben stood up and swung her into his arms. He carried her to the bed and lay down beside her. Moonlight fell across them and he ran his hand the length of her body. A rip of longing tore through Carina as Ben kissed the lobes of her ears before his lips came down on her mouth. She was on the brink of something from which there could be no return and did nothing to stop him until he nudged her legs apart. She stiffened and Ben lay still, gently stroking her hair and the side of her face.

'There's nothing to be afraid of, *carina*, my love.' He spoke her name as an endearment. 'It's time you learned the pleasure you've been missing.'

Carina remembered one brief moment of desperation that made her catch hold of his shoulders before her arms went round him. Her head was pressed down into the pillow and she smelled his clean, masculine scent. He was telling her he loved her, telling her she was beautiful. This was what she wanted; the feel of his body and his hands beneath her hips as they dissolved into one another, Ben taking her with him into the night, rising and falling in waves of sensation. She was aware of the pulse in her wrist and the surging of her heart. Sparks of electricity fired in her blood – there was no sense of time or space – only Ben in the warm, crushing darkness, the fusion between them and a wild, unknown thrill of surrender. Her last conscious thought was that she was disembodied and weight-less, floating through water with her arms locked around his neck.

A long time afterwards her surroundings became solid and she lay with her cheek on Ben's chest. She listened to the quiet rhythm of his breathing and was unprepared for the tears that filled her eyes. They slipped from beneath her lashes and Ben's arms tightened about her. He held her to him and Carina cried until there were no tears left and she didn't know if they were for what she had lost or gained.

CHAPTER SEVENTEEN

When she woke up the next morning, Ben had gone. The memory of their passion was as sweet as the scent of jasmine wafting in through the window. For the first time, she had learned what it was to be loved. How strange that someone as aloof as Ben had revealed this to her! How surprising he had been so infinitely tender. Until last night, she hadn't known what it meant to be truly alive. Recalling her abandonment in his arms, Carina experienced a thrill of pleasure. Others might be outraged, but how could she be, when he had made her happy?

There was a knock at the door and Bella came in. She opened the shutters and, stifling a yawn, Carina watched as she laid fresh logs in the grate. Her wrapper lay discarded on the floor and Bella picked it up with a disapproving look. She went out, then returned with a breakfast tray, and a skirt of worsted material with a cotton blouse.

'Thank you, Bella,' Carina murmured as she sat up.

'Nothing to do with me, ma'am. The captain asked me to provide you with clothes.'

She buttered a roll and drank her coffee while Bella remained at the foot of the bed. She seemed unwilling to be dismissed and Carina wished Ben had come instead. She thought of his words in the night and wondered what it would be like when they met again. The thought made her pulse quicken.

When she had washed and dressed, Carina sat at the dressing table. The mirror showed her cheeks were pink and a new brightness in her eyes. She looked better already, she thought. Bella picked up a box of pins and Carina told her she preferred to leave it down. The next moment the box dropped onto the table and the girl marched to the door. She stood there with her hands on her hips and her head lowered.

'Suit yourself, ma'am. Quality don't come to Monteleone any more – only women of a different kind!'

Bella flounced out of the room, leaving the door open. As her footsteps rattled down the passage, Carina's grip tightened round the hairbrush she had unconsciously snatched up. She was shocked by her rudeness – but Bella had seen the crumpled bedclothes and much else besides. She would relay every detail to the other servants and she must find Ben and make sure he stopped her.

Carina hurried downstairs to a hall that was cluttered with walking canes and coats. The front door was open and she took a moment to study the house that was Ben's home. Monteleone was a white two-storey building around a central courtyard and its air of normality heartened her. She couldn't see Ben outside, and, trying the first door she came to, entered an oval room with French windows.

Miniatures and bronzes crowded the tables beneath old mirrors and the portrait over the fireplace arrested her gaze. At first she thought it was of Bianca Scalia. The likeness was such that they might have come face to face, only the young woman was dressed in the fashion of a generation before. It must be her mother, Isabella del Angelo.

The resemblance was so striking, Carina felt goose pimples on her arms. She thought of Paulo's story and Bianca Scalia's connection with Monteleone. Bianca had spent her holidays here. It was at Monteleone that she and Ben had fallen in love all those years ago – and here they had said their final farewells.

The room felt oppressive and, loosening the collar of her shirt, Carina stepped out on to the terrace. She walked to the end and went down a flight of steps to a garden aflame with red hibiscus. The sky was dazzling blue, the moss soft and springy beneath her feet and she followed a path to where a wooden bench was placed against the wall.

Sitting down, she tried sort out the chaos of her emotions. What happened last night was momentous. Nothing would ever be the same again. She would never be the same. For the first time she could remember, she had woken this morning feeling at peace. There had been lightness in her heart until the altercation with Bella dispelled her euphoria. Who were these other women who came to Monteleone, she wondered? Was it possible that Bianca Scalia was still in Ben's life? She must go and find him. When she saw him again, she would be reassured.

Carina walked back to the house, not looking at the portrait of Donna Isabella as she passed through the oval room. She searched the ground floor, but there was no sign of Ben. She would talk to him later, she decided and returned to her bedroom. She lay flat on the bed and was half-asleep when she heard Ben's voice in the passage. There was no time to put on her shoes or straighten her skirt, but she was out of bed in her stockinged feet when he walked in.

Ben was wearing riding clothes and his face was streaked

with dust. He was so handsome, Carina felt a clutch at her heart as he walked over and kissed her on the forehead.

'I'm away for a couple of hours and return to find the household in an uproar. Bella Campi's handed in her notice. Apparently, she finds herself unsuited to the position of lady's maid.'

'Really? Then it saves you the trouble of dismissing her.'

'What happened? Why did she upset you?'

'She was unpleasant and insolent.'

'There's only one person at Monteleone whose opinion is of any account and that is Selida.' Ben took hold of her hand and played with her fingers. 'I'm glad to say she's offered to look after you herself. What did Bella say that so offended you?'

'She said you don't entertain society at Monteleone – only women of a different sort.' Carina ignored the flicker of amusement in Ben's eyes. 'You presume I accept things as they are—'

'I presume nothing. You shouldn't care what Bella thinks.'

'But I do care!'

'Then you're not the woman I thought you were.'

All her life she had known who she was and where she belonged. Carina had been secure in that knowledge – and the ground had shifted beneath her feet. Who was she now and where did she belong? She searched Ben's face for an answer and found a look akin to pity for a child who fails to understand the adult world. Then he smiled, dropped her hand and headed towards the door.

'Don't let it upset you, sweetheart. Your status as my guest is of no significance to anyone but ourselves. Dinner is served at seven o'clock and I'll meet you downstairs.'

CHAPTER EIGHTEEN

Ben left the room and Carina heard him speak to someone outside before Selida came in. She smiled encouragingly and beckoned her towards the wardrobe.

'I've found you some lovely dresses. We brought them here this morning when you were in the garden.'

Carina was astonished by the number of outfits crammed into the small space. There were summer dresses and skirts, capes and riding habits along with boots and a selection of bonnets. An entire wardrobe was laid open before her and Selida held up a dress of sprig muslin with the high waistline in the empire style.

'Look, isn't this delightful? I am sure it will fit you.'

The dresses were old fashioned, not one had a wide skirt or crinoline, but they were pretty and a welcome distraction. Carina allowed Selida to choose and when it was settled she would wear the sprig muslin, she tidied her hair and set off downstairs. Her newfound elegance gave her confidence and she hoped Ben would be impressed. As she walked into the salon, he looked at her appreciatively.

'That dress must be thirty years old, but it suits you well enough. You look lovely.'

An elderly man in a white jacket shuffled in to announce dinner was served and Ben offered his arm and led her to the dining room. The table was large enough for twelve, with two places set at one end, and Ben seemed content to eat in silence. Looking at him now in his fine clothes, no one would imagine him as a convict in chains, Carina thought. Ben behaved as if the other side of his life did not exist. What had kept him all day so that he hadn't visited her until late?

When at last they were alone, she finished her wine and asked. 'Tell me about Donna Isabella del Angelo. Was this her home?'

'In a manner of speaking. It was the family's summer residence.'

'Is it true she was your benefactress?'

'I'm sure there's nothing about me that you don't know already. Why don't you give me your account of my past? It's bound to be more entertaining than anything I can tell you.'

His tone was relaxed and Carina gathered her thoughts before she began.

'I know you were involved in the '48 revolution. When it failed you were driven into exile. Where did you go?'

'I lived in Dublin for a time.'

Ben's eyelashes dropped and she went on more cautiously. 'Were you brought up at Monteleone?'

'My brother and I spent part of our childhood here. We inherited the estate when Donna Isabella died.'

'Why did she leave it to you and not her daughter?'

The question popped out without thinking and Carina put her hands under the table and pinched the napkin on her lap. On the day she collapsed on the road, Ben warned her never to speak of

Bianca – but she couldn't help being curious. Donna Isabella would never have bequeathed the property to Ben and his brother when she had an heir of her own. If Monteleone belonged to Ben, then it was Bianca Scalia who had given it to him.

'Donna Isabella's life was in Palermo.' Ben said with some reserve. 'I expect she trusted us to look after the place.'

'So you returned to Sicily with a price on your head to take care of Monteleone?'

'I came back because I'm committed to the cause of Sicily's freedom. And this time we will be successful.'

He pushed his chair back, bringing the conversation to an end, and stood aside to let her pass through the door ahead of him. Carina went to stand by the fire and felt his breath on her shoulder.

'You're shivering. Shall I fetch you a stole?'

'I'm not cold, thank you.'

'Greta Mazzini is coming to call on us in the morning. I'm sure you'll get on famously. Now, stay by here and keep warm until I come back.'

'Where are you going?'

'I'll be home by midnight, I promise.'

'What business can you have at this time of night?'

Carina heard vexation in her voice. She had waited for Ben all day and he was going out again. She was his lover now, not his captive. It shouldn't be like this! Her lips trembled and she clenched her jaw as she walked out of the room without waiting for his answer. Reaching the hall, she lifted the front of her skirt and swept up the staircase. She hoped to hear Ben's tread on the steps and feel his hand on her shoulder, but when she looked down he was going out of the front door.

How could he be so indifferent with the memory of their recent intimacy? Carina thought of his hands on her body and the rapture she had experienced in his arms. This morning she had been happy. She had broken society's greatest taboo believing that Ben would stand by her. Did such matters mean nothing to him? An awful suspicion came into her mind. Last night she had convinced herself Ben loved her – but perhaps she was the same as any other woman he had taken to his bed – and no doubt convinced them that he was sincere too!

Disappointment dropped in her stomach as she closed the bedroom door and leant against it. She had let Ben seduce her because she was worn down by deprivation and dependency. How could she have been so easily persuaded? If he cared for her, he would have come to her this morning and not left her alone like this! She would lock him out, Carina decided, but the key was nowhere to be found. She searched the room, on every ledge and in every drawer, then finally dragged one of the heavy armchairs and jammed it under the door handle. It might not keep Ben out, but he couldn't fail to get the message.

Worries darted through her head as she put on her nightgown and climbed into bed. Had she made a terrible mistake? What if she fell pregnant? Dear God, what then? The idea was so terrifying Carina scrambled out of bed. She found a flint and relit the candle. On the desk were writing materials and she gathered them up before going to sit by the fire. Chewing the end of the pencil, she imagined herself in the garden and began to write.

Shine on, calm crescent moon,
Shine on, beyond our sight,
Dispel dark and dusky gloom,
Absolve with limpid light.

Look down, star mantled sky,
Look up, soft singing sea.
Firmament of mother earth
Forbid all melancholy.

Breathe deep, sweet jasmine'd air,
Arabian flowers' delight.
Children of southern moon
Console my heart tonight.

Carina stopped and started, changing words and crossing out lines. The poem helped to control her panic and she made a final alteration, then left the paper on the desk. She went back to bed and snuffed out the candle. As the clock struck twelve, she heard the front door shut. A few moments later there were footsteps in the passage and the door handle rattled, followed by the sound of splintering wood as the chair crashed on its side.

Carina was so tense she could hardly breathe. She lay as close to the edge of the bed as she could. She felt Ben's knees touch the back of her legs and his hands on her shoulders. He began to massage her muscles and she kept her eyes shut, trying to keep still, but when he reached for the fastening of her gown, she clutched hold of it and he moved away.

The candle flickered into light and Ben turned her over on to her back. Placing his elbows on the pillow, he looked down into her face.

'What's wrong?'

'I won't let you do this!' Carina began. 'I'm not like your other women—'

'I agree – you're far more desirable and a good deal more difficult.'

'I'm at no man's command—'

'As I've found out ...' Ben murmured and bent his neck to kiss her. Carina shut her mouth and he continued unperturbed. 'You remind me of a mountain cat my brother brought home. Alex was so sure he could tame that damn animal until it turned on him and mauled him half to death.'

It was the first time Ben had spoken of his twin and Carina looked him. She saw a shadow pass across his face and then he smiled.

'You're as wild as that cat and twice as dangerous.'

'Did he let the poor creature go?'

'I seem to recall he let it loose. It was shot dead the next week.'

'Well, at least he set it free.'

'But I'm not my brother, my love. I don't have his patience and nor do I have any inclination to tame you.'

'Ben, please! You know what we did was wrong—'

'There's no use shutting the stable door after the horse has bolted.'

He was mocking her and Carina twisted her head on the pillow, refusing to look at him.

'Listen to me, sweetheart.' Ben ran a finger down the inside of her arm.' I would love to spend every hour of the day with you, but I have other responsibilities. It doesn't mean I'm not serious in this matter.'

'But think what might happen if ... if ...'

'If you find yourself with child? Then I'll persuade you to marry me. I vowed long ago no offspring of mine would be born illegitimate.'

'Do you mean we'd live together as man and wife?'

'Not necessarily; I'm sure we can reach an accommodation that's acceptable to us both. You're a beautiful woman. It would be an honour to be your husband, even in name only. Besides, an annulment is easily obtained.'

Ben regarded marriage as a contract to be dissolved without a qualm of conscience – but she loved as fiercely as she hated. She would rather bear a child out of wedlock than submit to such an arrangement and her face tightened with determination.

'It would be a travesty of all that's right and decent.'

'Not if you prove you were forced into the marriage or your mind was unbalanced at the time.'

'By all that's sacred, I couldn't—'

'Hush now …'

Ben took her hand and guided it to his mouth, kissing the tips of her fingers. He hadn't listened to a word she said, Carina thought. She might have persisted, but he muffled her protests with his lips. She was aware of him removing her nightgown, leaning over and pressing kisses to her neck. Ben aroused feelings she had never known before. And now, for mercy's sake, what was he doing? The exploration of his fingers was insistent and Carina grabbed a handful of his hair and forced his head up.

'There's nothing to be ashamed of, sweetheart. It would be a sin against nature to waste that sweet ardour of yours.'

Ben looked down at her and the warmth in his eyes pierced Carina to the core. How could she resist when she had no desire to stop him? In his arms, fear and uncertainty slipped away. She would not think about tomorrow. Ben was no longer a stranger. She could close her eyes and see his face in the darkness. The passion between them was a raging fire, consuming her in its flames – and if this wasn't love, what else could it be?

CHAPTER NINETEEN

Darling Nonna,
I am glad to tell you I'm safe and well. You must have been so
worried, but my guardian angel protected me. I was rescued a week
ago and am now in the care of good people. When I return to
Palermo, you will see with your own eyes that I have come to no
harm ...

Carina chewed the inside of her mouth writing the last sentence.
She wanted to reassure her grandmother, but dare not say too
much. With the letter in her hand, she went downstairs to the
oval room where Greta Mazzini was waiting with Ben. Greta
wore a dark blue riding habit with a plumed hat perched on her
raven hair. She had a lively expression and an aura of vitality
that more than made up for her lack of stature.

'Greta is married to Stefan Bosco of Calatafimi,' Ben said as he
introduced her. 'But she's too proud of her connection to the
most dangerous radical in Europe to relinquish her maiden name.'

'Come now, Ben, only with my closest friends. To everyone
else I am Signora Bosco.' Greta spoke with a soft musical lilt

and smiled at Carina. 'Ben has told me of your predicament. I do hope I may be of assistance.'

There was generosity in her black eyes and Carina warmed to her. Greta was bright and friendly and she wondered how much Ben had told her. They were both waiting for her response, Ben with an amused, ironic look on his face, and she kept her tone light.

'I've been well taken care of since my arrival at Monteleone, thank you. Captain Mavrone has been very ... attentive.'

'Well, it was the very least he could do! Your intervention saved his life – and, along with it, any prospect of our success.'

'I'm indebted to Miss Temple in every way.' The insinuation was clear as Ben came to his feet. 'Now I'm afraid I must leave you, ladies. I've business to attend to and you have a great deal to discuss. Good day to you, Greta. I will see you later, Carina.'

He lifted Greta's hand to his lips and his fingers brushed Carina's shoulder as he passed her by. Her eyes followed him and when the door closed Greta moved her chair closer.

'Ben's a remarkable man but he can also be impossible. Has he explained anything to you – or is that why I'm here?'

'He told me you have offered to write to my grandmother and I'm very grateful. Would you be so kind as to enclose this letter from me? I want to reassure her that I'm safe.'

'Of course – I shall write to Contessa Denuzio later today.' Greta took Carina's letter and placed it in her pocket. 'The story is you were abandoned close to our estate in Calatafimi. We've given you refuge and you'll stay with us until you are strong enough to travel. Our home is far enough from Monteleone to avoid any suspicion you might be in danger.'

Their eyes met and there was wry humour in Greta's expression. Carina coloured slightly and asked.

'Is there news of the uprising in Palermo?'

'Only that it's been postponed. Maniscalco's purge played havoc with our plans. There's only one man who can deliver us – and that's Giuseppe Garibaldi.' Greta eyes lost their focus and her voice became wistful. 'You can't imagine a man such as he! He's a new Messiah who will change the course of history.'

Carina was struck by the way she enunciated his name and the faraway look on her face surprised Carina. What was it about Garibaldi that induced such reverence? She recalled Enrico speaking of him in the same tone – as if there were almost something mystical about the man. She fiddled with the tassels of her shawl and it was moment before she spoke.

'Are you certain Garibaldi will come?'

'He'll come in the name of Italian unity. And now Ben's returned, we must prepare for action. For all his greatness, Garibaldi cannot achieve victory without the Sicilian patriots – and we can't be free without Garibaldi.'

With the briskness of a woman with purpose, Greta stood up, put on her gloves and straightened her hat. Her eyebrows drew together in two black crescents as she peered into Carina's face.

'Ben's confident you will never betray us. He's less certain of your political views.'

Surely Ben knew which side she was on! Her uncle and aunt might support the Bourbons, while Paulo was ambivalent, but she and Gabriella were patriots. It upset her that Ben questioned her loyalty and resentment glimmered in Carina's eyes.

'You may assure Captain Mavrone my sympathies are with the patriots.'

'Don't be angry.' Greta touched her hand briefly. 'Ben is vigilant to an extreme. He's been betrayed too many times to trust anyone.'

Greta knew Ben better than she did and Carina forgot her momentary annoyance. There was so much she wanted to understand – so much Greta could tell her about Ben. If only they had more time. But Greta was already taking her leave.

'I thank Heaven you've joined us, Miss Temple. Ben tells me you have the courage and fortitude of a lion. I believe in Providence and fate has brought you to us for good reason.'

CHAPTER TWENTY

Ben stayed with Carina all that night and every other night in the weeks that followed. Sometimes they dined together and when he was delayed she ate alone and he joined her later, coming to her room in the quiet of the night. She no longer resented his absences. They served to prolong the anticipation of his return and Carina did not question why she was at Monteleone. Her family knew she was safe and Ben was the centre of her world. There was no thought of going home, no thought of anything except Ben and the forthcoming revolution.

Greta sent a note asking permission to take her riding and Ben lent her his horse. They cantered through fields of green wheat and, when they came to the beach of Capo de Vito, galloped by the edge of the sea. Greta was an accomplished horsewoman and Carina was flattered when she complimented her on her ability.

'There's nothing I love more than being in the saddle! I've always understood horses better than humans.'

'Which is why you ride superbly. Garibaldi could do with equestrians of your skill. Will you enlist when the time comes?'

'Does Garibaldi allow *women* in his army?'

'He's never discriminated and his late wife was always by his side. Despite my husband's reservations, I'm determined to volunteer.'

Carina could shoot and ride as well as any man and she could barely contain herself.

'Then I'll volunteer with you! In what capacity may we serve?'

'As couriers and such like. I don't care so long as we can take part!'

She flashed a smile and Carina laughed out loud. Greta was unlike any other woman she had met. Her company was exhilarating and she was dying to ask her about Ben. She picked her moment as they were heading up the hill towards Monteleone.

'Have you known Ben all your life?'

'For as long as I can remember. The boys were five years older and I thought of them as my brothers.'

'Were the twins very alike?'

'They were identical in looks – and north and south in character. Ben was a rebel while Alexander never spoke of revolution. There was no justice in his death.'

Greta rubbed her riding crop against her cheek and Carina felt her distress. It must have been heart-breaking for all of them, she thought, and devastating for Ben. She couldn't imagine losing a brother or sister, let alone a twin. In the early days she had the impression of Ben as a man disinherited and alone. If what Paulo said was true, then his political activities had led to Alexander's death. Scalia was to blame, but Ben carried the burden of guilt and her heart went out to him.

'Why didn't Princess Scalia try to save Alexander?'

'Once she married Prince Scalia, Bianca del Angelo cut all ties with Monteleone.'

'I heard she was very close to Ben—'

'Bianca was close to *both* brothers,' Greta stated emphatically. 'I've no time for malicious gossip – and nor, do I imagine, do you!'

Carina blushed and Greta's tone softened. 'Ben's a good man. I can't bear to have him maligned. He needs a woman with spirit like you. But be sure to stand up for yourself – and don't let him go breaking your heart.'

Greta went from dark to light so fast that it was hard to keep up. She had stood up for herself all her life, Carina thought – only her relationship with Ben was different to anything she had experienced before. She needed Greta's guidance and would never mention Bianca Scalia's name again.

'Come on, I'll race you to the top.' Greta touched her spurs to her horse's flanks and called to her, 'Let the best man between us be the winner!'

Later that evening Ben came upstairs and put his arm around her.

'Greta tells me you ride like an officer of the Light Brigade. Where did you acquire such an excellent training?'

'I was an only child and spent most of my time in the stables. Horses were my best friends.'

'Do you miss your home?'

Her childhood and England felt as far away as the moon, her memories of Melton faded as old daguerreotypes. Not wanting to encroach on their present happiness, she had refrained from talking about the past, but they knew each other better now.

'I grew up in Yorkshire until I was fourteen and then moved to London.'

'Tell me about your parents.'

'My mother died when I was born. She never had the chance to bring me to Sicily.'

'And your father?'

She hadn't spoken about her father since his death, not even to Alice. The way Ben looked at her, so still and quiet, made Carina feel she could tell him anything.

'My father was killed out hunting.' The memory had been suppressed so long that her words came out in a rush. 'He jumped a stone wall without knowing there was a dyke on the far side. His horse fell and Papa broke his neck. He died instantly.'

It came back to her as if it had been yesterday. Carina saw her father's broken body being carried into the house. She remembered her stunned bewilderment in the beginning and the onslaught of grief that followed. There was a pencil lying on the table and she picked it up, squeezing it between her fingers.

'On the morning of his funeral, I took my horse over the wall where he was killed. It's what my father would have wanted. My courage was all I had to prove myself to him.'

The snap of the pencil made her look down. There were marks where the lead dug into the palm. Ben took the pieces from her and threw them onto the fire.

'Courage is a great quality.'

'Then I was fortunate for I was born with more than my fair share.'

'No one's born with courage, my love. Some people are born without fear, but that's different. Courage is acquired by degrees, layer upon layer. Brave men and women aren't those who don't know fear, but those who overcome and are strengthened by it.'

There was a serrated edge to his voice. Ben was going to tell her about Alexander at last, Carina thought. She waited and it saddened her when he was silent – but another matter pressed more urgently on her mind.

'Greta Mazzini and I intend to ride for Garibaldi when the time comes.'

'A battleground is no place for a woman. Would your father have let you take such a risk?'

Probably not, Carina thought, only she had come a long way since then. If Greta could volunteer, then so could she! Whatever Ben said, she would have her way. Her cheeks dimpled prettily and she changed direction.

'Greta speaks of Garibaldi as the new Messiah. Have you met him?'

'I fought beside him last year with the *Cacciatore dei Alpi*. He's a brilliant military commander. I admire him most for his integrity and humility.'

Ben walked over to the desk. He picked up her poem and brought it back with him. 'I read this earlier. Did you write it?'

She nodded, aware of the keen look in his eyes.

'I didn't know you were a poet. Are you still so melancholy?'

'Only when you treat me like a child—'

Ben laughed softly and Carina turned her face up to him. He kissed her with one hand pressed hard against the muslin that covered her breast and guided her towards the bed.

'You're made for love, not for war, sweetheart. It's a damned sight more satisfactory than any battlefield.'

Carina felt mildly irritated. Ben might not approve now – but she would wear him down until he agreed. She was going to ride with Garibaldi and no one could stop her! Seeing her expression, his eyebrows lifted in mock horror.

'My darling, don't look so fierce! You might frighten me away.'

Ben's tone was light-hearted, but his lips spoke a different language. Carina let him undress her and he tossed her clothes to the ground, kissing her all the time until she was breathless. When he knelt between her knees she had a dizzying glimpse of the brilliance in his eyes. There was no tenderness tonight. His hand twisted in her hair as he pushed her up against the headboard and Carina raked her nails across his back. His unashamed hands ranged over her body, as if he wanted to possess every part of her not yet made his own and Carina responded with desire as fierce as his own. Their passion for each other was insatiable, on and on through the darkness and danger of the night, until they fell back exhausted.

Later, Carina lay beside him with her hand playing across his chest. Ben was awake and she wondered what he was thinking.

'I've told you about myself, yet know so little about you. Are there secrets in your past?'

'None that would interest you, my love. There's no mystery about me – no riddles to solve.'

As he spoke, Ben reached for her. He drew her head into the hollow of his shoulder and she could imagine the look on his face. She had seen that blank expression before, warning her away whenever she came too close. Ben had encouraged her to talk about her parents and confessed nothing of himself. What was it that he would not admit even as he lay in her arms? How much longer must she wait?

I'll wait forever, Carina thought. Against hope, against reason, against peace, I love this man. I will defeat him as he has defeated me. I love Ben and will never give in until I capture his elusive soul.

CHAPTER TWENTY-ONE

March brought sun and showers and Carina sensed events were on the move. Strange men who came to the house were taken to buildings beyond the stable yard and covered wagons lumbered up the road almost every day. Ben was away so much and she was lonely without him.

Carina went for walks and picked the tiny red flowers of St Joseph for Selida. From her, she learnt the twins came from a village in the mountains. Selida had been employed by Donna Isabella as their nurse and stayed on at Monteleone ever since. She told her the boys had been educated at home, before they were sent to Ireland where Ben trained as a soldier and Alexander studied at university.

When he was at home, Carina sometimes caught Ben watching her with a speculative look in his eyes. What was he was thinking, she wondered? Surely, by now he knew he could trust her? She wanted to ask him when the revolution would begin but Ben put a finger across her lips. He made love to her, but didn't tell her where he had been or what he had been doing.

One night he was later than usual and Carina could not sleep. She tossed and turned in bed and then made up her mind. If Ben refused to involve her, she must find out what was happening for herself. Once, when she wandered too far from the house towards the stables, a groom had stopped her and told her it was out of bounds. Carina had let it pass at the time, putting it down to the obsessive secrecy of Monteleone, but it was there her investigation would begin.

The next morning she told Selida she was going for a walk and descended the back stairs, making a detour past the kitchen. The cook was rolling pasta and the smell of tomatoes and garlic on the stove followed her down the passage. Looking out from the back door, she saw two stable lads grooming a horse in the yard. One was holding the stallion's head while the other oiled its hooves. She waited until they finished, then slipped behind the loose box, walking swiftly until she came to a courtyard with high walls.

In front of her were storerooms with wooden doors and steps leading down to some kind of a cellar. Carina listened to make sure no one followed and then tiptoed forward. The door was open so she went down until her head was beneath ground level. As she pushed the door inward, cobwebs swept her face and she put down her parasol to brush them away. She could see stacked shelves reaching up to the curve of the ceiling. Why, it was only an old wine cellar! Carina smiled at her own foolishness. There was hardly space to move, let alone hold a secret meeting.

A shaft of sunlight came through the door as she turned back and the breath went out of her lungs in a gasp. Instead of wine barrels, she was staring at weapons. There were muzzle-loaders and bayonets stacked in rows, along with pistols and muskets. Wooden crates marked with skull and crossbones stood unopened on the floor. Here, Ben had assembled the military equipment for the revolution! Monteleone was to be the headquarters and she would be at the heart of it!

The next moment Ben's voice exploded in her ear. 'What the hell do you think you're doing?'

There was a dangerous look on his face as he pushed her back into the dark interior. When he reached for the door, Carina thought he meant to shut her in but he left it open a crack, allowing a small amount of light into the cellar.

'Two of my men were watching you. They saw you come here and sent for me.'

'But the door was wide open.'

'The guards set you a trap. They don't trust you. In fact, they believe you're a spy.'

'Then tell them the truth—'

Carina broke off as Ben dropped into a crouch. He took hold of the front of her skirt and pulled it up above her knees. His hand slid from her ankle to her calf, running over her silk stockings to the top of her legs. She tried to keep her knees together but he forced them apart to search the inside of her thighs. When he straightened up, he unbuttoned her dress and felt roughly inside the bodice.

'Have you finished or shall I strip naked for you?' Carina cheeks flamed with mortification. Her hands were clumsy as she fastened the buttons and brushing her aside, Ben finished the job himself. Then he stood back, studying her face with the same scrutiny he had bestowed on the rest of her.

'I know how much you wanted my pistol and old habits die hard. If not a gun, what were you looking for?'

'I want to know where you spend all day and half the night.'

'You could have asked.'

'You wouldn't have told me! You never tell me anything!'

'I haven't told you because the more you know, the more dangerous it is for you. When you return to Palermo you will be interrogated – and possibly by Prince Scalia himself. The revolution is upon us, Carina. Indeed, I'm obliged to bring forward the date of your departure.'

Carina looked at Ben in disbelief. What was he talking about? She wasn't going back to Palermo. She was staying here with him. She heard his words but could not take them in.

'Baron Riso's staying here tomorrow night and will escort you back to Palermo. He's arranged for the British Consul to take you to your family. Between them, they'll conceal all traces of where you've been.'

Thoughts crowded her brain, one following so fast upon another that Carina felt stunned. How could Ben endure the idea of her being interrogated by Scalia? An overheard phrase drummed in her head. 'He's a man with a precise method of sucking the juice from the grape and then discarding the skin.' She couldn't remember where she had heard the remark, but it wasn't true of Ben. She refused to believe it.

'I've invited Greta and Stefan for the evening,' Ben continued with military efficiency. 'Francesco Riso believes you've been with them all the time. I've kept my promise, sweetheart. You will return home with your reputation unblemished.'

To hell with his promises! The day after tomorrow she would be gone from Monteleone. They might never see each other again. What about us, her mind screamed? Ben had asked her to marry him, for pity's sake! Furious, words sprang to her lips and Carina forced them down. Losing her temper would only make it worse. She lifted her chin and managed to ask quietly, 'When did you decide all this?'

'We received notice last week that Rosalino Pilo, one of

Garibaldi's best commanders, is on his way. Once Garibaldi hears the uprising is successful he will sail for Sicily.'

Compared to the great cause of Italy, their relationship was incidental and so, it seemed, was she. But Ben couldn't make her return to Palermo. She would write to Nonna and tell her she was delayed. Baron Riso could take her letter for Mr Goodwin to pass on. If Ben insisted she left Monteleone, she would stay with Greta Mazzini.

'I must get you back before your family take to their heels,' Ben's voice was kinder. 'Most of the nobility have abandoned Palermo for Naples already.'

Her eyes burned with obstinacy and Ben avoided her gaze as he led her up the steps. He escorted her across the yard and Carina walked on to the house alone. There's been a misunderstanding, she thought desperately. I must be cool-headed. Ben doesn't realise I'm committed to the revolution. It's the reason he won't tell me anything. I must talk to him and make him understand.

The rest of the day dragged by, and Carina took supper in her room. She hoped Ben would be early, but it was after midnight when he came to bed. His eyes closed straightaway, but she knew he wasn't asleep. She waited and then put her hand on his chest. Her fingers ran over his skin, skimming the flat surface of his stomach. Carina was astonished at her boldness. She wondered how much further she would go. Then his body tensed and Ben caught her by the wrist and pulled her hand away.

They lay face to face and Ben lifted her leg over his waist. Carina saw in his eyes the same hard elation she felt in herself. She moved astride him and tossed her hair back off her face. A smile played around her mouth and Ben swore softly. His resistance crumbled and he reached for her shoulders and pulled her down. He made love to her as if he wanted to impress himself upon her forever and her heart welled up with happiness. Ben couldn't love her like this and then send her away. Tomorrow, when she asked him, he would let her stay.

CHAPTER TWENTY-TWO

The twittering of small birds woke Carina soon after dawn. She had fallen asleep confident and woken up cold with apprehension. Supposing Ben denied her request? Would Greta be willing to have her to stay? If Greta wouldn't help her, then who could she turn to?

Ben had left early and, trapped in a state of nervous tension, the day seemed to last forever. It was past five when Carina heard Ben come in. She peered down from the landing to make sure no one was around before she crept downstairs to the library. She listened and then opened the door quietly. She needed to talk to Ben undisturbed and would wait for him here. He was bound to come soon.

Leaving the door ajar, Carina tried to rehearse her arguments, but could hardly think for the butterflies in her stomach. She ran her eye along the titles of the books. Dictionaries and periodicals were on the lower shelves with novels and poetry higher up. To distract herself, she climbed the library steps and took out the first volume that her hand touched.

It was an anthology of English verse and the flyleaf was inscribed with the name Alexander Mavrone. The binding had been stretched and she let the book fall open at will. The pages parted where a piece of folded paper acted as a bookmark and the lines of a poem by Byron were underlined in pencil.

> *When we two parted*
> *In silence and tears*
> *Half broken-hearted*
> *To sever for years ...*
>
> *They knew not I knew thee*
> *Who knew thee too well,*
> *Long, long shall I rue thee,*
> *Too deeply to tell.*
>
> *If I should meet thee*
> *After long years*
> *How should I greet thee?*
> *With silence and tears.*

Beneath the quiet rhythm and simple words was a depth of feeling that haunted Carina. The folded bookmark caught her attention and she blew away a fine layer of dust, and spread the paper open. A curl of flaxen hair lay in the crease. She touched it lightly and then snatched her hand away. The image of Bianca Scalia's face swam into her mind and she shut the book with a snap.

'Did you find what you're looking for?' Ben's voice came from the doorway.

How long had he been watching her, Carina wondered? She put the book back and came slowly down the steps.

'Your library is a revelation.'

'My brother's library,' Ben corrected her as he strolled forward, his gaze scanning the surface of his desk. 'Perhaps my correspondence is of more interest?'

'I'm not in the habit of prying.'

'Of course you're not.' He was mildly sarcastic. 'Now you're here, why don't you sit down?'

Ben pulled up a chair and Carina sat down. The piercing blue of his eyes made her heart pound, but it was now or never and she held her nerve.

'I've decided not to return to Palermo. I'm going to volunteer my services to Garibaldi.'

'You know that's out of the question.'

'Please hear me out.' Carina lifted a hand, her voice gathering strength. 'I shall write to my grandmother and tell her it's unsafe for me to travel. I'm better staying where I am for now.'

'Which isn't true. In a few weeks Monteleone will be the most dangerous place in Sicily.'

'Then I'll stay with Greta Mazzini and her husband.'

'That's nothing to the purpose. You'll only be safe if you travel with your family to Naples.'

'I've no wish to go to Naples. I want to take part in the revolution. Sicily is in my blood. I have the right to be a part of our nation's future.'

'Please be reasonable, Carina. I'm not sending you away for my own convenience.'

'Then why are you?'

'I've no choice. I brought you here to save you.'

'Not from yourself!' Carina saw a muscle in Ben's jaw twitch and went on quickly. 'I'm sure Greta will agree. I'll discuss it with her later.'

'Greta and Stefan can't look after you. They know that it's madness for you to stay.'

'Then I shall find somewhere else—'

'For God's sake, Carina! It's time you went home.'

He sounded exasperated. And with the collapse of her hopes, despair and anger took over. Carina struck out with her hands, pointing first to herself and then to him.

'I thought my home was with you! You said you were serious and I trusted you! Were you afraid I wouldn't succumb unless I was convinced of your integrity?'

'Oh no, I knew you'd succumb from the first moment we met. Integrity didn't come into it.'

His words fell on Carina with crushing brutality. Did Ben know the hurt he caused? Was he being deliberately cruel in order to distance himself from her?

'Don't you understand what I've become? How can I go back to my family *now*?'

It was the last argument she had left to use and Carina looked into Ben's face. She saw the shadow in his eyes and tension in the hard line of his jaw. She waited, but he was silent. His mind was made up and no appeal of emotion nor reason would alter his decision.

Carina came to her feet and fled the library. She ran upstairs, taking the steps two at a time. When she reached her bedroom she slammed the door shut and fell on the bed. Pressure had been building up all day and she burst into a storm of weeping. She cried until her eyes were sore and her head throbbed. How arrogant to think last night changed anything! She had thought Ben cared for her – but he cared only for himself. He had lied to her and she had fallen for the oldest deception of all.

Some time later, Selida came in and sat down on the bed. She put a hand on her shoulder and Carina muffled her sobs in the pillow.

'Benito doesn't mean to hurt you. He's suffered more than you will ever know. You're on his conscience. He only wants what is best for you.'

After she had gone, Carina went through to the washroom and splashed cold water onto her face. I've done everything in my power to reach you, she thought. I have given you all of myself. I touch you, but leave no imprint. I am as wind blowing over rocks.

Never in her life had Carina accepted defeat, not in the sense she faced it now. She had lost her way before and recovered. It was not in her nature to yield and, standing by the basin with water dripping off her chin, she spoke out loud, 'I won't let you break my heart, Ben. I am as strong as you are ...'

She would return to her family, but go no further than Palermo. When they left for Naples, she would find a way to stay in Sicily. With single-minded determination, Carina cast everything else aside. Selida had hung out a black evening gown, but it wouldn't do for her last evening at Monteleone. She searched the wardrobe until she found a dress the colour of poppies. Red for passion and red for Garibaldi.

The dress was of a later style and required stays, so she waited until Selida came back. Holding on to the bedpost, Carina made her lace her in until her waist was tiny. She soothed her eyes with pads soaked in cold water and buffed her cheeks to give them colour. Selida helped pin her hair into a chignon and, at her suggestion, she put a touch of cream to her lips. Then Carina thanked her and made her way downstairs.

Ben was walking across the hall as she came down and stopped to wait for her.

'You look beautiful this evening.'

She inclined her head as he ushered her into the salon where the others were gathered. Greta introduced Carina to her husband, Stefan Bosco, a tall man with a high forehead and gentle smile. Soon afterwards, Baron Riso arrived. He looked tired, Carina thought, as he bowed over her hand. Ben brought her a glass of wine and she settled herself on the sofa with Greta while the men talked together by the fire.

'I'm sorry you must leave us.' Greta's eyes were filled with concern. 'I worry for you alone in Palermo.'

'I've friends to support me and I won't be entirely alone. But what will happen when the authorities learn that I've been staying with you? They're bound to make enquiries.'

'We've had plenty of practice and know how to handle them.' Greta smiled mischievously.

'You must tell me all about your home. I need to be acquainted with every detail.'

'We're half an hour's ride south of Calatafimi. We have a smallholding with a few hectares of olive groves and …'

Greta went on and Carina did her best to pay attention as her gaze strayed to the far end of the room. Ben had discarded his jacket and looked relaxed, but she knew how swiftly his pose could transform into action. He was the true soldier among the men, she thought. Baron Riso's courtesy made it hard to imagine him in hand-to-hand combat and Stefan seemed more a professor than an infantryman. The only other warrior in the room was Greta. Carina could imagine her on horseback, wielding a sword amidst the fray. Would she be kept from the battlefield, too, because she was a woman? Had their hope of riding with the Garibaldi been no more than a dream?

Dinner was announced and Carina was placed next to the baron, at the opposite end of the table from Ben. During the main part of the meal, conversation was general, but once the servants withdrew, talk shifted to the current situation.

'When does Garibaldi plan to set sail for Sicily?' The question came from Stefan.

'He will leave Genoa when he learns of our success.' Baron Riso's voice was compelling. 'I thank God the voice of freedom will soon be heard! We have bombs and firearms stored in the Gancia Convent and the day is appointed. I trust the *squadri* will support us, Captain Mavrone.'

'As soon as we receive your signal, we'll come down from the mountains and fight beside you in the streets of Palermo,' Ben answered.

'I would like to offer my assistance. I'll be in Palermo and the family home is at your disposal.'

Carina's announcement was met by stunned silence. She looked down the table and saw Ben frown. She expected him to protest, but it was Baron Riso who replied,

'We don't wish you to put yourself in danger, Miss Temple.'

'And yet you jeopardise the security of your wife and children? I'll not be excluded from the dangers that others face!'

'Brava!' Greta's eyes were bright as she clapped her hands. 'We womenfolk are ready—'

'You've a long journey ahead of you, Carina,' Ben cut her off and stood up. 'I'm sure you wish to retire. Let me escort you to the stairs. Will you excuse us, please?'

He came round the table and offered Carina his arm. She wanted to say a proper goodbye to Greta, but he barely gave her the time. They walked through the salon to the hall where the sconces had been extinguished and, leaving her at the foot of the stairs, Ben went to fetch a light. He returned with a candle and, as Carina reached for it, lifted it away and placed it on the base of the bannisters.

'Are you determined to frustrate me?'

'I told you before, I want to be part of the liberation of my country.'

'What am I to do with you, Carina Temple? You're utterly impossible but I'll miss you, my beautiful woman.'

Ben's fingers traced the contours of her face and Carina did not move. Cool and calm, she waited with her mouth slightly open until his arm went round her waist. Ben kissed her slowly and gently, his mouth pressing open her lips with a warmth that caressed her whole body. Remember this, she thought. He will come back to you …

There was no warning of the sound that broke in on them. One moment Ben was kissing her and the next, released her so abruptly that Carina lost her balance. She flung out her hand and sent the candle crashing to the ground.

'Please forgive me,' Baron Riso's voice came from somewhere near the door.

'Not at all.' Ben bent down and retrieved the broken candle. 'Carina was about to go up.'

'I'll get another light.' Stefan spoke next and returned with a candelabra from the dining table. With her hand on the rail, Carina climbed the stairs. An oil lamp was burning on the landing and she stopped to look down. Stefan held the candelabra aloft and Baron Riso coughed, putting his hand over his mouth – only Ben appeared unaffected by the moment. There was humour and admiration in his eyes as he smiled up at her. Then he put a hand on Baron Riso's shoulder and the small group headed towards the library, taking the light with them.

★ ★ ★

Carina departed from Monteleone early the next morning. She had said goodbye to Selida, whose niece accompanied her. The young woman sat on the seat opposite and she wondered whose idea it had been to provide a chaperone.

She could see Monteleone standing on its hill and the plain below, distinguished only by complexion from the sea beyond. How she wished this part of the journey over! Her papers would be checked along the way and she must practice her lines. She had to be word perfect to be convincing, but she was leaving Ben and sorrow strangled her heart.

He was to accompany them as far as the border of the estate and, as the carriage came to a halt, Carina leant out, craning her neck in search of him. Ahead on the road, a group of armed men gathered round the cavalcade. One of them began a chant and was joined by the others.

> *Come join them! Come follow, o youth of our land!*
> *Come fling out our banner, and marshal our band!*
> *Come with cold steel, come with hot fire,*
> *Come all with the flame of Italia's desire.*
> *Begone from Italia, begone from us now!*
> *Stranger begone, for this is our hour!*

Carina could see Ben now, standing in his stirrups as he motioned the men to silence. Baron Riso spoke a few words and then Ben sat back in the saddle and aimed his rifle in the air. A single shot rang out and the patriots waved their black hats and began cheering. Ben signalled to the coachmen to drive on. He was on her side of the carriage and her gloved hand gripped the rim of the window. As they drew level, he leant down from the saddle and said something but his words were lost in the din. The whip cracked, and, as the horses broke into a canter,

Carina put her head right out of the window to look back. Dust flew up, stinging her eyes, and she had a last glimpse of Ben on his black horse before they swept around the corner and he was gone.

CHAPTER TWENTY-THREE

PALERMO, APRIL 1860

Carina opened her eyes and looked up at the ceiling of her bedroom in Palermo. Her heart was heavy and she longed for Ben. She missed his warmth and dark head on the pillow. It was the same every morning. Depression faded with the activity of the day, but Ben was never far from her thoughts. Be patient, she told herself. You only left Monteleone ten days ago. It's not yet time.

Dawn sneaked in through the shutters and she cast her mind back to her arrival home. Despite endless roadblocks and checking of papers, the journey had passed without incident. At the city gates soldiers with foreign accents challenged them and Baron Riso took her on to the consulate alone. Jane and Mr Goodwin were waiting and she was whisked off to the Palazzo Denuzio, where she found her grandmother with Paulo and Gabriella.

'It was terrible not knowing what had happened to you.' Nonna held her hand tight. 'We were frantic with worry until your letter arrived. Thank God our prayers have brought you safely home.'

And it must have seemed like an answer to prayer when she walked in that night, Carina thought. Her grandmother's eyes never left her face and she had to answer a hundred questions before she was allowed to bed. She learnt that Anna Maria was rescued by a fellow pilgrim and Prince Scalia had taken personal charge of the search. Troops were deployed deep into the Interior, hundreds of suspects arrested and interrogated but to no avail. It was as if she had vanished into thin air – and only when they heard from Greta Mazzini, did they know she was safe.

Carina met with Carlo and Anna Maria the following morning. Her aunt wept and declared it a miracle she was alive, while Carlo was permitted to ask only the mildest questions. Carina would submit a written statement to the head of police, Nonna insisted, but nothing more.

'Use your influence, for once, Carlo! The child has suffered enough without having to face the trials of the Inquisition. I demand this matter goes no further.'

Her uncle reluctantly complied, and a report was duly submitted. Paulo seemed the only one unconvinced by her story. He did not contradict her, but there was a mocking look in his eyes and Carina wondered if he believed a word she said.

Palermo was an occupied city and every day more troops arrived. Foreign mercenaries were brought in to reinforce the Bourbon army and the sound of marching went on day and night. 'Disordered times, dangerous times ...' Those were the words on everyone's lips. The city was rife with rumours and Carina watched and listened, her hopes rising and falling with every piece of news. Carlo Denuzio decided to send his wife and mother on ahead to Naples. Nonna refused outright at first and only finally agreed on condition that Carlo kept his word and Carina would not interrogated.

Church bells calling people to Matins began to peal out across the city and Carina dangled her legs over the side of the bed. Would she receive a reply from Jane today? The situation of foreign nationals in the city was becoming precarious and she must know it was urgent.

My uncle and cousins leave for Naples at the end of next week. She had written to her three days before. *He has booked Rose a passage to return to England and I cannot remain in Palermo alone. Do you think Mr and Mrs Goodwin might be kind enough to allow me stay at the consulate? I would be forever grateful if you could act as my chaperone. Alice and my grandmother will be content if they know that I am with you, and under the consul's protection. I beg you to help me, dear Jane! I cannot leave Sicily in her hour of need ...*

Carina could hear windows opening and footsteps on the stairs. The household was stirring and soon Rose would bring her breakfast. Matins must be over and she wondered why the bells were still ringing. Getting out of bed, she pinned her wrapper close about her and walked out on to the balcony. The streets around the house were deserted. There were no early morning hawkers selling bread and salami, no clattering of wagon wheels or the tramp of soldiers' boots. Apart from a group of nuns crossing the piazza, she could not see a single person.

The ringing of bells went on and her gaze scanned the churches and convents below with their campaniles rising above them. The pealing was coming from the old quarter of the city and now seemed to take on a different rhythm, ringing loudly and discordantly. Carina's heart stopped, then began to race. Could this be the signal for the insurgence? She was excited and terrified at the same time. And then, from nowhere, a flame of fire arched through the sky. There was a deafening explosion and she heard running feet behind her.

Gabriella appeared on the balcony in her nightgown, rosary beads in her hand. 'Lord save us, what's happening?'

'I don't know ... What's the name of that church down there?'

'The convent of Santa Maria Gancia—'

The cannon boomed again and a shell detonated with a force that rattled the glass panes in the window. Carina grabbed Gabriella by the arm and pulled her back inside.

'Holy Mary, protect them! Mother of mercy, save our loved ones ...'

Gabriella was on her knees and Carina didn't know whether to join her or tell her to get up. There were more loud bangs until, all at once, the bells fell silent. The quiet that followed was as chilling as the grave. Holding on to each other, the cousins stepped cautiously outside. A cloud of black smoke hung over the Gancia convent and Carina clasped a hand over her mouth. What had happened? Had the revolution been crushed as soon as it had begun?

'We must get dressed and find your father.' Carina tried to be strong but her voice shook. 'I'll meet you downstairs.'

Gabriella nodded, and, as she left the bedroom, Rose passed her in the doorway.

'Do you know what's going on?' Carina asked her.

'Gino says there's trouble in the east of the city. Seems it's all over now.'

Carina dressed quickly, not bothering with her hair. It might be nothing to do with the uprising, she thought as she ran down the stairs. Her uncle would know, but when she arrived in the gallery, both Carlo and Paulo had left the house. They had rushed off without saying where they were going or when they might be back.

Never had a day passed so slowly. The servants spoke in hushed tones and an eerie stillness hung over house. Carina and Gabriella could not eat and took turns walking up and down the gallery or slumped in chairs. Every moment they expected to hear carriage wheels on the cobbles but not until late afternoon were they alerted by noise in the courtyard. Both of them rushed to the top of the steps. Jane Parsons alighted from a *caleffini* and Carina ran down to meet her.

Jane instructed the driver to wait and put a finger to her lips, saying nothing until they were inside the house.

'I had to come and tell you myself.' She exhaled slowly as she sat down. 'The patriots were betrayed! Maniscalco's troops were waiting and drove them back into the convent. They rang the bells to call the people out – but there was no time! The doors were blown open by cannon. Three were killed and many more injured.'

She went on to tell them Baron Riso had been arrested and forced to march in chains all the way from the Piazza Bologna to the fortress of Castellamare. It was light and warm in the room but a chill wrapped itself around Carina.

'Those who lost their lives are true martyrs!' Gabriella spoke bravely but the blood had leached from her cheeks.

'Do you have news of Enrico Fola?' Carina asked, taking Gabriella's hand.

'I'm afraid not – I only know about Baron Riso because his wife sent a message to Mr Goodwin. I'm on my way to see her.' Jane plunged her hand into her reticule and retrieved a handkerchief. She held it to her nose a moment, then put it away and braced her shoulders. 'It's up to the *squadri* in the mountains now! They must keep the revolution alive in Sicily. For every man who died today, a hundred more will take his place.'

Jane's face was taut with strain as they went down to the

courtyard. Pietro stepped forward and Carina waved him away, handing her into the cab herself.

'Thank you for coming to tell us, dear Jane. Did you receive my letter?'

'We must no longer communicate by post,' Jane whispered as she settled herself inside. 'Of course you may stay at the consulate but travel only by *caleffini*. All the main streets are blocked and these drivers know every back alley and shortcut in the city. However, I expect your uncle will be delayed in Palermo rather longer than he anticipated.'

Carina watched as the two-wheeled gig trotted out through the gates. Purple bougainvillea cascaded over the walls and its garish display clashed with her dark mood. Ben had promised to fight alongside Baron Riso in the city and she imagined him waiting for the signal that never came. Renewed fear swept her. Now that the outcome of the revolution depended on the *squadri*; he would be in greater danger. And what of Enrico?

They were at the dinner table when Paulo came home. He threw his jacket onto a chair and loosened his necktie as he sat down.

'Papa sent me home to keep you calm,' he said and helped himself to a glass of wine, which he drank in one.

A plate was placed in front of him and Pietro served macaroni from a silver tureen. While they had no appetite, he wolfed down his meal. Paulo wouldn't eat like that if anything terrible had happened to Enrico, Carina thought. They remained silent until Pietro went out and Gabriella spoke first.

'Miss Parsons came by this afternoon. She told us the uprising has been crushed. Is Enrico safe? Please tell me!'

'Well, at least he's alive. He was arrested outside the convent.' Paulo cast Gabriella a pitying look as she crossed herself. 'They've taken him to the Vicaria prison.'

Gabriella lips moved but no sound came from her mouth and Carina answered for her. 'Enrico is a courageous man! Miss Parsons said that Baron Riso was also arrested.'

'Maniscalco believes your friend is the ringleader,' Paulo replied in a sanguine tone. 'Riso's in solitary confinement in the Castellamare – but there's no need to concern yourself unduly. Due to his rank he'll be granted a fair trial.'

Gabriella announced she would retire and Paulo went with her to the door.

'Try not to worry, Ella. Papa's promised to speak to the king on Enrico's behalf. He'll be home before we know it.'

Carina watched him hug his sister, his arm around her slight shoulders as he kissed the top of her head. She felt the warmth between them and Gabriella blew her a kiss before she went out.

Paulo closed the door and turned back into the room, scowling. 'How could Enrico be such a fool?'

'He acted according to his principles. He believes in a united Italy.'

'What are you talking about?' Paulo was derisive. 'There's no such nation.'

'I mean the new Italy that belongs to Italians – not to the Spanish or Austrians. The patriots sacrificed themselves for justice and freedom!'

'So you have been *mazzinified*! I hoped you had more sense than to be swayed by propaganda.'

Carina ignored the taunt and waited until Paulo sat down. 'What will happen to Enrico?'

'We must pray for clemency from the king. Scalia and Maniscalco's retribution is terrible to behold.' Paulo glanced at the tall case clock in the corner. 'Thirteen of the conspirators are condemned by court martial and will be executed at midnight. Can you imagine? The youngest is only fifteen years old.'

As the full impact of Paulo's words hit her, Carina's heart began to beat with hard, uneven jerks. She thought of the last time she had seen Enrico and the look on his face when he spoke of sacrifice. The memory was vivid and with it came to her a terrifying premonition. Enrico was alive, even if he was in prison, Carina told herself. He wasn't in danger and the events of the day were making her imagination run wild. She shook her head to get rid of unwanted thoughts, but the feeling of dread persisted and she could not shut it out.

Glancing across at Paulo, Carina saw his expression was bleak. An empty wine glass dangled from his hand. He must have witnessed terrible atrocities today and she admired him for keeping them from his sister. Gabriella was too young to withstand such horrors.

'We should visit Enrico, don't you think?'

'No one's allowed to see him, not even his family.'

'There would be no harm in trying.'

'I said no one.'

'Please can we—' Paulo stood up so abruptly the words died on Carina's lips as he came to stand over her.

'Don't even think about it! Your association with the rebels can only make Enrico's situation worse. Keep well out of this, I tell you!'

He had never spoken to her like that before and Carina stared at him. Did Paulo know she had been at Monteleone with Ben? No, it wasn't possible. There was no way he could have found out! She lowered her gaze and made an effort to sound contrite.

'I'm sorry. I didn't mean to interfere. Enrico's your friend and I know your family will help him. Let's pray the king is merciful. Now, if you don't mind, I'll follow Gabriella's example and retire.'

CHAPTER TWENTY-FOUR

It was barely light when Carina and Gabriella set out from the Palazzo Denuzio a week later. The landau was closed and heavy veils covered their faces as they handed their papers through the window for inspection. They could be turned back at any time and Carina was on edge every time they were stopped.

The visit had been hard enough to arrange and she couldn't have managed without Gabriella. It was her idea to involve Rose and Gino. They were sworn to secrecy and Gino instructed to make enquiries at the Vicaria on behalf of a young lady who wished to visit her brother. The prison guards said this 'sister' was by no means the first. They were inundated by such requests and prepared to oblige only if it was made worth their while. Between them, Carina and Gabriella had gathered a hundred scudi and divided the money into purses for Gino to distribute. Rose's task was to help them leave the house and make sure no one discovered they were gone. She would lock their bedrooms and wait for their return.

It was a day of showers and sudden gusts and they hung onto their bonnets as they hurried across the piazza. Gino was waiting with the landau in a side street and Rose had provided a basket of food. The journey passed in silence. Gabriella kept her eyes closed while Carina was too nervous to talk. She had never been inside a prison before. Paulo said 'gentlemen' were treated better than others, but the Vacaria had a gruesome reputation. They must be nearly there, she thought and lifted the corner of her veil to peer through the rain-spattered window.

Beneath stormy clouds, Mount Pellegrino hunched like a great beast over the fortress of Castellamare. It was a forbidding place and Carina shuddered as they went past. Somewhere inside there, Baron Riso was incarcerated. She hated to think of him in solitary confinement but now she could see the Vacaria. The prison's outer walls had small barred windows and a spiked rail running along the top. She nudged Gabriella, adjusting her veil as the carriage came to a halt. Gino opened the door and helped them out.

A rough-looking prison guard approached and said with a Calabrian accent, 'No more than ten minutes. That's what we agreed. So let's see what you've got in your basket.'

The basket was returned to the landau and its contents spilled on the floor and examined. When he finished, Gino handed him a purse and he gave a harsh laugh.

'Lover boy's a lucky fellow.'

Hardly, Carina thought grimly as they followed him to the entrance. Two guards joined them carrying truncheons and they passed through an arched vault and went down a steep slope. Most of the prison was underground, fortified by massive black stones with water running down the sides. Gate after gate was unchained, opened and locked behind them. There was no fresh air and the stench of human filth made Carina want to retch. She pinched the bridge of her nose and breathed through her mouth. It was worse than she could have imagined and when Gabriella stopped and bent over, she caught her by the shoulders as she was sick on the ground.

All around them the sound of groaning rose and fell. Lanterns in wall brackets gave out little light and the further in they went, the darker it became. The place was so cold they shivered despite their thick cloaks. The jailor stopped in front of a cave carved out of the rock. The cell was no larger than the inside of a carriage and the ceiling too low for a man to stand upright. At first Carina saw only one prisoner. Then two shadowy figures on the ground struggled to their knees and she realised they were manacled together.

Both men were dressed as common felons in devil's dust cloth. Heavy chains bound their ankles and wrists and their faces were black with grime. Gabriella shrank back as Enrico was wracked by a coughing fit. When he was able to raise his head, his eyes shone too brightly and Carina knew he was ill.

'We've brought you food, 'she whispered. 'Don't speak. Save your strength.'

'Papa's petitioned the king. This is for both of you.' Gabriella pressed her face to the bars and pushed through a loaf of bread.

'I don't want the king's mercy. It's enough you've both come,' Enrico spoke with difficulty. 'You're my guardian angels.'

Carina took a step to one side to allow Gabriella to talk to him while she passed cheese and fruit to the other prisoner. She had the impression he was taller and older than Enrico. 'What's your name?' she asked.

'Max Corso. Have you news of Francesco Riso?'

'He's in the Castellamare. We're told his rank means he will be given a fair trial.'

'That would require an act of God.' Max Corso's light-blue eyes fixed on her face. 'Your friend is extremely ill. You must secure his release. He hasn't the strength to survive in here.'

Dear Lord, her premonition hadn't been so wrong! Carina felt a slither of ice slip down her throat. Enrico will not die, she swore silently. I won't let it happen. We must find a way to save him. The basket was empty and her gloved fingers brushed Max Corso's hand.

'I promise to do all I can. Trust me—'

'Basta! Enough!' The guttural voice of the guard was close by her ear. 'Hurry up now!'

It seemed they had only been there a few minutes when it was already time to leave. Carina went quickly to Enrico.

'God bless and take care of you. Stay strong, dear friend.'

'We'll meet again when the revolution is accomplished,' Enrico whispered and then they were being led away and heading back towards the outside world. Gabriella stumbled and taking her arm Carina saw her lips move in silent prayer. If only she were blessed with her cousin's faith and Enrico's hope! Orderlies passed them with foul-smelling soup and a fuse of rage ignited inside her. When a rat ran across her shoes, Carina scarcely noticed. This was Satan's kingdom on earth and the Bourbon regime was rotten to the core. Those who perpetuated such inhumanity must be destroyed! The revolution was far more than a political struggle. It was a war against evil and she had joined the crusade.

She was tempted to instruct Gino to withhold the payments; but the guards would only take it out on the prisoners and she watched in silent fury as the money was distributed.

Gabriella slept for most of the way back, leaving her to deal with travel permits. Carina was too agitated to care how many times they were stopped. Enrico's situation was grave and they needed to act fast. A petition to the king would take too long.

Who else had the authority to order his release? The answer that came turned her stomach. The thought of petitioning Prince Scalia made her feel physically sick. No, she couldn't do it! Gabriella must entreat her father to speak to the governor. Carlo Denuzio had the ear of the king. He could say that Enrico had been wrongfully imprisoned and demand his immediate release.

They were nearly home and alighted the carriage at the far side of the piazza. Skirting the church as the bell in the campanile chimed eight, they came to the door where Rose was waiting. She escorted them discreetly past the kitchens and the servants' quarters, up the back stairs where a housemaid was scrubbing the stone. Gabriella had rehearsed the story that they had been to early Mass and Carina went with her to her bedroom. When she came to her own, she removed her bonnet and kicked off her filthy shoes. Then she stripped off her gloves, washing her hands and face before she lay down on the bed.

Paulo had warned her not to interfere, she thought. She was a wiser woman now than the girl who left London a few months before. Enrico wasn't her responsibility. The sensible course of action was for her uncle to plead Enrico's case, only she had no faith in him. Carlo Denuzio was too weak.

Carina slipped out of bed and began to pace the floor in her bare feet. She loved Ben and must protect him. One false move and she might endanger the patriot cause. There were a hundred reasons to not get involved, but if she did nothing Enrico would die. Carina recalled Scalia's interest at the Villa Pallestro. He would not ignore a supplication from her. It was a loathsome prospect, but there was no other way and she went over to the desk.

For a long time she stared at a blank piece of writing paper. Then she took up the quill and dipped it in ink.

Your Excellency,

There is a matter of great urgency I need to discuss with you and pray you will receive me at your earliest convenience. I beg you request permission from my uncle to attend upon your Excellency at the Palazzo Reale. The matter to which I refer is of a delicate nature and I would be grateful if the application came at your bequest rather than my own.

I trust upon your kindness and remain, sir, your most obedient servant ...

Carina signed her name at the bottom and addressed it to the prince under the direction of the Palazzo Reale. She sealed the envelope, inscribing her initials above the wax. Then she walked over to the bell pull. She would instruct Gino to deliver the letter this afternoon before she could change her mind. Prince Scalia was not a man to be easily deceived. If he responded to her request, the interview would be a trial by fire. She must be clever, duplicitous and use every weapon in her armoury.

CHAPTER TWENTY-FIVE

'Garibaldi is an unprincipled opportunist.' Carlo Denuzio was standing with his back to the window and in full flow. 'Piedmont will never join forces with him against our beloved king.'

They were in the salon, waiting for Paulo to return for dinner, and Carina was sitting beside Gabriella. Her cousin was concentrating on her crochet and did not answer.

The door opened and a footman entered, bearing a silver salver with a letter, which he carried over to her uncle. Carina watched as her uncle took a paper knife and sliced open the envelope. He took out a piece of thick writing paper and was unfolding it when Paulo walked in.

'I'm sorry to be late—'

Carina hushed him and indicated towards her uncle. Carlo read the letter, frowning, and then returned it to its envelope.

'I have received a summons from His Excellency, Prince Scalia. He requests an interview with you in the morning, Carina. I'm to escort you to the Palazzo Reale at nine o'clock.'

Carina let out a long breath. So, the prince hadn't forgotten, and had responded sooner than she expected! There was no way out now and she lowered her head.

'But, Papa, you promised Nonna! You can't break your word!' Gabriella's cheeks flamed as she stood up and faced her father.

'I agree. Our grandmother will have you flayed alive,' Paulo commented drily. 'Unless, that is, you intend to keep her in the dark?'

Carlo Denuzio took off his spectacles and held them to the light. He inspected them minutely and replaced them on his nose, shifting his weight from one foot to another.

'If you accompany me, Uncle Carlo, then I've no objection to an audience with Prince Scalia,' Carina said and looked up. 'It may provide an opportunity to plead Enrico Fola's case. There's no need to inform Nonna, it will only upset her.'

They were all staring at her, Gabriella with her mouth open, Paulo curious, while Carlo beamed with relief.

'Thank you, my dear. We must all do our duty in these difficult times. However, I advise you not to speak on Enrico's behalf. Evidence has come to light that he is not as innocent as we believed.'

The words hung in the air and Carina's gaze went to Paulo. He spread his hands in a gesture of hopelessness and she turned a sharp eye on her uncle.

'If I may not speak openly with Prince Scalia, then there's no purpose to the interview. You may tell His Excellency that is my answer.'

Carlo Denuzio didn't appreciate his authority being challenged and Carina wondered if he would give way. A glance at Gabriella and she saw her cousin had turned pale. A slight breeze came in through the window, stirring the warm air and Carina sat motionless until her uncle answered.

'You may speak to Prince Scalia as you wish. But I shall be with you throughout the interview, Carina. I've given you my advice and expect you to take heed of it.

Carina remembered his words as the carriage drew up at the front steps of the Palazzo Reale. She had hardly slept, but was alert as a sprung cat and she had considered every contingency. If necessary, she would agree to Scalia's demands but with no intention of honouring her word. The prospect ahead was daunting, and she must be on her guard from beginning to end.

She chose a suitably modest dress with a high collar and a bonnet trimmed with blue feathers. On her way downstairs, Carina caught a glimpse of herself in an old mirror and stopped to tilt the hat at a more rakish angle. There wasn't a hint of softness in the face that gazed back at her. Her eyes were hard and her mouth set in a determined line. It wasn't the face to beguile a man. She should appear more appealing and vulnerable. Turning her head, Carina fluttered her eyelashes and practised a pretty smile. She made her lower lip tremble as if she was about to burst into tears. That was better! She hadn't forgotten her old tricks and was on her mettle, ready for the battle ahead.

They were met by a court official who escorted them up the stairs to the palace. He held his mace of office high as they passed through the crowded hall and people fell back to make way. Carina's gaze passed over the petitioners. She could see fear and desperation on their faces and the furtive eyes of police spies as they mingled among them. No one was safe, she thought. How could her uncle align himself with a government that depended on torture and denunciation?

They climbed a second staircase, crossed an inner courtyard and came at last to the throne room. At the far end, dwarfed by the scale of the architecture, stood the throne raised on a dais and next to it the desk reserved for the governor of Sicily. Prince Scalia sat behind the mahogany escritoire and rose to his feet as they were ushered forward. According to the dignity of his station, he did not bow but proffered a hand first to her and then to Carlo. Flunkeys pulled up two chairs and Carina studied him from beneath her eyelashes.

His small stature gave a false impression. Prince Scalia was the most powerful man in all of Sicily, she thought and was conscious of his hooded eyes on her as she arranged her skirts.

'We've been most concerned for your welfare, Miss Temple.' Scalia spoke first. 'I'm glad to see you look better.'

'I thank you, sir. I am almost myself again.'

'Do I have your permission to ask Miss Temple a few questions, Carlo?'

'My niece submitted a written statement for Count Maniscalco.'

'I've read it and certain parts require greater clarification.' Prince Scalia's tone was impatient. 'Tell me, Miss Temple, do you have reason to suspect there was a political motive behind the crime?'

'I don't believe so. The men were common criminals.'

'Countess Denuzio told us one of them recognised you. Isn't that so, Carlo?'

'It was my wife's impression at the time.'

'A most unfortunate coincidence.' Carina's eyes met Scalia's dark stare. 'Their leader was an escaped convict who had seen us riding near the Villa Pallestro. No doubt he expected Your Excellency to arrange a ransom for my safe recovery.'

'Is that so?' The prince seemed genuinely surprised. 'Would you be so kind as to tell me what happened after you were kidnapped?'

In a toneless voice, Carina repeated the account she had given so many times before. She described the ambush and her subsequent abduction. Again, she stressed that she had been unconscious and didn't know how far they rode that day. When the ransom was not forthcoming, she was finally abandoned near to Calatafimi.

'I was cared for by the family of Stefan Bosco. They insisted I stay with them until I was well enough to travel home.'

Prince Scalia rested his chin on his fingertips, his unblinking eyes missing nothing. One false note, careless word or breath of anxiety, would betray her, but Carina did not falter. When she finished, he sat back in his chair and looked her in the face. 'Apart from general mistreatment, were you molested in any other manner?'

It was obvious what he meant and Carina shook her head silently.

'Why do you think they detained you so long?'

'I presume they kept me hostage against further reprisals by yourself.'

Carina answered too fast and Scalia was quick to catch her. 'So there was a political motive?'

'They were without decency or respect. It's painful to recall ...'

'Forgive me, my dear. I didn't mean to upset you.'

Carina took out her handkerchief to wipe her eyes and Scalia stood up. Carlo followed suit and the prince motioned to her to stay where she was.

'I would appreciate a moment in private with Miss Temple. It's difficult to speak of before an audience. Would you be so kind as to wait in the antechamber?'

Before Carlo could object, Scalia rang the bell on the desk. A side door opened and a stern-looking official marched forwards.

Her uncle was escorted out of the room and the prince came round the desk and took his chair.

'And what is this delicate matter you wish to discuss with me?'

'I'm most grateful to Your Excellency for granting me an audience. Enrico Fola has been wrongfully arrested. He is innocent of any crime. I'm here to plead for clemency on his behalf.'

'So you hope to save your liberal friends. Do you petition for the traitor Riso, too?'

'I've no interest in Baron Riso,' Carina lied smoothly. 'Enrico Fola is a friend of our family. I plead only for him.'

'You may rest assured, Enrico Fola's unlikely to face execution.'

'But he's extremely ill … If he stays in prison, he will die as surely as if you shot him by firing squad. There must be somewhere else he can be detained?'

'Is young Fola your lover?' Scalia's hand dropped over hers, his grip hard and painful.

'Enrico is sweetheart to my cousin, Gabriella.'

'In that case, we may reach an accommodation.'

Scalia let her go and stood up. He moved to sit at the far side of the desk and rested his hands on the arms of the chair. 'You're aware that mercy comes at a price?'

'I'm sure his family will pay any amount necessary.'

'My dear, don't let's dissemble further. In return for Fola's release, I expect you to render me a service.'

She had prepared herself for this. If Scalia demanded an assignation, she would consent and then make herself scarce. It was risky, but the prince wouldn't dare snatch her from under her uncle's roof. If it came to the worst, then she could always seek sanctuary in the consulate. She could promise him anything and still slip through his fingers.

Carina opened her fan and moved it slowly in front of her face. 'Pray, tell me what kind of service you require.'

'I want you to gather intelligence from the English community. We've reason to believe the British Consul is aware of Garibaldi's plans. You are well placed to find out what they are.'

The prince lifted his hand and took up a pen. He wrote a single line on a piece of paper and placed it on the blotter. Carina watched as he folded the parchment in two. He handed it to her and she placed it in her reticule.

'I'll send my carriage for you in ten days' time. The princess is in Naples so we may meet in private at the Palazzo Scalia. As for your young friend, when you provide us with information, he'll be sent home under house arrest. Are we agreed?'

'I will only agree on the day Enrico Fola's released from the Vacaria.'

'And why should I trust you?'

The emphasis was placed on the last two words and the look in his eyes implied: You think you can deceive me, but you're mistaken. I will get from you what I want ... Carina despised Scalia's machinations as much as the man himself, and her temper flared.

'I will give you my word. If that's not good enough for you, then I withdraw my petition.'

Carina met the prince's gaze defiantly until he picked up the bell. Moments later Carlo stalked in, his face puckered with frustration.

'Thank you for your patience, my friend.'

'Indeed ... Indeed. Now, how may I be of assistance?'

'A matter of importance has come up, a mission that entails your leaving for Naples at your earliest convenience. I'll come to it presently, but first I crave a further indulgence. Count Maniscalco requests your niece remain in Palermo a few days longer. They've arrested a suspect in Marsala. If Miss Temple can identify him, then judicial proceedings may begin.'

Scalia had come up with this in the last few minutes, Carina thought. His cunning took her breath away. She looked at her uncle and saw he was sweating. Carlo gave a small cough to clear his throat before he answered.

'I can't leave Carina without protection. It would be most improper—'

'I wouldn't ask such a favour, but His Majesty is in need of your counsel. By all means take Gabriella with you. Paulo may remain in Palermo as her guardian. I will personally guarantee their security in your absence.'

Lord, he was devious! The prince had made Carlo envoy to the king to get him out of the way. The suggestion of Paulo as her guardian was as calculated as it was absurd. The prince didn't trust her cousin and wanted to keep him under his eye. At a stroke, he had engineered an arrangement so that neither of them could escape.

Scalia held out a hand to signify the audience was over. They returned downstairs and she wasn't certain, exactly, what had been agreed – but a pact had been made. Passing the line of supplicants who waited in a disorderly queue on the stairs, Carina felt their despair. There was no mercy or justice in this place. The petitioners were downcast, as if they knew already their pleas would go unheard. Would she succeed where so many had failed? The interview had taken all her skill, but Prince Scalia held all the cards. It was up to him to make the first move. There was nothing more she could do now but wait and hope.

★　★　★

She could see but she couldn't open her eyes and Ben was walking away. Carina tried to call out but her tongue was frozen to the roof of her mouth. She was paralysed, suffocating in the darkness. If she didn't open her eyes she would die …

She woke up in fright, tucking her knees up under the coverlet as she stared into the black night. The nightmare was fading but a miasma of fear clung to her. Where was Ben? With Baron Riso in prison, she couldn't get a message to him. Scalia remained in Palermo and yet there came no word of Enrico's release. Maniscalco's agents had arrested a suspect in Marsala. If it was Ruffo or one of the others, they would betray her!

Stop this! Carina ordered herself. You're the one who requested the audience with Prince Scalia. You're not a coward and nor are you alone. Gabriella and Carlo left yesterday and Rose the day before, but Paulo is with you – and Mr Goodwin and Jane are still in Palermo.

The consul would be up to date with the latest intelligence and might have news of Ben. Scalia had given her a permit to travel freely in the city and would expect her to call at the consulate. That's what she would do, Carina decided. She would make arrangements in the morning. It had only been a dream – a dream and not a premonition. Tomorrow she would visit Jane and her courage would return.

CHAPTER TWENTY-SIX

I hope you are well, dearest, ran Alice's letter to Carina, who was reading it outside. *As I haven't heard from you these last weeks, I feel certain you are in better heart. We are now residing in Northumberland, which is greatly to my liking. Salford Manor is a comfortable house, situated south of Berwick and only two miles from the sea. When the weather is clement Anthony and I drive along the coast. As soon as you return to England, you must come to visit us …*

It was a warm evening and Carina returned the letter to its envelope as she waited for Paulo. The air was fragrant with orange blossom and she watched as bats swooped down in jagged flight. She was glad Alice was happy and Jane's news had made her spirits soar. General Garibaldi had set sail for Sicily and was expected to land within a fortnight!

Telegraph messages crackled to and fro between Palermo and Naples. Prince Scalia must be aware of Garibaldi's plans. Would he keep his side of the bargain now, Carina wondered? The ten days since their meeting were almost up and she would learn his intentions soon enough.

Jane had also told her the revolution was gaining momentum in the Interior. A squadron under Captain Mavrone had attacked and crippled a mobile column of the Neapolitan army just days before.

'Captain Mavrone? Are you sure?'

Carina's intervention was so sharp that Jane stared at her. 'I was with Baroness Riso yesterday. Her husband may be in prison, but she knows everything that's happening.'

'So this is where you're hiding.' Paulo's voice startled Carina as he sauntered through the door. 'I have good tidings! Pietro's bringing a bottle of wine to celebrate.'

'Has Garibaldi landed?'

'Enrico is home and under house arrest.'

'That's wonderful news! When was he released?'

'Yesterday, I'm told. I've sent a letter to Ella by the night packet. I don't suppose your audience with Scalia had anything to do it?'

'How is he? Have you seen him?' Carina felt a burden lifted off her.

'The house is under heavy guard and no one allowed near. On the square, Carina – what did you promise the old goat in order to persuade him?'

Pietro brought a lantern and tray, which he set on the table. He poured out two glasses of chilled wine and Carina took a sip before she answered.

'I told him Enrico was innocent. Prince Scalia may be more benevolent than we supposed.'

'Nonsense!' Paulo turned down the corners of his mouth. 'Scalia has no dealings with clemency – but I'm glad to say we're rid of him for a few days. The king's finally lost patience. Sicily's to have a new governor and Scalia is summoned to court. He departs for Naples tomorrow.'

It was almost too good to be true, Carina thought, Enrico was out of prison and Scalia about to leave for Naples. It had turned out better than she dared hope.

'How long will he be away?'

'Long enough for us to make our escape. We'll cross over to Naples as soon we hear he's on his way back. Our ships will pass in the night ...'

'I'm not leaving Palermo.'

'What are you talking about?'

'I want to stay and take part in the revolution.'

'Don't devil me, Carina! You're no more of a revolutionary than I am. If you want to stay, it's for another reason entirely.'

'What are you saying?'

'You're in love with Captain Mavrone.'

Carina had taken a gulp of wine and choked as she swallowed. Spluttering and gasping for breath, she grabbed a napkin, holding it over her mouth as Paulo went on.

'When I heard of your abduction I wrote to Enrico. He replied that you were safe and there was no need for concern. I thought it strange at the time. It was only when I returned to Palermo and learned you saved Mavrone's life that I rumbled you.'

Carina was too confounded to answer. She gazed at Paulo and he lowered his head so their eyes were on the same level.

'It's true, isn't it? Mavrone kidnapped you and you fell in love with him. That's why you want to stay in Sicily.'

'You're not as brilliant as you think you are.' Carina found her voice at last. 'Captain Mavrone did not abduct me. He rescued me from the brigands—'

'And left you in the care of Stefan and Greta Bosco for over a month.'

'Precisely; until I was strong enough to return home.'

'Balderdash! I haven't forgotten Baron Riso's reception—'

'Desist this minute, Paulo! I entreat you!'

'Then tell me the truth.'

Darkness had fallen and shafts of light beamed down from upstairs windows. The cicadas began their nocturnal chatter and soon they must go in for dinner. This was a conversation they would never have again. Paulo had known all along, Carina thought. There was no point lying to him now.

'If I trust you with my heart, you must promise not to betray me?'

Her cousin nodded and leant forward, his intent gaze on her face.

'I was happy with Ben, happier than I have ever been in my life.'

'I knew it!' Paulo punched an arm in the air. 'The first time I saw you, I said to myself: there's a girl after an adventure. You've exceeded all my expectations.' He paused, a frown furrowing his brow. 'Even so, you can't remain in Palermo alone. It's far too dangerous.'

'I've been offered refuge in the consulate. Jane Parsons will act as my chaperone.'

'And what happens if Garibaldi's defeated?'

'His army won't be defeated—'

'Garibaldi doesn't have an *army!*' Paulo expostulated. 'The Thousand, in their red shirts, are doctors, lawyers and heaven knows what else – but they're not trained soldiers—'

'The Sicilian patriots are well equipped and will fight alongside them.'

'And how many are they? Three, maybe four hundred, at the most? They don't stand a chance against a Bourbon army of twenty-five thousand. Mavrone might be killed. Have you thought of that?'

Of course she had. How could she know if Ben would come through alive? The only thing she knew for certain was that she must stay in Sicily. Carina had never told anyone of her premonitions. She was glad to have helped save Enrico, but if she tried to explain to Paulo, he would think she was out of her mind.

'I'm not staying only because of Ben Mavrone,' she answered after a moment. 'I truly believe in the cause. The Bourbon regime is evil. How can you remain immune to their cruelty and tyranny?'

'Because, despite the government's failings, I'm a realist. If your revolution is successful, which is unlikely, what do you hope to achieve?'

'The liberation of Sicily from bondage and oppression! You can't remain neutral, Paulo. Not now, when it's all about to begin!'

'There'll be bloodshed and countless lives lost – and, when it's all over, we Sicilians will carry on as we did before. We have a long history of invasion and learnt to live with occupation. You should have followed my example and kept out of it.'

Passive fatalism lay at the heart of Paulo's nature, Carina thought. She couldn't change him any more than he could pretend to be someone he wasn't and she waited for him to go on.

'What about Prince Scalia? How do you intend to deal with him?'

'I'm not in danger, if that's what you mean.'

'Not at present, but Scalia plays a long game. He never forgives those who outflank him.'

It was a timely reminder and Carina remembered then what she should have before. Prince Scalia had made his move and would expect her to respond. She couldn't afford to be complacent.

'We must convince the authorities I've left Palermo with you.' She rubbed her forehead hard, speaking her thoughts aloud. 'You'll book two berths on the ferry and register one in my name. After you've gone, I'll go to the consulate and disappear from sight. Scalia will believe I'm in Naples and no one will suspect that I'm here. Please, Paulo! I can't give over on this.'

A gong rang from upstairs and Paulo came to his feet. 'You realise Nonna will murder me?'

Paulo was waiting by the door and Carina hurried over and laid a feverish hand on his arm. 'It's up to you to reassure her! Say that, as a British citizen, the consul advises me to place myself under the protection of Her Majesty's government. He'll be responsible for my safety and she's not to worry.'

'And how do you propose we prevent Papa informing Scalia of your whereabouts?'

'You must blackmail him! If he breathes a word to Scalia, Gabriella will tell Nonna he broke his promise to her. He forced me to meet with Scalia, who interrogated me most cruelly.'

'Hang it all, Carina! I never knew you were so ruthless. No wonder you always get your way.'

'Not always—'

Carina broke off, unaware Paulo was watching her and that her expression changed, bringing sadness and uncertainty to her eyes. There was a time she believed that she could achieve anything she wanted. No longer. Ben was her nemesis and a ragged pain tore at her heart.

'Tell Nonna from me that if she's not back in Palermo by the summer, I'll come to see her in Naples.'

'With Ben Mavrone in tow, no doubt.' Paulo grinned and covered her hand with his own, pressing it against his arm as they went inside. 'The rascal will give you a run for your money – but if he's in your sights he doesn't stand a chance. Do you know, I feel sorry for the poor chap already?'

CHAPTER TWENTY-SEVEN

Carina did not move into the consulate and, after Paulo's departure, the household was reduced to a minimum. She installed herself in a bedroom next to the contessa's sitting room with its own door on to the veranda. The rest of the house was closed off, blinds drawn and the furniture covered in dust sheets; only Gino, with Pietro and his wife, remained on duty.

Prince Scalia had returned to Palermo and Carina dared not go out – but it was her decision to stay and she kept herself occupied. There were books to read and letters to answer. Many were from Harry Carstairs, who was upset he hadn't heard from her. He made no mention of a romantic interest for himself, but his correspondence was full of other gossip.

The London season is about to begin – and without the presence of Lord Danby! The scoundrel has finally had his comeuppance and been charged for unpaid gambling debts. There's even talk of him being asked to resign from the club. Can you imagine such a thing?

There was another letter too, from Alice.

*Please write soon, dearest. And reassure me you're in no danger.
The British newspapers are on fire with speculation about General
Garibaldi. Is it true he is on his way to Sicily? Will he really invade
the island?*

Carina's answer was deliberately ambiguous:

*I am sorry to have been so late in replying to your last letter. Great
events are taking place and everyone in a state of wonderment as
to how the present crisis will be resolved. We pray for news of
Garibaldi's arrival every day. My family and Jane Parsons are well
and send you their warmest regards.*

She was equally misleading to her grandmother:

*Mr Goodwin has taken me under his wing and Jane Parsons is a
delightful companion. I miss you all but I am in good spirits.*

Deception was paramount and she was becoming skilful at
artifice. Nonna and Alice would be appalled, Carina thought,
but it was crucial her family believed she was in the consulate
– and Prince Scalia that she was in Naples. How else could she
stay on in Sicily?

The army patrolled the streets day and night and Gino was
her only source of information. He told her of posters put up
by the secret committee, announcing 'Garibaldi is coming!'
They were torn down by the police only to reappear the next
day and the mood in Palermo was febrile. The government
ordered a demonstration of loyalty to the king and Gino
described what happened. Twice, Maniscalco shouted: 'Long
live the King of Naples!' to be greeted by silence from the huge
crowd. Then a single voice shouted 'Long live Italy.' The people

began to cheer and stamp their feet and the Royal Guard opened fire on them. More than a hundred people, including women and children, were wounded and twenty shot dead.

In the days that followed, Carina was stalked by doubt. Threatened with such brutal retaliation, the citizens of Palermo were frightened. She was frightened. Would the Sicilians find the courage to rise up for Garibaldi? Would they? Everything depended on the answer to that question.

Later the same week, Gino came running up the steps with a newspaper. Catching sight of the headline, Carina threw her hands in the air.

On 11th May, an act of flagrant piracy culminated in the landing of armed men at Marsala. It is estimated they number at least eight hundred and are commanded by Garibaldi.

The article was dated 17th May and was already out of date. What had happened since? She had to know and must send a message to Jane at once. The curfew forbade carriages, so Gino would have to go on foot wearing her uncle's badge and livery. The Denuzio name still counted in a city governed by the Bourbons and he was unlikely to be challenged.

'What news?' she wrote, then folded the paper and gave it to Gino.

Carina was on tenterhooks as she waited for his return. She stood on the veranda and looked up to mountains of the Conca d' Oro where a hundred bonfires glimmered in the darkness. They were lit by rebel groups as a threat to the government and symbol of hope to the people below. Was Ben with them, she wondered? She would like to think he was, but knew he was likely on more deadly business; harrying enemy battalions that ventured into the Interior.

By the time Gino returned, it was midnight and Carina had bitten her nails to the quick. Yes, he had given her letter to the doorman at the consulate. No, he didn't know if Mr Goodwin or Miss Parsons were at home because he hadn't enquired. Gino's expression suggested he had gone beyond the call of duty and Carina bit back her frustration and thanked him.

She was late up the next morning and walked into the sitting room to find Pietro standing by the door. He held a silver salver on which was placed a small white envelope. His expression was so serious, Carina felt the blood drain from her face. Could Maniscalco's agents be at the door? Gino might have been followed last night and they had come to investigate who was home. God forbid, it might be Prince Scalia himself! There was no one who could save her from him!

Carina plucked the envelope from the tray, took out the card and let out a small cry. 'Please show the consul in immediately!'

Pietro went to fetch him and Carina tried to compose herself. Relief followed so fast upon panic her cheeks were pink and she dabbed her face with a handkerchief, stuffing it up her sleeve as Mr Goodwin was shown in. He was wearing his official uniform with sash and badge, and looked uncomfortably hot.

'How good of you to call.' Carina proffered her hand and then walked out onto the veranda. 'Pietro, please bring some lemonade for His Excellency.'

Mr Goodwin came forward, taking off his gloves as he sat down. Pietro filled their glasses and then withdrew.

'Until last night, we had no idea that you were in Palermo. I have orders from London to evacuate all British citizens immediately—'

'So Garibaldi is marching on the city!' Carina broke in. 'Has there been a confrontation?'

'Indeed there has. Despite reports to the contrary, General Garibaldi won a decisive victory at Caletafimi.'

Good news at last! Carina was so excited she wanted to jump up and shout 'hurrah'. She restrained herself watching a small lizard run across the terrace, disappearing down the steps as Mr Goodwin continued.

'Sir Rodney Mundy and I called on Count Maniscalco to enquire as to measures being adopted for the security of British personnel and property in the city. It was made clear to us if the patriots incite the people to rebellion, the city will be shelled by artillery fire. Hence my visit.'

'How close are the Redshirts? Do you know?'

'No one knows. Every scrap of information is contradicted by the next, which is exactly how Garibaldi wants it. The element of surprise is crucial to his advance.'

'And the *squadri* in the mountains? Do you have news of their campaign?'

'Skirmishes continue with casualties on both sides. Garibaldi lost one of his best men recently.'

Carina gripped the sides of the cane chair and asked in a whisper. 'Do you have his name?'

'Rosolino Pilo was killed two days ago. Acting on false intelligence, Garibaldi ordered him to occupy the high ground above Monreale. Four columns of Bourbon infantry were in the town. He died with a pen in his hand, trying to summon reinforcements.' Mr Goodwin stopped, alerted by the look in Carina's eyes. 'My dear, I hope he wasn't a personal friend?'

'Rosolino Pilo was an outstanding soldier. It's a terrible blow indeed.'

'I've secured you a berth on Admiral Mundy's flagship anchored in the harbour.' The consul nodded, rearranging his face into a formal expression. 'The port is packed with refugees and my wife and Miss Parsons are expecting you to join them. You will be taken on board first thing tomorrow.'

She had sought his protection and Carina was embarrassed. It felt shabby to turn down the offer, but when the Redshirts entered Palermo it was here that Ben would come to find her. She could not leave now!

'I'm very grateful, sir, but I prefer to remain at home. We're out of range of Bourbon cannon and stocked with provisions. The house will be kept securely locked until hostilities are over.'

'If Garibaldi tries to take Palermo, the Bourbon government will destroy the city. Houses belonging to the liberal nobility have already been ransacked—'

'But my uncle's not of the liberal persuasion, sir. No Bourbon troops will be sent to his home.'

'Please consider my proposal and send a message to the consulate by this evening.' Mr Goodwin finished his lemonade and stood up. 'It is my duty to ensure your safety. However, if you're determined to place yourself in danger, there's nothing I can do prevent you.'

The consul made a stiff bow before Pietro escorted him out. I've made him angry, Carina thought, but Jane will understand. A poem was streaming through her head and she must set it down. She hurried to the bureau and collected a sheaf of paper. Carrying the inkwell outside, she put them on the table and started to write.

> *A thousand men, no more, no more,*
> *A thousand men, no more,*
> *For Italy and Freedom*
> *Sailed to Sicilia's shore.*
> *For Unity, Italia's name,*
> *A thousand went to war*

O sons of brave Italia
Praise be forever more!

Twenty thousand five and more,
Twenty thousand five.
Enemy with cannon fire
Redshirts to survive.
'Italy or death' they swore!
Gallantly they charged,
Garibaldi to the fore,
God above their guard!

A thousand men, no more, no more,
A thousand men, no more,
For Unity, Italia's name,
Cast strangers from our shore.
For Sicily and Freedom
Raise high the tricolour!
O sons of brave Italia,
Praise be forever more!

The poem came so fast that she scribbled the words, smudging the paper and staining the blotter. When she had it right she would translate it into Italian. It was her tribute to Garibaldi and, given a chance, she would present it to him. A gust of wind blew the papers off the table and Carina went down on her hands and knees, scrabbling on the ground to retrieve them. She stood up and saw black clouds over the mountains. The Sicilians were deeply superstitious, but the oncoming storm was not a bad omen. Garibaldi and the Redshirts would be victorious!

CHAPTER TWENTY-EIGHT

Early on the 27th of May, when the first shell was launched on Palermo, Carina was asleep. The cannon boomed again and she put a pillow over her head to block out the noise. A shell screamed over the house, its vibration knocking the clock on the mantelpiece to the floor and she leapt out of bed and ran outside. Her grandmother's apartments were too low to see the city, but she could hear church bells pealing. They had been silent so long, Carina was terrified they might stop but they were ringing from every quarter of the city. The people had risen in support of the revolution – or else Garibaldi had already captured Palermo!

She was going too fast. If the government had surrendered, the bombing would be over, but the whine of shells started again. The sound of them was ear-splitting as they ripped off roofs and tore masonry apart and one landed so close the house was shaken to its foundations. At any moment the wooden veranda might collapse. How could this be happening? A barrage from the harbour couldn't reach this far and Carina shook her head in disbelief as she hurried inside.

She had told Pietro and Nella not to come in, but Gino was here. Throwing open the wardrobe doors, she took out the first outfit her hand touched. Without a crinoline, the skirt was too long so she caught up folds of material and tied them in a knot above her knees. Then she found a pair of low-heeled boots and sat down to lace them up before setting off down the dark passage.

Instead of fresh coffee, her nostrils caught the whiff of sulphur as she unbolted the front door. Above the din, Carina heard the whinnying of frightened horses. Gino would be with them in the stables and she called to him. The boom of cannon drowned out her voice so she waited for a lull and then shouted again. There was too much noise and she would have to go and find him. Carina was halfway across the courtyard when a shell exploded outside the walls. Its detonation was so powerful the top of the gate was ripped off and she was thrown backwards. Sitting on the ground, she tasted mortar, thick as chalk in her mouth, and rubbed her sleeve across her face as Gino came running towards her.

'You must take cover, signorina. In the cellars or the garden?'

Gino helped her to her feet and Carina tried to think. If they received a direct strike, the house would collapse with the cellars buried beneath it. The garden would be safer – but first, she must find out how long the bombardment was likely to last. As she ran up the stairs with Gino beside her, she recalled the day Paulo had shown her his father's sabre, demonstrating it so carelessly he had cut his hand.

'Get the count's hunting guns. Make sure they are loaded! And bring me his sword! The one hanging on the wall.'

It was dark in her old bedroom and Carina stopped to catch her breath. Then she heaved open the shutters. The bells were still ringing and the sound gave her courage as she stepped out onto the balcony. The sky was the colour of blood and the barrage coming from a squadron of Neapolitan battleships outside the harbour. Shells were being launched, not only from the sea but also from higher ground. Everywhere she looked, there was devastation. A gaping hole was gouged out of the church roof and she saw lifeless bodies strewn over the terraces below. Huge tongues of flame leapt in the air, showering cascades of sparks down and setting houses on fire. One shell followed another in quick succession and there would be no end to it until Palermo was flattened!

A sob thickened her throat as Carina went back into the bedroom. God help them all! The Bourbons would rather murder Sicilians than surrender. Should they open the gates and offer refuge to those fleeing from the destruction? The house would be swamped and more killed if they received a direct strike – better they escaped the inferno of the city into the countryside.

She bolted the shutters and headed back, meeting Gino half-way down to the courtyard. He had the sword, but no guns. Her uncle had locked them away or taken them to Naples and the sabre was so heavy she had to use both hands to grasp it by the hilt.

'Get an axe from the woodshed! They're killing our people!'

Gino ran down ahead and, as she came to the bottom of the steps, Carina stopped and stared at the gate. There were loud voices outside and a hard object was being rammed into the wood. She stood, petrified, as the hammering went on until the gate caved in and Bavarese mercenaries poured into the court-yard. Their faces were blackened by smoke and their uniforms covered with blood. Drunk on violence and liquor, they were shouting and raising their fists in the air. Then they caught sight of her and fell silent. One of them swaggered forward and spat on the ground at her feet.

Carina looked at his filthy beard and greedy expression and such anger filled her that terror fell away. She lifted the sabre so the blade was pointing at his heart, her eyes like fire in her white face. As the mercenary made a lunge, a volley of shots rang out and the man's face snatched sideways. He leapt in the air and then fell at her feet with half his head blown off.

The sabre dropped from her hands as more shots were fired. All around her was a kaleidoscope of movement and noise. Chunks of masonry came crashing down and a hand caught her by the arm and pulled her out of the way. Carina glimpsed a hunter's black hat and the red tunic of the Garibaldini. She squeezed her eyes shut and opened them again. The courtyard was crowded with Redshirts and the Bavarese were being rounded up. She stared at them stupidly before turning to the slender figure beside her.

'By the devil!' Enrico Fola's expression was thunderstruck. 'What on earth are you doing here?'

Enrico and his troops gathered around her and the dead soldier was dragged away. His body left a trail of blood on the ground and Carina thought she might be sick. Gino appeared with the axe, jaw dropping as he took in the scene.

'Why aren't you with the British contingent?' Enrico asked curtly.

'I was offered a berth on Admiral Mundy's flagship ...'

'Then why the hell didn't you take it?'

His harshness so unnerved her, Carina nearly burst into tears. 'I thought ... the bombardment couldn't reach us ...'

Enrico appeared to be in charge and yet uncertain what to do. Carina stood twisting her hands until one of the soldiers shouted the grounds were clear and he made up his mind.

'You'll have to come with us. Leave your man here to guard the house. We'll give him guns and ammunition. Get your stuff – but only as much as you can carry in one hand – and hurry!'

Enrico was pale but his voice rang with authority and Carina dashed down the passage to her bedroom. She collected a few belongings, stuffing them into a bag, and hurried back. A makeshift attempt had been made to repair the gate and Gino was armed with Bavarese guns. Carina spoke briefly to him and then followed Enrico outside.

He broke into a run and they headed downhill, avoiding the streets crowded with people fleeing the bombardment. Adrenaline gave strength to her legs so Carina managed to keep up until they reached the ancient quarter where Enrico slowed to a walk. The thunder of cannon seemed further away in this no-man's-land. Faces peered out from behind half-closed shutters before they moved quickly out of sight. Then, without warning, Enrico halted. Carina looked over his shoulder and saw they had come to a wide street.

Stretched across the road and less than thirty paces away, an overturned cart formed the basis of a barricade. An assortment of planks and barrels were piled on top and it was manned by Redshirts. There seemed to be a hiatus in the fighting until shell rocketed out of the sky and exploded in front of them. Cobbles were torn up and shrapnel rained down, but no one moved until Enrico gave the command.

'*Avanti*! To the barricade!'

One moment they were squashed together in a doorway and the next bolting down the street with Carina dashing after them. As she reached the barricade, a sharp pain tore into her upper arm. Enrico threw her to the ground, protecting her with his body. There was blood seeping through her dress and he cut the sleeve from cuff to shoulder.

'Let's hope it's only a flesh wound. I'll bandage it, as best as I can.'

He worked fast, wrapping a tourniquet tight around her arm before he climbed up to join the others. The Redshirts were returning fire, standing up and ducking down, while she crouched beneath the ramshackle structure. Bullets ricocheted around her and fusillade seemed to go on forever until the gunfire ceased. Carina heard cheering and lifted her head. Enrico came down and helped her to her feet and her eyes went from his face to the men on the barricade. They were waving their muskets and clapping each other on the back. Enrico was laughing and then she was laughing too, the pain in her arm forgotten as she threw her arms about his neck.

'We must hurry to the Piazza Pretoria,' Enrico said, disengaging himself. 'Before the day's out we shall raise the tricolour in Palermo!'

Carina's heart was on fire as she fell into step with the men. Enrico could have led her through the gates of Hell and she would have followed him. For the rest of her life she would remember this day, she thought, marching through the streets of Palermo with the applause of a free people ringing in her ears. Women and children stood on the balconies, shouting greetings while boys in rags ran on ahead, turning somersaults as if leading a military band in a carnival. When a shell landed not far in front, a young boy sprinted forwards and threw himself onto the smoking missile. He extracted the fuse and then leapt high in the air, holding the piece in his hand – to be rewarded by clapping and cheering for his daring performance.

Arriving in the Piazza Pretoria, the atmosphere was markedly different. The square was crammed and the hot sun beat down on an army of wounded and exhausted men. Injured soldiers sat with their weapons at their feet, passing water skins from one to another as donkey carts arrived with more casualties. Redshirts on stretchers were passed over the heads of the crowd and Carina saw a soldier, with skin hanging off his face and blood pouring down his neck. He seemed to be staring at her before his knees buckled and he went down in the dust. Suddenly she began to shake uncontrollably. Afraid she might collapse, she undid the knot in her skirt, letting it fall to the ground.

'Where are the casualties being taken? I'd like to help …'

'That won't be necessary, ma'am,' the officer with Enrico answered. 'Garibaldi has set up a hospital in the Royal Palace. We have more nursing volunteers than we need.'

'You're in need of medical attention yourself, Carina. I've friends to take care for you.' Enrico took her bag and turned to the officer. 'May I leave my platoon under your command? I must see to my companion.'

She was relieved, dammit! She was worn to the bone and her arm throbbing. Carina longed to breathe fresh air and escape the misery surrounding her. She was so weak that Enrico put his arm round her waist, supporting her as they picked their way between rows of casualties.

'I'm taking you to my old tutor and his wife. You'll stay with them until the bombardment is over.'

Carina was too dazed to answer. They came to a side street where it was cooler and stopped in front of a house at the far end. Enrico used the stock of his musket to bang on the door. The shutters were closed and he hammered again, shouting to those inside.

'Enrico Fola wishes to speak to Monsieur Carot. Please open the door!'

There were voices inside speaking in French; a man's raised in argument and the quieter tones of a woman. A few moments later Carina heard the creak of bolts being drawn. The door opened a hand's width and an elderly gentleman peered through the gap. He might have shut the door in their faces if Enrico hadn't placed his foot across the threshold.

'It's me, *maitre*! Enrico Fola at your service. Please don't be alarmed. I beg your assistance. This young woman is injured.'

Monsieur Carot's spectacles slid from his nose to hang from a chain around his neck as he stared at Enrico. 'I cannot believe it! Does your father know about this?'

'My father's in Naples. I'm in charge for the present.'

'But you're … you're …'

'I am myself, dear friend. May I present Miss Temple – the granddaughter of Contessa Denuzio.'

It was absurd to be making formal introductions at such a time, Carina thought, as Enrico's hand pressed into the small of her back. He pushed her forwards and Monsieur Carot stepped out into the street, looking one way and then the other.

'First the bombardment – and now the red devils camped next door! I never thought I'd live to see this day. *You*, Monsieur Enrico! *You* in Garibaldi's uniform!'

He bent to draw the locks but Enrico put a hand on his shoulder. 'I can't stay, but I'd be grateful if you could provide for my friend. She needs medical attention—'

'*La pauvre petite!*' Madame Carot came bustling through, taking in the situation at a glance. 'Don't you fret, Henri. I'll take care of her, Monsieur Enrico – be off with you now and don't bring any of your new friends back with you. Where are you hurt, young lady?'

She spoke to all three of them in the same breath, her eyes on Carina as she led her to a chair. 'You're very pale, my dear. You should sit down.'

Madame produced a phial from her pocket, which she uncorked and waved under Carina's nose. The smelling salts cleared her head and Carina caught Enrico's quick smile before he lowered his head and stepped into the street. She wanted to tell him to be careful, but the door slammed shut and Monsieur Carot slid the bolts before she could get the words out of her mouth.

CHAPTER TWENTY-NINE

'But, monsieur, the bombardment is over! Surely you'll permit me the benefit of fresh air?'

They were sitting at the kitchen table and for the last few mornings the conversation had been the same. Every time she begged to go out, Monsieur Carot refused point blank. Her wound had festered and, as Madame Carot applied hot bran poultices to draw out the poison, she told her of the desolation the Redshirts had inflicted on Palermo. Carina did not believe her. Now her injury had healed, she was desperate to get away.

In that instant there was a loud rap at the door. Before anyone could stop her, Carina ran to open it. Enrico was standing on the doorstep wearing freshly laundered uniform, and she took him through to the kitchen where he spread his arms in apology.

'Forgive me for not coming before now.'

'Have they gone?' Monsieur Carot asked.

'The last ship, taking Bourbon troops to the mainland from Palermo, sailed last night.'

'*Sacre Coeur!*' Madame Carot pressed her hand to her mouth

while her husband's gaze rested nervously on Enrico as he continued.

'General Garibaldi secured an armistice and there's has been a ceasefire for four days. Surely you're aware of that?'

'We've had no news. We were waiting for you.' Carina was impatient. 'Please tell us everything.'

They sat round the table and listened as Enrico described how the battle lasted three days and nights with victory balanced precariously between the two sides until the Bourbons were confined to an area surrounding the Royal Palace. Cut off from supplies and reinforcements, they called a truce and proposed a conference on board Admiral Mundy's ship. At this point Carina made a small sound, then nodded vigorously, urging Enrico to go on.

'Miss Parsons sent you many messages, Carina. I'll come to that later. A cease-fire was agreed and Garibaldi appealed to the citizens of Palermo for help. Men, women and children worked all night, building barricades and repairing weapons. General Lanza was so confounded by their support for Garibaldi, he telegraphed the king and received the order to evacuate by return.'

'So Garibaldi's in charge of Palermo?' Monsieur Carot enquired fretfully.

'*La municipalite c'est moi.* That's what he said, only in Italian.'

Madame Carot's cup rattled in its saucer and Carina shot Enrico a cautionary glance, which he ignored.

'The general's taken up quarters in the Royal Palace. You're invited to a reception there tonight, Carina. Miss Parsons told Garibaldi how you refused to take refuge aboard ship and stayed to help the Redshirts. You are quite a heroine!'

'But that's nonsense! I don't believe Jane said any such thing!'

'Why else does he want to meet you? I'm here to take you home so you can make yourself ready for this evening.'

Enrico did his best to reassure Monsieur and Madame Carot while Carina fetched her belongings. She thanked them for their kindness and, once in the carriage, her eyes began to sparkle.

'I couldn't believe it when I saw you at the palazzo. How did you escape from house arrest?'

'I was rescued by agents of the Secret Committee. They bribed the guards and took me to the *squadri* in the mountains. Fortunately, I had time to recover before Garibaldi attacked Palermo.'

So it was Enrico, and not Ben, stoking the fires and watching over Palermo, Carina thought as they jolted along. Flagstones had been ripped up to make barricades and the roads were precarious, with potholes and mounds of rubble to negotiate. Some of the finest buildings in the city had been destroyed, but from the burnt-out ruins came the sound of laughter and sing-ing. Tricolour flags were draped from shattered windows and Enrico assured her the palazzo was in good order. He had called by yesterday and the servants were preparing for her return.

'What's the purpose of this evening?' Carina enquired.

'To celebrate our victory and rally the support of the munic-ipality. One and all are fascinated by Garibaldi – whether they attend is a different matter.'

'Have you news of Captain Mavrone?' Finally, she asked the question foremost in her mind.

'Mavrone's well and promoted to colonel. I am sure he'll be there tonight.'

His tone gave nothing away, but disquiet stirred in Carina and Enrico turned towards her.

'Nothing stays the same in times of war. We must prepare ourselves for change. I only wish Gabriella was here to share in our victory.'

'Have you heard from her?'

'I've written, but my letters are returned unopened.'

Carlo meant to punish Enrico for his politics, Carina thought, and she wasn't having any of it.

'Then we must arrange this among ourselves. Nonna loves Gabriella. Between us, we'll find a way to circumvent my uncle.'

They drove into the courtyard and she outlined a plan as it came into her head. She would write to her grandmother and enclose a letter from Enrico to Gabriella. He must bring one for her tomorrow. If the contessa agreed to act as go-between, they could correspond under her seal. There was no time to say more for they had arrived and Pietro was letting down the steps.

Enrico led her to the door and Carina waited until the gig drove out through the gates. She went inside and walked to the sitting room, barely aware of Pietro as he took her bag to the bedroom. Tonight she would be reunited with Ben! Every day for the last two months had been destined to lead to this evening. Suddenly, she was apprehensive. Would Ben be pleased to see her? 'Nothing stays the same …' Enrico's words came into her mind. Was he trying to warn her? Pietro said there had been no visitors. Ben was in Palermo, but he had not come to find her. How would it be when they met each other again?

CHAPTER THIRTY

Carina was among the last guests to arrive at the Royal Palace. She had been busy all day and visited every room in the house. The main gate was repaired and Carlo's sabre polished and hung back in his study. It was there Pietro found her to inform her the carriage would be at the front door within the hour.

She took time to have a bath and wash her hair. By all accounts General Garibaldi was a man of simple tastes, so she chose a plain silk dress with a scalloped neckline, and left her hair loose. Only at the last minute did she remember her poem and ran back to collect a copy from her bureau. It was written out on a single piece of vellum and she folded it in her reticule.

As she climbed the steps of the palace, Carina thought of her last visit. Where were Scalia's police spies now, she wondered? The palace was transformed, the marble-columned hall festooned with red, white and green banners as ordinary citizens of Palermo mingled with the Revolutionary Guard. There were smiling faces everywhere she looked. Men and women in national dress conversed with gentlemen in tailed coats and ladies in crinolined skirts and she joined a line at the bottom of the stairs.

'Miss Temple! We've been waiting for you. Come on up!'

Jane made herself heard above the hubbub and Carina looked up and saw her friend with Mr Goodwin. They were at the head of the queue, beckoning to her, and she made her way up, muttering apologies to the ladies and gentlemen who stood aside. When she reached the top, Jane kissed her and the consul shook her hand.

'We're so proud of you!' Jane's face radiated happiness. 'Mr Goodwin was in high dudgeon when you refused Admiral Mundy's offer. I told him you always acted upon your principles.'

Jane's opinion might be different if she knew the half of it, Carina thought. Then the municipal brass band struck up, playing loudly and rendering further conversation impossible. Passing through the upper hall, she looked around for Ben. There were Redshirts gathered by the open windows, along with fellows in check jackets with notebooks who looked like newspaper correspondents. Drawing near the terrace, Carina craned her neck, hoping to catch a glimpse of him outside.

'We must wait our turn, my dear,' Jane spoke in her ear. 'General Garibaldi has promised us a private audience.'

Ahead of them, officers were selecting a small number from the line and taking them out to the terrace. Carina saw Baron Riso leaning on a stick and Admiral Mundy in full naval uniform. She thought she glimpsed Greta Mazzini's dark head, but there was no sign of Ben. She was flushed with nerves and she fanned herself until a soldier came to fetch them. He led the way, whisking them past others, and brought them up behind Admiral Mundy. As the admiral stepped aside, Carina found herself face to face with Garibaldi.

The general held out his hand and Carina had the absurd idea she should curtsy. Her first impression was of his eyes, brown or very dark blue, deeply set with well-defined eyebrows. It was an open, pleasant face and his gaze was mesmeric. She understood immediately the effect he had on those who met him and couldn't have looked away, even had she wanted.

'Miss Parsons told me of your bravery, Miss Temple,' Garibaldi's voice was deep and melodic. 'We owe a great debt to people like yourself.'

'I'm sure Miss Parsons greatly exaggerated.'

'I hope you'll stay for dinner after the reception.' Garibaldi smiled, his clear gaze on her face. 'I've a great many people to greet, but afterwards we'll celebrate in true Sicilian style. Please honour me with your presence at my table.'

'We shall be delighted. The honour is entirely ours,' Jane answered.

Carina had not uttered more than one sentence in the whole exchange. Yet, in her simple dress with her hair about her shoulders, she had secured a place at Garibaldi's table. Tonight she would be the envy of every female heart in Palermo! It was silly to be gratified, but she had been hidden away so long a delicious kind of warmth enveloped her. Baron Riso limped over to talk to them. He made little of his ordeal but his shoulders were stooped and his hair had turned white.

A sudden quiet fell upon the company and Carina looked to the doorway as a tall, statuesque beauty stepped out onto the terrace. She had long blond hair and wore breeches and a military jacket. Ignoring those waiting in line, she walked straight up to Garibaldi and kissed him on the cheek.

'Who is she?' Carina whispered to Jane.

'Her name is Anne Lamartine. She sailed with the Thousand ...'

Everyone was looking at the tall beauty, but Carina had seen the man who followed. Ben was tanned and clean-shaven, his hair falling across his forehead as he loped down the steps. For a moment she thought he might not see her and walk straight past. Then, as if caught by the strong pull of her gaze, he stopped and swung round. His glance swept from her pink cheeks to the low neckline of her dress and came back to her face.

Before they could say a word, Baron Riso stepped between them. He greeted Ben, kissing him twice in the Sicilian fashion, and then presented him to Jane and Mr and Mrs Goodwin. Carina had pictured this moment so often in her mind but never like this! A noise like the roar of the sea filled her head until Anne Lamartine's voice shafted through her senses.

'Do hurry up, Benito! The general wants to know what you've been doing these last few days.'

The Frenchwoman was standing beside Garibaldi with her thumbs tucked into her belt. She spoke Italian with a heavy accent and Carina saw Ben frown. She thought he meant to ignore her, but Jane was smiling and urging him on. He waited a moment and then, with a brief apology, walked over to the general.

Ben couldn't be with that woman! It was pure coincidence they had arrived together, Carina thought. First impressions were often wrong. She only had to get through dinner and they would meet up afterwards. Then a hand touched her shoulder and she turned to find Greta Mazzini beside her.

'I'm so happy to see you. I knew you would stay in Palermo. I told everyone you wouldn't desert us!'

The genuine pleasure of seeing Greta helped Carina endure the next hour and later, when she looked towards Garibaldi's entourage, Ben had gone. Anne Lamartine was holding court, her gestures as affected as her manner of dress. Jealousy was not an emotion Carina recognized in herself, but Lamartine was a show-off and the type of female she instinctively distrusted.

The crowd began to disperse and, from the corner of her eye, Carina saw Ben standing at the top of the steps. Guests drifted off and now only Redshirts and the British contingent remained. Dinner was announced and she noticed how Garibaldi brushed the interruption aside. This was her opportunity and she touched Jane's shoulder.

'Please excuse me ...'

Carina did not miss Jane's shrewd look as she left her and walked over to Garibaldi. There was a soft glow in her eyes as she took the poem from her reticule and handed it to him.

'These are a few poor verses I wrote after the battle of Calatafimi. Please accept them with my deepest admiration.'

Garibaldi glanced down at the lined paper, reading it over before he put it in his pocket. He offered Carina his arm and spoke to Anne Lamartine.

'Please join us at our table, madame. And bring Greta Mazzini and Colonel Mavrone with you.'

Carina gave the Frenchwoman a cursory glance, noting how Lamartine pursed her lips as she tucked her hand into the crook of Garibaldi's arm. He led her across the terrace and as they passed by Jane, she made a signal indicating she had been waylaid. The general stopped to talk to Ben and she pretended to admire the view as they discussed arrangements for the next day.

Carina was aware of Ben standing to attention and, as they were about to move on, Garibaldi said, 'May I present Colonel Mavrone?'

'We've met before.' Ben answered in a level voice. 'A pleasure, as always, ma'am.'

'Along with our dear friend, Rosalino Pilo, Colonel Mavrone kept the fire of revolution alight. We couldn't have defeated General Lanza without the noble *squadri*.'

'And without Garibaldi, Sicily would not have won her freedom.' Carina smiled.

'I expect not.' The general had an easy way of casting flattery aside. 'Now, I've kept everyone from their dinner long enough. We must eat our macaroni pie before it gets cold.'

Ben stood back and Carina saw a flicker in his blue eyes. He didn't care for her audacity but she would rather annoy him than be ignored and she lifted her head and walked on. In the great hall trestle tables were set out, laden with food and flagons of wine, and Redshirts stood around talking. Catching sight of Enrico, she waved to him. He lifted his arm, then, seeing who escorted her, dropped it to his side. Guests were left to find their own places and, as soon as Garibaldi sat down, everyone followed in a disorderly scramble.

Benches scraped the marble floor and Anne Lamartine forced her way to the front. Carina was on Garibaldi's right. She hoped Ben might be next to her, but Stefan Bosco was on her other side. The general had invited Jane, too, and she looked around until she spotted her seated at a table some distance away.

There was no formality between Garibaldi and his officers as they talked together, and, when supper was over, Carina glanced down the table to where Lamartine sat opposite Ben. She watched her put a cheroot between her lips, inhaling before she handed it to him and said something that made him laugh. Pain slashed at Carina's heart. Never before had she felt inferior to another woman and she could not bear Ben's indifference.

He was behaving as if there had never been anything between them and Carina leant closer to Garibaldi so that her bare arm brushed his sleeve. Her eyes were luminous beneath their thick lashes and she gave him her rapt attention until he swung his leg over the bench and turned his back on the others. How long had she been in Sicily, he asked? What had brought her to the cause? Garibaldi spoke to her as if she was the only person in the room. No one could tell, from her bright eyes and brittle smile, the chaos raging inside. It was well known that Garibaldi liked to retire early and Carina hoped Ben noticed it was past eleven before the general stood up.

'Friends and comrades, you have given all of yourselves for your country. Seek only the glory of Italy – for the destiny of our nation is that of all the world. May we thank God for the strength to drive out the vermin who have devoured all that is rightfully ours.'

He spoke slowly, articulating each word, and Carina's eyes sought out Ben. He was leaning forward, listening attentively, and she willed him to look at her. He only had to turn his head a fraction to catch her eye, but he seemed oblivious to her presence. Heartbreak swept her and hot tears pricked her eyes. She was afraid she might give herself away before Garibaldi's next words banished everything else from her mind.

'I've been presented this evening with a poem by Miss Carina Temple. Her verses say more eloquently than I can, the emotions that are in my heart tonight. Hear them and be proud!'

Garibaldi began reading her poem and Carina forced herself to sit still. Her verses weren't meant for this! They were a personal tribute, not a public oration. For mercy's sake, the lines didn't even scan in Italian! She felt hot colour rise in her cheeks as he came to the end.

For Unity and Freedom
Raise high the tricolour!
O sons of brave Italia,
Praise be forever more!

When Garibaldi finished, there was a moment of silence. Then someone shouted 'Bravo!' and there was a loud rumbling of applause. People were clapping and stamping their feet and Garibaldi held up his hand for silence.

'I thank you, Miss Temple. You risked your life to stay in Palermo during the bombardment. We're blessed by your courage and the beauty of your verse.'

Carina didn't know where to look. Garibaldi expected her to answer. The whole room was waiting and there was a stranglehold in her throat. Not knowing what she was going to say, she made as if to stand up when a male voice pre-empted her.

'Generale, you must come at once! There's an urgent message from Messina.'

Carina thanked God for the staff officer's intervention. Without another word, the general left the table and strode towards his private apartments. He walked with his head held forward, his legs carrying his sturdy body with a swagger and she was aware of a different man, determined and ruthless, with no time for prevarication. Before he went through the door, Carina knew he had dismissed her from his mind.

Following Garibaldi's departure, guests pressed in on every side. Stefan clapped her on the back and Greta hugged her. She saw Jane trying to get through and being blocked by others. A man with a ginger moustache, who said he was from *The Times* of London, asked for a copy of the poem. Carina declined, but it was half an hour later before she could get away and by then the room was almost empty.

Tobacco smoke clung to the air and she looked for Jane and Enrico. She was desperate to go home, but she couldn't leave without saying goodnight to her friends. They were probably outside on the terrace, she thought. It was dark and cool as she stood on the steps. Carina breathed in the sweet night air, listening for Jane's voice among the masculine tones of her companions. She was about to go to her when Ben spoke at her elbow.

'A pretty poem. Well done.'

She turned to face him. There was not enough light to see his face clearly and she answered coolly, 'I'm glad you think so. I'm on my way to say goodnight to my friends. So, if you'll forgive me—'

'Forgive you for what – for flirting outrageously with Garibaldi? You certainly made an impression.'

'Really? And why do you say that?'

'Because the general is receptive as any man to feminine wiles. You can behave as you wish, but he has a reputation to maintain.'

Ben was goading her, but she refused to rise. Carina stayed silent and his hand touched her arm.

'I must talk to you alone. It's impossible here. May I call on you tomorrow?'

For the first time in the evening, relief stole over Carina. Ben was annoyed with her for flirting with Garibaldi and nothing more! She was acutely conscious of his hand on her arm, the physical connection between them so powerful his lightest touch made her tremble. If only she could take him home with her now! Once they were alone there would be no need for explanations.

'There you are, Benito!' Anne Lamartine's voice cut between them. 'I've been looking for you everywhere! I hope I'm not disturbing a secret tryst?'

Her gaze switched accusingly from Carina to Ben as she came down the steps. For all her masculine dress, Lamartine exuded sensuality and Carina wished her at the other end of the earth.

'Why don't you introduce us, darling?' Lamartine's hand dropped possessively on Ben's shoulder. 'You know any friend of Garibaldi is a friend of mine.'

'Miss Temple, may I present Madame—'

'I'm afraid I can't delay,' Carina interrupted rudely. 'Good night to you, Colonel Mavrone.'

With a withering glance at Ben she pushed past him, forcing Lamartine to step out of her way and heard her raise her voice.

'What an ill-mannered creature! And as for that poem, did you ever hear anything so sycophantic?'

Nothing would induce her to stay a moment longer. She would send her apologies to Jane and Enrico in the morning and she hastened through the hall. The tables and benches were stacked on top of each other, wax from the dying candles dripping on the floor and sticking to the soles of her satin slippers. When she came to the staircase, she ran down. As she reached the hall, Ben called down from above.

'Carina, wait!'

Carina hesitated. Why hadn't he sent Lamartine packing? The strain of the evening had left her exhausted and disappointment clouded reason. Women swarmed round Ben like flies. Why should she wait when he had Lamartine, and plenty others, to entertain him?

She could see the landau on the forecourt with Gino asleep, his head bent sideways, and hurried across the gravel. She would drive home herself, Carina decided. She hitched up her petticoats to climb onto the driving board and, with a crack of the whip over their heads, set the horses off at a canter.

Gino woke up and grabbed the headboard as the carriage skidded round a corner, narrowly missing a wall. He shouted at her that she was risking the horses' legs taking them at such a pace, but Carina did not slow down until they began to climb. By the time they crossed the piazza and trotted by the damaged church, she was calmer. Had she been unfair to Ben? She didn't think so – and one thing was for certain: he would not be permitted to call until he rid himself of that woman. They weren't at Monteleone now. If he wanted to see her then he must show her more respect.

CHAPTER THIRTY-ONE

'Signorina, there's a gentleman to see you.'

It seemed she had only just gone to sleep when Nella opened the shutters.

Carina rubbed her eyes. 'What time is it?'

'Seven o'clock, ma'am. A gentleman called earlier, but I sent him away.'

'Did he leave his name?'

'No, ma'am, not even a card.'

'Please inform him that I don't receive visitors before ten o'clock.'

'But he left his horse with Gino—'

'Then kindly ask Gino to stable his horse and instruct the gentleman to return later.'

Nella's expression implied she would rather resign than do any such thing and Carina reluctantly sat up.

'All right, then ask your husband to tell him. Where's Pietro anyway?'

'He's in the courtyard talking to the gentleman.'

'Please pass on my instructions. And I'll have my coffee while you're about it, thank you.' Carina watched as Nella scuttled out of the bedroom. What did Ben think he was doing, disturbing the household at crack of dawn? Not only was Gino obliged to provide for his horse, he was passing the time of day with Pietro! Whatever next? She wouldn't be surprised if he ordered breakfast while he was about it.

Carina had gone to bed upset and woken up fractious. She was in no mood to be hurried and it was past ten o'clock when she walked into the sitting room. Ben was sitting in an armchair, reading an old newssheet and came to his feet as she entered. He returned the newspaper to the rack and Carina noted he wore the same red shirt and breeches as the night before. She hoped he was sorry, but there was an air of confidence about him and in the way he spoke.

'The newspapers fail to give Garibaldi the credit he deserves. We were on the brink of disaster at Calatafimi – and he alone saved us from defeat. The general was accidentally hit by a rock and shouted the enemy was throwing stones because they'd run out of ammunition. It wasn't true, but he gave us the courage to make a final assault.'

Carina made no comment and walked past him out onto the veranda. Opening her parasol, she descended the steps and heard Ben's boots crunch on the gravel behind her. She walked on to where a statue of Venus presided over a stone bench scattered with cushions and sat down.

'How very enticing.' Ben glanced up at the naked goddess as he joined her. 'Do you receive all your visitors in such charming company?'

'Only those I wish to talk to in private. What brought you here at such an unearthly hour?'

'I was afraid you might not receive me after madam's performance last night.'

'You're right. Is she your lover?'

'How could you possibly think such a thing?' Ben's eyes creased at the corners as he smiled. 'A woman addicted to glory and gunpowder is hardly my type.'

She had forgotten how handsome he was with laughter in his eyes. Ben's smile melted her heart. Carina desperately wanted to believe him, but she was guarded.

'Why didn't you come to find me before now?'

'Our intelligence indicated you had gone to Naples with your family. Besides, I had a few other things on my mind. Cannon fire and nights without sleep can make a man forgetful. What other excuses can I think of?'

'That you no longer care for me?' The cloying scent of carnations filled the air and a bee buzzed close by her head. Carina waved it away. Ben thought for a moment before he answered.

'I've missed you, sweetheart. Life's been very dull without you.'

'Even in the midst of revolution?'

'Even then. I heard you were wounded in action?'

'A bullet grazed my arm. It was nothing.'

'May I see?' Carina undid the buttons of her cuff and pulled her sleeve up above the elbow. The wound had left a small scar and Ben's finger passed gently over the bruise. Then he took her hand, turned it over and pressed his mouth to her palm.

'You're an exceptional woman, Miss Temple. Has anyone ever told you so?'

Ben was about to make a declaration! For one mad, fleeting instant Carina was convinced of it. She saw the flame in his eyes and held her breath before he caught her in an embrace that sent the parasol spinning to the ground. Bending her back over his arm, he kissed her like a man starved. With her head on his lap, he slid one hand across her collarbone and his fingers dipped inside her bodice. Warm, swimming giddiness enveloped her, and Ben kissed her until the sky was no longer blue but a million different colours. When he raised his head, the light was so bright she put a hand over her eyes to shield them. Ben helped her into a sitting position and picked up her open parasol, shaking off the dust before he gave it to her.

'Shall we go inside?' His voice was hoarse and a ribbon of sweat slid down Carina's spine. There must be somewhere they could go! There were too many people downstairs and rest of the house was shut up. Ben would have to come back later when Pietro and Nella had gone home. Carina straightened the neckline of her dress. When she answered, her voice was as strained as his. 'You said you wanted to speak to me.'

'I hoped we might converse somewhere more comfortable.' Ben opened her hand, circling her palm with his fingers. 'I want to talk about the next few months. Garibaldi intends to invade the mainland while the momentum is with him.'

Carina wondered what he was leading up to. She wasn't interested in Garibaldi's plans for the future. Her only concern was for them.

'I would like to take care of you, Carina. When the army moves on, I want you to stay in Palermo.'

Carina rested the handle of her parasol on her shoulder to shade her face from the sun. From the recesses of her mind came the memory of Ben making her leave Monteleone. She had begged him to let her stay and he had been implacable. It was different now. She was an independent woman and could do as she wished.

'I'm going to ride for Garibaldi with Greta Mazzini. I'm as good a horsewoman as she is.'

'I know you are, but Greta has a husband to look out for her. Stefan's in the rear guard while my duty is to lead every charge beside Garibaldi. I can't be responsible for you.'

'I'm not asking you to be responsible. I can look out for myself.'

'The campaign ahead is far more dangerous than anything we've encountered so far. We might be defeated and driven back. You must stay in Palermo so you're safe.'

He made it sound as if it was for her sake, and happiness drained out of Carina. Moments before, she had been confident. She had even imagined Ben was going to propose. He had raised her hopes only to dash them. Enrico was wrong, she thought. Ben was the same as ever and nothing had changed. 'On what terms do you propose I stay?' She asked, breaking the silence at last.

'I hoped we might continue as at Monteleone. I'll return to Palermo as often as I can.'

'Are you asking me to be … your … your mistress?' It was a difficult word to get out. Ben wanted her, but not enough to take her with him. He needed her, but not enough to make a lasting commitment. Even if he loved her, it wasn't enough to give up his precious freedom. And if he didn't love her, what kind of woman did he think she was? Her heart told her any kind of arrangement was better than none. She must stay close to Ben. To lose him again would be unbearable, but her brain reminded her of the past. He'll make love to me and then leave, she thought. I can't let him do this to me. Where's your pride, Carina Temple?

She fought a hard, swift battle with herself and stood up.

'I'll not be your mistress, Ben. I had no choice at Monteleone. Now that I'm a free woman, I respect the code of morality that society demands.'

'You've always broken the rules and been proud of it! What's happened that you no longer have the guts to follow your instincts? "I had no choice …"' Ben's voice seared with scorn as he mimicked her words. 'You wanted me as much as I wanted you – and you still do. Damn your code of morality! Where was it when you were in my bed?'

He was so angry that Carina thought Ben might pick her up and shake her. Hot words rushed up and she flung them at him, not caring that they hurt. 'You're the one who's a coward! You don't dare to love and that's the truth! You haven't the guts to risk your wounded heart.'

They were standing so close Carina saw Ben flinch as if she had struck him. There was a flash of pain in his eyes before his lashes dropped and she turned on her heel and started back towards the house. Halfway there, she broke into a run. As she came to the steps, Ben caught up and grabbed her by the arm.

'I pledged to marry you if you were carrying my child. It doesn't appear to be the case, but I've been faithful all the same. What a bloody waste of time!'

Neither of them had noticed the two figures on the veranda. Ben released her and as Carina looked over his shoulder she saw Enrico with another man, standing under the awning in the shade. They must have heard every word and she blushed to the roots of her hair. She had forgotten Enrico was to call today and wondered vaguely who was with him. Looking back at Ben, the anger of moments before had vanished from his face. He was amused by her embarrassment and she glared at him. Then, mustering as much dignity as she could, she lifted the front of her skirt and went up the steps.

'Good morning. I'm sorry to have kept you waiting.' She sounded breathless as she held out her hand to Enrico.

Enrico saluted as Ben appeared and he touched the back of his hand to his forehead.

'I'm glad to catch up with you, Captain Fola. The general has a staff meeting at three o'clock and requests your attendance.'

Ben walked over to Carina and bowed. 'Thank you for the tour of the house and garden, Miss Temple. I shall report to General Garibaldi on the state of your property. I'll see myself out.'

With that he was gone and Carina was left speechless, staring after him. She tried to collect herself as Enrico presented his companion and then sank deep into a chair. She had no interest in the Englishman and did not trust herself to speak. Staring into the middle distance, she let the two men make conversation.

'You may recall we met at the reception last evening, Miss Temple.' Mr Barrow's voice distracted her. 'You were kind enough to say I might have a transcript of your poem.'

She remembered him now. He was the correspondent from *The Times*. She was sure she never said any such thing, but Carina was in no frame of mind to argue. She rose and went over to the bureau. Searching among her papers she found an early draft, which she gave him. It no longer mattered what became of her poem. Mr Barrow could claim he wrote it himself for all she cared! The only thing she desired was to be left alone. Pleading a headache, she took the letter for Gabriella from Enrico and then rang the bell for Petro to show them out.

CHAPTER THIRTY-TWO

She had hoped for too much, Carina thought. Ben had offered his protection and pride made her refuse. She wasn't sorry for what she had said – but she had been so sure they would be together. What was her future without him? If she refused to accept his proposition, how could they ever set things right between them?

Her mind went round and round searching for answers. If only they could talk, but Ben made no attempt to see her again. I can't stop loving him because we had an argument, she thought. War has its own rules. Who knows what might happen? Ben could be wounded or killed. I must find a way to be close to him. I've the skill and courage to ride with the Redshirts – but how is this to be arranged?

Temperatures soared during the day but when the scorching sun set behind Mount Pellegrino, sea breezes refreshed the city and life returned to normal. A steady flow of correspondence arrived from her grandmother, each letter containing one for Enrico from Gabriella.

Dearest Carina, Nonna wrote. *We were concerned when we learnt of the bombardment and glad to know you were safe on Admiral Mundy's flagship. I am most grateful to Mr Goodwin and Miss Parsons for taking care of you. As you can imagine, there is great consternation at court. The king and queen remain in Naples for now. How long they will stay, depends on Garibaldi's intentions ...*

Enrico came regularly and Carina longed to ask for news of Ben, but every time she thought of him she struggled to hold back tears. I can't go on like this, she thought in despair. I have to find out if Greta Mazzini is still in Palermo. She's the only person who can help me.

The next time Enrico brought a letter for Gabriella, she rustled up her courage and asked him.

'I believe she's staying at a pensione in the centre of town.' Enrico gave her a straight look. 'Stefan's gone home to look after the farm at Calatafimi. They have an unconventional marriage, as you probably know.'

She didn't know, but Carina nodded. 'They were very kind to me. I would like to call on her. Do you have an address?'

Enrico scribbled the directions on a piece of paper and, when he left, Carina called Pietro and requested the landau be made ready.

'But it's impossible, signorina! Tomorrow is *Festinu*. The procession of Santa Rosalia is tonight! No carriages are allowed in the city.'

How could she have forgotten? The feast day of Palermo's patron saint was the most important celebration of the year. Carina asked Pietro to order a *caleffini*. She remembered Jane telling her the drivers knew every route in the city and one of them would get her to the centre.

Less than an hour later, she was in a gig and on her way. The driver told her the pensione was close to the Piazza Garibaldi and dropped her off as near as he could. From there, she would have to go on foot. There were hundreds of people milling around and a murmur of excitement ran through the crowd as the procession of St Rosalia approached.

The statue of the saint was dressed in white, placed high on a boat-shaped chariot and illuminated by a forest of candles. As she came nearer, children dashed in front of the horses to throw blossom in her path. A young woman fell to her knees in the middle of the road, bringing the procession to a halt and those next to Carina genuflected. She bowed her head and when the statue moved on everyone began to sing.

> *Notti e ghiornu farìa sta via!*
> *Viva Santa Rosalia!*
> *Ogni passu e ogni via!*
> *Viva Santa Rosalia!*

Santa Rosalia was a real person to them, Carina thought as she joined a stream of people heading towards a piazza where a band was playing. Wall brackets lit the dark alleys and she checked each door until she came to the pensione. The upper windows were open and music and laughter drifted out into the night. She lifted the heavy knocker and a housemaid opened the door and showed her upstairs. Someone was singing a Venetian barcarole and as Carina hesitated by the entrance, Greta glanced round.

'At last! I've been waiting for you every evening. Where've you been all this time?'

Greta was wearing national dress; a black jacket and red skirt adorned with flowers. Her hair was tied up in a scarf and her black eyes shining as she presented Carina to the company.

'I'm sure you all remember our distinguished poet, Carina Temple?'

There was a round of applause and Carina was introduced to the pianist, whose name she didn't catch, and a French woman called Angela Pourri. A group of Redshirts came forward and one seemed vaguely familiar.

'Our guardian angel, if I remember correctly? Max Corso at your service, ma'am,' the soldier said. 'It was a mercy you secured Enrico Fola's release.'

Carina looked at the young man with blonde hair and blue eyes. At first she couldn't think who he was. Then it came to her. He was the prisoner who had been with Enrico in the Vicaria! Max Corso was younger than she had thought, no more than twenty-five, and good-looking with regular features.

'I'm sure it had very little to do with me. When were you set free?'

'On the day Garibaldi entered Palermo. The citizens blew open the gates and stormed the prison. They attacked the guards and carried us out as heroes.'

'It was a wretched, evil place. I thank God you survived.'

'I'm fortunate to be blessed with the constitution of an ox. We heard Fola's sentence was commuted by order of Prince Scalia himself. You must have gone to extraordinary lengths.'

Carina smiled and moved on. Prince Scalia had taken to his heels with the rest of them. He could do her no harm, but the memory of that time made her shudder. She wondered how Max Corso had found out. If he or anyone else asked her, she would deny her involvement outright. Everyone in the world had a secret and this one was hers. It was the only truly worthwhile thing she had done in her life and she would take it with her to the grave.

'Come on! It's time for a tarantella!' Greta exclaimed as the pianist struck up a lively tune. She had never danced a Sicilian folk dance before, but Carina found herself on the floor between Greta and Angela with a tambourine in her hand. The men danced in a circle around them, clapping in time to the music. Then it was the women's turn and she was on her feet, picking up the rhythm and clapping the tambourine on her hip and in the air as they snaked through the men. They danced in circles and spun round in pairs, the tempo becoming faster and wilder until the dance ended with a loud cheer.

They were all hot and breathless and Greta declared they must go to the piazza for an ice cream.

'This is the one night of the year that we're safe. There are no pickpockets when *Santuzza* is in town. They wouldn't dare!'

The party began heading for the door and Greta was halfway down the stairs when Carina called to her. 'Please, Greta, can you wait for a moment? I must speak to you before I leave.'

'You can't possibly go home tonight!' Greta looked up briefly. 'You can sleep my bed and we'll talk tomorrow. Now come along or we'll miss all the fun!'

When Carina opened her eyes, Greta's head lay on the pillow beside her; she was asleep. They had strolled back from the piazza in the early hours and Carina had slept in her petticoats. Her dress hung haphazardly from a hook in the wall and the smell of coffee wafted up from downstairs. A church bell was tolling and she counted to seven. She didn't want to disturb her friend, so she quietly washed and dressed, waiting until Greta stretched her arms and yawned.

Coffee was sent up and she perched on the end of the bed with a cup in her hand while Greta propped herself upon pillows.

'So, we must talk about Ben?'

'No, not at all.' Carina was taken by surprise. 'I came to ask you about riding with the Redshirts. I need to know who to speak to.'

'You should ask Ben. He has the authority.'

'He won't let me volunteer. He insists I stay in Palermo.'

'The reason Ben doesn't want you near the battlefield is because he cannot be distracted in any way.'

'So no one is distracted by Anne Lamartine?' Carina protested.

'Precisely; you are different.'

'But you don't understand! We had an argument. I refused to—'

'You refused to be left behind?' Greta drew up her knees and rested her chin on her hands. Her eyes were kind and her voice firm. 'The next confrontation is likely to be the bloodiest of the campaign. Ben wants you to stay in Palermo so you're safe.'

'And if Garibaldi is victorious, may we volunteer then?'

'I sincerely hope so. In the meantime, I must return to Stefan in Calatafimi. I've an appointment with the general this afternoon and will request he sends for us both when the time's right.' Greta curled a lock of hair round her finger and tucked it behind her ear. 'There's something I must ask you, Carina. Max Corso told me you appealed personally to Prince Scalia for Enrico Fola's release. Do you know about the vendetta between Ben and Prince Scalia?'

Carina nodded silently and felt her face stiffen as Greta went on.

'The whole world can change, but devils remain constant. A vendetta lasts until death, no matter the circumstances. You must be careful – especially if you and Ben have feelings for one another.'

She had brought the conversation back to Ben and Carina finished her coffee and put down her cup.

'I don't know if Ben has feelings for me – or for anyone else.' She answered in a low voice. 'Have you met Madame Lamartine?'

'Anne Lamartine is a vain, ambitious woman. Her quarry is Garibaldi and she'll use any means she can to stay close to him. She may try with Ben, but she won't get far.'

How can you be sure? Carina wanted to ask. She was desperate for reassurance, but in the depths of Greta's eyes she saw compassion and stayed silent.

'When Ben returned from his years of exile, he was a changed man,' Greta spoke with care. 'He had no love or trust to offer any woman. At least, I believed that was so, until I saw him with you. I was struck by your effect on him from the first day I met you at Monteleone.'

So much had changed since then, Carina thought. The young woman, brimming with the golden confidence of youth, had gone forever. Her presence at Monteleone had had no lasting effect on Ben. She had learnt that men only cared for women if it is on their terms. She had refused Ben his, and there was an ache in her heart as she looked at Greta.

'I cannot stay in Palermo when the army leave. I won't be able to endure it.'

'Then we must both be patient.' Greta slipped out of the bed and went over to the wardrobe. She searched among the clothes until she found a clean shirt. 'I take it you can ride astride?'

'I rode astride when I was young and can borrow my cousin's breeches and boots. What happens if Garibaldi's defeated?'

'He will return to Palermo and consolidate his power in Sicily. He won't be defeated in the long run.'

Ben had tried to explain all this to her, Carina thought, and she hadn't given him the chance. But Greta was to meet with Garibaldi today. She would put her name forward and it was enough to give her hope.

'Thank you with all my heart.' Carina embraced Greta as she said goodbye. 'You have no idea how much this means to me.'

'I have every idea.' A smile touched Greta's mouth. 'There may be a rift between you now – but don't give up on Ben. He needs you.'

If only that were true, Carina thought as she walked back to the piazza – and it was Ben who had given up on her, rather than the other way around. Passing through the crowd, she was cheered by the festive atmosphere and excited voices of children. Men and women were dressed in their best clothes and only black-frocked priests, fearful of Garibaldi's anti-clericalism, walked by with their heads down. At the far corner stood a line of *caleffini* and she was about to cross over when a clatter of hooves made her look round.

Two riders were coming down the street and, with a lurch in her heart, Carina saw Ben in the lead with Lamartine close behind. She pushed back into a shadowed corner as they went past and stopped by the fountain. Lamartine swept off her sombrero, laughing as she shook out her hair. Then Ben tossed a coin to a boy to hold their horses and they strolled towards a trattoria.

Carina waited until they were inside before she skirted round the other side of the piazza. Hidden behind a cab, she watched as they joined Max Corso and Angela Pourri. Max pulled up extra chairs at their table and Lamartine sat close to Ben. She took off her gloves and placed her hand on his arm.

Carina wanted to cry. Until now, she had believed that somehow she and Ben would be reconciled. Oh God, how could one ever know anything? Seeing Ben with Lamartine drove everything Greta had said from her mind. Ben had discarded her as carelessly as a piece of old rag. He could have any woman he wanted. So why choose Anne Lamartine? Had he lied about her, too, on the morning after Garibaldi's reception?

Carina scrambled into a cab and gave directions to the driver. As they set off, she leant back to keep out of sight and dug her nails into the leather upholstery. I hate him, she thought with hot violence. I hate Ben for making me feel worthless and ashamed. I wish he had never come into my life.

CHAPTER THIRTY-THREE

It was past nine o'clock and Carina's hair was wet from the bath when she went out onto the veranda. She had arrived home at midday and survived the afternoon without breaking down. Now, everyone had gone and she was alone. There was an ocean of tears inside her, but if she started to cry she might never stop. I won't let Ben destroy me, she thought. I must find the courage to live my life without him.

With all the will of her strong character, Carina told herself it was over between her and Ben and reached for the carafe. She poured a generous quantity of wine into her glass and gulped it down. Pietro had left an oil lamp on the table and she placed it on the floor to prevent it attracting mosquitoes. There was a rumbling of thunder in the distance and an electric storm was on its way. Soon it would burst over the city and cool the sweltering streets. How she longed for rain to wash away her misery!

She had not eaten all day and Carina picked at the food Nella had left before she pushed the plate aside and helped herself to more wine. Behind her, the house lay dark and still. It was stiflingly hot and she must open the door to her bedroom to let in some air. She felt giddy as she stood up and walked unsteadily along the veranda. She wasn't drunk – just a little off balance – but she forgot the lamp was on the floor and stumbled over it on the way back. Crouching down, she set it on the table and fumbled around until she found the tinderbox. She dropped the first match, but her second attempt was more successful – the flame caught light.

Carina picked up the decanter and was surprised to find it almost empty. The wine eased the pain in her heart and she needed a little more to help her sleep. Just one more glass would be enough. Leaning back in the chair, she hitched her nightgown up to her knees and stretched out her legs. There was a bird caught in the creeper on the balustrade and she could hear it rustling the leaves. She should get a stick and set it free – but there were flashes of lightening over the sea and the storm almost here. First she must clear away her supper.

The tray was so heavy Carina had to brace her arms to lift it and she would have to come back for the lamp. She was about to go in when she heard the crack of a branch near the steps, followed by the sound of breaking glass as the decanter tipped off the tray onto the ground.

Pietro had locked the gates hours ago and no one could be in the garden! One of Gino's dogs must have escaped the kennels and was prowling around looking for scraps. Still holding the tray, Carina stood barefoot amidst the shattered glass, her eyes fixed on the darkness at the top of the steps. There was a shadowy movement and then the head and shoulders of a man emerged.

'You!' Carina stared at Ben before the fright he had given her detonated a reaction. 'What the devil do you think you're doing?'

'The front door was bolted and no one answered the bell. I was obliged to scale the wall.'

Ben walked over to her and took the tray from her. Placing it on the table, he hunkered down and picked up the shards of glass, depositing them in a pile on the tray. He rubbed his hands to shake off the dust and Carina wondered why he took the trouble.

'I didn't mean to frighten you. I apologise—'

'If you had any manners, you'd have gone away. As it is, you're not welcome.'

'Calm yourself, Carina.'

There was a note of command in his voice, but Carina had seen a fruit knife on the tray. She grasped hold of it, waving it in front of his face.

'You're trespassing on private property. I don't want you here. Go away!'

'If you send me away, you'll miss what I have to say. I've an important message from General Garibaldi.'

'That's not true. You're lying—'

'Have I ever lied to you?'

Of course he had, so many times she had lost count. Her brain wasn't functioning properly and she wished she had drunk less wine. It crossed her mind that Ben might have intercepted Greta at headquarters and prevented her speaking to Garibaldi. What if he had? She would speak to the general herself and Ben couldn't stop her! There was something that was different about his appearance. For a moment Carina couldn't place what it was – and then saw he was wearing the jacket of a cavalry officer.

'Did you steal yourself a new uniform? I can't say I like it.'

'I've been given command of a cavalry regiment.'

'Why? For courting favour with Garibaldi's concubine?'

'I didn't come here to trade insults. Do you want the general's message or not?'

Carina put one hand on the back of a chair to steady herself. There was a jug of water on the table and she put down the knife, concentrating hard as she filled a glass. She drank to the last drop and hiccupped.

'Well,' she said, finally, 'what is it?'

'Garibaldi is leaving Palermo later tonight. He instructs me to inform you that he returns on Sunday and requests an audience at eleven o'clock. He has business to discuss with you.'

'What kind of business?'

'How do I know? If he wasn't so occupied with preparations for the campaign, I'm sure he'd have come himself—'

'But he sent you, didn't he? Why you and not a friend of mine like Enrico Fola?'

'I volunteered because I am leaving in the morning. I came to say goodbye, Carina.'

Ben had not come to undo Greta's work. He had come to say goodbye, no more and no less. 'Let thy servant depart in peace …' Words from her father's funeral; nonsense jangling in her head. Ben was holding out his hand and Carina stretched her arm, stiff and straight, across the table. He lifted it and brushed her fingers lightly with his lips.

'Your departure is very sudden …' It was a ridiculous thing to say, but the whole situation was ridiculous, with her in her nightgown and Ben so formal in his uniform. Carina wanted to laugh or make a joke to ease the tension, but she couldn't laugh in case she began to cry and she had to keep talking.

'Who else is coming with you?'

'I ride out in the morning with Enrico Fola and the *Cacciatori d'Etna*. All soldiers who are fit enough to fight will follow within a week.'

'I see …' But she did not see because tears filled her eyes. Ben was leaving her and they might never meet again. She had convinced herself she hated him, but now she couldn't bear to let him go. As Carina searched for words of farewell, the cicadas ceased their chatter and in that long moment, in the long, hot night, the absence of their company was deafening. Ben glanced upward and a flash of lightning turned the veranda dazzling white. There was a crash and heavy rain slammed down on her head. Ben moved so fast she couldn't think of what he was doing. He grabbed her hand, dragging her with him towards her bedroom.

Another flash ripped across the sky as Ben came in and shut the door behind him. Water dripped from his hair onto his face and he gazed about the room, his expression changing to one of surprise. Then he ran a hand through his wet hair and laughed.

'I didn't intend to confine you to your bedroom. I thought we were taking refuge in the salon.'

Carina watched as Ben shook himself, scattering drops of water onto the polished floor. He walked across the room, unfastening his jacket and slinging it over the chair. The way he moved reminded her of when they had been on the run. It was as if the storm exhilarated him, stripping away his veneer of sophistication and she eyed him suspiciously.

'I hesitate to offer advice, but you should get out of your wet clothes.'

There was devilment in his blue eyes and Carina knew her shift was soaked through and transparent. The next crack of thunder shook the glass panes in the window, but she did not move.

'Don't be alarmed, sweetheart. I'm aware you're a paragon of virtue and will leave as soon as the storm is over. There's nothing to fear.'

How casually he said the words! There was nothing to fear because Ben had another woman to warm his bed and would return to her tonight. That thought was the last thing Carina remembered clearly of what followed. His mocking tone set loose madness in her brain and she looked around wildly for an object to hurl at him. As she made a grab for a bronze statuette, Ben crossed the room and caught her in his arms.

'Get out of my life!' She beat her hands on his chest and screamed at him. 'I don't want to see you again! Never again! Never! Leave me alone—'

Carina sobbed as she gave way to days and nights of strain and Ben crushed her against him.

'Hush, Carina, that's enough.' Her wet cheek was pressed against his shirt, his fingers stroking her hair and his voice gentle. 'It's all right – be quiet now. Please don't cry, my love.'

He put his hand under her chin and tipped her head back so Carina was forced to look at him. She couldn't hide what was in her heart and the terror of losing him was plain in her eyes. Ben lifted her up and carried her over to the bed.

'Try to rest. You're exhausted. You need to sleep.'

He laid her down with her head on the pillow. As he straightened up, Carina thought he meant to leave and caught hold of the front of his shirt. Kneeling up on the bed, her arms reached up and hooked around his neck. There was no shame or pride left. She clung to him as if her life depended on it and when he tried to free himself, cried out.

'Please don't go! Not yet—'

'I don't want to take advantage of you – not in the state you're in.'

'Stay with me, please. Stay just a little while!'

'Then give me a chance to get undressed.'

Ben sat on the edge of the bed and Carina watched through half closed eyes as he stripped off his shirt. He bent down to take off his boots and when he came to her, took her shift by the hem and pulled it over her head. Streaks of lightning illuminated the room through the slatted shutters and he studied her as if he had never seen her naked before. His hands moved over her body and he kissed the corner of her mouth, his lips lingering and caressing her neck.

Tonight when he tried to leave, she had begged him to stay. Ben was a sickness in her soul and Carina longed to be soothed by the comfort of his arms. Then she thought of Anne Lamartine. Did Ben make love to her with the same tenderness? How many women were there for him? In the name of mercy, how many more beside herself?

Carina sat up. Ben had hurt her and the urge to smash the pain inside was the same impulse that made her turn on him. He reached for her shoulder and she struck out and caught him across the cheek with the back of her hand. She would have hit him again, but he pulled her down on the bed beneath him. She was saying she hated him, saying she loved him until his lips covered her mouth and the retaliation of his body obliterated all else.

Ben possessed her completely and carelessly, their union as primitive as the violence that preceded it. Never before had Carina called out her love and need for him as she did now. Their passion for each other was undiminished, stronger than ever, carrying them to fulfillment black as night and bright as the blinding light of day – a beginning and an end, like death itself.

Ben lay with his head on her shoulder, her lips touching his forehead long after the storm had passed. Carina was only dimly aware of him getting up. He must have opened the shutters for the draught, the scent of wet leaves coming into the room. He pulled the sheet up to cover her and she felt his weight compress the mattress. His hand brushed her face, wiping the damp hair off her forehead and he kissed the side of her cheek.

'Take care of yourself, my beautiful woman.'

Carina was too drowsy to speak or open her eyes and did not hear him leave. His footsteps were silent as he picked up his boots to put them on outside. Before he had gone from the room, she was asleep.

CHAPTER THIRTY-FOUR

The sun shone in a clear blue sky as the paddle steamer headed for the open sea. Hanging over the ship's rail, Carina caught sight of the schooner belonging to the famous author Alexander Dumas. The scene was so colourful it was hard to believe they were on an expedition to war. Boats in the harbour were decked with flags and crews of frigates at anchor shouted jubilantly as the old paddle sounded its horn. Garibaldi had left Palermo, taking his army overland two weeks before, and the campaign that would carry the revolution to Italy was about to begin!

Last night Carina had written to Alice, in haste:

Please forgive a brief letter. You will have heard of Garibaldi's success in Palermo. Now he plans to cross to the Straits of Messina and lead the Redshirts onto the mainland! He has recruited Jane Parsons and myself as auxiliary nurses and we leave for Messina tomorrow. We are not allowed near the field of battle and in no danger. In case I cannot write again, I will do so as soon we reach Naples ...

Passing the headland of the bay, the steamer picked up speed and Carina thought of Ben. On the night of the storm she had been overwhelmed by her love for him. She didn't care if the servants talked or what they thought. Garibaldi and the revolution had changed everything. The old order had been swept away and this was a new world where everyone was free. Alice and Nonna might not agree, but one day they would understand. She couldn't worry about them now, not when they were on their way to the front.

Arriving at Garibaldi's headquarters, Carina had found Jane and another woman with him. The general was eating an orange and wiped his hands on his handkerchief before he introduced her to Jessie Mario, the wife of one of his staff officers.

'Jessie's the most important woman in my campaign. She's a political writer as well a doctor,' Garibaldi said admiringly, of the broad-shouldered Englishwoman. 'I've asked you here this morning, ladies, to request your assistance. I'm concerned that our ambulance arrangements are inadequate for a sustained military campaign. We have doctors among the Thousand but no nurses.'

'There are plenty of nurses in Palermo,' Jessie responded robustly.

'I'm not talking about Palermo, Jessie. We need medical facilities for the field,' Garibaldi answered. 'I came to fight the cause of all Italy and not of Sicily alone. The time has come for us to cross to the mainland.'

They all knew that in going ahead without explicit support from Piedmont, Garibaldi was taking a great risk. The Bourbon army was ready to defend Messina to the last man. Yet hearing him speak and meeting his calm gaze, how could they refuse? As the meeting drew to a close, the general thanked them in turn. They were almost out of the door before he called Carina back.

'Greta Mazzini tells me you're a skilled horsewoman and wish to volunteer. If Jessie can spare you, I give you my word you'll ride with the Redshirts. It will be arranged once we gain the mainland.'

She had been right to put her faith in Greta, Carina thought as they left the palace. Jane, normally so calm, was pink in the face and pressed her hands to her cheeks.

'To think we will be part of the great campaign!'

'And you'll be a second Florence Nightingale, I suppose,' Carina teased her.

'Don't be frivolous. You may prefer gallivanting about on a horse, but I'm happy to follow the example of that eminent lady.'

Since then, life had been such a bustle there hadn't been time to think or a minute to spare. Under the supervision of Jessie Mario, she and Jane collected medical supplies, rolled bandages and filled bed ticks until everything was ready to be shipped. They visited the hospital to learn first aid and Carina went to bed each night exhausted.

A confrontation between the two armies was expected any time and soon their training and preparation would be put to the test. She had written to Greta, arranging to meet her in Messina, but beneath the brave exterior lay tension and fear. No one knew what the next few days would bring and Carina was as nervous as everyone else. Pray God Garibaldi would defeat the Bourbons and Ben would be unharmed!

It was dusk when the steamer dropped anchor in a bay west of the town of Milazzo and Jane and Carina were taken by mule cart to their lodgings. They drove past fields bordered by plated cactus and as they bumped along the darkening road, Carina plied the driver with questions. He replied with grunts and she persisted until he answered, 'I don't know who's winning and I don't care.'

The man spat a piece of chewed tobacco on the floor and she could get no more out of him. They had to wait until they reached the village where Jessie Mario was waiting. The wagon drew up at an old farmhouse where she stood in the doorway, holding a lamp as they alighted.

Jessie paid their driver and led them inside. There was soup on the table and she sat down with them.

'Action commenced at first light. It's been a bloody battle. Over eight hundred of our men were killed or wounded.'

'Dear Lord, why so many?' Carina asked.

'The Bourbon army is well disciplined and performed with credit. They suffered half as many casualties as we did.'

'Then there must be a great deal for us to do!' Jane said briskly. 'Shall we start tonight or in the morning?'

'In the morning. We've set up a hospital in the Capuchin convent. The wounded will be brought in during the night.'

Jessie showed them to their quarters at the back of the house. The room was spartan, furnished with a couple of chairs and a table on which stood a basin and a pitcher of water. There was a large bed for the two of them and Carina kicked off her shoes. Without a thought for modesty, she stripped off her dress and folded it on a chair, only taking the time to wash her arms and face before she lay down.

When she awoke, Jane was already up and Carina dressed quickly. She could hear cannon fire not far away as she pinned her hair under a starched cap and then went through to the kitchen. After breakfast, Jessie outlined their duties for the day. They were to nurse the most severely wounded and assist the doctors in whatever way needed. She handed them two large white aprons with ties at the neck and waist.

'Remember all that you've learnt. You may be shocked by what you see today and must have stout hearts.'

They made their way to the square and passed by a squadron of Redshirts preparing themselves for combat. Their equipment was battered and there wasn't an officer among them, but the soldiers waved and one blew Carina a kiss before he gathered up his musket and marched away. The sight of his jaunty swagger made her proud. Jessie needn't fear they would be faint-hearted, she thought, but when they reached the Capuchin convent, her confidence left her.

Passing through shady cloisters, they came to a refectory where wounded men lay shoulder to shoulder on straw pallets. Two doctors were performing surgery on the ground and the floor was running with blood. The place was filthy and Carina ran back to fetch a mop and bucket. Some of the injured were unconscious while others groaned, clutching wounds where dried blood stuck to their torn uniforms. The dirt and stench of unwashed bodies in the blistering heat, the staring eyes and swollen tongues of the dead made Carina want to vomit. Then a hand touched her apron and she looked down to see a young soldier with blood frothing on his lips. He was mouthing soundlessly and she dropped to her knees.

'Drink please …'

'Yes. I will bring you water.'

She was already on her feet when Jessie stopped her, telling her she must go and help the doctor in her place.

'But this man is dying!'

'Then we will need his place for others. You will work with Dr Bernadotti.'

Carina was thankful that Jessie gave her no choice. How else could she have endured the horror of that day? Swarms of flies crawled over open wounds and the smell of gangrene nauseated her. No amount of training could have prepared her for the shattered bodies and faces burnt black by gunpowder. If only she could block her ears to the screams and shut her eyes as the scalpel cut into putrid flesh.

The only way to carry on was to concentrate on the task in hand. Carina cut thread, forcing it through the needle eye, and tore strips of cloth for tourniquets. With a basin of water, she took the doctor's instruments, wiped them and handed them back. As soon as one patient was attended to, surgery was performed on the next. There was no quinine and only a limited amount of iodine. Chloroform was kept for the worst cases and cheap brandy the main antidote for pain. She poured it down the throats of young men who gagged and choked. Carina held them still, trying not to look, until the doctor finished stitching up and moved on. They must have performed more than twenty operations before Dr Bernadotti took his bag of instruments from her.

'I visit the field this afternoon and will need you again this evening. Take some time in the fresh air. You must keep up your strength.'

The doctor shuffled off with the gait of an old man. Carina was exhausted but she could see Jessie cradling the head of a solider in her lap as she removed shrapnel from his neck. She could not rest while Jessie and Jane worked on. When Jane came to find her, the three women went outside. Too tired to speak, they sat sipping tea and nibbling sweet cakes brought by the monks. Dr Bernadotti returned and stirred plenty of sugar into his coffee before he drank it and put the tin cup on the ground.

'They're bringing in more casualties this evening. We don't have enough doctors to perform surgery. You're a trained doctor, Mrs Mario. You will deal with the gunshot wounds.

Miss Parsons will help you and Miss Temple will continue as my assistant.'

So the endless process of cutting and patching up began again and all the time more casualties were coming in. For those they saved, twice as many died. Orderlies with grim faces wrapped still-warm corpses in sackcloth and carried them away. There was no time to change mattresses or to provide clean straw, no time for kindness or consolation. The living, dying and dead followed each other in a morbid procession until, close upon midnight, Dr Bernadotti declared they must stop until morning.

Carina walked home with Jessie and Jane and they ate in silence. Warmed by soup and bread, they took turns to wash before they fell into bed. Carina awoke early and, afraid she might lose her nerve, set off ahead of the others. She arrived at the convent to find Dr Bernadotti already at work. He told her to clean his surgical instruments, so she sat on a stool with a bucket of water, scraping off particles of skin and clotted blood. When would this nightmare end? What good was the agony of surgery when bodies were carried off with such depressing frequency? There were only ten nurses among a hundred patients and, despite endlessly scrubbing floors and boiling bandages, death became commonplace.

Conscious only of the misery around her, Carina hadn't noticed it was getting dark when Jane came running to find her.

'Dottore, I must speak to Carina. Can you spare her, please?'

Carina was fixing a tourniquet and Dr Bernadotti did not answer. Hearing the urgency in Jane's voice, she stood up and wiped her hands on her apron. Jane's face was ashen and deadly fear went through her heart.

'What is it, Jane? What's happened?'

'Come outside with me.' Jane took hold of her hand. 'You must be brave, dear. We've just learned Enrico Fola was killed in yesterday's action.'

Carina stared dumbly at Jane. Enrico had been killed! No, it couldn't be true! Not Enrico. Oh God, poor Gabriella! She wanted to howl like an animal but Jane's grasp tightened, forcing her to listen.

'Jessie has sent for you. She needs you immediately.'

'Tell Jessie I'll come later!' Carina's self-control snapped. 'You're the one meant to be helping her, aren't you?'

Her eyes were half-blinded with tears, but she saw the distinctive jerk of Jane's chin.

'Colonel Mavrone has been brought in. He's critically wounded. Jessie wants you to attend him.'

Carina was too shocked to understand and Jane went on rapidly. 'He's in a coma. I told Jessie you're his friend. They hope Colonel Mavrone might respond to a familiar voice. She wants you to talk to him.'

Her brain swirled with panic. Enrico was dead and Ben was critically injured. He was here in the hospital! Her knees were shaking and Jane held her arm as she led her towards the cloisters. The monks had evacuated their cells to provide more space and Jessie was talking to a young doctor at the far end. They looked so serious Carina stopped, heedless of Jane tugging at her sleeve, until Jessie walked back and dismissed her with a nod of her head.

'Colonel Mavrone has been unconscious since this morning. We hope it's bruising and not bleeding in the brain. Talk to him and try to make him respond. Stay with him until I come back.'

Jessie took her to the cell where half a dozen men lay next to one another on the floor. Carina was aware of the doctor's hand on her shoulder and he indicated a figure nearest the wall.

Lifting her skirt, she climbed over the bodies crammed into the small space, and knelt down beside Ben. He lay on his back, with his jacket rolled up under his head, and blood seeped from a bandage below his hairline. His eyes were shut and his breathing so light she put her ear to his mouth. When she spoke his name, there was no reaction. Searching in her pocket for a clean handkerchief, Carina found water and squeezed it into his mouth. The liquid trickled down the side of his jaw and she put her finger between his lips. They were cold and she held his wrist and took his pulse. The rhythm was faint, but she could feel it. Ben was alive.

'It's me, Carina,' she whispered. 'I'm here to take care of you.'

A soldier lying close by called for his mother but Carina was powerless to help him. All her attention was on Ben. She kissed his forehead and tasted blood on her lips.

'Wake up, my darling. I'm with you now. Please open your eyes.'

Not a muscle in Ben's face moved as she crouched beside him and Carina lost track of time. It could have been minutes or hours later when she heard footsteps stop outside the cell. Turning her head, she saw two orderlies standing in the doorway holding a sackcloth shroud.

'There's no one for you in here,' she hissed at them.

'But we were told—'

They came forward and bent over the man lying next to Ben. To her mortal shame, Carina realised they had come for the young soldier who had called for his mother. She had shown him no kindness and there was none for him now. With rough efficiency, the men pulled off his boots and dumped him in the sacking. Then they slung his weight between them and carried him out.

'I won't let them take you, Ben. I swear they won't have you. Please, darling. You must wake up!'

Still there was no response and Doctor Calvi came into the cell with two stretcher-bearers. There was scarcely room to move, but they laid another wounded soldier down on the straw pallet. He, too, was the son, brother or husband of someone who loved him. He too would die alone with no one to comfort him or say a prayer – but not Ben! She would stay with him until he opened his eyes and his heartbeat was steady.

Carina watched anxiously as the doctor lifted Ben's wrist and placed a hand over his mouth.

'Did he respond in any way?'

'Yes. I'm sure he did.'

'Dr Bernadotti asked me to find you.'

'I can't leave. Colonel Mavrone recognised me ...'

Her voice trailed off as the doctor took her arm and helped her to her feet.

'You can come back later. Nothing will change in the next hour.'

Doctor Calvi tried to reassure her, but he was taking her away from Ben. Looking back from the door, Carina saw his eyes were still closed and when they came to the cloisters, Jessie told her to sit down. Too worn out to protest, she sat on the ground and Jessie went to fetch her coffee, returning with a Garibaldini officer.

'The women are exhausted, dottore. Is there no one else?'

'We'll stay for one more hour,' Jessie answered. 'Then we'll go home.'

'If my wife's mind is made up, I'll not sway her,' Alberto Mario conceded. 'How is Colonel Mavrone? The general sent me to find out.'

'It depends on what happens in the night. He will either regain consciousness or his brain will cease to function.'

'He knew me!' Carina lied and came so swiftly to her feet the little group stared at her. 'I must go back to him at once.'

'Dr Bernadotti needs you.'

'Someone else can assist the doctor! I'm the only one who can help Colonel Mavrone.'

'His survival depends on the will of God.' Jessie's retort was like a glancing blow. 'Please report to Dr Bernadotti immediately and take him some coffee.'

She didn't believe in the will of God! How could a merciful God permit the obscenity of this place? Blasphemous words sprang to her lips and Carina bit them back, her eyes angry and defiant.

'You can stay with Colonel Mavrone all night, if you wish.' Jessie's tone softened. 'I'm only asking for an hour of your time.'

A mug of coffee was thrust into her hand and Carina made her way to the refectory and put the coffee down beside Dr Bernadotti. She was clumsy and dropped an ice bladder pressed to an amputated arm to freeze the severed nerves.

'*Merda*, woman!' The doctor swore under his breath. 'Are you too weak to do the job properly?'

'I'm sorry …' From then on, Carina's hands were steady. She fetched fresh swabs as Dr Bernadotti stitched the wound of a boy no more than twelve years old. He clung to Carina, crying in her arms until he fell asleep and she held his head on her lap.

'Let no one say Sicilians lack courage.' The doctor leant over her shoulder. 'I've seen greater bravery here today than on any battlefield.'

'Let no one say Sicilians lack courage.' Carina repeated his words as she walked back to the cell where Ben was waiting.

She wasn't sure she believed in God, but she prayed all the same. 'Don't let him die. Please, God, let Ben live. Please save his life,' she whispered as she peered into each cell, her footsteps resounding on the stone floor until she came across a young nurse.

'Have you seen Doctor Calvi?'

'He was here not long ago.'

'The officer in the end room? What news of him?'

'The orderlies collected a body not long ago.'

The girl had made a mistake! How could she know which cell the orderlies had visited? If someone had been taken away, it wasn't Ben. I'll see him when I look in. He will be there … Carina ran down the corridor and stopped at the last cell, her fingers clutching the rough wood of the doorframe. She waited until her eyes became accustomed to the dim light and then looked inside.

Every part of the floor was occupied and she let out a breath of relief. Unhooking the lamp, she climbed over the bodies and fixed it on a nail in the wall above where Ben lay. Nothing appeared to have changed, but something was wrong. Carina sensed it at once and instinct, stronger than fear, impelled her to look down. Where Ben had lain, a soldier with a shattered arm was stretched out with a knapsack under his head. She heard a cough behind her and cast a terrified glance towards the passage. Dr Calvi stood in the doorway and his expression told her what she already knew. In her absence, Ben had been taken from her and this man, one of the last casualties of the battle of Milazzo, had been given his place.

CHAPTER THIRTY-FIVE

Jane's face came slowly into focus. I must have fainted in the hospital, Carina thought listlessly. Then memory came back and her voice came out in a rasp.

'Is he dead?'

'Try not to think of Enrico Fola.'

'Is he dead? Tell me!'

'I told you yesterday.' Jane looked puzzled and then her expression cleared. 'You mean Colonel Mavrone? No, he's not dead. He walked out of the hospital on his own two feet.'

Carina blinked, trying to take in her words. 'I thought they'd taken him away ...'

'He regained consciousness and discharged himself. Dr Calvi came to tell you but you collapsed.'

The sun came through the window and relief was choked by pain. Ben had survived, but Enrico was dead. Dear, honourable Enrico. Why him of all men? Carina thought of his beautiful hands and eyes like pools of deep water. Poor darling, little Gabriella. She had known with such terrible certainty and prayed that she was wrong. Premonition was not a gift. It was an affliction and in the old days she would have been burned as a witch.

She was aware of Jane sitting with her back to the window, her needle moving in and out of the material as she repaired an apron. For a long time, neither of them spoke. Then Jane folded her mending and looked across the room.

'You're not allowed in the hospital today. I'm staying here until lunchtime. You must keep quiet this afternoon.'

After Jane had gone, Carina slept again and later felt strong enough to get up. She washed and went through to the kitchen where she found Jessie. She had come to collect oranges for the hospital and Carina helped her gather them from the larder.

Jessie pinched the oranges with her fingers, picking out the ripest. 'Head injuries are always unpredictable. Colonel Mavrone should have stayed where he was. Alberto says he's gone off to lick his wounds in private.'

Jessie's apron was full and she looked Carina in the face. 'You were right. He did recognise you. He asked Dr Calvi what you were doing in the hospital.'

Ben had frightened her out of her mind, but he was alive and Enrico was dead. Carina wanted to cry but her eyes had burned dry, her grief too deep for tears. There was so much to do in the hospital and she returned to work the next day. Every time she nursed a dying soldier, she imagined it was Enrico and her distress was fuelled by silent anger. She believed in the revolution – but too many men had died. What cause on God's earth could be worth such terrible suffering? Those who fell on the battlefield were fortunate compared to the wretches who lingered here. For that small mercy granted Enrico, Carina was grateful, but for the rest she felt only sorrow.

A week later Dr Bernadotti arrived at the hospital and made an announcement.

'General Garibaldi has negotiated the evacuation of enemy forces from Messina! All of Sicily is liberated at last! The sacrifice of our gallant soldiers has not been in vain!'

Everyone cheered the doctor in the dark refectory that afternoon. Soldiers with amputated arms and legs shouted 'Bravo!' from their straw pallets and even the weakest whispered a faint hurrah. Faces emaciated by pain brightened and men on crutches waved one feebly in the air. Garibaldi's victory lifted spirits as no amount of nursing could and, for the first time, Jessie and Carina left the hospital early.

The village was deserted and they strolled home, swinging their nursing hats by the ribbons.

'You and Jane have proved excellent nurses. I'm proud of you both.'

'Wait for us, ladies!' Alberto Mario shouted from behind them. He caught up and there at his side was Ben, with a clean bandage over his wound and a bruise like an ink stain spread across his forehead.

'We missed you at the hospital. I wanted to thank you.' Ben's gaze went from Carina to Jessie and Alberto. 'May I speak with Carina in private?'

The village square had a stone ledge along one side and Ben led her over to sit under an oriental plane with thick leaves that blocked out the sun.

'I'm very sorry to hear about Enrico.' He put his arm round her shoulders. 'He was a fine man and a brave soldier.'

Unshed tears choked her and Carina was beyond utterance. Tremors started to move up through her abdomen and down her arms. Her breath came in short, ragged gasps and Ben held her to him until the paroxysms ceased.

She sat up and smoothed back her hair, patting it flat against her head.

'Enrico was in love with my cousin,' she said, wiping a hand across her face. 'Gabriella is in Naples. Will they publish lists of casualties over there?'

'To the last name, and invent many more besides. Sadly, your cousin will find out soon enough.'

'How did Enrico die?'

'He fell in the first cavalry charge. He is buried with our other brave men who died in the battle.'

From somewhere in the distance, Carina heard the bray of a donkey and cartwheels on cobbles. It was unbearable to think of Enrico buried in a mass grave. She half expected him to walk round the corner and greet her with his quick smile. Turning her head, she noticed Ben was pale beneath his tan and touched his cheek.

'I was afraid I might lose you as well.'

'It will take more than a knock on the head to finish me off.' Ben took her hand, his fingers moving from her wrist to her elbow in long low sweeps. 'I came to know Enrico well this last month. He said you were responsible for his release from prison. He implied you even went so far as to appeal to Prince Scalia.'

Max Corso must have told Enrico, Carina thought. The risk she had taken had been for nothing and Ben must believe her because if he didn't, she would get up and leave.

'Enrico would have died if he'd stayed in the Vacaria. Prince Scalia was the only person who could save him. I know he's your enemy, but I had no choice.'

'And what did Scalia demand in return?'

'He asked me to find out Garibaldi's plans from the British Consul. As it turned out, events moved so fast he found out without my help.'

'It was a noble and brave act, Carina. There's nothing more terrible than to rot to death in prison. Enrico died with honour. I hope that may be some small consolation for your cousin.'

Ben's brooding gaze went through and beyond her. His hand stilled and Carina knew he was thinking of Alexander. They were identical twins. Alex would have been the same height as Ben with dark hair and blue eyes. Did he talk in the same way and move with the same grace? Would she have been able to tell them apart? Alexander. Monteleone. Bianca … She had suppressed her suspicions for so long, why did she have to think of Bianca Scalia now? I must ask Ben, Carina decided. We love each other and I trust him to tell me the truth. It was a delicate question and she decided to begin with Alex.

'Please tell me about your brother.'

'Alex was the steady, sensible one.' Ben's gaze came back to her. 'He was a scholar and hoped to become a teacher. He was more of a gentleman than myself. You'd have liked him.'

'Would he have approved of me?'

'I dare say he would. He had an eye for a beautiful woman – that was one weakness we shared.'

Ben let go of her hand and cupped his palm around the nape of her neck. He kissed her gently and, when he drew back, there was a glow like a small flame in the depths of his eyes.

'I couldn't believe it was you in the hospital. I dreamt you were an angel sent from heaven to collect me.'

'Garibaldi asked me to assist the medical corps.'

'Well, I'm glad he persuaded you to forget your other idea. We lost three of our best couriers in the battle.'

If she told him of Garibaldi's promise, they would have a quarrel. Ben was recovering from a serious injury and she must not upset him. How could she explain she had no vocation for nursing – that the only thing she wanted was to be with him? Bianca Scalia was put aside and she swung to a different tack.

'Stars above, Ben! How could you disappear from the hospital like that? You were at death's door.'

'Do you think I'd have survived long in there?'

Soon Ben would re-join his regiment, Carina thought. He could be taken as swiftly and cruelly as Enrico. She would rather die than be without him and this might be her only chance. She must ask him now.

'Please will you take me with you when leave?'

His eyebrows went up and Carina's resolve wavered. Ben was studying her face in that disconcerting way of his, his gaze penetrating and guarded. What else could she say? She had seen the desperate faces of women searching for names of loved ones on casualty lists and would not be one of them.

'I want to be close to those I love, not laying out their corpses.'

Ben looked down at his scuffed boots and spoke without looking up. 'I'm to lead an advance party across the Straits. Garibaldi is determined never to suffer such heavy losses again. The main army will only follow once we've secured a position on the mainland. You know I cannot take you with me.'

'Then I'll cross over with General Garibaldi.'

'You will travel with Jessie Mario and the ambulances.'

'Relief nurses arrive from Palermo tomorrow and I'm released from my duties.'

'Please, my darling, we can't go through this again.' Ben raised his head and looked at her through tired eyes. 'Believe me, there's nothing to be gained by competing with Lamartine for Garibaldi's favours.'

It was an unnecessary jibe and Carina stood up. Ben came to his feet and put his hands on her shoulders.

'War's no time to make commitments, my love.' There was both frustration and tenderness in his voice.' God willing, the

Pioneers will gain the headland successfully. I promise we will be together in Italy. Is that good enough for you?'

Everything she had fought for so long was in the balance but they must not have an argument. If Ben couldn't take her, then she had to manage this by herself. Somehow, she must find a way to follow him and soon Greta would be here to help her.

A group of people strolled into the square and caught Carina's attention because of their smart clothes. They looked like foreign tourists. One of them seemed to be pointing towards her. Then a young man detached himself from the group and began to walk across the square. He was dressed in the finest broadcloth jacket and peg top trousers Carina had seen since leaving London. As he broke into a run, her heart stopped. She forgot Ben was standing beside her and waiting for her answer. Her mind went blank as Harry Carstairs swept her up in his arms and spun her round.

'Your poem was in *The Times*! You're famous, Carrie! You've been away long enough and are free to come home!'

CHAPTER THIRTY-SIX

'You must give us your news first. We've heard nothing from England in weeks.'

Jane was insistent as they sat together on the small patio behind the house. Carina had brought Harry home and he was smoking a pipe.

'You can't imagine the brouhaha when Carina's poem was in *The Times*! Every newspaper in England covered the sailing of the Thousand. The country is infected with Garibaldi fever. He's regarded as the hero of our age! Anyone who knows him is exalted.'

How fickle people were, Carina thought. She was glad her poem had been published and more so that Jane was keeping Harry occupied. She needed time to collect herself. Harry had given her a shock and by the time she had recovered and looked for Ben, he had gone. She watched as Harry unrolled his tobacco pouch and took out a small amount, compressing it with great attention. He hadn't changed, she thought. With the addition of a top hat and cane, he might have been about to take a stroll down the Mall.

'How did you learn we were here?' Jane was inquisitive as Harry lit a match and drew on his pipe.

'Sir Oliver Temple gave me permission to enquire at the Foreign Office. Mr Goodwin advised them of your whereabouts and they passed the information on to me. I travelled with correspondents from a dozen newspapers.'

'How long do you intend to remain here?' Carina asked pointedly.

'I'll stay until you're ready to come home to England.'

Harry spoke of England as home but it was no longer her home. And why had he thought it necessary to ask for Oliver's permission? He knew she despised her uncle. Carina's foot began to tap a rhythm on the ground and Harry hurried on.

'Faith, I don't mean right away! Another sea voyage would be the death of me!'

Jessie appeared at the door to call them in for supper. She had invited Harry, along with her husband Alberto, who was waiting in the kitchen.

'One more Britisher!' Alberto declared as Harry was introduced. 'We have more foreigners than Italians fighting for our nation's freedom.'

'Now don't you start getting at Mr Carstairs!' Jessie said as they sat down at the table. 'He's a gentleman and not used to your soldierly talk.'

'Well, thank heavens he's not another journalist. I've had enough of those vultures feeding on our pickings.'

'The pen's as sharp a weapon as the sword,' Jane retorted firmly. 'The British newspapers have changed the world's view of Italy. We should be grateful to them.'

'And since when have newspaper editors won Garibaldi's wars for him?'

'Come now, Alberto, stay quiet and eat your supper,' Jessie scolded mildly as she ladled out soup. 'A full stomach will put you in better humour.'

They ate in silence for a time. Alberto polished off his plate with a crust of bread and then turned to Carina.

'I'm glad we found you this afternoon. Colonel Mavrone was most anxious to speak to you.'

'I can't think why … He seemed to have recovered well.' Carina stumbled over her words and blushed, annoyed with herself. 'Do you know when Garibaldi plans to cross the Straits?'

'The British are with him all the way!' Harry interjected. 'The Prime Minister and many others have contributed to his funds.'

'A thousand Redshirts wrapped in English banknotes!' Alberto smiled at Harry.' Garibaldi will take his decision in the next few days. Now, where's that spaghetti you promised me, Jessie?'

When supper was over, Jessie and Jane insisted Carina leave the clearing up to them and sent her outside with Harry. They drank coffee and, as Harry talked, she tried not to think of Ben.

'I'm glad you've come round to Miss Parsons. I wrote to your aunt and dare say she's relieved that you're together.'

'And why did you do that?'

'I thought it polite to tell Lady Farne I was setting out to find you.'

'Did you also inform your father? I take it he gave you his blessing?'

'Better to keep the old man in the dark. He dislikes foreigners and abhors revolution.'

His response nettled Carina. Her own father had served in the navy and met her mother when he was stationed in Sicily.

As far as she knew, Harry had never left England before and displayed an irritating superiority that was common to his kind.

'Garibaldi's campaign has nothing to do with you, Harry. You should have stayed away.'

There was a full moon and Carina saw happiness wiped from Harry's face. She didn't mean to be cruel, but his arrival was a complication she could do without. Her life with Ben was about to begin and she must explain this to Harry. It was his first night and she would talk to him tomorrow, Carina decided as she walked with him to the gate and gave him the lantern.

'I hope you've found decent lodgings. The accommodation in Milazzo may not be up to the standard you're accustomed to.'

'I've booked a pensione beneath the castle and am assured the beds are clean. Will I find you here in the morning?'

'Yes, if you're up early enough. We're handing over to the medical team from Palermo tomorrow.'

Harry held the lamp up so that its light shone down on her face. 'To be honest, Carrie, I didn't come to join the revolution. You know why I'm here—'

'Be off with you now! It's time we were all in bed.' Carina cut across him not wanting to hear his next words, her gaze following the bobbing light of the lantern until it disappeared. Harry had written to Oliver and Alice. Why hadn't he forewarned her? Was he afraid she might have stopped him? They were friends, not sweethearts! She had learnt to bat away uncomfortable thoughts, but Harry was as dogged as she was – and the sooner she told him about Ben, the better.

Disquiet scratched her as she thought of Ben. He wasn't yet fully recovered and could have a relapse. The Neapolitan navy might sink his boat. Anything might happen to him and they hadn't even said goodbye. Ben had more lives than a cat, she told herself. There was no use worrying about him, but she wished with all her heart Harry had not come. She was bound to make him unhappy. If only she could pack him off home on the next boat for England.

CHAPTER THIRTY-SEVEN

Two days later, with Carina free of nursing duties, Harry hired a pony and trap. They drove to visit Garibaldi's army, bivouacked on the beaches where the Redshirts were preparing for the invasion of the mainland. The men's faces had the same determined look Carina had seen in Palermo. They were scorched in the sun by day and chilled by sea mists at night but morale was high for the Pioneers had successfully crossed the Straits. Ben was safe and Carina longed to be with him.

'A penny for your thoughts.'

Ben was so strongly in her mind, Carina did not hear Harry.

'I said, a penny for your thoughts.'

She was wearing a wide straw bonnet and Carina fiddled with the bow as she turned her head. 'I must talk to you, Harry. Please stop the trap so we can speak?'

'I told you already; I don't want to know about the last six months. You've done your penance and now it's over.' Harry flicked the reins on the pony's back so she broke into a trot. 'I hope Garibaldi is in no hurry for I've no stomach for bloodshed.'

'Then why don't you go home? You can tell your friends in White's how you served in Garibaldi's campaign without ruining your best coat!'

Harry's mouth twitched and his cheeks went red. She should be ashamed of herself, Carina thought – but if only he would listen to her! She had tried to tell him about Ben so many times. Harry regarded her sojourn in Sicily as a punishment – when it had been the best time of her life. His refusal to let her speak maddened her. When he dropped her off in the village without giving her another opportunity, she made up her mind. Harry was afraid of what she had to say but it could be put off no longer. This evening, without fail, she would tell him she was in love with Ben. She would sit him down before supper and make him hear her out.

'There you are, my friend!'

Carina heard a familiar voice and saw Greta Mazzini running down the road. She wore a red tunic that reached below her knees and was out of breath as she wrapped her arms round her.

'I've been looking all over for you. I couldn't believe it when I received your letter. Just imagine, Carina Temple as a nurse!'

'I wasn't as bad as all that – but not so good either!' Carina laughed. 'I'm so glad you're here. Is Stefan with you?'

'Yes.'

'Come back to the house and I'll tell you everything.'

It made her happy to be with Greta and, as they walked the short distance, Carina told her about the meeting with Garibaldi and the horrific casualties after the battle of Milazzo. Greta had heard about Enrico and held her hand as they spoke of him. There was a horse tethered outside the farmhouse and they went inside to find Alberto Mario standing by the sink, pouring water from a pitcher.

'I've just ridden from Messina and am dying of thirst.' Alberto gulped down the water and refilled his glass. 'I hoped to catch Jessie on my way to meet Colonel Bavari at the barracks.'

'Then I'll make some coffee.'

'No, thank you – I'm already late. Garibaldi leaves tonight and I'm sailing with him. Please will you tell my dear wife?'

'And when do we follow?' Carina grasped Alberto's arm. 'The general promised us we could ride as couriers. We're waiting for his summons.'

'What are you talking about?' Alberto's gaze went to Greta. 'Miss Temple is a nurse—'

'Garibaldi gave me his word,' Greta replied with a winning smile. 'He won't be surprised, but he may need reminding.'

'I'll come with you now unless you speak for us!'

'Then it appears I have little choice,' Alberto Mario said, removing Carina's hand from his sleeve. 'Does Jessie know about this?'

'No, but I'll tell her as soon she gets back.'

'I'll pass on your message.' Alberto strode towards the door. 'When you arrive in Reggio, report to staff headquarters.'

'So we'll ride with the Redshirts, after all!' Greta grinned as he went out. 'It's lucky Alberto Mario's used to strong-minded women! And now I must go and find Stefan. Shall we meet on the ferry tomorrow?'

Greta took care not to mention Ben, Carina noticed as she waved her off. When Jessie and Jane came home, she told them Alberto's news and her own plans. Jane raised her eyes to Heaven and Jessie said she was sorry to lose her, but they didn't try to change her mind. Too animated to go to bed, the women talked late into the night until, one by one, they fell asleep around the kitchen table.

They were woken at dawn by a loud banging on the door.

Rubbing the sleep out of her eyes, Carina went to open it and found Harry on the doorstep, dressed in plaid trousers and green frock coat.

'Garibaldi's landed in Italy! Four thousand Redshirts sailed overnight and are camped near Reggio. I'm travelling with the newspaper reporters. I hope victory will be secured by the time I get there!'

There was no time to delay. Jane was to accompany the ambulances the next day, while Jessie and Carina were in the advance party. They spent the morning loading bandages, medicines and surgical equipment on to a mule cart and, with her bag containing Paulo's breeches and boots, Carina sat between Jessie and the driver as they lumbered down the dusty road to the beach.

The trawler requisitioned as a ferry was packed to the gunwales and Greta had saved a place for them in the stern. Once their precious cargo was stowed, Carina sank down on a pile of sacking with her grip bag under her knees. They had been on the go since dawn, but she was too excited to be tired. Greta had brought a basket of food. She handed out cheese and bread with slices of watermelon and Carina's gaze travelled over the crowded deck. Anne Lamartine was standing in the bow, accompanied by an officer of the *Cacciatore d'Etna*. As the boat moved away from the beach, she took off her hat, waving it above her head and shouting, 'Viva Garibaldi! Viva Italia!'

The Frenchwoman's long hair flew out behind her like a banner and everyone on board took up the chant, apart from Carina. Gradually the singing died away and the passengers became quiet, all eyes fixed on the opposite shore. Carina made out a long, sandy beach. A flotilla of fishing boats rowed out to greet them and, within an hour, the passengers were disembarked and the trawler set off to collect its next load.

Greta left them to meet up with Stefan and, as their supplies were being loaded onto a wagon, news came through that Garibaldi had taken Reggio. The Redshirts had entered the town by night and, after an hour of ferocious hand-to-hand combat, the enemy had surrendered. The bells were ringing when they arrived and an ecstatic crowd was out on the streets. As Carina alighted, two boys caught hold of her hands and dragged her into a dance. She lost her bonnet and would have been swept away, if Harry hadn't appeared and pulled her free. He retrieved her hat and Carina tucked it under her arm.

'Isn't it wonderful? This is what it was like after the liberation of Palermo.'

'I have to say the Latin temperament is too ebullient for my taste.'

'Oh, Harry, don't be such a dry stick. Don't you want to join in?'

'I'd prefer supper and a good night's rest.'

For all his assumed diffidence, Harry's eyes were bright and when they gained the corner of the square, he clapped Alberto Mario on the back.

'Well done, sir! A tremendous victory!'

'Indeed it was.' Alberto managed a weak smile. 'Now, Miss Temple, you're to come with me. Garibaldi is expecting you.'

'You're not serious! You can't let Carina consider such rashness.'

Not Harry too, Carina thought with a ripple of annoyance. Taking no notice of him, she turned to Jessie. 'May I borrow your husband for ten minutes?'

Jessie offered to keep her bonnet and Carina followed Alberto down the main street to where Garibaldi had taken lodgings at the edge of town. Two soldiers guarded the entrance and stood to attention as they saluted Alberto.

'From now on you're on your own. Good luck.' Alberto cast a glance over his shoulder as he headed back. 'What's Jessie supposed to do with Mr Carstairs in your absence?'

'Tell her not to worry about him. Harry can look after himself.'

The guards moved aside and Carina did not hear Alberto's reply. The door swung open and she stepped into a smoky kitchen with a low ceiling. Ben standing by a window and Garibaldi sitting at the table with Lamartine leaning over his shoulder. A newspaper was spread open and he was reading aloud. When he caught sight of her, he stopped and stood up.

'I'm glad to see you, Miss Temple. You are most welcome. Come in, come in.'

The general introduced her to his senior members of staff and Carina recognised the names of the gallant men who had fought at Calatafimi and Palermo, the heroes of Milazzo and Reggio. It was beyond her wildest dreams to be among them but when they came to Ben, he bowed and turned abruptly away. I should have told him in Messina, Carina thought with sudden misgiving. He's angry because this isn't what he planned. I should have been patient and waited.

Garibaldi indicated the chair next to his own and as she sat down, Carina met Lamartine's hostile stare.

'Well, what a surprise.' The Frenchwoman said, throwing back her hair, 'When did you arrive, Miss Temple?'

'I travelled from Messina on the same boat as you, along with Jessie Mario who's in charge of the ambulances.'

'We've no need of your rags and plaster now! Isn't that so, Generale? From now on our progress will meet with no resistance.'

Garibaldi leant forward, absorbing himself in the broadsheet, and Lamartine pitched her voice higher. 'How will you occupy yourself? Are we to be favoured with more of your charming poetry?'

'I'm here to ride with General Garibaldi and the Redshirts to Naples.'

Garibaldi put down the paper and everyone stopped talking. Carina was conscious of Ben watching her from where he stood by the window. There was a moment of suspense before the general answered. 'I gave you my word in Palermo and I intend to honour it, Miss Temple. You will ride in the company of my personal bodyguard.'

'But she has no experience—' Lamartine exclaimed.

'Great courage is required for nursing our wounded soldiers.' Garibaldi interrupted her mid-sentence. 'Miss Temple is an excellent horsewoman. I pray no more blood will be shed between fellow Italians, but her training can only be a benefit. We leave at three and I suggest we now retire.'

Garibaldi rose, the two women flanking him on either side, and spoke to Carina first. 'I propose Miss Temple stay here as my guest tonight. I'm sure Colonel Mavrone will make the necessary arrangements for you, *chere madame*.'

He made the announcement as if she had already given her assent and Carina felt colour rush into her cheeks. Ben can't leave me here, she thought wildly. He knows I want to be with him not the General. Why doesn't he say something? Her eyes searched his face, but Ben ignored her appeal. There was a hard line to his mouth and he looked her over briefly before turning to Lamartine. 'Shall we go?'

Garibaldi had foisted Ben with Lamartine while she had no choice but to stay here! The implications of spending the night with Garibaldi became clear and Carina's gaze bored into Ben's back as he went out of the door. Too late, she understood why he warned her not to compete with Lamartine. Garibaldi was a man who took whatever was on offer and that was how her eagerness had been perceived. She had disappointed him once, at the reception in Palermo, and he would be incensed when she did so again. But that was nothing compared to what Ben must be thinking at this moment!

Had she learnt nothing in all this time? It wasn't her fault. Ben should have insisted she went with him! Instead, he had abandoned her and now matters were beyond her control. The kitchen emptied, and when everyone had gone, Garibaldi led her up a narrow staircase. Carina was in such a panic she stumbled and he gave her his hand. They reached the top and a figure in a nightcap shuffled onto the landing.

'This is my manservant, Basso. He'll give up his bed for you tonight. He is used to sleeping on my floor.'

Carina was too distraught to feel any kind of relief. Ben would think she had deliberately set out to secure the general's attention when it was the last thing on her mind. He would be furious. There was a suffocating feeling in her throat and she did not answer.

'Try to get a good night's sleep.' Garibaldi stroked one side of his moustache as he looked at her. 'Thank you for saving me from Madame Lamartine this evening. Don't worry, my dear. Colonel Mavrone will come to his senses by the morning.'

As he lifted her hand to his lips, Carina supposed Greta must have said something to him. If he knew about her relationship with Ben, then he should have sought his permission beforehand! Garibaldi was inspirational, charming and utterly ruthless. He had manipulated them all to his advantage – but he didn't know what Ben was like and anxiety left her speechless.

'Basso will provide you with the uniform of my bodyguard in the morning.' Garibaldi's gaze was calm and unrepentant.

'Don't be concerned, Miss Temple. No one will question your honour when you ride at my side into San Giovanni tomorrow.'

Carina stayed awake so long worrying, she had only just fallen asleep when Basso woke her. Stiff from lying on the narrow pallet, she stretched her arms to ease her cramped muscles. Basso brought her warm water, clothes and a comb. She put on Paulo's boots and breeches and a red shirt with a belt and holster. Then she tugged the comb through the hair and tucked it under the distinctive cap of Garibaldi's bodyguard. She packed her clothes and gave her bag to Basso before going downstairs to join Garibaldi and his officers.

Sitting round the kitchen table drinking strong coffee, she listened as they planned their strategy for the day. Ben was not present and Lamartine only made an appearance as they walked down the street to mount up in the square. Carina was allocated a sturdy cob and was adjusting the length of her stirrup leathers when the Frenchwoman rode up beside her.

'A word of advice, if I may?' Carina made no reply and Lamartine nudged her horse closer. 'All men are bastards. Don't ever expect them to be faithful. They're all selfish bastards – to the very last one of them.'

With that, she touched her spurs to the horse's flanks and rode off. She should know, Carina thought – but to whom was she referring? Had she been with Ben last night? The thought made her feel sick. Garibaldi said Ben would come to senses by this morning, so where was he? Catching sight of Greta, she rode over to her.

'I hoped to find you with Garibaldi yesterday evening.'

'Stefan preferred to keep away. We stayed in town and dined with your friends.'

There was no time to find out more for they were off. With Garibaldi at their head, the cavalcade left Reggio while its citizens slept. Once the town was behind them, they headed inland, riding in single file through terrain bleached bare by heat and lack of rain. The sun came up, turning the landscape blazing white and they had been in the saddle for over three hours before Garibaldi reined in.

The general stood in his stirrups and put his spyglass to his eye to survey the layout of the land. Carina saw a fortified town by the sea with encampments along the beach. Columns of their own infantry, who must have marched during the night, were strung out in battle formation and as close to the enemy as they could get. No one spoke until a plume of dust rose from the road. The main body of cavalry was approaching and when Garibaldi gave the signal, they began their descent, slowly at first and then at a canter as the general galloped ahead.

Garibaldi's grey horse and red poncho made him stand out and Carina watched nervously as a volley of shots from the battlements of San Giovanni exploded around him. Seemingly indifferent to danger, he dismounted and climbed onto a rock, shouting to his men not to return fire. The general stood there alone, a dramatic and formidable figure, showing himself to five thousand Redshirts as they swept up the coast.

In their black hats with bayonets and daggers in their belts, they looked like an army of bandits, Carina thought as she followed the others to take shelter behind rocks. Bullets whistled overhead and black canister shot rained down so she pulled her neck scarf over her nose and mouth. Her instructions were clear; she must stay close to Garibaldi at all times. She was ready to mount up when, in front of her, she saw an infantryman lying wounded and unconscious on open ground.

Tossing the reins of her horse to an officer nearby, Carina grabbed a medical bag and ran forwards. A shell exploded, covering her with earth and grass as she ducked and knelt beside the injured man. She wound a tourniquet round his thigh, using her teeth to secure the knot, then beckoned to the men behind her. As the soldier was dragged to safety, she dashed back to the rocks. Enemy fire began to slacken and Carina counted time between the volleys until they stopped altogether. She stood up and spoke to the captain who held her horse.

'What's happening?'

'Garibaldi's negotiating a surrender. You're meant to be with him, aren't you? You'd better hurry up!'

Looking around, Carina saw the other members of the bodyguard had gone. The field was aflame with Redshirts and Garibaldi could be anywhere among them! She had forgotten her first duty and as they cantered down the hill, the captain shouted to her. 'Better stick closer to the chief from now on!'

They had reached Garibaldi's entourage and Carina saw him sitting cross-legged on the ground, smoking a cigar, as relaxed as if he were on a country picnic. He gestured to her to join them and one of the men handed her a water skin, which she tipped into her mouth. Succulent peaches and slices of black bread were passed round and they watched as the gates of the town opened. A small detachment of Bourbon officers marched up the hill towards them. They looked uncomfortable, sitting on the ground in their gold-braided uniforms, and one of them made a long speech.

Garibaldi sat in silence, puffing on his cigar until the senior officer demanded the Redshirts withdraw.

'I can make you prisoners or push you into the sea!' the general's voice rang out. 'You may return home in defeat or retain your rank and serve under my flag. The choice is yours, but I'll not hold back all day.'

The enemy could not hope for a conditional surrender, but went on blustering until Garibaldi pulled his hat down and gave an ultimatum.

'I never make bargains and I refuse your offers on any terms. You have twenty minutes before I attack.'

He took out his watch and the Bourbon officers scrambled to their feet. They hurried back towards the town and Garibaldi shouted for his mount. His mood changed in a lightning stroke and Carina ran to her horse and vaulted onto its back. With his bodyguard behind him, he galloped down the hill, cavalry and infantry closing in on all sides and brought them to a halt close to the gates.

The horses snorted and stamped and Carina's heart beat faster than the seconds ticking away. Her gaze scanned the high castle walls and she saw a white flag hoisted on the battlements. A loud cheer came from the ranks of the Redshirts and was echoed from inside the walls. Precisely twenty minutes after he had given his ultimatum, the garrison of San Giovanni surrendered and Garibaldi took the town without firing a shot.

CHAPTER THIRTY-EIGHT

She had been born for this moment, Carina thought as she rode into San Giovanni. Her heart overflowed with pride for the men who had given their lives so that Italy might be free. The sacrifice made by Enrico and many others had achieved far more than unity. It had broken the bonds of slavery forever.

All the same, she was alert as she rode close behind the general. The Bourbon soldiers looked wretched, smoking cheap cigars and spitting into the gutters, but they were still armed. Carina's hand rested on the stock of her revolver and the bodyguard hemmed him in until they reached the centre of the town, where Garibaldi rode forward and spoke from the saddle.

'Soldiers, you too are the sons of Italy and are at liberty! Anyone who wishes to join my army may apply to General Cosenz. Those of you who want to go home may do so.'

This unhoped-for clemency was too much for the defeated men of King Francis. Their reaction was spontaneous. As they threw down their rifles and rushed towards the general, Carina thought they meant to pull him from his horse. She drew her gun to fire over their heads and then saw they were kneeling and trying to kiss his boots. Doors and windows were thrown open and people poured into the streets, cheering and shouting as they crowded around him.

Mothers held up their children to be blessed and an old woman dressed in black limped past with tears pouring down her cheeks. '*Il nostro gesu Christo!*'

'Not quite ... but it makes a change,' a Genoese officer who rode beside Carina remarked drily. 'Last week they called him the Devil Incarnate. Garibaldi won't want his sanctity impaired by such earthly beings as a bodyguard, so we'd better make ourselves scarce. If we don't find stabling in the next hour there'll be none to be had.'

He was right, Carina thought as they rode up the narrow streets, making their way against a flowing tide of people. This was Garibaldi's victory and his moment of triumph. There would be time later to offer him her congratulations. She twisted her neck, looking for Ben. She hadn't seen or heard of him all day. The Redshirts had suffered minor casualties, but she would have heard if he was injured. There was no sign of Greta or Stefan either and she hoped he was with them.

The captain negotiated a price for livery and invited Carina to join him for supper in the square where the patron gave them a front table. His wife took her inside to wash and she wiped her face and scrubbed her hands, rolling up her sleeves to scrape off dirt and pieces of shot from her arms. It was stiflingly hot and she shook out her hair and tucked her cap into her belt. Then she went back to the table where two more members of the bodyguard had joined the party.

Spicy pasta was washed down with red wine. The food and company eased her fatigue, but Carina was restless. More than once she turned in her chair to search for Ben. The square was heaving with people, but he was tall enough to stand out and she couldn't see him anywhere. Instead, her gaze alighted on Harry. He cut an eccentric figure in his green frock coat among the ragged uniforms of the Redshirts and Carina stood up and waved.

Harry saw her and came straight over. His face was flushed and his voice too loud. 'Where were you last night? I thought I'd never see you again.'

'There was no need to worry.'

'We expected you to come back. I waited up until daybreak.'

'I stayed the night at Garibaldi's headquarters.'

'Is it a habit of the general's to offer hospitality to single ladies?'

'Please keep your voice down!' Aware of her companions, Carina tried to calm him. 'I'm a member of the general's body-guard. There are other women besides myself.'

'But not many who share his lodgings overnight!' Harry made no attempt to lower his voice.

'Well, now you've found me, why don't you join us?'

'I need to talk to you urgently. You must come with me this minute!'

Harry was insistent and Carina apologised to her comrades, trying to gather her strength as she left the table. Harry took her by the hand pulling her along. The brightly lit square was left behind and they walked through dark, narrow streets until they came to the town gates. There was no one about and through the archway Carina saw the coastline of Sicily with the setting sun tipped on the horizon. On any other occasion the view would have been spectacular, but she was alarmed by the wild look in Harry's eyes.

'This may be the last chance we have to talk – that's if you carry on as you are—'

'I thought you were coming to Naples!'

'There's something I must say to you, Carrie. I should have told you long ago.'

Carina's eyes went sharply to Harry's face. She knew what was coming and threw up her hands in an attempt to stop him.

'I'm in love with you! Always have been but never had the courage to tell you until now.'

'Don't! You don't know what you're saying!'

'You could love me – I know you could, if only you'd give me a chance.'

'But I do love you, Harry. You're my oldest friend.'

'I don't want your friendship. I want you to be my wife!'

Harry took her hands in his and bowed his head. His grip was so strong Carina thought he might break her fingers.

'You're hurting me!' Her voice lifted in desperation. 'I've tried to explain so many times! I love someone else—'

'I don't care what you've done.' Harry's arms went round her. 'You've had your fill of adventuring, darling. Come home and marry me before I lose you to General Garibaldi or anybody else—'

'I'm afraid that's out of the question, Mr Carstairs.'

The sound of Ben's voice gave Carina such a fright that she let out a cry. She wrenched herself from Harry's embrace as Ben emerged from the shadows. He walked towards them and did not favour her with a glance.

'You see, Miss Temple is already betrothed – to me.'

How she collected her wits Carina didn't know. Harry was staring at her, his eyes glazed with shock and Ben's tone was demonic.

'You may deny our betrothal, Carina. But I hope you have the honesty to admit to Mr Carstairs you're my mistress.'

Harry had gone white, his mouth tight beneath his moustache and his expression was so stricken, Carina thought he was going to faint. She reached for his hand and he flung her aside with such force she fell on her knees. With his arms by his sides, his hands balled into fists as he looked down at her.

'Is this true? Are you this man's mistress?' he demanded in a cracked voice.

The lines on Harry's forehead and around his mouth narrowed as he battled to keep control. Yes, she would tell him Ben was her lover! She was desperate for Harry to know – but not with Ben standing over her, forcing her to confess. The words stuck in her throat and Harry's eyes slid away. He turned on his heel and stumbled towards the shelter of the streets. When he reached them, he clutched at the walls like a blind man. As he disappeared from sight, Carina leapt to her feet and turned on Ben in fury.

'How could you be so cruel? Who do you want to hurt, Harry or me? Which of us do you hate the most?'

'Mr Carstairs has a right to know the truth.'

'I was going to tell him—'

'I'm not surprised he's so upset.' Ben stemmed her words. 'I couldn't credit the way you pursued Garibaldi yesterday. Oh, the sweet poison of a woman's charms ...'

'I didn't know he would ask me to stay. I came to find you!'

'It was perfectly obvious what you were after.'

'Garibaldi behaved impeccably—'

'Did he now? How very disappointing for you.'

Carina could feel the barely controlled violence in Ben. The steely glint in his eyes indicated how far he might go, but never in her life had she lacked courage. Not once, in all the time she had known him, had Ben admitted he was wrong. He hadn't declared openly he loved her as Harry had done! Who did he think he was to defame her? She wanted to hurt him as much as he had hurt Harry and her voice filled with venom.

'You said no commitments! Well, you needn't have bothered! I never belonged to you and never will. It was lust – not love – that drew us together!'

Ben sucked in his breath and the side of his lip curled down in disgust. Carina saw in his eyes the same contempt she had witnessed before. In that instant she hated him. She hated him with a rage that made her want to smash his face with her fists. As she struck out, he caught her by the wrists and twisted her about. Carina kicked at his shins with her boots, shouting and swearing, as he pushed her ahead of him. When she dug her heels into the cobbles and threw her weight back, he jerked her arm painfully, not caring if he hurt her. This wasn't the man she loved! She was at the mercy of a rough and cruel stranger. What did Ben mean to do? Where was he taking her?

'I've arranged accommodation for us outside of town,' he answered as if she had spoken aloud.

With only the moonlight to guide them, Ben made her walk in front until they came to a house lit by red lanterns. The windowpanes were stained scarlet and above the door was a sign: *Senora Vacavi's Establishment.* There was a piano thumping inside and, through the thin net curtains, Carina glimpsed soldiers with scantily dressed girls. Ben had brought her to a brothel and her voice broke with rage.

'How dare you bring me here?'

'If you're too tired to walk, I'll carry you inside.'

'I'm not going into that place!'

'Tonight, for once, you'll do as you're told.'

'I won't go in, do you hear?' Carina shouted. 'If you try to force me, I'll scream the place down! I hate you ... you bastard!'

'And a bastard's what you deserve, Carina – not a great man like Garibaldi, nor even a pretty gentleman like Mr Carstairs.'

'Damn you, Ben Mavrone! You're a famous liar!'

'Leave it now, both of you, please!'

Greta Mazzini's voice came out of the night and Carina flinched in surprise. Ben released her and Greta stepped from darkness into the garish light. Carina saw a revolver holstered at her side and stared at her in bewilderment. How could Greta be here?

'Stefan's found lodgings. You're staying with us tonight. He's waiting with a wagon just over there.' Greta faced Ben, her hand resting on the stock of her gun. 'Shall we go? It's been a long day.'

'I'm sure Carina's grateful for your hospitality, but I must decline.'

'I'm sorry, Ben, but you're coming with us.'

Greta's tone was uncompromising. Carina glanced at Ben and saw the frightening glitter gone from his eyes. For a time the three of them stood in silence. Then he shrugged and set off in the direction indicated.

It was inconceivable Ben could be made to walk at gunpoint by his best friend, Carina thought as he led the way along a narrow path beneath the walls. Greta walked directly after him while she trailed last. When they came to the road, Stefan was waiting and squeezed her hand as he helped her into the back. Ben climbed up beside him and Greta on the driving board. They headed away from San Giovanni and down a bumpy track to a farm building, waiting outside while Stefan stabled the mule. As they went into kitchen, Greta unloaded her gun, dropping the bullets into her pocket.

'Carina will sleep in my bed tonight. You can share with Stefan or sleep here, Ben; whichever you prefer.'

The smell of cigar smoke drifted upward as Carina followed Greta up the stairs and closed the bedroom door. She undressed, leaving her clothes on the floor, and slipped into bed before Greta blew out the candle.

'How did you know?' she whispered in the darkness.

'Stefan was with Ben all evening. When Ben followed you and Mr Carstairs, Stefan came to find me. We were afraid this might happen.'

'What are you saying?' Carina was too dazed to comprehend her meaning.

'We couldn't let Ben do something stupid. We're too fond of you both.'

'Oh, Greta, Ben was brutal to Harry. And to me. I couldn't believe it of him.'

'Perhaps it was the only way for Mr Carstairs to accept the truth.'

'He frightened me. I thought Ben had gone mad.' Tears started in Carina's eyes and Greta's arms went round her.

'Sicilian men are driven mad by jealousy. Why else do we have so many crimes of passion in our country? No Sicilian will let another man near the woman he loves.'

'But I'm not his woman and he doesn't love me.'

'That's where you are wrong.'

Greta kissed her on the cheek and lay down. Carina was dropping with exhaustion, her heart numb with pain. Nothing made sense anymore. She must wait until morning and then ask Greta what to do. Greta understood Ben far better than she did. Thank God for her this evening. Thank God for Greta and her good friendship.

White clouds scudded across a blue sky and Carina could hear the tinkling of sheep bells in the distance. The house was quiet when she woke up, so she assumed the others must have left already. Near the basin she found a note from Greta saying there was coffee in the kitchen and they would return later.

Had Ben stayed here overnight, she wondered, or had he walked back to San Giovanni?

Carina tried to isolate in her mind the mistakes they had both made. She had failed to believe Ben when he gave her his promise. She was too impatient and Ben too quick to condemn her. She had underestimated Garibaldi and Ben had believed the worst of her. Hatred was the counter side of love, but it was Ben's capacity for cruelty that hurt the most. He had wanted to humiliate her and would have done so if Greta hadn't intervened. She still loved him, but the darkness in Ben was as impenetrable as the darkness of Sicily itself. How could they go on after last night?

First things first. She would have something to eat and then walk to town to collect her horse and find Greta and Stefan. She must report to Garibaldi's headquarters and was bound to run into Ben. She wouldn't have the courage to face him unless they were with her. Carina dressed and noticed that her holster was empty. She couldn't remember where she had left her gun, but it must be in the house somewhere. She picked up her boots and carried them down the narrow staircase.

'Good morning. Did you sleep well?'

Ben's voice startled her and Carina looked around the kitchen. He was alone and she sat down at the kitchen table without answering. As she put on her boots, Ben poured coffee into a mug and placed it in front of her, along with freshly baked bread he must have brought back with him. Through the open door Carina saw his horse unsaddled and tied to a rail in the shade. Ben had been waiting for her.

'Stefan and Greta dropped me in town early,' Ben said, tipping his chair back in the usual way. 'I called on Harry Carstairs and asked him to accept my sincere apologies. I said I was drunk and my allegations were totally unfounded.'

Carina took a sip of coffee. It was so bitter she almost spat it out. She could not rage at Ben now, but nor could she bring herself to meet his gaze.

'Did he believe you?'

'He said he hoped never to set eyes on me again. He asked me to leave before he had me thrown out. I don't blame him.'

'What do you want, Ben?'

'I want to say I'm sorry. My conduct last night was unforgivable. There was no excuse.'

Her revolver was lying on the table. Ben picked it up and Carina watched as he broke it open. 'So, she took your bullets too. Never let it be said Greta Mazzini is not thorough. You'll need to get more ammunition.'

He put down her gun and Carina lifted her head to look at him. Ben was unshaven and there were dark shadows under his eyes. He hadn't slept, she thought and waited for him to go on.

'If Harry Carstairs proposes again, you should accept his offer. I was mistaken in my opinion of him. He will make a good husband.'

'I hardly think you're qualified to offer advice.'

The ghost of a smile touched Ben's lips and then faded. Carina dipped the roll in her coffee and chewed it slowly. She was glad of the breeze coming through the window and took her time.

'What came over you, Ben?'

'I was jealous and lost control.' Ben ran a hand through his hair, pushing it off his forehead. 'I'm not a good man, Carina – not even a half decent one like your friend. I've hurt too many people.'

Carina studied the coarse grain in the wood of the table. It might help Ben to damn himself, but it wasn't enough for her to forgive him and soft anger stirred inside.

'How could you be so vile? What were you thinking?'

'I was thinking you were a beautiful flirt who'd stop at nothing to get what she wanted. Me, Garibaldi, riding with the Redshirts – that it was all a game to you before you returned to your safe life in England. The fact I was wrong makes no difference.'

The low note in his voice brought Carina's head up and Ben leant forward and put his elbows on the table.

'We cannot change the nature of our souls. Even you, with your dogged persistence, won't succeed in that endeavour. A better man than myself would have let you go long ago. Lord knows, I tried—'

'I've one question,' Carina interrupted. 'Why are you jealous of Harry?'

For a long moment, Ben said nothing. When he finally answered, Carina sensed the effort it cost him.

'Harry Carstairs can give you everything you deserve. He'll make you happy and I will not. The time has come for us go our separate ways.' Ben paused and drew a long breath. 'I hope one day you can find it in your heart to forgive me.'

The finality in his voice hit Carina like a blow to the stomach. How much easier to fight in hot blood than with cold logic! They had both asked themselves the same question and Ben reached his conclusion. He articulated what he believed to be right – but she had vowed never to give up. She had fought so long and so hard. They couldn't let it end like this! Ben could change. She could change. They could find a way back together.

Ben was watching her face and made an impatient gesture with his hand.

'For God's sake, Carina! You can't make everything right with your bloody-minded tenacity. I'm jinxed. I've destroyed anyone who has come close to me and I will destroy you. I don't mean to – but that's the way it is. We're going to put an end to this right now.'

'I love you—'

'I recall you saying much the same to Mr Carstairs.'

'You were unforgivably cruel to Harry—'

'And what about you?'

Carina did not reply. For as long as she could remember, Harry had been her steadfast friend. His only fault was in loving her too much. She wasn't the person he believed her to be – but she couldn't think about Harry now. Ben wasn't jinxed! It was just another excuse not to commit himself. She must have faith. How could she convince Ben there was still hope – that it wasn't too late for them?

Carina began to chew the nail of her thumb and Ben broke the silence first.

'Harry's devotion is such that he'll forgive you anything. Marry him, Carina. For the first time in your life do what is right for yourself.'

'And if I refuse?'

'Then we're both damned.'

Ben stood up and went to the window. He had his back to her and Carina looked down at her hands. With their callouses and torn nails, they reminded her of the lonely child and unhappy girl she had once been. She had exorcised her demons while Ben was still tormented by his. He wanted to save her from himself, but she would not help him.

Ben is the only man I will ever love, she thought. It doesn't matter that I don't always understand him. No human being truly understands another. I love him and can endure anything if he's with me. Without him I am lost.

Carina breathed in to fill her lungs. Then she rose from the chair and walked across the room. Standing behind Ben she leant her head between his shoulder blades. The side of her face pressed into his back and she felt the tautness in his muscles.

'It's not my nature to do what's right. You should know that by now.'

Ben turned slowly and looked down at her. 'Have you been listening to a word I said?'

'I'm prepared to take the risk.'

'Then you're out of your mind.'

'Maybe so ...'

'I can't promise never to lose my temper again. What will you do then?'

'I will kill you.' Carina answered with quiet force. 'I don't want to marry anyone else. I want to be with you.'

'I've no desire to ruin your life, sweetheart.' Ben's gaze shifted over her shoulder. If she hadn't known better, Carina might have thought there was someone standing behind her. Then his eyes came back to her face. 'Above all, I want you to be happy.'

'I can only be happy with you. I love you, don't you understand?'

Ben looked at her so long and hard, the suspense was excruciating. How could she know what was going on in his head? Carina saw surprise and self-deprecation in his face; then something new to her, the look of a man resigned to his fate caught unawares by a last-minute reprieve. She was so tense she twisted a lock of her hair around her finger, tugging until it hurt.

Then, without warning, Ben went down on one knee. 'Will you marry me, Carina Temple?'

He held out his hand and Carina thought he was joking. Looking into his blue eyes, she saw that he was serious and her breath came fast.

'When?'

'Tonight. Tomorrow. As soon as I can get a licence.'

'By the devil, Ben Mavrone, you're a hard man to pin down!'

'Will you be my wife – for richer or poorer, for better, for worse and all that?'

'Why?'

'Why do you think? Because I'm in love with you, darling.' Ben took hold of her hand and pressed it to his lips. 'Are you going to keep me on my knees all day? For the last time, Carina Temple, will you marry me?'

'I will.'

Ben stood up and pulled her to him. He held her so tightly she thought he would crush the life out of her, kissing her with a passion that made her dizzy. One hand was at the collar of her shirt and she clung to him, overrun with happiness and relief. By a hair's breadth they had snatched victory from the jaws of defeat! Her love for Ben was invincible and Carina was ablaze with triumph. Whatever lay ahead, whether for better or for worse, they would be together. The man she loved was secure in her heart and she would never let him go.

CHAPTER THIRTY-NINE

Dearest Alice,
I am writing this in the town of San Giovanni and will explain
everything to you when we reach Naples. I have the most wonderful
news! Tomorrow I am to marry Colonel Ben Mavrone. I know this
will come as a shock, but please trust me. I met Ben this spring and
came to know him well after the Redshirts entered Palermo. He is
the best of men and I love him dearly. As soon as the campaign is
over, I will bring him to England to meet you. Then you will
understand my happiness ...

Carina was awake, but too tired to open her eyes. Her spine was
pressed against Ben's stomach and, for the first time in weeks,
they were alone, lying on the softest spring mattress in the
whole of Naples. How Ben had found the hotel, she had no
idea. It was late when they arrived and the double bed and snug
apartment seemed like paradise.

And what a day yesterday had been! They had travelled the
final lap of the journey with Garibaldi on a train that was
crammed to bursting. Enthusiastic demonstrations greeted

them at every station and when they reached Naples and Garibaldi descended onto the platform, a crowd of supporters surged towards him. Knocking down barriers, they swept past the guard of honour, drowning out the welcome speeches of the officials. Ben had shouldered a way through the melee and they had managed to get to the open carriages before the procession through the city began.

Once or twice Garibaldi took off his hat and inclined his head, but he neither waved nor smiled. Only when they passed the port, where the sailors hung like monkeys from the riggings and broke into a cheer, did he raise his arm in a salute. Arriving at the Royal Palace, vacated by the king only days before, he addressed the crowd from the balcony.

'This is the beginning of a new era for Italy! Today we pass from the yoke of servitude to become a free and great nation. I thank you for your welcome. I thank you for your courage in the name of all Italy.'

Something had surprised Carina then. She and Ben were standing beneath the balcony and her gaze strayed to the group of people behind Garibaldi. One man caught her attention because he was wearing court dress. She had imagined for a moment it was Prince Scalia, but she must have been mistaken. The king had fled north to Gaeta and taken his court and ministers with him. Snuggling closer to Ben, she dismissed the memory and let her mind drift back over the last weeks.

Ben had found a priest in San Giovanni and they were married quietly in a small chapel with Greta and Stefan as witnesses. There was no time to invite anyone else. Greta gave her a clean red shirt and helped tie her hair with a white ribbon. As she stepped forward to stand beside Ben, Greta pressed a small bouquet of white carnations into Carina's hand. They had taken their solemn vows and, hearing Ben's voice pledging his love and fidelity, Carina thought her heart would break with joy.

She had been with Ben and the Pioneers ever since and Carina had never ridden so hard or so fast in her life. This was the life he loved, she thought. She noted every detail about him, the way he took decisions, his easy manner with subordinates and the warmth in his eyes when they met hers across the campfire. When Ben slung their bedrolls down side by side on the ground, she had wished they were alone, and last night was her reward. Not waiting to have supper, Ben had dropped their bags on the floor and taken her straight to bed. Thinking of it, Carina stirred restlessly.

'Are you hungry, my love? Shall I order breakfast?'

'I'm starving. I said so last night, but you wouldn't listen.'

'I recall other appetites demanded satisfaction first.'

His hands were under her hair, lifting her head, and Carina's lips fluttered against his mouth. When he made love to her all other thought was scattered to oblivion. It was only later, as she looked up at cherubs and satyrs painted above the bed, Carina remembered. It *was* Scalia she had seen yesterday! How could he have been in the official ceremony for Garibaldi? Could Bianca also be in Naples? Had Ben seen him too, and drawn the same conclusion?

Carina slipped out of bed and wrapped a sheet round her as she went to the window. The street below was crowded with men and women waving banners and chanting Garibaldi's name. She leant forward to get a better view until a whistle from the opposite balcony made her step back.

'Your beauty isn't wasted on the menfolk of Naples, my love. A little more modesty, please, or we'll have the entire male population of the city barracking our hotel.'

Ben smiled and Carina gave a toss of her head as she went to the antechamber and immersed herself a tub of cool water. Ben came through and knelt down. He tried to duck her head under water so she threw the soap at him and when she scrambled out, he climbed into the tub himself.

'I've been looking forward to a bath for weeks!' Carina feigned indignation. 'You might have let me enjoy it.'

He made a lunge for her, but she escaped and put on her clothes before she tugged the bell pull to summon the porter. After some time the man appeared, yawning as he buttoned up his jacket.

'We would like coffee and as much bread as you can find.'

'But everyone's out in the streets, signora.'

'But you're here and I'm sure you'll be kind enough to fix something for us. My husband has an appointment with General Garibaldi. We mustn't keep him waiting.'

Garibaldi's name had a magical effect and within half an hour Carina was sitting by the window, dipping panini into milky coffee. When Ben emerged from the bathroom, he had shaved off his beard and her heart skipped a beat. Oh how she loved him! His good looks and engaging smile caused havoc in a woman's heart – and she must take care not to lose him in this riotous city.

Ben sat down and flicked a breadcrumb off the front of her shirt. His hand lingered a moment before he sighed and withdrew it to fill his cup with coffee. Carina wondered if she should tell him her suspicions about the prince. She didn't want to spoil the happiness of the morning but had vowed to keep nothing from him.

'I thought I saw Prince Scalia with Garibaldi yesterday. Could it be possible?'

'Scalia and Liborio are snakes in the grass. As soon as they deserted one master, they crawled straight to the next.'

'How can Scalia remain at liberty? I don't understand.'

'One of Garibaldi's strengths is pragmatism. The king is holed up in Gaeta, but he's determined to reclaim Naples. The general knows the populace is fickle. He's prepared to accommodate a few turncoats until Victor Emmanuel accepts the crown.'

'But Scalia's the most evil man in the two Sicilies—'

'And one of the most powerful in Naples. He has greater influence here than in Palermo.'

'Mercy! Will we never be rid of him?'

'Scalia will be punished in time. Garibaldi will deal with him when he's no longer of any use – but I agree. I find it reprehensible he does business with murderers.'

Ben stood up, and walked over to the cabinet where he had left his revolver. He checked the hammer before tucking the gun it into the holster. Carina was prepared for a shift in his mood but it passed swiftly.

'And now, and now, sweet wife, I must attend to your trousseau. I'm going shopping.'

'May I come with you?'

'Heavens, no! What would the couturiers of Naples say? Trust me, darling. I'm told I have an excellent eye for feminine fashion.'

He was bound to be away hours, so Carina set about fixing her coiffure. Her hair had grown long and she brushed it, combing out the knots, before she attempted a chignon. Standing in front of the glass with a mouthful of pins between her teeth, she tried to remember how Rose had put it up. It was far harder than she knew. No sooner was her hair rolled in one place than the pins fell tumbling to the floor. In the end she gave up and waited impatiently for Ben to return.

He walked in, his arms stacked with boxes, which he tossed on the bed. Packed within layers of tissue, were dresses and petticoats, underclothes and corsets, and Ben made her try everything on. He had rather too expert a hand, she thought, as he laced her into stays and fastened buttons until she stood before him in a dress of moiré silk. Carina was impressed by Ben's good taste, including a delightful bonnet with a wide brim and ribbon that matched the colour of her eyes.

'Thank you, my darling.' She stood on tiptoes to kiss him. 'They're lovely.'

'This is our honeymoon and you look beautiful. I shall be the envy of every husband in Naples.'

There was undisguised admiration in Ben's eyes and Carina took him by the hands and whirled him round the room. He laughed and told her she was behaving like a child, but she didn't care. Ben arranged for a lady's maid to come each morning to dress her hair, and she did not think about Prince Scalia or Bianca again. The weather was perfect and Naples a vibrant, bustling port surrounded by antiquity. They drove out to the slopes of Vesuvius and looked in wonder at the volcano. Another day, they visited a museum packed with treasures from Pompeii where the mosaics were fresh as yesterday and sculptures so lifelike they looked like flesh and bone.

Ben cut a dashing figure in the city and Carina was aware of the impression he made when entering a room. She noticed the eyes of other women following him and how they blushed as he bent over their hands. More confident than she was in conversation, Ben could be provocative or as tactful as a diplomat. She never knew what he might say next or which opinion he would favour. Carina listened to him talk of matters about which she knew nothing and regretted her lack of formal learning. She wanted to be Ben's equal in every way and was ashamed of her ignorance.

'But you have youth on your side!' His eyes danced when she told him. 'You've plenty of time to learn about the world. There's no need to rush.'

Nevertheless, Ben took the trouble to explain current issues to her and bought her newspapers to read. He asked her questions and listened to her answers, encouraging her to form her own views. He could be serious or funny, making her laugh until she cried. When he gave her a book of Keats's poetry, he said that he preferred her verse to all the Romantic poets put together. He was teasing, Carina was sure, but she was pleased with the compliment.

On the surface Ben was sophisticated and urbane, but he never lost the look of a man who has lived with danger too long to be careless. He was unstintingly generous and attentive, yet his core of isolation remained. Occasionally, Carina turned her head and caught a brooding look on his face. His mind was far away and his expression so serious she wondered what he could be thinking. The moment he felt her eyes on him, Ben would get up and kiss her or tell her a story to make her smile.

Then, for two consecutive days, he left her alone in the hotel. He gave no explanation of where he had been and Carina knew better than to interrogate him. Ben had always been secretive and she wouldn't look for shadows in the sunlight. She had known how it would be and there were no regrets. Ben was her beloved husband and, for the most part, seemed as delighted with married life as she was herself.

One evening they were invited to dine with Garibaldi at the Palazzo D'Angri, arriving late to find the antechamber crammed with journalists. Scores of hands darted in the air, beseeching them with questions until they reached the private apartments where Garibaldi embraced Carina. He congratulated Ben on his good fortune and she was overjoyed to find

Greta and Stefan among the guests, along with Jane and Jessie and Alberto Mario.

'We've only just heard of your marriage. Congratulations to you both!' Jessie wagged a finger at Ben. 'You've found yourself a remarkable woman, Colonel Mavrone. Make sure you take care of her – no more running off as you did after Milazzo!'

'I've been dying to talk to you. Do you mind if we sit down?' Greta took her hand, leading Carina to an open window.

She was pale and Carina looked at her with concern. 'What's wrong, Greta? Are you ill?'

'I'm told the sickness is normal and will pass in a month or so.'

'You don't mean? You're not—'

'In an interesting condition? Yes, I am! Can you believe it? Stefan and I've been married for five years. We'd almost given up hope.'

'Why, it's wonderful news! When did you find out?'

'I saw the doctor yesterday and the baby's due in April. Stefan's mortified that he let me ride as a courier. He insists we return to Sicily at the earliest opportunity. And you, dearest? Are you happy?'

'Oh, Greta … When I think how Ben and I almost lost each other. We owe all our happiness to you. How can I ever express my gratitude?'

'By coming home and following my example.' Greta opened her fan to cool herself. 'I shall spend my confinement with my mother and rely on you to visit every day. Now I've found a woman after my own heart, I intend to keep her my friend forever.'

The others joined them and Jessie cast a knowing glance over Greta. 'Well, Senora Bosco, it's fortunate your services are no longer required on the battlefield.'

'What news of the ambulances?' Ben asked.

'They arrived from Reggio yesterday. I'm glad to say we've been allocated the finest convent in Naples as our hospital. Never again will we be unprepared as we were at Milazzo.'

'Garibaldi hoped no more blood would be shed between fellow Italians,' Carina said quietly.

'No king gives up his throne without a fight and the Bourbons are the worst of the lot.' Alberto Mario answered. 'I'm afraid it's not over yet.'

The next night they went to the opera at the Theatre San Carlo for Verdi's *Nabucco*. Carina hoped to hear the famous chorus, but the audience was over-excited and the performance constantly interrupted. The opera stopped and started so many times, they left at the interval, walking along the marina before returning to the hotel. When she thought about Harry, Carina hoped he had returned to England, and tried not to feel guilty. She must write to him but nothing was so important that it couldn't wait. Happiness was not a dream. It was here and now and every moment too precious to waste.

They were sitting at a pavement table in the morning sun and waiters in long aprons hurried from table to table. Smartly dressed men did business over coffee and Ben was reading a newspaper. At the far end, a man sat with a book propped in front of him. Carina noticed him because, more than once, he lifted his head to stare in their direction. When she caught his eye, he looked quickly away and soon afterwards summoned the waiter for his bill. The next day she saw him again. She was with Ben, buying cigars, and he was standing outside the shop window.

Touching Ben's arm, she indicated with her head. 'Who is that man?'

'Which one?'

'That bald fellow over there. I am sure he's following us.'

'You're a beautiful woman, darling. Every man in Naples would follow you if they had time.'

He wasn't taking her seriously and when Carina looked again, the stranger had gone. Ben was right. Why shouldn't the man frequent the same restaurants and visit the same shops as they did? He was probably one of the many journalists who followed Garibaldi from Sicily and now had nothing to do. During the next few days there was no sign of him and Carina put him out of her mind.

She had discovered the Villa Denuzio was an hour's drive from Naples and sent a letter to her grandmother.

Darling Nonna,
I am sorry not to have written before but these last weeks have been
a whirlwind. I pray you are well. Please, can I come and see you
soon? I have some good news I wish to convey to you in person ...

An answer, written in a spidery hand, was delivered to the hotel the same evening. Nonna wrote that Carlo and Anna Maria were in Gaeta on the command of the king, while she remained in the villa with Gabriella and Paulo. She looked forward to Carina's visit. When might they expect her?

Carina replied there was someone she wanted her to meet and she would bring him for lunch the day after tomorrow. She was confident Ben would win Nonna over but when she thought of Gabriella her mood darkened. She felt so desperately sad for her. What could she say that could possibly be of any consolation? They were driving home and, with these thoughts on her mind, Carina sighed as she rested her head on Ben's shoulder.

'You're tired, my love. I'll take you back and then I must return to headquarters.'

'But you were there only an hour ago.'

'Something's come up.'

When they arrived at the hotel, Ben walked her to the door and Carina entered the dark lobby alone. She was about to go upstairs when she heard her name and looked round as Harry rose from a high-backed chair. He walked over and then, as if it were the most natural thing in the world, invited her to join him in a glass of lemonade.

'I've been looking for you but only thought of enquiring at the Palazzo D'Angri this morning. They told me you were staying here.'

'I meant to write to you. Dear Harry, I'm so sorry.'

Harry poured her a glass of lemonade. He sat straight and stiff in his chair and took a sip of juice.

'When I heard you were married I couldn't believe it.'

'Can you forgive me?'

'Nothing to forgive, old girl. Had a feeling something was up and hoped I was wrong.' His sentences were patently rehearsed. 'I sail for England on Friday and couldn't leave without saying goodbye. We've been friends for too long.'

'Dear Harry, you're like a brother to me—'

'And too much of a fool to realise it!'

Carina dropped her gaze to her lap. It was awkward enough and she didn't want to make it any worse. There was a commotion in the street outside but no one came in and Harry put down his glass.

'I know it's not my business, but are you sure you made the right decision?'

'I promise you I am happy. I know Ben behaved badly in San Giovanni and I apologise. He was upset that night but he's a good man and I truly love him.'

'Will you stay in Italy?'

'Sicily will be our home but we'll visit England once the campaign is over. I want to see you and introduce Ben to Alice.'

'Does Lady Farne know of your marriage?'

'I've written to her and will tell my grandmother tomorrow.'

Harry began to fiddle with his watch chain. He was disinclined to continue the conversation and Carina studied him over the top of her glass. His hair was bleached the colour of pale straw and he looked older than his twenty years. How she wished she hadn't had to hurt him! There was a long silence, then he took a card from his wallet and, in a curiously formal gesture, placed it on the table in front of her.

'Please will you do me the honour of dining with me tomorrow evening? I would like to be on better terms with your husband before I leave. I'm staying at the Hotel Garibaldi. Shall we say seven o'clock?'

'Why, thank you! How very kind.'

Carina stood up to kiss him but Harry put on his gloves and shook her hand. After he had gone, she made her way up to the bedroom. Harry had left an English newspaper and she was lying on the bed reading it when Ben returned. She would have jumped up and run to him but the serious look on his face stopped her.

'I'm afraid there's trouble in Palermo. The Sicilians are claiming Garibaldi's deserted them. He's asked me to take charge of the situation.'

'Why you? Why not someone else? How long will you be away?'

The questions followed one upon the other and Ben sat down on the bed beside her.

'I'm the most senior Sicilian officer in Garibaldi's command.'

'When do you go?'

'At first light tomorrow.'

'But we're visiting my grandmother—'

'I know and I'm sorry. I will pay my respects as soon as I return.'

Carina swung her bare legs over the side of the bed. There were other officers who could do the job just as well! Why did Garibaldi have to choose Ben? He was a well-respected and high-ranking officer, she reminded herself. Ben was under the general's command and must obey orders. He had other responsibilities, apart from attending upon her.

'I've booked you on the same ferry as Greta and Stefan on Thursday. I'm not leaving you alone for long, my darling.'

Thursday? Why, today was Tuesday! It was the day after tomorrow and Ben was taking her with him to Palermo! How silly to think he would abandon her in Naples. Those days were behind them. She was his wife now and he would never leave her again.

Ben came to bed and pressed her hand against his heart so she felt its strong, steady beat. Carina sought his mouth impatiently. She held him close to her and when he tried to raise himself up, pulled him back down. She was intoxicated with this man who was her husband. She loved the taste of him, the feel of his hard body and his cool skin. Ben kissed her, gently at first, and then passionately. He turned her over, his lips brushing her shoulders as he lifted her onto her knees. Carina felt his body against hers, his finger tracing the deep groove of her spine and she abandoned herself to him entirely. He is mine, she thought …

Carina lay with her head on his lap, her hair spread across his stomach as Ben propped himself up on the pillows, not knowing if she stayed awake or dozed in the hours that followed. The clock struck three and she heard him moving around the room.

She kept her eyes shut until he came back and knelt by the bed, taking her in his arms.

'I've paid the bill and left you money with your travel papers in the desk. Stefan has your ticket for the ferry. Remember your pistol, sweetheart. Promise to have it on you always.' He took her face in his hands and kissed her forehead and then her lips. 'I'll see you in Sicily, my darling. Behave yourself while I'm away.'

Ben stood up, collected his knapsack, slinging it over his shoulder as he walked towards the door. He stood for a long moment with his hand on the knob looking back at her and then went out. As the door closed, Carina experienced a sense of loss so acute she bit down on her knuckle to stop herself crying. She didn't know why she was so upset. They would only be apart for two days. It was no time at all. Her love for Ben was making her soft, she thought as she walked over to the window.

Carina watched Ben cross the street below, his stride long and purposeful as he headed towards the port. When he was lost from sight, her gaze travelled over the tiled rooftops to the bay. The sea was smooth as polished gunmetal and he would have a good crossing. Tomorrow was a busy day. She must try to get some rest and she went back to bed, curling up in the place where the sheets were still warm.

CHAPTER FORTY

There was no warning of the sirocco that swept up the western seaboard late that afternoon. The morning had dawned bright and it was only as she left Naples in a hired diligence, Carina realised she had forgotten to tell Ben about meeting Harry. The dinner engagement would be more difficult without him, but she must go all the same. As they arrived at the Villa Denuzio, she looked out and saw a pretty pink stucco house surrounded by mimosa trees. Paulo came striding across the gravel to open the door. He gave her his hand and peered into the interior.

'Where've you hidden him? We expected your husband. Nonna will be disappointed.'

'Mercy, how do you know?'

'Papa was informed. He told Nonna you married one of Garibaldi's officers without asking her permission.'

'It was a private ceremony! How could he—'

'No doubt the priest told the bishop, who told the cardinal, who told the pope, who told my father. It doesn't matter. What have you done with him?'

'Ben had to go to Palermo this morning.'

'So the damned man's deserted you already?'

The teasing note was still there, but Paulo's face was drawn and Carina saw the dark look in his eyes as he led her up the steps.

'Oh, Paulo. I'm so sad about Enrico. You must be devastated.'

'Enrico was too fine a man to die. What a stupid, tragic waste!' Paulo answered roughly as they stood in the cool of the hall. 'What difference does it make if we're ruled by a dictator or a king? It's not a cause worth dying for!'

Carina wanted to tell him he was wrong, but Enrico had been Paulo's friend. Caution checked her and she asked, 'How is Gabriella?'

'My sister is stronger than I am. You will see.'

As they walked through the house, Carina had an impression of the same dilapidated grandeur as in Palermo, rooms full of old pictures with faded furniture and windows shuttered to keep out the light. Paulo took her out onto a terrace where Nonna was sitting in a wicker chair under a canopy of vines. She asked Paulo to leave them for a while and Carina took a seat beside her.

'I hoped to be the one to tell you, Nonna. I wanted you to meet Ben and for you to give us your blessing. Sadly, he received orders to return to Palermo this morning.'

'Then I look forward to making his acquaintance at another time,' Nonna answered brusquely. 'I gather I've been misled as to your activities over these last few months. I hope you will now do me the courtesy of telling the truth?'

Carina was determined to be honest, but it was harder than she anticipated and would have been impossible had Ben been there. How devious she sounded, admitting that she had lied on her return to Palermo! How sordid her confession that she had been with Ben and not Greta Mazzini all that time! She faltered more than once and Nonna listened in silence until she came to the wedding. 'We were married in the parish church of San Giovanni. I should have asked your permission. I'm sorry, but there was no time.'

'Carlo will be vexed your union had the benefit of clergy. He hoped it was a secular arrangement that might be annulled.'

'I'm sorry if I've disappointed the family.' Carina coloured slightly. 'I love Ben and would do the same again tomorrow.'

'A gentleman would have sought my permission. Did your husband fear it wouldn't be forthcoming?'

'You may not consider Ben a gentleman – but he's good enough for me.'

'Even so, I cannot condone your duplicity.'

They were stern words and the two women fell silent. Nonna looked small and old. The skin of her face was creased and her neck bent with the strain of holding up her head. Her grandmother was frailer than when they had last been together, Carina thought. And she had changed too, far more than she realised. How otherwise could she have lied so blatantly to Nonna and Alice? She had hoped Nonna would be pleased and smarted under the reprimand. Six months ago she would have defended herself, but Carina held her tongue. Nonna was an old woman. How could she understand the extent of her love for Ben?

Bees were humming in the lavender and Carina looked over the garden walls to the sunburnt fields beyond the gate. There were clouds massing on the horizon. She wondered if it would rain and whether she should leave before lunch – but she couldn't go without seeing Gabriella.

'I'm not made of stone, Carina,' her grandmother said at length. 'I understand that for you love is everything. It was the same with your mother.'

'Then why are you angry?'

'Because you should have told me the truth. Were you afraid I might be shocked? When I was young it was considered the greatest misfortune not to experience a grand passion. I know what it is to be ruled by one's heart.'

Nonna's mottled hands folded over the top of her cane and her gaze turned inward. Her grandmother had lived through the age of the Romantics, Carina thought. She had been alive at a time when Byron was in Italy. How presumptuous to assume she knew nothing of love! She dismissed her hurt, smiling at Nonna, who beckoned her closer.

Carina shifted her chair, lowering her head, and her grandmother traced a cross on her forehead.

'I give your marriage my blessing, dear child. Ben Mavrone has made you happy and that is all that is important. If your mother were alive she would bless you both. It's time we had some good news in this house.'

A breeze rustled the vine leaves as Paulo and Gabriella came through the door. Gabriella's face was white as a china doll with dark smudges beneath her eyes. She was so thin her shoulder blades stuck out through the thin muslin of her dress and Carina was shocked. During lunch, she took care not to speak of Sicily. Afraid of saying anything that might break Gabriella's brittle composure, she described San Giovanni and Garibaldi's progress to Naples. Paulo pretended not to listen, but she was aware of Gabriella's covert attention and, when they returned to the terrace, Nonna made an excuse to leave them alone.

Gabriella walked to the balustrade, resting her elbows on the top. Her back was turned and Carina spoke gently, 'I know how much you loved Enrico and he loved you, dearest. I'm so very sorry.'

Only the stiffening of muscles in her neck gave any indication that Gabriella had heard. She doesn't want my sympathy, Carina thought. If Ben died, I would be the same. Sympathy doesn't make you strong – it only makes you cry. She searched her mind for inspiration and noticed Gabriella wore a band of red, white and green ribbons around her wrist.

'I wish you could see the tricolour flags and banners on display in Naples. Every balcony of every house proclaims the New Italy! All that you and Enrico believed in and fought for has been realised.'

'Enrico was proud of you.' Gabriella gave a slight lift of her shoulders and turned to face her. 'He said you were valiant. That was the word he used.'

'Foolhardy, more like! Did he mention that he saved my life?'

'He told me everything. I'm so grateful you made it possible for us to write. His letters are a great comfort.' Gabriella paused and a tear slid down either side of her nose. She took out her handkerchief and wiped them away. Then, with a fortitude that defied her years, she went on.

'It's God's Will that Enrico was taken from us. I cannot count his loss against the greatness of what has been achieved.'

Faith glowed in her dark eyes and Carina felt a lump rise in her throat. Her cousin was awash with sorrow, but behind her suffering lay a hinterland of courage. Gabriella is the valiant one, she thought. She's the youngest and bravest of us all.

'The triumph of Liberty gives me strength to endure,' Gabriella went on after a long pause. 'If only Paulo could understand that Enrico didn't die in vain. Will you talk to him, Carina?'

She could try but it would do no good, Carina thought. Paulo did not share Gabriella's idealism. He might never accept Enrico's sacrifice but he was a survivor. With his charm and agile mind, he would carve out a career for himself, under whichever regime prevailed. Her cousins had steel in their bones, the same gritty resolve she felt herself, and she was proud of them.

'Will you promise to visit us in Naples when we return from Sicily?' Carina lifted her hand to her cousin's cold cheek. 'And bring Paulo with you! He's far too curious to resist.'

'Holy Mary! I forgot to congratulate you on your marriage! Do you know that Enrico and Colonel Mavrone became friends? He told me all about him in his letters.'

'What did he say?'

'Enrico considered Colonel Mavrone the finest leader of men in the Sicilian army. He was also of the opinion you were in love with each other – and both too proud to admit it!'

It wasn't often she was lost for words, but Carina was never to remember how she answered or whether she responded at all. Paulo joined them and they sat outside talking until the first drops of rain began to fall. She said goodbye to Nonna and Paulo held an umbrella over her head as he escorted her to the carriage. At the last minute Gabriella came running out of the house and thrust a cloak through the window.

'Take this or you'll be soaked before you reach Naples …'

'And next time don't forget to bring your husband!' Paulo shouted.

The force of the storm unleashed a downpour on their heads and they ran back to the shelter of the portico. As the diligence moved off, Carina leant out to wave. Her cousins were standing on the top step and an image of them burnt into her mind: Paulo, with his arm bent at the elbow like an artist's maquette and Gabriella, standing on tiptoes waving her white handker-chief, until they were hidden by a curtain of rain.

CHAPTER FORTY-ONE

By the time they reached Naples, the rain had stopped and a wind was getting up. She would call in at the hotel and change before dinner, Carina decided, and engaged the driver to wait and take her on. The lobby was empty and the porter absent from his desk so she fetched her key herself. Then, with a quick look around, she lifted her damp skirts and went up the stairs. No one had bothered to light the lamp on the landing and when she reached her bedroom door, she stopped outside and felt through her skirts for her gun.

The pistol was in place, strapped to her thigh, and Carina turned the key to let herself in. She hung Gabriella's cloak over a chair and took off her wet shoes. As she was tidying her hair, the window banged shut, making her jump. She was as nervous as a kitten – but was only because Ben wasn't here and she must hurry or be late for Harry.

Carina searched for a dry pair of shoes and was about to put them on when she heard the creak of floorboards behind her. As she swung about the blood froze in her veins. The door was wide open and a heavily built man stood on the threshold. She stared at him, her eyes wide with shock. Her first terrified impulse was to try and make a run for it. She might just bolt past him and get downstairs but he was blocking the doorway.

'I believe you have come to the wrong room, sir.' She tried to keep her voice steady. 'If you ask the concierge, I am sure he will redirect you.'

The stranger stood where he was, menacing and silent. Without taking her eyes off him, Carina slipped one hand into her pocket. She reached through the opening in her skirt and touched the stock of her pistol. Before she could remove it from the holster, the man stepped into the room. In two strides he was at her side and towering over her. Carina screamed before a blow sent her flying backwards. She fell against the table and tried to save herself, but a second blow sent her to the floor. Her body smashed onto the marble and she lay stunned.

She was dimly aware of the stranger beside her, lifting her into a sitting position. His hand was round her neck and a pad of material was clamped over her nose and mouth. Carina recognised the smell of chloroform and clawed frantically at his fingers. She tried not to breathe, but her lungs were bursting and she choked against the gag as she inhaled. With each breath her movements became weaker. Her vision blurred and she saw solid furniture melting in front of her eyes. She was falling, plummeting off a cliff into a swirling vortex, and seconds later collapsed on the floor unconscious.

Carina had the sensation of being cast adrift on a sea that was rolling and pitching beneath her. Her head ached and drowsiness pulled her under. Awareness slipped away until she was forced awake because she was going to be sick. Bending her head to one side, she retched. Then she dropped her chin on her chest until the nausea and giddiness passed.

Taking long, slow breaths, Carina opened her eyes. She was tied to a chair with her arms bound. Light from a flare flicked ghostly shadows over the walls and she was in a low, vaulted cellar with a portcullis gate. Over her own rasping breath, she heard the scratching of rats. Vermin infested this dark, dank place and she cast about desperately, trying to think what had happened. There had been a stranger in her room. He had drugged her and brought her here. She thought of the man who followed her and Ben, but there was no obvious connection. For the love of God, where was she?

There had been harrowing accounts in the newspapers of cells dug into the hills, where opponents of the old regime were condemned to a living death. They had been evacuated by the Redshirts but there might still be a guard. Carina called out. Her cries echoed around the chamber and came back to her and she let out a whimper of terror. No one would even know she was missing! Harry would wait in vain and assume she had forgotten or changed her mind. He wouldn't think to raise the alarm. But if she had been brought here to die, why was a torch still burning?

Whoever he might be, her abductor meant to return. Carina felt the weight of the holster strapped to her thigh. It was hidden beneath her skirts. Thank God he hadn't found the pistol! She began to rock backwards and forwards, trying to loosen the rope that bound her arms. She twisted her wrists, working at the knot. Then, from a long way off, she heard the sound of voices.

'Help me! I'm down here!'

There were hurried footsteps and a shadowy hulk stood outside the gate, stooping to turn the key. As the gate swung open, her kidnapper emerged from the darkness.

'Now you're awake there's someone who wants to talk to you.'

'My dear Carina, this is a long-awaited pleasure.'

The big man stood aside and Carina turned her face towards the voice. With an attention to detail that distanced shock, she noticed that Prince Scalia was dressed for dinner. He had removed his gloves and held one hand over the other, stroking the signet ring on his little finger.

'Fetch me a chair and leave us alone. Come back in half an hour. Make sure we're not disturbed in the meantime.'

The man found a stool and Scalia locked the gate behind him. He dropped the key into his pocket. His face was close to hers and Carina felt her skin crawl. She should have guessed Scalia was behind this – but what did he want? Enrico was dead and he had joined forces with Garibaldi. She was no longer his enemy. Fear and revulsion made her heart pound, but she kept them out of her voice.

'I've friends in Naples who will be looking for me.'

'No one would think of searching here. Did you really think I was taken in by your charade in Palermo, Carina? I knew by then you had fallen in with the rebels.'

'So why did you release Enrico Fola?'

'Fola was of no consequence to us. I hoped to entice to you into my bed – but I've no taste for second-hand goods, particularly cast-offs from Captain Mavrone.'

Scalia sat with his legs wide apart and his hands clasped. Ben should have killed him when he had the chance, Carina thought and lowered her gaze to hide what was in her eyes.

'You can't keep me a prisoner here.'

'I've no intention of keeping you a prisoner. Our business won't take long ...'

Scalia paused and Carina was swept by disgust. She loathed this man, with his small white hands and cruel face. Raising her eyes to meet his gaze, her lip curved contemptuously.

'Do I revolt you, Carina? The scars you find so unattractive are your husband's doing.'

'To avenge the murder of his brother!'

'You don't believe in that old fiction, do you?' Scalia gave a hollow laugh. 'Mavrone never forgave me for stealing Bianca from him.'

'That's not true—'

Carina broke off as the prince stood up and kicked the stool aside. He reached into the pocket of his waistcoat and took out a small heart-shaped locket, which he dangled in front of her face.

'Bianca sailed for Sicily with Mavrone this morning. They've spent time together in Naples. I have a record of all their assignations. She left this behind so that I would know she was with him.'

Carina recognised the locket. She remembered Bianca fidgeting with it the first time they met, clasping it as a talisman in the Villa Pallestro. She was never without it. Scalia must have ripped it off her neck – but it wasn't evidence of Ben's infidelity. The prince was playing a grotesque game. Bianca hadn't gone to Sicily. Where was she, she wondered suddenly?

'Let me show you the portrait my wife wears so close to her heart.'

Scalia leant down and snapped open the clasp. Carina glanced at the tiny painting inside. The portrait looked like Ben, but it wasn't him.

'The portrait is of Alexander, the man you executed,' Carina spat the words at him.

'It's of Ben and not his brother. Come now, my dear. You know as well as I do that your husband's still in love with my wife.'

Unwanted memories swam to the surface: Ben's unexplained absences these last few weeks and the look on his face when she had first spoken of Bianca. But Ben had arranged for her to be with him in Sicily. He hadn't betrayed her and Scalia was lying. She watched, transfixed, as he threw the locket aside and took a small dagger from his belt. Its blade was no longer than that of a man's finger and Carina went cold with horror. Scalia wasn't going to kill or rape her. Cruelty was his life's blood and he had something else in mind, something that made the gorge rise in her throat.

'You're the weapon I shall use against Mavrone. He'll never look at you again without being reminded of me. This is the last act of the vendetta.'

Carina tried to tip the chair backwards, but Scalia put one foot on the seat to hold it upright. He bent over her, his smile extended by the scars. His eyes shone feverishly, saliva brimming at the corner of his mouth. Carina couldn't bear to look. She squeezed her eyes shut and felt the knife slice open the front of her dress, Scalia's fingers moving from her throat to the top of her basque. The cold edge of the blade touched her skin and her mind reeled in terror. God save me! Then agonising pain spiralled upwards and she fainted.

A hand was slapping her face, becoming harder until Carina was forced awake. She was lying on the floor with Scalia standing astride her. A burning sensation in her chest made her groan as she pushed back on her elbows.

'Goodbye, Signora Mavrone. I don't expect we'll meet again.'

Scalia put on his gloves as he walked towards the gate. Warm air bathed her skin and Carina felt blood trickling from her chest down to her stomach. Her fingers stretched out and as her hands touched damp straw, she stared at them. The rope had come undone! Scalia had untied her or else it had fallen off, and she could defend herself.

'I will kill you for this!'

The prince turned to face her, but Carina was no longer on the ground. She was kneeling up with the pistol in her hand. Somehow, she had removed it from the holster and the barrel was aimed at his heart. Scalia was telling her to give it to him. He was walking towards her and holding out his hand. Her finger crooked on the trigger, but the hammer caught the edge of her cuff. She tore at the material with her teeth to free the action and he halted, the pupils of his eyes dilating.

'Don't be a fool. Give me the gun and I'll let you go.'

Carina steadied her wrist and pulled the trigger three times in quick succession. A deafening explosion accompanied each shot. Through a cloud of burning gun-smoke, she saw Scalia stagger. He swayed on his feet but did not fall. She thought she had missed him and raised the gun to fire again. Now there were four scorched holes in his waistcoat turning from black to red, spreading into a pool of blood across his chest. Scalia fell on his knees. One hand clawed the air, and then he toppled forwards and lay still.

The prince lay on his stomach with his neck twisted towards her. His eyes were filmy and blood lathered his lips. A rigour made his body hunch up and a rattling sound came from his throat. Carina dropped the gun. She thought she would be sick or faint again, but did neither. Her mind seized on one thought – she must escape before the other man came back.

Scalia's dead eyes were staring at her and the key was in his pocket. It was safer to stay low and she crawled across the floor on hands and knees. Gritting her teeth, she groped in one pocket and then the other. The prince's arm moved in a final spasm and she cried out in fright – but she had the key and she staggered to the gate. The flare had burnt low and she had to feel for the keyhole with her fingers. The key was in, but wouldn't move. Wiping her hands on her skirt, Carina tried again. The lock gave way and she leant against the heavy gate and shoved it open.

A moment later, she was running down a tunnel in pitch darkness. She tripped over the hem of her dress and fell. Her face hit the ground and Carina tasted mud in her mouth. Lifting her head, she saw a slither of light in the distance and stumbled on. Scalia's accomplice must have heard the shots! He would be waiting to ambush her. She must be careful. With her back grazing the wall, she inched forward, listening for footsteps, but the only sound she heard was the howling wind outside.

When she came to the light, Carina crawled through a narrow opening, grimacing as she squeezed through the earthen tunnel. Fresh air touched her face – the fresh air of the living world not the fetid stench of the subterranean prison – and she was standing on a rocky escarpment. She wiped the back of her hand across her eyes and made out an outline of buildings not far below. Dark clouds buffeted across the moon and, between them, Carina caught a glimpse of the metallic sea. A surge of relief energised her and she began to run, not stopping until she came to a stone paved street where the wind was funneled into gusts.

It was the sirocco, the hot African wind detested by Sicilians. Its wailing lacerated her brain and she crouched down, her hands clasped over her ears. The wind sounded like Prince Scalia screaming. Carina imagined him hurtling towards her with blood pouring out of his stomach. Deranged by the vision, she stared wild-eyed up the street. A wine barrel had broken loose from its moorings and burst open, bumping down and spilling its contents as it gathered speed and went past her.

She began to walk, keeping her balance by running a hand running along the wall. Three men were coming up the hill towards her and stopped beneath a street lamp. Her mind was rank with death and Carina saw their shirts were red as the blood on Scalia's body. They were devils sent from hell in vengeance! With a muffled scream, she darted past them and careered blindly on, swerving round corners and down flights of steps until she came to the bottom of the hill. There she stopped and bent over to drag air into her lungs.

The wind was no longer warm and she shivered as it gathered up pieces of confetti, the remnants of a victory parade, and sent them swirling in a storm of snowflakes. Carina looked nervously over her shoulder. Why was she so afraid? Who was it that followed, keeping his distance hiding in the shadows? A man passed on the other side of the street, holding on to his hat as he bent into the wind. Robert Danby cast a furtive glance in her direction and hurried on. Snow would muffle the sound of carriage wheels and she must get home! How far away was she from Mount Street?

Wincing with pain, Carina forced herself on until she came to a cobbled square. On the far side was a hotel with lamps burning in the windows. She limped over to the entrance and read the sign above the door. The Grand Hotel Garibaldi. Of course! What in the world was she thinking? She was in Naples and not London – and this was where she was meant to be! How could she have forgotten Harry was expecting her for dinner? She hadn't had time to dress properly. Carina couldn't remember what had kept her, but Harry would understand.

She felt she had achieved a miraculous feat and stepped into the foyer with her head high. As she knew he would be, Harry was waiting. She saw him get up, his jaw dropping as he clutched the back of the chair. He was staring at her as if she were a madwoman. The wind slammed the door shut and a concierge came out from behind his desk, shouting at her and waving his arms about like a pantomime character. He looked so funny that she burst out laughing; a high-pitched, hysterical laugh that ended as Harry's arms went round her.

CHAPTER FORTY-TWO

OCTOBER 1860, NORTHUMBERLAND

She was asleep and dreaming she was at Melton. Paddy was in the loose box, grooming Papa's bay hunter. He looked up and smiled. Carina saw him clearly before he disappeared. Now she was in Palermo with Nonna – or was it her mother? They looked so alike. She tried to reach out to them but they vanished. Faces assembled in strange disguises, then fractured into tiny pieces. Nothing was real ...

Voices at the edges of her memory; Harry asking questions, harsh and insistent. Carina wanted him to go away. He stopped her listening, listening for the only voice she wanted to hear.

She tried to turn her head and a woman said softly, 'Stay quiet, dearest. There's nothing to fear. I am with you.'

Carina opened her eyes. She was lying in bed and Alice was beside her. She was holding her hand, gently stroking her fingers. Alice wouldn't let her go.

'You had an accident in Naples. Harry Carstairs brought you home. You arrived yesterday.'

She wanted Ben. Where was he? Carina felt tears rolling down her cheeks.

'Please don't cry, darling.' Alice wiped her face with a handkerchief. 'You're safe now. Trust me ... all will be well.'

'Camomile tea will calm her anxiety.' A man's voice with a northern brogue. 'She needs rest, peace and quiet. Our Northumbrian air will do her good ...'

But she wasn't in Northumbria. She was in Italy. She wanted to tell them but she had forgotten how to speak. Darkness closed in again.

When she awoke, Carina was sitting in a chair wrapped in blankets. She didn't recognise this room with blue curtains. She was due to catch the ferry to Palermo. Where had she left her cloak? She tried to stand up.

'Not yet, dearest.' Alice touched her arm. 'You're not strong enough. Dr Crawley says you can come downstairs in a few days.'

Carina shook her head. Her lips struggled to form a question. It came out in a soundless whisper. 'Where am I?'

'Don't upset yourself, dear one. I'll explain everything once you are well.'

Carina closed her eyes. Pigeons cooing outside the window. The yapping of a small dog. Sounds drifting through her head in snatches. She wanted to sleep, but something was changing. She was losing control, her mind rushing upward towards an invisible surface. She had been safe deep down on the seabed but Alice was drawing her into the light. Suddenly she knew where she was. She was staying with Alice and Anthony in Northumberland. She was meant to be in Sicily with Ben. He was waiting for her. Her heart cried out for him. Why was she here?

*   *   *

'I must speak openly with you, Mr Carstairs.' Alice was sitting with her back to the window. 'I'm afraid Carina's return to England has done her more harm than good.'

'Are you suggesting I should have abandoned her in Naples?'

'You were placed in a difficult situation.'

'What else was I supposed to do?' Harry sounded peevish. 'I hate to think what might have befallen Carina if I hadn't been there.'

Alice held her sampler up to the light. A stitch seemed to be at fault and she took out her scissors to snip the thread. 'Carina wrote to me of her marriage. She sounded happy, therefore her present state of health has come as a great shock. Pray, tell me what you know of her husband.'

'I only met Colonel Mavrone once. Didn't take to the fellow. He's certainly not a gentleman – but I never thought he'd assault Carina.'

'Did she say he had done so?'

'When she arrived at the hotel, she was wild with terror and covered in blood. They must have had an argument. Ben Mavrone's a jealous man with a savage temper. It's obvious he was the culprit!'

'How much did she tell you?'

'Nothing beyond Mavrone's name, over and over again. Anyone would have understood she wanted me to know who had attacked her. When I suggested calling a doctor she went berserk. It took two glasses of brandy to calm her down.'

'And what happened on the voyage home?'

'At first, she seemed calm but distracted, suffering from the shock of the attack, I dare say. I tried to question her, but she became angry and increasingly withdrawn. Sometimes she would talk to herself in Italian, but I couldn't get a sensible word from her. I hoped she would be better once we arrived in England. It grieves me to see that so far it's made little difference.'

'And you consulted a doctor in London before coming north.' Alice spoke in the same quiet voice. 'What was his professional opinion?'

'That her wounds are superficial and will heal, ghastly though they are – but the mental shock will take much longer. He insisted that Carina must never set eyes on her assailant again if she's to have any chance of full recovery.'

'But we don't know what Carina wants, do we? It's possible there's more to this than she's able to tell us at present. Do you think she's in love with Ben Mavrone? Why else did she marry him?'

'Asked myself the same question a hundred times.' Harry stopped and blew his nose loudly. 'I believe Carina was obliged to marry Colonel Mavrone – for the sake of appearances, if you take my meaning?'

'And not because she's in love with him, is that your meaning, sir? You know very well my niece has never felt obliged to conduct herself in accordance with proprietary.'

'Maybe so, ma'am, but I'm sure that Carina was afraid of him.' The stamp of Harry's footsteps began on the hardwood floor. 'The morning after the assault, I went to their hotel. Mavrone had taken to his heels so I bribed the porter to let me into the bedroom. The place was a shambles. A stroke of luck that I found Carina's travel documents.'

'Were you able to confer with her grandmother before leaving Naples?'

'I didn't have time to find out where she lived and Carina was in no state to enlighten me. I left a letter for Colonel Mavrone. Told him I was bringing her here. The man knows where she is. If he's innocent and wants her back he'd have come by now, or sent a letter.'

'So you took it upon yourself to remove Carina from her husband, without her or anyone else's consent?'

'Someone had to save her from the blackguard!' Harry's voice rose, loud and agitated. 'The scoundrel assaulted and deserted Carina. The sooner she starts proceedings for a divorce, the better—'

'A divorce! Whatever are you talking about?'

'I'm prepared to stand up in court and bear evidence against Colonel Mavrone. Happy to do so, ma'am. The man deserves horse whipping!'

'My dear sir, it's not your place to pass judgement on Carina's husband.' Alice put her sewing on the table and stood up. 'I'm confident that we will hear from Colonel Mavrone soon. Are you certain you gave him our address?'

'Do you doubt my word, ma'am?'

'Indeed I do not. You have been a good friend to Carina and I'm grateful. However, we have encroached upon your time too long.' Alice's voice was unnervingly calm. 'Your parents must be anxious for your return. I will ask Anthony to make arrangements for your journey south as soon as is convenient.'

It was the note of anger in Alice's voice that made Carina stop as she went past the morning room door. She was on her way to the garden, and, hearing voices, paused, her bonnet under her arm as she listened. She could see Alice, but not Harry who was standing by the hearth. To begin with, she didn't understand what they were saying. When Ben's name cropped up she was confused by Harry's answers. Why did he say Ben had attacked her? Harry knew she loved Ben. She wasn't afraid of him! What was he talking about? Harry went on and on, taking no notice of Alice and when he spoke of divorce, Carina pressed her hand to her mouth. She heard his offer to testify against Ben, followed by her aunt's firm dismissal, and ran up upstairs to her room.

Carina locked the door and slung her cape and bonnet onto a chair. She perched on the edge of the four-poster bed with her arms around her body and her head bowed. She had suffered concussion as a child. From the moment of falling off her pony until she woke up, all memory was wiped from her mind. It was the same again now. She remembered meeting Harry in a hotel lobby but nothing immediately before or after that, until she had found herself in a ship's cabin. Bewildered and disoriented, she had looked out of the porthole and seen the rock of Gibraltar. A cannon boomed a salute from the castle and it was then she realised they were on their way to England. Harry hadn't saved her. He had stolen her from Ben!

Flashes of memory, fleeting and insubstantial, disturbed her recollection of the rest of the journey. When Ben came to her in dreams, it was like dreaming of the dead and she knew she was being punished. She had done something terrible. Her mind was unfreezing and it was all coming back. She had shot Prince Scalia! Why had she killed him? He had hurt her, she knew – the scars she bore told her that afresh every day. But there was something else, something her mind only let her remember now: Scalia had said Ben was in love with Bianca. She didn't believe him, but she had shot him all the same.

She had been too ill until now to understand. Scalia had unhinged her mind and she had murdered him. Dear God! Carina's jaw began to tremble so she had to clench her teeth to stop it. Don't think about it, said a voice in her head. This has to be gone through with, but not yet. Wait until you're stronger.

Alice is sending Harry away. You'll be better once he's gone. Alice will help you. Don't think about it now ...

In the days after Harry's departure, Carina did her best to put herself back together. Slowly, carefully, she began to talk again. Rose came from London with a portmanteau of clothes and she let her fuss over her. When they spoke of Sicily, it was only of small things. Rose attended to her hair, but Carina insisted on dressing herself. She had become used to it, she said, and gradually her health improved.

Alice encouraged her to take the pony and trap for short excursions. Driving along the coast near Bamburgh helped clear the fog in her mind. What happened after she left Naples, she wondered? Greta and Stefan would have gone to the hotel and found her missing. Ben would have learnt of her disappearance when they arrived in Palermo. He must know that she hadn't left Italy of her own accord! Once he returned to Naples and read Harry's letter, he would set out to find her.

On waking each morning Carina forced hope into her heart. Today there would be a letter from Ben. Post was delivered regularly, but there came no news of his imminent arrival. There was good reason for the delay, she told herself. The weather had been atrocious and the postal system on the continent was famously unreliable. Alice had told her that a final battle between the two sides was expected any day. How could Ben leave Italy when the future of the revolution hung in the balance? She could not – would not – believe that Harry had spoken the truth.

How could I not love thee, my heart was aflame?
No one before thee, beloved thy name—

Carina began a poem, then tore the paper into tiny pieces and threw them on the fire. Why was there no word from Ben? If he could not travel then at least he could write. She tried to summon up her old resilience. She would go and find him, she decided, then changed her mind. The man who had abducted her knew that she had killed Scalia. When she landed in Italy, she would be arrested and charged for murder.

There was no going back and, try as she might, the suspicion implanted by Scalia could not be rooted out. Ben had spoken of annulment. Now Bianca was free, was it what he wanted? Did Harry have proof they were together? Was that the reason he was so willing to testify against Ben? 'All men are bastards. Don't expect them to be faithful.' Anne Lamartine's words circled her mind like vultures. She had only loved one man and trusted him completely. Now, the very action that prevented her returning to Italy had set Bianca free to fall into his arms …

Upset by the smallest mishap, Carina often found herself on the verge of tears. She was nervous of strangers and shut herself away when visitors came to the house. Alice tried to comfort her, but the only person she could talk to was Ben and he wasn't here. Perhaps she should write to him. Where was he now, she wondered? What if he was with Bianca? She could not bear her suspicions to be confirmed in the cold formality of a letter. It would send her mad.

When Carina caught sight of herself in the mirror, she saw a white-faced stranger with sunken eyes. I look like a terrified child, she thought. I was always so strong, I believed myself indestructible. How could I fall so in love with Ben that all my happiness, even my sanity, depends upon him?

In the stony reality of his absence, Carina stopped asking herself what the next day might bring. She, who always fought her way out of trouble, was trapped in a situation from which there was no escape. She had never known this type of misery and helplessness. Cut off from those around her, she felt locked behind glass in a world where she no longer belonged. She went on living, getting through each day without feeling she was alive. Time passed her by and gradually hope ebbed away.

There was a night when Carina dreamt Ben was in bed beside her. She heard him breathing and slid her hand over the cold sheet. Her eyes flew open and she sat bolt upright, weeping until she was exhausted. I can't go on like this, she thought in anguish. If I can learn to live without hope, then I will live without despair. I must accept the truth. Ben doesn't love me. I must crush him out of my heart and lock down my pain. No one will ever hurt me like this again.

'This is splendid news!' Anthony Farne lowered the newspaper and looked across the morning room to Carina and Alice.

'It's reported Garibaldi fought one of the greatest battles of his career at Volturno. The Bourbons were routed and Victor Emmanuel is proclaimed King of Italy.'

'I'm delighted to hear it,' Alice exclaimed. 'What will the great man do now?'

'Garibaldi was offered an estate, a dukedom and enough money for a lifetime, but refused them all. He's retired to his home on Caprera, taking only two horses named Calatafimi and Milazzo. You were fortunate to have born company with such a man, Carina.'

Carina continued leafing through the sketchbook of Alice's Sicilian watercolours. The names touched a raw nerve. She didn't want to think about Garibaldi and looked out of the window to where leaves of beech and maple were dying in a burst of autumn colour.

'I wonder if I may take the trap to the picnic house by the beach this afternoon?'

It was a beautiful October day and the sun was warm as Carina drove through the park to the beach. When she came to the small stone bothy, she hitched the pony to the post and left her bonnet and cape in the trap. She unlocked the door of the hut and took out a chair, sitting in the sun for a while before she decided to walk down to the sea. The tide was out and her boots sank into wet sand as she stood at the water's edge. Seagulls swooped overhead and she watched as they dived low on the incoming tide.

A wave swept over her feet and Carina turned to make her way back. A flock of birds rose up and flew away all at once. She could see the pony standing on the dunes with its neck arched and its ears pricked forward. The pony whinnied and she looked over her shoulder. A horseman was riding by the sea and she recognised Anthony's big chestnut hunter. She had been away too long – Alice was worried and sent him to find her.

Carina held a hand over her eyes and stopped to wait for him. The rider seemed taller than Anthony as he approached. She admired the way he rode with long stirrups, giving the horse its head as they cantered across the sand. Dear God, was it a trick of light that made him seem suddenly familiar? For a moment her heart stood still. Surely, she was mistaken?

Curbing an irrational urge to run, Carina walked so fast by the time she reached the dunes, she was out of breath. She stopped at the top of the bank and put her hands to her sides. How ridiculous she must have looked scuttling across the beach like that. How stupid to lose her head! She only had to put the chair back and lock up before she drove home. Then, it seemed the next moment, she heard the clink of irons as the horse was pulled up, followed by a soft thud of boots on the sand.

She hadn't let herself believe it was Ben. Yet he was here and standing right behind her! She could feel him in her bones and a spasm of pain made her put her hand to her chest. She splayed out her fingers and pressed down until the ache subsided. Keeping her eyes on the chair in the porch, Carina waited until she was calm. She knew why Ben had come. He had travelled a great distance and she must hear what he had to say. Unclenching her fists, she dropped her arms to her sides and turned to face him.

CHAPTER FORTY-THREE

Ben was standing beside Anthony's horse with his arm resting on the animal's neck and his hand tangled in its mane. How long had it been, Carina wondered, one month or two? His hair was windswept and his face lined and weary. She looked at him and felt no leap of happiness. There was an iron chain around her heart and she passed her tongue over her lips.

'How did you know I was here?' she asked.

'Your aunt gave me directions and Sir Anthony lent me his horse.'

'I meant in Northumberland. Did you get Harry's letter?'

Ben led the horse up the bank and looped the reins next to those of the pony. He reached inside his jacket for a crumpled piece of paper and handed it to her.

'Read this, if you will.'

Carina spread the note open and scanned the brief contents.

*Miss Temple instructs me to inform you she has placed herself
under my protection. Should you attempt to write or to meet with
her, she will seek your indictment on the charge of grievous harm
against her person.*

Harry Carstairs

Surely, it must be a forgery? Carina read it again. Harry's signa-
ture was unmistakable. She felt her palms prickling and her
hands begin to shake. The letter fluttered to the ground and
Ben stooped to pick it up.

'When Greta and Stefan arrived in Palermo without you, I
caught the next ferry to Naples. Mr Carstairs's letter was waiting. Did you instruct him to write to me?'

So Ben had arrived in Naples the same day they sailed for
England. They had missed each other by only a few hours.
Harry had deliberately misled him – But why? Carina saw disil-
lusionment in Ben's eyes and answered stiffly.

'I didn't know Harry had written until a few weeks ago. He
told my aunt he had informed you that he was bringing me
here. He assured us you were aware of my whereabouts.'

'Did he now? So, Harry Carstairs isn't quite as honourable he
would have us believe? I suppose he's still in love with you and
hoped to get me out of the way. But let's not pin all the blame
on him. Did it not occur to you how I might feel when you
disappeared without any kind of explanation?'

She hadn't let herself, Carina thought. In her madness and
misery, she had been tormented by the thought of Ben and
Bianca together. Why make it worse by speculating on how
Ben felt when he found her gone? Relief, she imagined now.
There was too much to disentangle and she did not answer.

'I searched all of Naples and then paid a call on your grandmother. She received me kindly and I was sorry to alarm her.

When Lady Farne's letter arrived, she sent your cousin to tell me. It was only then any of us knew you were alive. Honestly, Carina! How could you be so careless of those you left behind?'

'I wasn't myself. I cannot remember ...'

'Will you try, please? I know you've been ill, your aunt has told me that much. So, unless you prefer to be outside, I suggest we avail ourselves of the hut.'

Ben guided her towards the door and picked up the chair as they went past. He placed it inside and motioned for her to sit down. Carina remained on her feet. Whatever he had to say, she preferred to hear it standing up. Her glance passed over him, taking in his travel-worn clothes. Ben felt like someone she had known long ago. How could it be like this?

'What happened to you after I left Naples? Please tell me, Carina.'

Ben held his hand out to her and Carina folded her arms across her chest. Before the coldness in her face, his expression hardened. He took a cheroot from his case and struck a match to light it, blowing a ring of smoke into the air.

'You're aware Riccardo Scalia is dead,' he said.

It was a statement, not a question and Carina was silent. She stood, looking out of the door and concentrated on tiny particles of dust dancing in the light.

'His body was discovered after you left Italy.' Ben continued. 'The authorities treated it as a political assassination. They were unable to identify the killer and Garibaldi has since declared the case closed.'

He was giving her the facts, but Ben couldn't feel the emptiness inside. Did he suspect that she was involved? It seemed like a lifetime ago. What did it matter now?

'I've had no news from Italy,' Carina chose her words carefully. 'I don't suppose anyone was very sorry.'

'I was questioned by the police on my return from Sicily. They showed me the gun used to kill Scalia. It was very similar to the one I gave you. Tell me, do you still have the Colt pistol?'

'Harry took charge of my affairs. He may have left it in Naples—'

'But you're not sure?'

'I suffered from memory loss.'

'Do you remember why you ran away? Was it to get away from me?'

'And if it was?'

'I'm sorry you didn't have the decency to tell me yourself. I am your husband – or did you forget that as well?'

Ben was twisting what she said, making it sound as if it was all her fault, and resentment fired Carina's spirit.

'I haven't forgotten. Surely that's why you're here? You've come to obtain an annulment of our marriage.'

'An annulment? On what grounds, may I ask?'

'Adultery with Bianca Scalia. I've been kept well informed.'

'Is that what you think – that Bianca and I left Naples together?'

Carina ignored the bitterness in his voice. They had come to the point sooner than expected. At last, the truth was out in the open. She must get this over before she lost her nerve.

'Why not? You've been in love with each other for years.'

'Or so Riccardo Scalia told you!'

'Yes, if you must know—'

'And you *believed* him?'

'He showed me Bianca's locket, the one she always wears. He said she left it to prove that she was with you. He said you were lovers …'

The words died on her lips as Ben dropped his cigar butt on the floor and crushed it beneath the heel of his boot. He was looking at her as if she had said something so stupid it was beyond credibility. Ben was good at this kind of thing, Carina reminded herself. He would try to manipulate her and she must not let him.

'Do you think I'd have married you if I loved another woman?'

'I don't know what to think? How can I when you never confide in me? You warned me never to speak of Bianca. Why was that – unless you had a secret to hide?'

Carina wasn't aware she raised her voice and threw out her arms. Ben's hands came down on her shoulders and he leant his face so close to hers she felt his breath on her cheek.

'I'm not in love with Bianca and she did not travel to Sicily with me. Scalia had her committed to a hospital for the insane six months ago.'

There was a dark look in his eyes, not of anger but the pain of returning memory. Ben was as tense as a cat ready to pounce and Carina braced herself for whatever was coming next. When he spoke, his voice was so low she strained to hear his words.

'Riccardo Scalia lied to you. Bianca is not my lover. She is my sister.'

How she came to be standing outside, Carina did not remember. Ben must have moved the chair to let her pass for she was aware the tide had come in and water covered the beach. In her mind she was in the library at Monteleone, reading Lord Byron's poem: 'They knew not I knew thee who knew thee too well ...' It was rumoured Byron wrote the verse for his half-sister by whom he fathered a child. Nothing was impossible. Ben might have been in love with Bianca. He had gone to see her in Naples. There were meant to be no secrets between them – so why hadn't he told her?

Carina heard Ben speaking, his voice reaching her from a distance.

'My brother and I were the result of a liaison Donna Isabella had before she married Bianca's father. We were brought to Monteleone after her husband died and didn't discover the truth until years later. Before he proposed to Bianca, Scalia made extensive enquiries and discovered our true parentage. Donna Isabella was terrified the scandal would destroy her daughter's prospects. She told us everything on the day we were packed off to Ireland.'

'And your father?' Carina turned her head slightly.

'Patrick Mavrone was stationed in Sicily after the war. Quite a shock when his illegitimate sons turned up years later – but he did his duty by us. He paid for our education and gave me refuge when I was in exile.'

'I came across a bookmark in your brother's book, a lock of Bianca's hair.'

'I placed it there when Alex died.'

Everything fitted into place and Carina believed him. She should have felt sorry for Bianca, but Ben could have been talking about someone she had never met. Ben was the man she had loved more than life itself; yet she felt as far removed from him as when she first saw him riding on the beach. She had thought her love was invincible and she was wrong. Her heart had turned to stone.

Carina stood motionless, her attitude as unyielding as her state of mind and Ben's arm went round her shoulders.

'I've come to take you home, sweetheart.'

'Please will you leave now?' Throwing him off, Carina backed away. 'If you hurry, you can catch the last train. Take Anthony's horse! I'll arrange for its collection later.'

'What the devil—?'

'I'm not coming home with you!'

'Why not?'

'Because I prefer to stay here. I'm better off in England.'

'Not in your aunt's opinion. She's invited me to stay until you're well enough to make the journey.'

'Name of Mercy, do I have to spell it out? I don't want to return to Italy. I'm never coming back!'

'What are you afraid of, Carina? Did Scalia make a coward of you?'

'Yes, I'm a coward.'

'You've never been a coward in your life.' Ben spoke without raising his voice.' Do you know what I think? I think you're one of those women who love the thrill of the chase and lose interest once they've hunted their prey to ground. Did I fail to live up to your expectations, Carina? Were you bored by the constraints of married life? Give me an honest answer, but don't dare say you're afraid of loving me.'

Carina looked at the sandy turf and rushes growing at the edge of the dunes. Ben's taunts were deliberate, forcing her to where she didn't want to go. Her pulse was beating at such a rate, she felt dizzy. She tried to hold on, but her mind was moving too fast. Hellish memory crashed in, shattering the paralysis that guarded her spirit and she was back to the darkness and terror of that night. She saw Scalia's contorted face, saliva dribbling from his mouth. She smelt his blood and felt the sweat on his fingers as he touched her. Carina reached for the collar of her dress, her hands working frantically at the buttons until they were undone. Then she pulled the bodice open down to her corsage and stepped forward.

'Here's your answer, Ben! See what hatred and revenge have done to me!'

The wounds had healed, their scars vivid on her pale skin.

Two lines were scored diagonally one across the other, running from the tip of her collarbone to the rise of each breast, in the mark of vendetta. The same blasphemous cross was burnt into the trees of Calabria and carved into rocks on the hillsides of Sicily. Carina saw in Ben's eyes the awakening horror she experienced every day in her room. Her voice dropped to a whisper.

'Scalia said it was the last act of the vendetta. I killed him because of you. I damned my mortal soul on your account.'

Ben was the only person on earth who could share this with her. She did not expect an appeal for forgiveness. It was hardly Ben's style, but she longed for him to say something that might help through the years ahead. If he had put his arms around her, she would have accepted any strength he had to give but he was too shocked to speak. Ben turned away, his profile rigid as he stared out over the charcoal sea. Everything they had been through together was drawing to a close.

The trembling in her hands ceased and Carina refastened her bodice. 'Go home to Sicily and seek whatever comfort you can. Leave me to find my own peace.'

Ben turned his head and gave her a long look that went through her in the absent, brooding gaze she knew so well. She must get back and convince Alice there was no point in prolonging his visit. Carina began to walk to where the pony was hitched to the post. Ben would not call her back or try to stop her. If he had spoken it might have acted as a spur, but he was silent and the short distance to the trap felt like a progress to the gallows. Carina was exhausted but, tired as she was, her mind ran on. Nothing in life will be so hard again. Don't pity the man you are leaving behind. Ben will manage well enough without you. He always has …

Carina unhitched the driving reins and climbed up onto the driving board. Reaching down, she retrieved her cloak and wrapped it around her shoulders. The chestnut stamped restlessly as they moved off and she turned the pony's head away from the sea down the rutted track that led to the house.

It was past nine o'clock when Carina went to bed. Rose had brought her supper on a tray but she could not eat while Ben was in the house. She had begged Alice to find him lodgings in Salford village. Her aunt looked at her despairingly and said she would not dream of being so inhospitable. Colonel Mavrone must stay tonight and leave in the morning. It was the very least they could do for him. She had even gone so far as to put Ben in the room adjoining her own, and was now entertaining him downstairs.

It was a cold, still night and sounds carried. Carina heard dinner being cleared and the servants going to bed. When Alice tapped on her door she snuffed out the candle and pretended to be asleep. The door opened and then shut. Ben would be having a cigar with Anthony and come upstairs later. She had taken the precaution of locking the connecting door and would stay awake until the light beneath it went out.

She had been half-dead before but now every nerve in her body was on fire. Her heart would not be quiet. She hadn't intended to confront Ben this afternoon. She had put all the blame on him when it was not his fault. I've done exactly as Scalia intended, she thought. He marked me in order to hurt Ben and destroy our love. Harry deceived us both – but I was the one who lost faith – not Ben. He came to take me home and I sent him away. Tomorrow he will leave my life forever. What if I still love him? Don't be a fool, an inner voice answered. You told Ben all he needs to know. He will never look at you again without horror and disgust. How can you live together as man and wife?

There were footsteps in the passage and Carina sat up as she heard his bedroom door shut. Her curtains were open and there was enough light to see the key safely in the lock. Ben was undressing and she waited for him to try the door. The light from the oil lamp dimmed. Soon he would extinguish the candle and she lay back on the pillows. Noises that usually went unnoticed were loud, the murmur of wind in the leaves and the distant hoot of a barn owl. Ben must be asleep, so why was there still light beneath the door?

The clock on the landing chimed eleven and Carina got out of bed and tiptoed across the floor. She put her ear to the door. There was no sound from his side. With her heart in her throat, she turned the key. She glanced around the dressing room with its dark oak furniture and saw Ben's motionless form on the bed. Just as she had thought, he had fallen asleep and left the candle burning on the table beside him.

With her hand at the neck of her nightgown, Carina crossed the threshold and stopped. Alexander came so forcefully into her mind that she could not move. She imagined him standing by the bed. He was the same height as Ben, with the same profile and dark hair, only younger as he had been in the minia-ture. If she wasn't careful, her sixth sense would bring him to life and she would hear him speak. Alex was Ben's identical twin, she thought. They had been conceived as one. The empa-thy and understanding between them was unlike any other. When he died, Ben had lost a living part of himself. Every time he looked in the glass he saw, not his own reflection, but the image of his dead twin. How could he ever accept that Alex was dead and he was alone?

It struck Carina with sudden, blinding clarity. The part of Ben hidden from her belonged to his twin. It was Alexander and not Bianca he kept in his heart and no one could take his place.

Now, at last, she understood his distrust and fear of commitment, the pain and madness that drove him to revenge. Ben had suffered terrible and inescapable grief. Selida had tried to tell her, but she had not listened. She had wanted more from Ben than he was able to give.

The image of Alexander faded as she walked over to the bed and looked down. Ben was asleep with one arm bent under his head on the pillow. His handsome face was ravaged by exhaustion and her heart wrenched. She felt more sorry for him than she had felt for anyone before. The vendetta and all that had followed had led to this moment. If he stayed with her, Ben would be reminded of Alex's murder every day for the rest of his life. He deserved to be free of his past. And, if she loved him, she must let him go.

Self-sacrifice went against the very grain of her nature and Carina fought with her conscience. I can't do this! I'm not noble and unselfish like Gabriella. I love Ben with all my heart. How can I give up the one person who is more precious to me than anything in the world? God give me the strength to do what is right, not for myself, but for Ben.

A tear fell on her cheek and she wiped it away. Carina lifted her hair off her face and traced a cross on Ben's forehead. He did not move and she held her breath and bent down to kiss him lightly on the lips. A draught came through the window as she straightened up and snuffed out the candle. She could see the open door to her bedroom and was about to make her way back when Ben's fingers encircled her wrist. Carina let out a gasp as he shifted over and drew back the bedclothes. His face was in shadow and she stood trembling until he reached for her and pulled her next to him on the narrow bed.

Ben put his arms around her and she lay with her head in the crook of his arm. Her whole body was shaking until his warmth and stillness infiltrated her senses. Tension and sorrow left her and peace fell on her spirit. 'I love you. I love you,' she whispered in the darkness, hoping Ben might hear, but he was already asleep.

Carina woke up as Ben left the bed and went to shut the window. She heard him use the bellows to blow the embers alight, and, when he came back, turned on her side to face him. He put his hand on her cheek and drew his finger over her lips and down her chin. How she loved the feel of his hands, the comfort of him close to her. Looking into his eyes, Carina felt he could see into her soul.

'I'm not leaving without you, sweetheart.'

'But how can I return to Italy? I'll be charged with murder.'

'Enough evidence of Scalia's atrocities has come to light for Garibaldi to have him arrested and executed. You saved him the trouble of a public trial. No one apart from ourselves will ever know.'

'But Scalia wasn't going to kill me. I shot him in retaliation.'

'God will reward you for ridding the world of a monster.'

'How can you be so certain?'

'Scalia committed crimes for which he will be damned. His treatment of Bianca was beyond forgiveness.' Ben's voice was heavy with impotent anger. 'He locked her up in a lunatic asylum on grounds of mental instability. When I found her in Naples she was barely alive. Greta and Stefan helped me move her to the convent of Santa Lucia. Now she's in the good care of the nuns, I pray she will be at peace.'

So, Prince Scalia was aware Bianca was half-sister to the twins and yet he executed Alexander all the same. Did Greta and Stefan also know the truth?

'Selida is the only person alive who knows that Bianca is my sister.' Ben read her mind. 'When Alex died, I vowed never to let anyone close to me again. I was insane during the years of my exile and afraid to go back to that time. How could I expect you to understand?'

'You could have tried.'

'And you could have written to me. Why didn't you?'

They had both made the same mistake, Carina thought, both too proud to admit weakness and seek reassurance from the other. Only honesty could save them now.

'I was never certain that you loved me.'

'Why else would I marry you?'

'You're a possessive man. You didn't want anyone else to have me.'

'Oh, my darling. The moment I laid eyes on you I knew you were put on this earth to cause me trouble. I had never met a woman like you. I was captivated by your beauty and courage. When Ruffo dropped you into my lap I knew I had met my match. I should have been kinder but you fought so hard, you drove me beyond restraint. I wanted to protect you and sent you away from Monteleone so that you would be safe. I did everything in my power to forget you, but I could not. Then there you were in Palermo on Garibaldi's arm. Every time I tried to hold on to you, you flew away. Every time I tried to leave you, you caught up with me.'

Ben had cared for her for longer than she had known. How could she have ever doubted him? There was so much she had failed to understand. I should have believed in him, Carina thought. She was silent and Ben took her face in both his hands with his thumbs beneath her chin.

'Your stubborn, unconditional love saved me, my darling. When I failed to persuade you to marry Harry, I convinced myself Scalia was no longer a threat. I should have known better. Name of God, I never meant you to come to any harm.'

Carina had never before heard him speak with such emotion. She looked at Ben and, for the first time, saw him as he really was – a man who needed to love as much as to be loved. Their hearts and minds were at one but there was something she had to say, even now, at the risk of losing her last chance of happiness.

'I won't let you take me back out of duty, Ben. I'd rather die than endure your pity.'

'Pity's not an emotion you arouse in those who love you, Carina. Besides, how would I dare face Greta if I came home without you?'

Ben's fingers moved to the ribbon of her nightgown. He undid the bow so it fell open to the waist. Carina's hands went up to cover herself and he took hold of them and placed them by her side. She felt his lips touch her skin, his mouth moving along the lines left by Scalia's knife. He planted tiny kisses on the scars and her closed eyes were wet with tears. When he raised his head, she pressed his cheek to her own and he took her in his arms.

'Never take your love away from me. I love you and cannot live without you. I will love you until the end of time, my darling, brave, beautiful woman.'

ACKNOWLEDGEMENTS

I owe a debt of gratitude to three remarkable women:

Joanna Frank, editor of the first draft, for her advice and faith in the book.

Diana Beaumont, my literary agent, for her guidance and perseverance.

Genevieve Pegg, publishing director of HarperNorth, for her creative skill in preparing the book for publication.

Thank you to my family, above all, for your unfailing loyalty, support and encouragement. This book is for you, with my love.

AUTHOR'S NOTE

This is a work of fiction. The historical events are true but, apart from General Garibaldi, Francesco Riso, Jessie and Alberto Mario, the characters in the book are products of the author's imagination. Any resemblance to actual persons, living or dead, is purely coincidental.

Harper North

BOOK CREDITS

HarperNorth would like to thank the following staff and contributors for their involvement in making this book a reality:

Hannah Avery
Fionnuala Barrett
Claire Boal
Charlotte Brown
Sarah Burke
Alan Cracknell
Jonathan de Peyer
Anna Derkacz
Tom Dunstan
Kate Elton
Mick Fawcett
Simon Gerratt
Alice Gomer
Monica Green

CJ Harter
Elisabeth Heissler
Graham Holmes
Nicky Lovick
Megan Jones
Jean-Marie Kelly
Alice Murphy-Pyle
Adam Murray
Genevieve Pegg
Rob Pinney
Agnes Rigou
Florence Shepherd
Emma Sullivan
Katrina Troy

For more unmissable reads,
sign up to the HarperNorth newsletter at
www.harpernorth.co.uk

or find us on Twitter at
@HarperNorthUK

Harper
North

DOS Tips, Tricks, and Traps

Chris DeVoney
with Norman Hale

Que® Corporation
Carmel, Indiana

Dedication

To Andy, Aaron, Adam, and Darin, my four executive sanity assistants.

C.D.V.

Publishing Director
David P. Ewing

Acquisitions Editor
Terrie Lynn Solomon

Developmental Editors
Lois Sherman
Kathie-Jo Arnoff

Editors
Mary Bednarek
Lisa Hunt
Shelley O'Hara
Mark Simpson

Technical Editors
David Nickolich, CDP, CSP
Jeff Booher
Tim Stanley

Production
William Hartman
Jennifer Matthews

Proofreader
Peter Tocco

Indexer
Sherry Massey

Composed in Garamond by

Page Design by
William Hartman, Hartman Publishing

About the Authors

Chris DeVoney

Chris DeVoney is President of DeVoney and Associates, Inc., a writing, research, and technology analyst firm. Mr. DeVoney received his B.S. degree from the University of Gloucester and has been involved in the microcomputer industry since 1975. Mr. DeVoney has written and edited numerous books and articles about microcomputers. He is the author of *Using PC DOS*, 2nd Editon, *MS-DOS User's Guide*, 3rd Edition, and contributing author of *Managing Your Hard Disk*, 2nd Edition, all published by Que Corporation.

Norman Hale

Norman Hale actively experiments with computers and DOS. His most recent article in *PC Magazine* (October 31, 1988) deals with advanced batch file techniques.

Contents at a Glance

Table of Contents

Part II: Controlling Your Hard Disk

Part III: Customizing Your System

11 Using a CONFIG.SYS File

Part IV: Troubleshooting Your System

Part V: Appendixes

Acknowledgments

Que Corporation thanks the following individuals for their contributions to this book:

Lois Sherman, for assisting with developing the chapter structure and directing the early development of this book.

Kathie-Jo Arnoff, for her editing and review of this book and for directing the editing, author review, and production stages of the book project.

Mary Bednarek, for revising parts of the text and working with the authors during the final development of this book.

Shelley O'Hara, for her editing work, ensuring accurate, clear, and easy-to-read text.

Tim Stanley, for his revision and technical edit of many parts of this book and for providing technical assistance on this project.

Jeff Booher, for technical editing many parts of this book and providing technical assistance to the editing staff working on this project.

Joanetta Hendel and Stacey Beheler, for their invaluable support to the developmental and editing staff working on this book.

Bill Hartman, for the design and production work on this book and for his willingness to make numerous modifications while producing this book.

The author thanks the following for their contribution

Scott Brooks and the staff of IBM's Communications department.

Marty Taucher and the staff of Microsoft's Public Relations department.

Bill Krueger and the staff of Intel's PCEO group.

Bill Gordon, Vericomp Publishing.

Mark Kolad, Kolad Research.

Tim Leslie, Ecosoft, Inc.

Paul Mace, Paul Mace Software.

Alan Steggemoller, Carmel Valley Associates.

The many inhabitants of the MS, IBM, CONSULT, and PC Magnet forums of CompuServe, including Barry Simon, Ward Christensen, and David Frier, for their perils, suggestions, and solutions.

Trademark Acknowledgments

Que Corporation has made every effort to supply trademark information about company names, products, and services mentioned in this book. Trademarks indicated below were derived from various sources. Que Corporation cannot attest to the accuracy of this information.

Conventions Used in This Book

DOS Tips, Tricks, and Traps uses certain conventions to help you more easily understand the text.

Messages that appear on the computer screen appear in this book in a `special typeface`, as in the following sample message:

`This is a screen message`

The system prompt (`A>`, `C>`, etc.), which appears on-screen, also appears in a special typeface.

The notation for issuing commands and running programs appears, in fullest form, in lines like the following:

`A>`*dc:pathc***COMMAND** *optional information /switches*

Two different typefaces are used to distinguish between optional and mandatory parts of a command. Items in **boldface** are mandatory; you must always give this part of a command. In this example, to issue the command called **\COMMAND**, you must type **\COMMAND** as it appears.

Items in *italic characters* are optional; you give these items only when needed. *dc:pathc*, *optional information*, and */switches* are optional variables. You substitute the appropriate disk drive and path name for *dc:pathc*. You substitute a file name or other item for *optional information*. You use the appropriate character or characters for */switches*.

Uppercase letters are usually used in the examples, but you can type command lines in either upper- or lowercase letters. In a few command lines, the case of the letters makes a difference. When the case is significant, the difference is specifically mentioned in the discussion of the command. Otherwise, you can safely use upper- or lowercase letters, or both.

Introduction

To increase your productivity, you need to look beyond your applications. Although you perform most of your work inside your application programs, there are additional concerns. Your application programs derive their power from DOS and the hardware of the computer. DOS, in turn, derives its power from the hardware of the computer. Your computer's capability and speed depend on the various components, sometimes individually and sometimes as a unit. Understanding this chain of power allows you to see ways to improve efficiency and to increase productivity—the goals of this book.

To understand the relationships of the various system parts and the role you play in determining performance, consider the analogy of motorized vehicles, from motor scooter to semitractor-trailer. The performance, efficiency, and desirability of a vehicle is determined by a number of factors: acceleration, top speed, room, mileage, comfort, cargo space, load capacity, and so on. Likewise, the performance of your computer system is determined by a number of factors: speed, capacity, memory, and so on.

You make purchase decisions regarding your computer based on performance factors just as you decide what features you want for your car. Some features are inherent to the computer you buy. Some features cannot be changed except by changing the feature itself, while other features can be changed with options.

Some combinations of basics and options increase performance, but the wrong mating can limit those increases. Putting an ultra-fast disk drive on a slow computer does not yield the same benefits as putting the same drive on an ultra-fast system. (This is comparable to putting a turbo-booster on a Volkswagon rather than on a racing engine.)

You can use the tips in this book to make an informed purchase decision. The purchase may be a new computer, a replacement component, or an add-on. As you expand and maintain your system, you determine performance by the hardware and software you choose.

Simply finding the right equipment is not enough. You must effectively use and maintain that equipment to reap the most rewards. This need brings in two additional considerations: operating conditions and maintenance. Do you drive your car on Sundays only, or do you drive to and from work every day on gridlocked, construction-filled roads? Similarly, you must consider how you use your computer: the amount of data you must process, the method and order you use to process data, and the time spent processing the data.

To work most effectively, you must know your computer needs. This book does not apply to just one situation. Instead, the book offers advice for all types of users and their various demands. You can find particular tips, tricks, and traps that pertain to your needs and apply them to enrich your operating conditions.

The efficiency of your car also can be enhanced or undermined through its maintenance. Dirty air filters, worn spark plugs, bald tires, and so on deter performance. For computers, you must perform two types of maintenance: physical (hardware) and logical (software and the way you use hardware and software). This book abounds in tips, tricks, and traps for best maintaining your computer system.

A last important consideration is you—the driver. As the user of the computer, you react to the sum of the hardware, software, and operating conditions. Your knowledge can determine the shortest, safest, and most productive route. This book seeks to steer you on this route.

The tips, tricks, and traps in this book are a culmination of my experience in using DOS since 1982. Much of the information is personal experience; some information is gained through other users. As stated in my other books, I use the *trial by ordeal* method of learning an operating system. Some appropriately call this *working on the bleeding edge of technology*. Many of the traps are based on these mistakes.

About This Book

DOS Tips, Tricks, and Traps has three underlying philosophies:

- Provide needed background information
- Offer shortcuts or productive alternatives to common operations
- Balance appropriate risk with appropriate reward

Background Information

The first philosophy is to offer needed background information on a subject. This background may be needed for several reasons.

First, perhaps the subject is one that often confuses even the intermediate computer user. The subject of processor and memory type, for example, can be confusing: 8088/8086 versus 286 versus 386, real versus expanded versus extended memory. The processor affects memory type, and memory type affects performance. Without background information, unraveling the related performance factors is difficult.

Second, the justification of a tip, trick, or trap may not be obvious without the background information. In addition to combating confusion, background information justifies some of the suggestions in this book. Disk cachers or interleave-setting programs may require the purchase of third-party programs. When spending money, a Missourian attitude ("show me") is appropriate. By knowing the why and what of the subjects, you can quantify the benefits.

Another possibility is that the lack of knowledge about a subject might be dangerous. For instance, running some disk utilities under COMPAQ® MS-DOS® V3.31 or DOS V4 can cause problems. Previous versions of some disk utilities react violently to large disks partitions and can destroy information. Knowing about the differences alerts you to use only the tools certified to work under the new DOS versions.

Shortcuts

The tips and tricks reflect my personal operating philosophy of practiced laziness—doing the least work to get the most results. In some cases, the tip or trick is an easier way to accomplish a task. In other cases, the tip or trick reflects an approach to work around a function missing in DOS. And in some cases, the tip or trick is simply a different approach to a common problem.

Risks Vs. Rewards

The final philosophy underlines a difference between this book and *Using PC DOS* and *MS-DOS User's Guide*. Those two books assume that paranoia is healthy. This book assumes that *some* paranoia is healthy.

Consider, for example, the approach to backing up. All hard disks fail—hence the reason for backup. Predicting the exact time for the failure is impossible. You know that if certain events occur—dropping the hard disk from a height of three feet or more, having the computer struck by lightning, having a key component fail, or scrambling key logical areas of a disk—the disk will fail.

Backing up is a housekeeping task (no productive work is created), and the task consumes resources (diskettes, tapes, time, and money). The issue is not whether you should back up—the issue is how often you should backup.

The attitude of other books is basically *you cannot back up enough*. That advice is appropriate for beginners who do not understand the catastrophic results of a hard disk failure nor the risk/reward ratio of infrequent backups.

The advice in this book is *back up enough*. This advice is appropriate because you understand the causes and ramifications of hard disk failure and the effort required to recover from a disaster. If you don't need the data, you don't need to back it up. If the time to re-create the destroyed data is less than the time to back up, you don't need to back up this data. The remaining data is a risk/reward game. The reward is spending your resources on other tasks. The risk is the difficulty in re-creating the information.

Some paranoia is healthy, but too much paranoia is counterproductive. The amount of applicable paranoia is an informed choice. The conscious decision on when to back up—and other decisions—is based on risk versus reward.

How This Book Is Organized

DOS Tips, Tricks, and Traps is organized into four basic parts. The first part of the book deals with how to make the most of your disks and drives. The chapters in this part (Chapters 1–5) offer tips, tricks, and traps about the CPU and memory, disk drives, disk performance, and more.

Part II presents suggestions for managing your files, diskettes, and hard disk. Chapters 6–10 give you advice about subdirectories, file management, batch files, and backups.

Part III shows you ways you can customize your system. These chapters (11–13) cover CONFIG.SYS, device drivers, ANSI.SYS, and the video screen and keyboard.

Part IV offers troubleshooting advice. Chapters 14 and 15 provide tips, tricks, and traps for avoiding and repairing logical and physical damage.

What This Book Contains

The following is a chapter-by-chapter description of what this book contains.

Chapter 1, which lays the groundwork for tips, tricks, and traps in other parts of the book, explains some confusing aspects about the CPU, memory, and expansion bus, particularly the subjects of expanded and extended memory. The chapter also covers the major differences between the 80386 and other CPUs, and gives advice about changing or expanding your system.

Chapter 2 illustrates the similarities and differences among various types of disk drives and helps you become a more knowledgeable user of disks and disk drives. You can learn to gain the best performance from your present hardware or change it to meet your needs.

Chapter 3 shows you a number of ways you can improve disk performance. The topics discussed in this chapter include RAM disks, disk BUFFERS, FASTOPEN, disk cachers, and defragmenters.

Chapter 4 explains formatting disks and diskettes. The tips, tricks, and traps illustrate the differences between physical (or low-level) and logical (or high-level) formatting. Advice on partitioning hard disks also is included.

Chapter 5 shows you how to use and protect your diskettes. The chapter focuses on three subjects: handling diskettes, using DISKCOPY, and traveling with a computer. You learn to avoid damaging your diskettes through inadvertent operations. Specific tips are given for traveling with a laptop or transportable computer.

Chapter 6 centers on the need to establish and use subdirectories effectively. The chapter provides tips, tricks, and traps for organizing subdirectories: naming them, structuring them according to the programs you use, installing programs within them, and storing DOS and its utilities within them. The chapter also provides tips for manipulating subdirectories with PATH, APPEND, and SUBST.

Chapter 7 discusses file management: naming files, using file attributes, erasing files, moving files, copying files, renaming files, replacing files, and unerasing files.

Chapters 8 and 9 focus on batch files. Chapter 8 deals with batch file basics, and gives you tips, tricks, and traps on using subcommands within batch files. Chapter 9 goes into the more advanced techniques of redirecting input and output, and using environment variables.

Chapter 10 introduces some general guidelines on backing up and presents some strategies in planning how different types of backups can meet your needs.

Chapter 11 shows you how to use DOS's configuration file, CONFIG.SYS, to alter the functions and performance of your system. This chapter also discusses the DOS V4 INSTALL directive and its potential uses. Chapter 12 shows you how to use particular device drivers in your system configuration.

Chapter 13 discusses customizing your video screen and keyboard. The chapter shows you how to create special characters and boxes using the built-in facilities of your computer, and offers many tips, tricks, and traps about using ANSI control codes.

Chapter 14 describes logical damage—how you can avoid it and how you can repair it. The chapter covers handling lost clusters, damaged file allocation tables, cross-linked files, and other problems.

Chapter 15 defines physical damage. You learn how to use DOS error messages to pinpoint and resolve your problems.

The book includes three appendixes for quick reference. Appendix A offers some general facts about disks and DOS. Appendix B includes tables of ASCII codes, and Appendix C provides ANSI escape codes.

A thorough index helps you locate the particular information you need among the tips, tricks, and traps.

What Versions of DOS Are Covered

This book primarily covers PC DOS and MS-DOS versions 3.3 and 4.0. However, many tips, tricks, and traps are applicable to all versions of DOS V3. Some of the information is applicable to DOS V2.

In this book, the tips, tricks, and traps are applicable to both PC DOS and MS-DOS. The discussion states explicitly when the information presented is either implementation specific or version specific.

Note that this book does not cover the visual shell of DOS V4. Most readers of this book operate DOS from the DOS prompt. In the interest of continuity and clarity, the visual shell is not discussed in this book.

How To Use This Book

You should use *DOS Tips, Tricks, and Traps* as a tool, like a dictionary. The book is designed to give you quick access to solutions that offer immediate help with DOS.

Here are some of the times you will reach for this book:

- When you've tried to do something apparently simple, you've gotten an unexpected result, and you're sitting in a quandary
- When it looks as though you can't get there from here with DOS, but you think there ought to be a way
- When you know how to get the job done, but you are sure that a quicker and easier solution exists

Because *DOS Tips, Tricks, and Traps* is organized by topics, you also can read sections straight through. The chapters generally have several subsections. Each subsection is composed of a list of tips, tricks, and traps on that particular topic. The text in many subsections is progressive: earlier tips lay the groundwork for later ones. Therefore, you may sometimes want to read straight through this book the way you read an ordinary book.

However, each tip, trick, and trap is designed primarily to stand on its own. Usually you will be reading one or only a few tips, tricks, or traps at a time. You can use this book to go directly to the solution for your immediate problems.

You will find that a particular entry does not refer to other entries even though the material in other tips, tricks, and traps may be relevant to the one you are reading. The book is designed this way in order to avoid cluttering the text with numerous cross references. To find all the important references to a particular topic, you can refer to the book's thorough index.

As you read through a section looking for particular information, keep in mind the format of the tips, tricks, and traps.

A *tip* is a helpful hint that tells you a better way to use a DOS or system-related command. Tips remind you about procedures that are often forgotten or frequently misused.

A *trick* is an innovative solution to a frequent problem or a solution to a problem that DOS was not designed to handle. In many cases, tricks involve several steps that were discovered by experimenting for some time. Applying these tricks can save you from duplicating the same time and effort.

A *trap* is a pitfall or problem that may slow you down or prevent you from finding a solution. Knowing DOS's limits ahead of time can help you avoid traps. Whenever possible, the traps contain a "workaround" solution that bypasses the limitation.

Learning More About DOS

If you are new to DOS and need a comprehensive tutorial, try either Que's *MS-DOS User's Guide*, 3rd edition, or *Using PC DOS*, 2nd edition. If you would like more information on the programming aspects of MS-DOS, you may want to purchase a book that covers the inner workings of MS-DOS, such as Que's *DOS Programmers' Reference*. Other Que publications that may interest you include *Managing Your Hard Disk*, 2nd edition, and *DOS QueCards*.

PART I

Making the Most of Disks and Drives

Includes

Using Your System's Power: CPUs and Memory

Knowing and Protecting Your Disk Drives

Improving Disk Performance

Formatting Disks and Diskettes

Using and Protecting Your Diskettes

1

Using Your System's Power: CPUs and Memory

Four hardware elements provide the fundamental horsepower for your computer: the central processing unit (CPU), memory, the expansion bus, and disk storage. This chapter is devoted to the first three subjects: the CPU, memory, and the expansion bus.

This chapter explains some confusing aspects about the CPU, memory, and expansion bus, particularly the subjects of expanded and extended memory. Questions about these subjects are among the most frequently asked to DOS help-magazine columns and user groups.

The chapter also gives advice about changing or expanding your system. The various tips, tricks, and traps will help if you are interested in replacing your system, expanding the memory of your system, or adding an expansion board to your system. The material in this chapter can help separate "vendor fact" from "vendor hype."

The chapter lays the groundwork for tips, tricks, and traps in other parts of this book. For example, the information in this chapter is needed for installing certain device drivers, using certain peripherals, and running certain applications programs.

To understand your computer system, keep one eye on a microscopic view of the CPU and memory while occasionally using the other eye for a macroscopic view of the entire system. The CPU is the heart of the system, but it is constrained by other items, including memory and the expansion bus (see fig. 1.1). In turn, the amount of memory you place in a system is constrained by the type of CPU, and the use of that memory is constrained by the CPU and the software that the CPU executes. Also, the speed of the expansion bus can constrain the speed of memory and other peripherals. These circular constraints on the system are common to all mechanisms. As you read this chapter, each piece of the system puzzle falls into place.

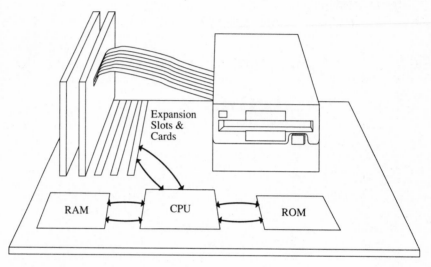

Fig. 1.1. Although the CPU is a major factor in computer speed, the rate of information flow between the CPU and each major subsystem (RAM, ROM, and devices connected via the expansion slots) determines true computer speed.

The use of memory imposes limits on PC DOS and MS-DOS, and DOS limits the use of memory. In addition, certain applications programs and the latest operating systems require more memory than the DOS "limit." To understand these limits, you need to understand your computer's CPU and memory, the subject of this chapter.

CPU Power

Like a car's engine, the CPU provides the horsepower for your computer. Although many different CPUs exist, DOS works only with the six Intel-derived (based on Intel chips) CPUs listed in table 1.1.

Table 1.1
Central Processing Unit Characteristics

CPU	Top clock speed	Physical memory addressing	Width of data movement	Register width	Types of computers
8088	8 MHz	1M	8 bits	16 bits	PC, IBM PC XT™, and most original clones
8086	8 MHz	1M	16 bits	16 bits	PS/2™ Models 25-30 and others
80286	20 MHz	16M	16 bits	16 bits	IBM® PC AT, PS/2 Models 30/286, 50, 50z, 60, AT clones
80386SX	24 MHz	4G	16 bits	32 bits	COMPAQ 386SX
80386	24 MHz	4G	32 bits	32 bits	PS/2 Models 70-80, COMPAQ 386, clones

Unless the difference is significant, this book uses the term *8086* to mean either the 8086 or 8088 and the terms *386* or *80386* to mean either the 80386 or 80386SX. Also, DOS is used generically to refer to all implementations of DOS. If the implementation is important—for instance, the material applies only to IBM PC DOS or only to MS-DOS, the specific implementation is used.

Table 1.1 presents various facts about the processors and ranks them in relative order of power, based on five factors:

- The width of data movement (or data-bus width)
- The CPU's clock rate
- The CPU's register width
- The amount of addressable memory
- The mode of addressing memory (not indicated in the table)

Some factors affect computer performance more than others. However, all five are considered in rating the power of the CPU. The first three factors—width of data movement, clock rate, and register widths—affect the overall performance of the computer and are discussed in this section. The last two factors—the amount of addressable memory and the mode of addressing memory—relate to the amount of memory available to the computer and programs. These two factors are the subject of this chapter's "Memory and the CPU" section.

Data-Bus Width

1.1 Tip: CPUs with wider data buses work faster.

The *width of data movement* refers to the number of data bits moved at one time between the CPU and memory. Many internal computer operations involve 16 to 32 bits (2 to 4 bytes) at a time on the system's internal data bus. (The *data bus* is the system of lines that connect the CPU with memory.) Moving 2 to 4 bytes during one operation speeds performance. A CPU that moves 16 bits at a time is faster than a CPU moving 8 bits; a CPU moving 32 bits is faster than a CPU moving 16 bits.

Computers are classified by the data-bus width. Notice that the 8086 is rated higher than the 8088, and the 386 is ranked higher than the 386SX. The two pairs of processors are "half cousins." The 8088 executes the machine-language instructions half as fast (8 versus 16 bits at a time) as the 8086. The 386SX handles 16 bits at a time versus the 386's 32 bits.

You should note, however, the exceptions to these specifications. Some operations, such as manipulating a single byte or bytes in different locations, can cause a lower-rated CPU to perform certain work faster. Practically, these exceptions are rare and negated by other elements, such as the system clock speed.

System Clock Speed

1.2 Tip: CPUs with faster system clock speeds usually perform more work.

The second horsepower factor is CPU speed or *system clock* speed. The system clock is the basic timing signal that coordinates the movement of information between the CPU, memory, and other devices. The CPU clock speed, rated in megahertz (one million cycles per second; abbreviated MHz), is the popular number bandied about by vendors. Faster system clocks generally mean faster operations—which means more work performed in the same amount of time.

The 8088/8086's top speed is generally 8 MHz, although some of these CPUs can border 10 MHz. The current top speed for the 286 is 20 MHz. The current Intel speed demon is the 386, which tops at 25 MHz; a yet unreleased model of the 386 is rumored to run at 40 MHz.

Even within the same family, CPUs are not created equal. Each CPU line has several models, based on the maximum-rated system clock speed. For example, the 386 has three basic models running at 16 MHz, 20 MHz, and 25 MHz. These speeds, which are based on the construction of the chip, are established by the CPU manufacturer. The faster the CPU, the higher the price.

Remember that the CPU's clock speed is only an indication of the speed of the system. Some computers running at the same CPU clock speed are faster than others. This topic is covered in another section of this chapter.

1.3 Tip: Because wait states slow system performance, choose systems with low wait states if you want maximum speed.

The system clock is a good approximation of the CPU's power. However, the infamous wait state can jade comparisons. When memory cannot offer its information as quickly as the CPU can retrieve the information, a *wait state* is inserted. For each wait state, the CPU waits one system clock cycle for the information to become available. This wait state slows the overall operation of the system.

Ordinarily, a processor running at 12 MHz is faster than a processor running at 10 MHz. If the 12 MHz processor must suffer 1 wait state each time memory is accessed, however, the performance of a 10MHz processor without the wait state is almost as fast. Generally, 1 wait state slows potential performance by 8 to 12 percent.

Register Width

1.4 Tip: CPUs with larger registers perform complex operations in fewer instructions and less time.

CPUs vary in their capability to execute instructions. If two CPUs run at the same system clock rate and execute identical machine-language instructions, the higher-rated CPU generally performs more quickly.

For two reasons other than top system clock speed, CPUs can be more powerful: they can execute some identical instructions in less time, and they have additional instructions that can perform the same task in less time. The latter reason (instruction set) is based on the number and size of the CPU's registers.

A *CPU register* is a working area for instructions and data within the CPU chip. The fastest CPU operations involve register-to-register work, which is typically several times faster than register-to-memory work. More registers mean faster internal operations and less memory accesses. Larger registers (16-bit versus 32-bit registers) mean that complex operations are performed in fewer instructions or in less time. The overall result is speedier operations.

When comparing apples to apples (executing the identical instructions on two different CPUs running at the same clock rate), the higher-rated CPU will perform the instructions in less time. When comparing red apples to golden apples (different instructions for the same task at the same clock rate), the higher-rated CPUs perform the work in less time. This means that when software is written specifically for the higher-rated CPUs, the software will perform the task faster than software written to work with all CPUs.

Comparing different instructions at different system clock rates is an apples-to-oranges comparison. Although these benchmarks give some idea of the relative differences in power between the CPUs, the benchmarks are meaningless for determining the exact gain in speed.

Before moving on to the next tip, I should mention that the 286 CPU is imperceptibly faster in executing certain string manipulation operations than the 386. Although this time difference is meaningless, it does exist.

Expansion Bus

1.5 Trap: Don't use the CPU and system clock as the only performance criteria. The expansion bus also is important.

Would you believe that a 12 MHz, 80286-based computer can outperform a 16 MHz or 20 MHz 386-based computer? If the operations involve extensive input and output (such as heavily disk-oriented operations), the result is astonishing. Because of the speed of the expansion bus, the slower 286-based machine is actually faster.

The expansion bus of many computers runs at a different effective system clock rate than the CPU and the system's motherboard memory. For example, some 8 MHz systems run a bus at 6 MHz. Some 10 MHz through 12 MHz systems run at 8 MHz, and some 16 MHz or faster 386 systems run at 10 MHz.

Note several reasons for the slower speed. First, because the bus is not designed for higher speeds, it may not operate reliably at a high speed.

Even IBM's Micro Channel Architecture (MCA) bus of the PS/2 Models 50 through 80 is rated for a top speed of only 10 MHz.

Second, some cards do not need to work at a high rate if an outside device restricts the pace of operations. For example, tying a communications adapter that runs on a 25 MHz bus to a modem running 2400 baud is a waste.

Finally, many expansion cards cannot keep up with the frantic pace established by the CPU. The cards use parts that are too slow for the CPU's top speed. To handle the slow expansion-card problem, computer manufacturers run the expansion bus at a slower clock rate and allow the boards to insert wait states that idle the processor while it waits for the expansion card to respond. This method allows the CPU and its system board to run as quickly as possible, which speeds operations that do not involve the expansion bus.

The specific example that prompted this trap was a PC network installation. The file server was a 386-based system running at 16 MHz. When this computer malfunctioned, a 12 MHz 286-based computer was used as a backup. The network suddenly seemed faster. Both computers had the same amount of memory and the same disk drives and adapters. A quick examination revealed that the 386-based system ran its expansion bus at 10 MHZ, but the 286-based system ran at 12 MHz. The difference in bus speeds resulted in a 15 percent improvement in network performance. Don't assume that a 386 is faster than a 286: examine the entire system before you make a choice.

Memory and the CPU

The remaining CPU elements concern memory—a major performance factor in a computer system. Types of memory can be classified based on four factors: type of memory (ROM versus RAM), the amount of memory (particularly RAM), the addressability of memory (real, expanded, or extended), and the construction of the memory (dynamic, static, or static column).

One factor is well ingrained in most computer users: the difference between ROM and RAM. ROM, read-only memory, is nonvolatile and nonchanging and is used for programs and information that should always be present in the computer. RAM is the "blackboard" memory of the computer (writeable and readable by the CPU). RAM is the memory that the CPU, DOS, and programs use to hold changing information.

Another factor is the amount of memory in the computer system. The amount of memory, particularly RAM, is basically determined by the CPU. RAM is a predominant performance-limiting resource of the computer. Because more RAM means more horsepower, the 386's vast memory addressability of 4 gigabytes (4 billion bytes) is usually preferred to the 8086's 1 million-byte limit. (Remember that some of the memory space is used by ROM.)

All memory, including RAM, is not equal. One difference is how the CPU addresses memory, which accounts for the third factor. This difference, based on addressability, relates to the CPU's hardware and the software instructions needed to access memory. The terms *real*, *extended*, and *expanded* become important. These terms and the differences are defined in the next sections.

A final factor is the type of memory chips. All RAM is not alike. You can use several types of memory: dynamic, static, and static columns. Almost all 8086 and 80286 computers use only one type of RAM; therefore, the type is not important for these computers. However, 386 systems may use any or all three types of memory. Memory is rated at varying speeds, ranging from 60 to 300 nanoseconds (billionths of a second; abbreviated ns). The speed of RAM is critical to all computers. Both factors are discussed in the section on expanded memory later in this chapter.

Linear Memory

1.6   Tip: Remember that most memory is addressed linearly.

A basic concept in addressing memory is linear memory. *Linear memory* is memory that is addressed directly by the CPU in a sequentially ascending manner—one location after another.

For example, an 8088 or 8086 has 20 hardware lines used to address a memory location. These addressing lines, which carry a simple on-or-off status, select which memory location will be written or read by the CPU. The collection of these lines is called the *address bus*. With these 20 addressing lines, the 8088 or 8086 can address 2^{20} memory locations, for a total of 1,048,576 (or 1 megabyte) locations. The first memory location is numbered 0; the remaining locations are numbered and addressed in an ascending order up to the 1M point.

Another example is the 286 processor, which has 24 memory addressing lines. Given 24 addressing lines, the 80286 can address a total of

16,777,266 locations (2^{24} locations, a total of 16 megabytes). The 386 has 32 address lines and can handle 2^{32} locations (4,294,967,296 or 4G of memory). As you will see in later tips, the CPU does not always address this memory in a linear fashion.

Linear memory does not mean that the memory locations must be addressed one after the other; it does mean that the memory appears to the CPU as one location after another. Later tips on real, expanded, and extended memory show you how hardware and software barriers can segregate memory.

Real Memory

1.7 Tip: The first 640K of RAM is known by several names, including *real memory*, *640K memory*, *DOS memory*, and *conventional memory*.

The term *real memory* is a misnomer because the entire first 1M of memory is real memory, not just the first 640K. When used in the context of RAM, however, the term *real memory* implies 640K of RAM. The remaining three terms refer to the 640K of RAM that DOS uses normally. When discussing the differences among types of memory, this book uses the term *conventional* memory.

1.8 Tip: Real memory works on all CPUs.

The 286 and 386 have multiple operating modes (see fig. 1.2). In one operating mode, *real mode*, the 286 and 386 act like an 8086. In real mode, the CPU uses *real memory*, the memory below the 1M point that is available to all CPUs. Because the 286 and 386 must be specially instructed to use the memory above 1M, the 1M point is a "magic" limit. In practice, the 286 and 386 generally labor under the same memory restrictions as the 8086.

1.9 Tip: You can use extended memory with only 286 and 386 computers.

The memory above 1M used by the 286 and 386 is called *extended memory*. The 286 and 386 normally address extended memory by using another operating mode, *protected mode*. In protected mode, the CPU protects programs and their data from overwriting each other in memory. Often, protected memory and extended memory are synonyms.

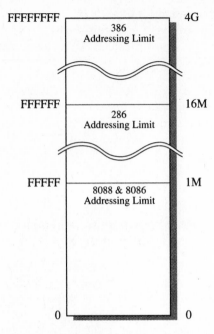

Fig. 1.2. A map of addressable memory by the various CPUs. The 386 addresses 4,000 times more memory than the 8088/8086. (The map is not drawn to scale.)

1.10 Tip: Because DOS uses primarily real mode, DOS has a "magic" 640K limit.

This tip answers the question, "If some computers have more than 1M of RAM, why doesn't DOS use it?" DOS is written to work on an 8088 or 8086, or on a 286 or 386 working in real mode. Because DOS is not written to use protected memory, most DOS programs and many applications programs are not designed to load into or run from the additional memory offered by the 286 or 386. The explanation resides in the legacy of the original IBM Personal Computer.

The design of the IBM PC sliced the 1M memory address space into two groups: 0 to 640K and 640K to 1M (see fig. 1.3). The memory space from 640K through 1M (a total of 384K, and occasionally nicknamed *high real-memory* or *high memory*) was dedicated for use by the read-only memory (ROM) on the system board and plug-in adapters. The remaining memory space was reserved for RAM. This memory is used by DOS and other programs and is appropriately called *low memory*. This split-memory scheme is used in all IBM Personal Computers and clones, including the Personal System/2® family.

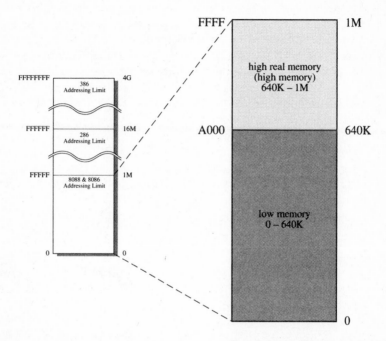

Fig. 1.3. The first 1 megabyte of memory (real memory) in all personal computers is broken into two segments. Low memory, from 0 to 640K, is devoted to user RAM. High memory (from 640K to 1M) is reserved for adapters and system ROM. For 286-based systems, a computer with 1M of RAM is broken into 640K of low memory and 384K of extended memory.

Because DOS uses real mode, only 1M of memory is potentially available. If you subtract the 384K of memory space dedicated to other uses, only 640K of memory space is available for RAM to work with DOS—the "magic" 640K DOS barrier.

A 286 computer with more than 640K of RAM has two different sections of RAM. The first section runs from 0 to 640K; the second section starts at 1M and runs up in memory address space. This split memory explains why 1M of RAM is not 1M, but 640K plus 384K of extended memory.

With a 386 computer, the RAM may be split into 640K and 384K, or it may be contiguous. The 386 works with memory differently from the other CPUs. The difference is explained later in this chapter.

Some applications programs and tools are specially written to take advantage of the extended memory of the 286 and 386—for example, VDISK.SYS, the PC DOS RAM disk; and RAMDRIVE.SYS, the MS-DOS RAM disk. DOS loads the RAM-disk software into real memory (memory beneath the 1M point), but the software can use extended memory (the actual RAM that acts as a disk) for its data. The program itself, not DOS, moves itself into protected memory and switches the CPU between real and protected modes. Because the switch must be made when the program calls on DOS for any activity, few programs that run under DOS actually run from protected mode.

1.11   Trick: Some programs can use nearly 64K of extended memory as conventional memory.

Some programs use the first 64K of extended memory of the 286 or 386 as conventional memory—for example, Microsoft® Windows/286 and its device driver HIMEM.SYS (see fig. 1.4). The program and device driver take advantage of a quirk in the 286 processor that gives the first 64K of extended memory two uses: normal protected memory and exceptional conventional memory.

The 286 can actually address more than 1M in real mode. By flipping the 21st memory-addressing line on the 286 CPU, the 286 addresses memory from 0 to 1.064M (minus 16 bytes that the memory manager uses) without using additional instructions or entering protected mode.

The Microsoft device driver and extended memory manager HIMEM.SYS provide programs with a standard method for using this first 64K of extended memory. Only specially written programs can use this additional 64K of memory (minus 16 bytes), but the trick allows programs such as Microsoft Windows/286 to free 50K of conventional memory space for other uses. (The device driver uses 10K of space, and another 4K is internal to Windows.) HIMEM.SYS and other extended memory programs are discussed in Chapter 12.

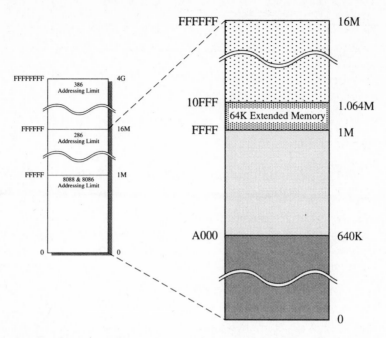

Fig. 1.4. Using an extended memory manager, the first 64K of extended memory can be addressed as an extra 64K of real memory.

Expanded Memory

Extended memory is protected memory. *Expanded memory* is bank-switched memory. Extended memory is linear, an ascending extension of memory. Expanded memory is a method to shoehorn up to 32M of RAM into a 64K to 96K space.

Expanded memory literally plugs a gap in the memory of the PC. As the PC evolved and IBM and other manufacturers filled the upper 384K of memory space, gaps in memory addresses became apparent. Expanded memory fits groups of 16K blocks of RAM into the gaps.

Expanded memory has several nicknames: *EMS memory* (Expanded Memory Specification, the name of the original specification); *LIM memory* (for Lotus®-Intel-Microsoft, the joint designers of the specification); and *EEMS* (Enhanced Expanded Memory Specification). EEMS was developed by AST Research and Quadram Corporation and is a superset of EMS/LIM memory.

Expanded memory, EMS, and LIM are almost interchangeable terms. Extended memory is sometimes referred to as *AT memory*. Because of the confusion between extended and expanded memory, however, this book distinguishes between these two whenever possible. *LIM* refers to the software—the expanded-memory manager or programs that use the expanded-memory manager. *EMS* refers to the expanded-memory hardware. This books uses the term *expanded memory* to cover the general principles of all expanded memory, which includes both the hardware and the software.

1.12 Tip: The expanded-memory manager coordinates the use of expanded memory.

To use expanded memory, you need certain hardware—either a special memory board or a 386-based computer. For software, you need an expanded-memory management program. The two elements contribute to a scheme that works with any computer, from an original PC to the latest PS/2.

Expanded RAM, which is organized into 16K blocks called *pages*, works by using several peekholes (frames)—empty address spaces in the first 1M of memory (see fig. 1.5). Four or more pages of RAM are selected by the expanded-memory management software and exposed through these peekholes by the expanded-memory board circuitry. When the page is selected, the CPU can read or write to the RAM page. When not selected, the page is hidden from the CPU.

Expanded memory plays a "now-you-see-it, now-you-don't" game with the CPU. The memory board contains *ports*—hardware switches used for input and output between the CPU and devices. The ports control which physical 16K page of RAM is exposed to the CPU and at what memory address. The expanded-memory managers direct the CPU to write to the ports; the ports change the physical memory that is exposed to the CPU.

Several technical names describe this exposing and selecting of RAM sections. Because the CPU's view of the expanded-memory pages is "switched" off and on, the most commonly used term is *page switching* or *bank switching*. Another common name for the expanded-memory scheme is *page mapping*, which refers to the way the pages of RAM are mapped (addressed) into and out of the peekhole.

By playing addressing games with the CPU, any 8088, 8086, or 80286 can use up to 32M of memory. The expanded-memory paging scheme is the

only way that an 8088 or 8086 can address more than 1M of memory and
the only way an 80286 can address more than 16M of memory. The 386
also can use expanded memory, but the 386 is a special case discussed
later in this chapter.

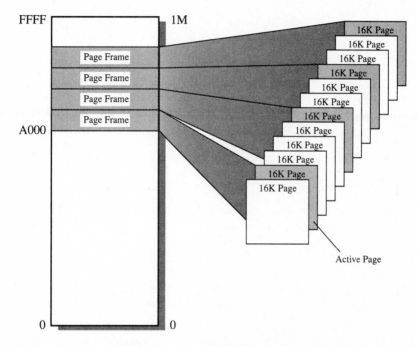

Fig. 1.5. EMS memory works by swapping 16K pages of physical memory on the EMS board
into page frames in conventional memory. Page frames are usually located in empty 16K
spaces in high real memory. When exposed through the page frame, the physical page is
accessible by the CPU as conventional memory. A page frame can use any EMS page, but only
one page at a time.

With expanded memory, applications programs potentially can access an
additional 32 megabytes of RAM. The applications program calls on the
expanded-memory manager to coordinate the use of expanded memory.
Because expanded memory works with any CPU and any personal
computer, applications programs that use expanded memory can run on
any computer.

1.13   Tip: Specially written programs can take full advantage of expanded memory.

Many programs, such as Lotus 1-2-3® and DOS V4's VDISK, use expanded memory to hold data, not additional parts of the program's instructions. The programs reside in conventional memory; expanded memory holds data—the spreadsheet or the file—on the RAM disk.

Only a few carefully crafted programs can actually reside in and run from expanded memory. One such program is Borland's SideKick® Plus desktop organizer. SideKick Plus stores most of its program instructions and data in expanded memory. When it needs more conventional memory, the program puts a copy of conventional memory into expanded memory, uses the freed conventional memory, and then restores the conventional memory. This swapping of memory is an ingenious method of getting more from the DOS 640K "limit." In addition, using expanded memory for the swapping tasks is generally faster than using a RAM disk or hard disk.

All computers can use expanded memory. As with extended memory, however, special programs must be written to take advantage of the added memory space. Most programs use expanded memory for data space, not as space for holding additional program instructions.

1.14   Trap: Remember that some programs require LIM V4, the newer expanded-memory software.

Be aware of the differences between the original expanded memory specification, LIM V3.2, and the current specification, LIM V4.0. Some programs, such as Microsoft® Windows V2.0, require the newer version of LIM. Your program's documentation will state whether LIM V4 is required or whether you can use LIM V3.2 or V4.

The outdated LIM V3.2 allowed only 8 megabytes of RAM and only 4 pages of memory (64K) at a time. LIM V4 allows 32M of expanded RAM, the use of more than four 16K pages of memory at one time, and improved support for running programs from expanded memory. Some programs depend on two other features of V4: the frame (peekhole) address can be changed, and expanded memory can be used anywhere in real memory by remapping real memory.

Fortunately, EMS boards built for the V3 specification can use V4 software. The V3 boards, however, cannot use the two additional RAM pages or the program support of V4. A memory board built for LIM V4 is needed in order for you to use the additional features. In other ways, the LIM V4 software works identically with the older boards.

Expanded Versus Extended Memory

1.15 Tip: More DOS programs use expanded memory than extended memory.

For every DOS program that uses extended memory, there are 50 programs that use expanded memory. Lotus 1-2-3, Microsoft® Excel and Windows, Borland's SideKick Plus, and many other applications use expanded memory more effectively than extended memory. Unless you are running OS/2™, expanded memory is more suitable to your programs.

1.16 Tip: To expand memory on an 80286 system, choose a memory board that offers both expanded and extended memory.

When I purchased my workhorse computer (a Sperry® IT, an AT-clone), I knew I would someday use OS/2 on the computer (then rumored to be named DOS V). Knowing that the new operating system would use extended (protected) memory rather than expanded memory, I bought an extended memory card. I was the proud owner of a personal computer that held more RAM than most minicomputers—3.5 megabytes.

Since that time, I've conceded my mistake and have purchased combination memory boards that offer expanded *and* extended memory. The reason? Combination memory boards are more versatile.

Very few programs use extended memory. If your programs require additional memory, you need a memory board that offers expanded memory. But for a few dollars more, you can buy a memory board that offers both expanded and extended memory. These combination boards are not only more versatile, but worth the extra expense. As later tips demonstrate, you may want to use both types of memory in your system.

The IBM memory expansion boards for the PS/2 Models 50 and 60 are combination expanded and extended memory boards. When you buy an IBM memory board for these systems, you buy the capability to use the additional memory in either mode.

1.17 Tip: The speed of expanded and extended memory depends on the system and software.

More programs support expanded memory because it can be accessed faster than extended memory on some 80286-based systems, particularly on 6 MHz or 8 MHz AT-class machines. System clock speed, EMS board construction, and the software instructions used to access memory make the difference.

The ROM BIOS of the 80286 computer can switch the processor from real to protected mode by issuing the CPU software interrupt 15 instruction (abbreviated INT 15; the 15 is a hexadecimal number).

Although the Personal Computer AT and its look-alikes were designed to use the protected memory of the 286, the design did not prove efficient. Neither the INT 15 instruction nor the internal hardware executes the switch between real and protected mode efficiently. The number of system clock cycles needed to enter protected mode, use the protected memory, and reenter real mode is extensive. If you run expanded and extended memory while running at speeds of 6 MHz to 10 MHz, expanded memory is almost 20 percent faster than extended memory.

In machines designed to utilize protected memory (such as the PS/2 Models 30/286, 50, 50Z, and 60), the ROM BIOS and hardware execute the interrupt 15 switch much quicker. The relative speeds of extended and expanded memory is within 1 percent.

Several other variables affect the speed of expanded and extended memory. First, various expanded memory boards shift gears somewhere between the 8 MHz to 12 MHz system clock range. When operating at lower clock speeds, the expanded memory boards transfer 16 bits at a time; at higher speeds, expanded memory boards transfer 8 bits at a time. This shift at higher speeds can make extended memory faster than expanded memory.

The efficiency of the EMS management software is a second variable. Some EMS software is not coded as efficiently as others. The more efficient code produces speedier operations; therefore, one EMS board may work faster than another.

The third and final variable is the applications software. The 286 has a LOADALL instruction that allows programs to access protected memory without actually switching the processor into protected mode. By using LOADALL instead of the INT 15 switch, programs can access extended memory faster than expanded memory.

If your software does not offer the option to run in both expanded and extended memory, the issue is moot. However, programs such as VDISK and RAMDRIVE offer both modes. If you have expanded and extended memory, you might test which is faster for your system. Run the software in expanded memory; then run the software in extended memory. You may be surprised at the difference.

LIM-ulators

1.18   Tip: If you have only extended memory on an 80286-based AT-class computer, you can use a LIM-ulator with most programs that use expanded memory.

If you have only extended memory, you can gain many of the benefits of programs that use expanded memory. Some programs and device drivers permit extended memory to masquerade as expanded memory. Expanded memory emulators, nicknamed LIM-ulators, simulate many of the functions of expanded memory.

Two LIM-ulator programs, Softbytes from Veritech and FLASH™ EMS from Software Masters, offer a combination of device driver and controlling program. Some extended memory board manufacturers provide a device driver called XEMM.SYS or REXX.SYS that performs the emulation. After loading into the computer, the device drivers and programs use a combination of DOS memory and extended memory to perform the bank-switching functions of expanded memory.

The cost of using these expanded-memory masqueraders is a steep reduction in DOS size and performance. The device driver or program itself occupies about 4K of DOS memory—a minor amount. Unfortunately, because conventional DOS memory must be substituted for expanded memory, an additional 16K to 64K of DOS memory is consumed.

Expanded memory emulators are slower than expanded memory, and the time difference is staggering. On an 8 MHz PC AT, the time difference between real expanded memory and an emulator is about 60 to 1. This 60-to-1 time difference occurs each time the applications program requests a different 16K page of expanded memory.

Depending on the application, however, you may not notice a significant difference in performance. If the applications program does not perform "massive" page switching, as the WordPerfect Library™ does, you see little difference. With 1-2-3, the size of your spreadsheet determines the depreciation. Most moderately sized spreadsheets take only a few seconds more to recalculate. Large spreadsheets (500K or more) take about 30 seconds or longer to recalculate.

LIM-ulators for the 80286 also cannot emulate perfectly the EMS specification. This specification allows programs to remap the 16K expanded memory pages into any blank area in the first 1M of memory. The 80286 hardware cannot provide this remapping. For this reason, two major applications, Javelin® and Microsoft Windows/286, cannot use LIM-ulators. Most other programs, however, can use the expanded memory emulators.

1.19 Tip: Take advantage of the LIM-ulator's capability to use disk storage for emulating expanded memory on 8088- through 80286-based systems.

Even if you don't have an extended memory board, LIM-ulators can approximate expanded memory by using disk storage on an 8088- through 80286-based system. Programs, therefore, can create data using expanded memory that is as large as disk storage. Both FLASH EMS and Softbytes use floppy or hard disk storage space and work on 8088-, 8086-, and 286-based computers.

The previous warnings about LIM-ulators still apply. The performance penalties are significantly increased. The difference between using real expanded memory and using a hard disk drive on an AT-class computer to emulate expanded memory is 200 to 1. Using a floppy disk as a substitute for expanded memory inflicts a 1,000 to 1 penalty.

LIM-ulating via a disk drive is strictly a matter of cost versus need versus performance. LIM-ulators are inexpensive. If you need to emulate EMS memory for most programs, LIM-ulators provide the "impossible"—a software solution to a hardware problem. If the performance sacrifice is unacceptable, buy an expanded memory board.

1.20 Trap: Don't use a LIM-ulator for a RAM disk or cache.

If you have extended memory, use the extended memory features of the RAM disk or disk cache. Using an emulator when you can use the real thing inflicts needless performance penalties on the RAM disk or disk cacher.

If you don't have extended memory, using a LIM-ulator for a RAM disk or cache is nonsense. The LIM-ulator uses conventional memory that you could devote to the RAM disk or cache. Also, the LIM-ulator is using the disk drive for its emulation of expanded memory. You add the 1,000-to-1 performance penalty to your use of the disk and gain no benefits.

The 386 CPU and Memory

1.21   Tip: The 386 CPU can treat extended memory as expanded memory.

All memory on a 386 computer is expanded memory. Although I confuse the issues by making this statement, the statement highlights the advantages of the 386 CPU.

You need either of two hardware pieces for expanded memory: an expanded memory board or an 80386 CPU. The expanded memory board contains the circuitry for performing page-switching and remapping. The 80386 itself has the hardware for performing the same page-switching and remapping.

The 386 can shuffle physical memory into many different logical (apparent) orders. Although a program thinks it has 128K of contiguous memory, the program could actually be using 32 different 4K chunks of memory. The remapping is transparent to the applications program; the 386 processor handles it by using *page mode* and hides the process.

The result is that 386-based systems can treat extended memory as expanded memory without any additional hardware circuitry. The only software piece needed is a small control program that enables page mode on the 386.

This control program is usually provided by the system manufacturer. PC DOS V4 provides XMAEM.SYS for its 386-based systems. COMPAQ 386 systems use CEMM.SYS. An extended version of CEMM.SYS is sold with the Softbyte/386 and 386-to-the-Max packages, 386 versions of the Softbyte emulator software. (CEMM, Softbytes/386, and 386-to-the-Max are written by the same author.) Another similar package is Quarterdeck's QEMM/386.

The control program is a LIM-avator (LIM activator), not a LIM-ulator. With a LIM-ulator, extended memory emulates expanded memory via software. The LIM-avator, however, activates the 386's hardware to treat extended memory as expanded memory, duplicating the page switching performed on EMS boards. All applications programs that use LIM V4 expanded memory can run on a 386.

The difference between the 286 and 386 is evident when you expand the memory of your computer. Most 286 systems have a choice of memory expansions: expanded, extended, or combination expanded and extended.

On 386 systems, you need only extended memory boards. The inherent power of the 386 plus the small control program turns extended memory into expanded memory. On 286 systems, charading extended memory as expanded memory lowers performance. The speed loss of using the control programs on a 386 is minuscule.

1.22   Trick: You can use the 640K through 1M region of real memory to run programs on a 386.

Another superiority of the 386 is its capability, through page mode, to use RAM in the high real-memory region of 640K through 1M. Because the 386 can make the physical memory appear to be addressed anywhere, programs can be loaded into a section of physical memory and logically appear to DOS and themselves that they run from real memory. The trickery is activated by the control program.

You can use this trickery to place ROM information into RAM. Because ROM is slower than RAM, placing a copy of ROM information into RAM speeds performance. (In fact, the PS/2 Models 70 to 80 can copy automatically the ROM BIOS into RAM.)

You can use this 640K to 1M RAM area also for *terminate-and-stay resident* programs (abbreviated TSR). By loading the TSR into high real memory, conventional DOS memory is freed for use by other programs. This trickery does not work with all TSRs. Some TSRs do not work well from high real memory. Some hardware and software combinations, such as those used with local area networks, preclude using some of the high real-memory space for RAM.

1.23   Tip: You can run multiple DOS programs on a 386.

You can run multiple programs on an 8088 (see fig. 1.6). For example, TSRs are a long established form of running multiple programs under DOS. Also, multitasking programs such as Software Carousel and Quarterdeck's DESQview™ allow any two or more non-TSR programs to run at once.

However, you can run any two or more DOS programs on a 386 without restrictions on program size, use of expanded or extended memory, or use of DOS interrupts. The 386-based computer has the horsepower to run several programs without serious performance degradation.

For hardware, you must have enough RAM. For software, you need a multitasking supervisor such as Microsoft Windows/386 or DESQview working with its QEMM/386 control program.

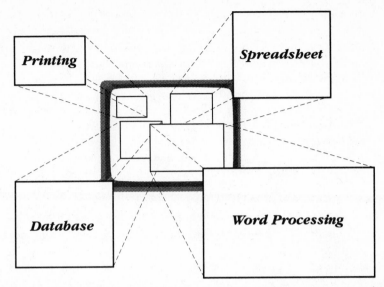

Fig. 1.6. With multitasking supervision, a single 386 computer can act as several 8086-based DOS computers at one time.

The 80386 has a hybrid operation mode, called *virtual 86 mode*, that crosses real mode, paging mode, and protected mode. This mode allows the 386 hardware to act like a series of 8086-based computers. The important magic used in virtual 86 mode is that each program thinks that it is running in the first 640K of memory.

The memory-paging hardware of the 386 hides the fact that the program may be anywhere in physical memory (above or below the 1M point) and that the program may be in several different chunks of physical memory. The same paging hardware also allows the program to use any extended memory as expanded memory.

Protected mode also stops programs from escaping from their apparent 640K space; therefore, programs cannot overwrite each other in memory. In protected mode, programs are assigned a segment of apparent memory of 640K bytes. The 386 will not let the program write data outside of its 640K boundary (which could cause the system to crash). But the 386 doesn't restrict the program from writing in its own 640K segment.

Only the 386 can run any two or more DOS programs with these protections. The 8088 and 8086 do not have a protected mode. The 80286 has a protected mode, but cannot fool a program into thinking that it is running from real memory when it is running from protected memory. Also, the 286 cannot duplicate the magic of making a program see chunks of noncontiguous memory as one larger, continuous chunk.

However, a hardware add-on board called the All-Charge Card adds the memory-paging hardware to 286 processors. The result is similar to having a 386, but not identical. You still need special software, such as DESQview, to use these features. Also, some software does not run as well, and software written specifically for the 386 does not work.

Programs such as Windows/386 and the DESQview-QEMM/386 combination handle the loading of programs into different memory partitions and arbitrate conflicts when two or more programs try to grab the same DOS or system resource (such as the printer, modem, or disk drive). Although each supervisor has some restrictions on which programs may require some supervisor setup, almost any program runs without any change—even most programs that write directly to the screen or try to read the keyboard directly. The programs that occasionally cause problems include communications programs (which need additional processor attention so that characters are not dropped).

Both Windows/386 and DESQview are worthy of investigation. You can get true multitasking capabilities without pitching your established software. Some programs do not need Windows or DESQview to multitask. The debugger from Borland, Turbo Debugger, uses virtual 86 mode. Normally, a debugger such as DEBUG or Periscope™ must share the 640K DOS space with the debugged program. If the buggy program is too large, the debugger and program cannot fit in memory; therefore, the debugger is useless.

To circumvent this problem, Periscope can be placed on a memory board outside of the 640K DOS space. Instead of a separate memory board, Turbo Debugger uses the 386 to put the program and a small piece of the debugger in one 640K session while the rest of the debugging program is in another 640K session. Not only can large programs be debugged, but the multiple session approach lets you watch the executing program while the debugger displays its information.

The 386 has many advantages over its less powerful brethren. Speed and larger RAM sizes are the usual focus. The page-mapping hardware makes memory expansion a simpler choice (because all memory can be treated as expanded memory). However, the feature that is not fully used today, virtual 86 mode, may be the best reason to buy a 386-based system. No other processor does it better (*it* being the capability to run multiple DOS programs).

1.24   Tip: Some 386 computers running at the same system clock speed outperform others.

All 386-based computers are not equal. The clock speed may be one difference, but less obvious differences include variations in the computers' internal construction. At the same clock speed, the type of RAM and memory cache used account for a clock-speed difference of 25 percent among 386-based systems.

Putting the difference into perspective is important. A 25 MHz 386 system is 4 to 7 times faster than an 8 MHz PC AT. System clock speed is not the only performance factor; the 25 MHz clock is just over 3 times faster than the 8 MHz clock. If you need a computer that is 7 times faster rather than just 4 times faster than a PC AT, knowing the differences in computer construction is important in selecting the right system for your needs.

In 8088 through 286 systems, memory speed is simply a matter of using fast enough RAM. However, at system clock speeds of 16 MHz or faster, major differences come into play. The RAM used in the 8088, 8086, and 286 is not fast enough for the 386.

Two types of RAM can be used in a computer: dynamic (abbreviated DRAM) and static (abbreviated SRAM). The key differences include size, money, power consumption, and access time. Dynamic memory is not only physically smaller than static memory, but it is also cheaper and consumes less power.

On the other hand, one of the many advantages of static memory over dynamic memory is a faster access time. Dynamic memory requires a precharging time before its contents are ready. A dynamic RAM whose access time is 100 ns requires a precharging time of 90 ns. (One nanosecond is a billionth of a second.) The result is that the effective access time of 100 ns is actually 190 ns. Dynamic memory is adequate below 16 MHz. The chips are fast enough, but at 16 MHz or higher, the access time of dynamic memories limits the speed of the CPU.

Static memory does not require precharging time; therefore, the access time of static memory is the true access time. The fastest dynamic memory is in the 60 ns range. The fastest static memory is 15 to 25 ns using silicon chips and 6 ns using a different, but more expensive, chip construction.

Another contrast is that the sequence of addressing dynamic memory is different than the static memory sequence. Under many conditions, static memory can offer more information than dynamic memory in the same amount of time.

Manufacturers balance performance and cost by using a blend of memory in the computer. Some manufacturers (such as COMPAQ in some of its 386 systems) use the static column approach. *Static column* is a hybrid dynamic memory disguised as static memory. Static columns fall somewhere within all the price and performance differences of static and dynamic memory. Static columns can move more information than dynamic memory in the same amount of time.

Other systems use two types of memory. Most memory is dynamic or static column; a small section of very high speed static memory also is used. In addition, circuitry copies sections of information from dynamic memory into static memory. As long as the CPU uses the information from static memory, the highest performance is achieved. This scheme is called a *memory cache* and is used by COMPAQ in its 25 MHz models.

The larger the memory cache, the faster the machine. Most caches start at 64K and top at 256K. However, even the caching scheme can make a difference. If the CPU writes to the cache and slower dynamic memory at the same time (called *write-through*), the CPU can bottleneck occasionally as it waits for the slower dynamic memory to respond. If the cacher handles the writing to RAM independently, the system is faster. The difference in performance is 8 to 12 percent.

Adding Expansion Cards

1.25   Tip: Buy the right expansion card for your computer's expansion bus.

Two traps are buried in this tip. One trap is that the wrong expansion card will not fit physically into the computer system's expansion bus. The other trap is that buying the wrong expansion card can limit your system's performance.

Table 1.2 lists the three major expansion buses for IBM Personal Computers and clones.

Table 1.2
IBM Expansion Buses

Bus	Expansion Slot Size	Compatible Computers
PC	8 bit	PC, XT, and XT clones
AT	8 and 16 bit	AT, PS/2 Model 30, and many 286 and 386 clones
MCA	16 bit	Models 30/286, 50, 50Z, 60, and clones
MCA	16 and 32 bit	Models 70, 80, and clones

Note that the MCA bus is different from the PC and AT buses. PC or AT bus boards will not fit in an MCA slot, nor will MCA boards fit in a PC or AT slot.

Even though PC and AT buses are similar, you cannot fit an AT-style board in a PC slot; a PC-style board, however, will fit in an AT slot. Some adapters, such as communications or printer adapters, only come in PC-bus style. These cards are designed to transfer information 8 bits at a time. Because the external device connected to the adapter is the drag on performance, you don't have any problem using these cards.

However, certain adapters are performance barriers: memory boards, disk adapters, network adapters, and video adapters. All four are used extensively by the computer and affect operating performance. Using an 8-bit board when a 16-bit version is available unnecessarily drags down the performance of the system. An example is an 80286-based computer using a cheaper XT-like disk adapter card. When you use an AT-like disk adapter, the disk performance on the system increases 80 percent. Neither the disk drive nor computer changes, only the disk adapter.

Adding Memory

1.26 Tip: When you buy more memory chips for your system, make sure to buy the memory with the right access time.

Memory is priced by its access time. Memory with slow access time is cheaper than memory with faster access time. Buying memory that is too slow causes hardware failures. The board either inserts too many wait states, or you suffer parity errors or bad memory errors. You can use chips faster than required, but you simply spend more money than necessary.

Check your expansion board for the correct speed. Most expansion boards require 150 ns or faster DRAMs. At 8 MHz, 120 to 150 ns DRAMs are required. At 10 to 12 MHz speeds, 100 ns to 120 ns DRAMs are needed. At 14 to 16 MHz or faster, 80 ns DRAMs or 100 ns SRAMs are required. Faster speeds require static column or static RAMs.

1.27   Trap: Don't mix and match memory chips freely.

You cannot use dynamic memory chips where static columns or static memory are required, or vice versa. Also, don't mix RAM with different access times in the same row on a memory board. The slight difference in access time between certain chips can disrupt the system.

1.28   Tip: Have enough RAM in your system to satisfy your programs and your performance needs.

How much memory is right for you? The answer depends on you and your use of the computer. Demanding users or demanding usage require 1 to 3 megabytes or more of memory. Many users are comfortable with 1 megabyte. Others feel that 512K or 640K is more than adequate.

Remember that the absolute speed advantage is in using conventional memory. Programs and data work fastest from conventional memory, not from expanded or extended memory—even in 386-based machines. But if conventional memory is insufficient, you need to use expanded or extended memory. The question then becomes, "For what will you use more than 1M of RAM?" Among the potential uses are increased program functions and system performance.

The best amount of memory is the smallest amount to do productive work and get the best performance from your system. If you can benefit from the advantages of more RAM, buy more. If in doubt, gain experience with your computer and then decide whether you need more RAM. Even at the lofty prices caused by the 1988 RAM chip shortage, RAM is still a bargain.

2

Knowing and Protecting
Your Disk Drives

Despite their differences, the various types of disk drives have much in common. This chapter includes tips, tricks, and traps that illustrate these similarities and differences and help you become a more knowledgeable user of disks and disk drives.

The disk drive information is designed to help you achieve the best combination of hardware (by adapting or changing your hardware) or gain the best performance from your present hardware (by adapting or changing your software). For more information on both floppy and hard disk drives, see Que's books *Managing Your Hard Disk,* 2nd Edition; *MS-DOS User's Guide,* 3rd Edition; and *Using PC DOS,* 2nd Edition.

Disk Drive Capacity

2.1 Tip: The storage capacity of a disk depends on the number of cylinders, media surfaces, and sectors used.

All disk media are circular. The band of the surface used for recording information is called the *recording area* or *data area.* The data area is broken down further into the smaller concentric bands called *tracks* (see fig. 2.1).

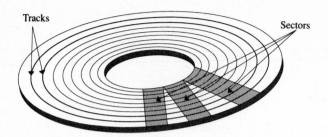

Fig. 2.1. A disk's tracks and sectors.

Most diskettes have two sides and are therefore called *double-sided floppy diskettes.* Hard disks, however, use two or more rigid steel, vertically stacked disks, called *platters*, which are also divided into tracks. Some hard disks devote the surface of one platter, the *servo surface*, to recording-head tracking information. An imaginary *cylinder* is formed by connecting any given track on a hard disk media surface with the same numbered track on different media surfaces (see fig. 2.2).

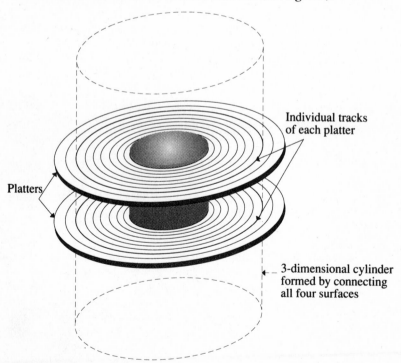

Fig. 2.2. Tracks, sectors, and cylinder.

Each track on the media is subdivided into *sectors*. The potential number of sectors per track is a function of the recording mechanism and media type. The smaller the magnetic field, the more sectors per track. To use more sectors, the media must withstand more magnetic flux changes per inch.

Table 2.1 lists statistics on the various track and sector layouts and provides some additional DOS information. Disks that use 8 sectors per track are relics from DOS V1. 360K (introduced by DOS V2) and 720K (introduced by some implementations of MS-DOS with V2.11; by PC DOS with V3.2) diskettes use 9 sectors per track. 1.2M diskettes use 15 sectors per track; 1.44M diskettes use 18. Most hard disks use 17 or 25 sectors, but the number varies.

Table 2.1
Table of Disk Characteristics

Disk Capacity	Tracks	Sectors	Heads	Introduced with DOS Version
160K minifloppy	40	8	1	V1.0
320K minifloppy	40	8	2	V1.1
180K minifloppy	40	9	1	V2.0
360K minifloppy	40	9	2	V2.0
10M hard disk	varies	17	varies	V2.0
1.2M minifloppy	80	15	2	V3.0
20M hard disk	varies	17	varies	V3.0
720K microfloppy	80	9	2	V3.2
30M hard disk	varies	17	varies	V3.2
1.44M microfloppy	80	18	2	V3.3
hard disk extended partitions	varies	17	varies	V3.3
32M+ partitions	varies	varies	varies	V3.31/V4.0

Floppy diskettes cost less than hard disks but store less information. Diskettes (and certain type of hard disks) are removable, which means that the alignment of the media to the disk drive's recording heads is imprecise. To compensate for this imprecision, the floppy disk's recording heads are slightly larger and generate a wider magnetic field. (The wider the field, the less data the media can accommodate.) Floppies therefore provide a lower total number of bytes per initial outlay. In addition, the floppy media is flexible, which means that the media-to-recording-head distance can vary, introducing even more imprecision.

Given the limits of the media and its use, floppy disk storage capacity cannot be improved to any extent without a significant increase in cost. Floppy disk drives are meant to be inexpensive. Major improvements that would give a floppy disk capacities that rival hard disks would price the drive out of the market. Also, drive manufacturers have a greater incentive to improve hard disks—the bang-for-the-buck is greater.

Compared to floppy drives, hard disk drives have several advantages that affect their storage capacity. Because the hard disk media is mounted, rigid, and precisely aligned with the recording heads, greater recording precision is possible. A more costly and precise mechanism is used on hard disks to step the arm that holds the recording heads.

In addition, the hard disk's recording head is smaller and more costly than the floppy disk's. Floppy disk drives record either 48 or 96 tracks per inch. Using a data band just smaller than 7/8 of an inch, the read/write heads of the drive record either 40 or 80 tracks. The width of the hard disk's recording band, however, is smaller. As a result, more tracks are created per circular inch of media—200 to 700 per inch—but at a greater cost.

Disk Drive Performance

The top disk drive performance factors include the following:

- Speed
- Transfer rate
- Access time
- Interleave
- Fragmentation
- Caching

The first four factors relate to the hardware of the computer. Transfer rate and access time relate to the speed of the drive, and interleave refers to the physical distance between sectors. Fragmentation is a natural consequence of disk drive use. Caching can be an added option, a built-in option, or both. More information on both caching and fragmentation can be found in Chapter 3, "Improving Disk Performance."

The following tips explain the first four factors. Some factors cannot be changed; others can. Depending on your system, some factors should be changed, particularly if you have a hard disk system.

Disk Drive Speed

2.2 Tip: Match disk drive speed with the computing power of your system.

Hard disk drive pricing is based primarily on speed. A disk drive much slower than the computer is a drain on computing power. A disk drive much faster than the computer is an overly expensive investment. The trick is to use a disk drive as fast as the computer, or nearly as fast.

As you read the following tips, remember that you must change the hardware associated with the disk drive in order to change some of the speed factors; other factors can be changed by changing the way you use the drive.

Data Transfer Rate

2.3 Tip: Use caution when you interpret disk drive transfer rate specifications.

The *data transfer rate* is the speed at which information moves from the disk to the computer or from the computer to the disk. The rate is expressed in either kilobits (Kbits) or kilobytes (K) per second for floppy disks. On hard disks, the rate is sometimes expressed in Mbits (megabits) and M (megabytes) per second.

The three types of transfer rates are burst, average, and real. *Burst data transfer rate*, or maximum data transfer rate, is the speed of information transfer if every factor is perfect (the recording heads are in the right spot, the interleave is optimum, the computer and disk drive can absorb or transmit the information without delay, and so on). Because all these factors are seldom correct, the burst transfer rate usually applies only to short amounts of information.

The *average data transfer* rate is the effective rate at which larger amounts of data move between your system and disk drives. Average data transfer reflects the point at which other capabilities of the disk drive affect the performance of prolonged data transfer.

The rate that drive manufacturers cannot quote is the *real data transfer rate*, the rate at which information moves between the disk drive and your computer. The quoted transfer rates do not include other factors that reflect true disk performance. Real data transfer rate depends on your computer, the disk drive, the operating system, the applications software, and other factors. Each factor imposes a limit on the real data transfer rate.

When you consider the specifications of any disk drive, remember that burst and average data rates represent the ideal. In practical day-to-day use, however, these rates may become interesting fictions.

2.4   Tip: Transfer rate is more sensitive to the disk drive controller on a hard disk system than to the controller on a floppy drive system.

Two elements—the computer's adapter and the electronic controller for the disk drive—place upper boundaries on the transfer rate for a disk. No matter how "fast" the disk drive stores and retrieves information, data cannot be moved faster between the computer and disk drive than the interface and controller can handle.

Floppy disk drives usually use an integrated controller-interface adapter board that is plugged into the computer. The intelligence for operations is located on the controller interface, not on the floppy disk drive.

Most floppy disk drives use the same type of controller interface. Because of their slowness, floppy drives do not tax the transfer rate of the controller and, therefore, the controller interface for floppy disks is not a concern.

For hard disks, the adapter card that is placed in the computer is the disk drive controller which communicates with the hard disk drive's logic board. Unlike floppy disk drives, the hard disk's intelligence is split between the controller and the drive's own logic board. The floppy disk drive must be instructed to start its motor, move a certain number of tracks, wait for a given sector, and begin reading or writing. For a hard disk, the controller requests a given cylinder, head, and sector; the logic board does the remaining work. The controller guides the hard disk drive; with a floppy diskette, the drive must be led through each step.

The interface between the drive's logic board and the controller is dictated by the logic board. Different interfaces have different upper boundaries on data transfer rate. In addition, different controllers can have functions and features that boost drive performance. The interface type between the drive and controller and the controller itself therefore become important performance factors.

Hard disk drives fall into three speed classes based on the interface used by the controller: ST-506, ESDI, and SCSI. *ST-506* is the name of the first Winchester disk drive produced by Seagate Technology, which dominates the low end of the hard disk market. The ST-506, commonly known as the Seagate® interface, is used on most "low-end" disk drives. The top speed of the interface is 5 megabits/second (Mbit/sec.) or 625K per second. This drive-interface combination is used on most PC, XT, AT, and lower-end PS/2 computers.

ESDI, nicknamed *ED-see,* the abbreviation for Enhanced System Device Interface, is a higher performance device interface. Like the ST-506, the interface is a serial bus, but it can be used with other devices, ranging from tape backup units to optical scanners. The current top speed of ESDI is 15 Mbit/sec. (1.875M per second). ESDI is used on many fast 286 systems and most 386 systems.

SCSI, nicknamed *scuzzy* or *sexy,* is the abbreviation for Small Computer System Interface. SCSI evolved from the ST-506 Interface, and like ESDI, SCSI is actually a bus for intelligent devices. Unlike ESDI, SCSI is a parallel bus. The maximum transfer rate for the bus is 25 Mbit/sec. (more than 3M per second).

Of the three standards, ST-506 dominates the low end and ESDI dominates the high end. Because SCSI is about 25 percent more expensive than ESDI, and because the ST-506, ESDI, and SCSI do not work with each other, SCSI's role in the PC world has been minimal.

Because of the popularity of the Apple Macintosh® II, which has a SCSI interface available, marketplace forces will probably increase the number of SCSI devices and decrease the price differential. Eventually, SCSI may become a force in the PC drive world, but for now, Seagate and ESDI rule.

Access Time

2.5 Tip: Track-to-track access time and average access time vary widely among hard disks but vary little among floppy disks.

Average access time is the time it takes the recording heads in the disk drive to move from one random location to another and obtain the start of the requested information. *Track-to-track access time* is the amount of time it takes the recording heads to move to an adjacent cylinder and access the recorded information. Both figures are rated in milliseconds (ms, thousandths of a second). Both times are functions of disk rotation speed and the stepping mechanism inside the disk drive.

Access times are almost uniform for classes of floppy disk drives. The access times of hard disk drives, however, vary greatly. This variation leads to interesting games among hard disk manufacturers. The most interesting aspect is that a single component of access time—seek time—gains the most attention.

Access time is a function of three different components: settle time, latency, and seek time. Two of these components are fixed by disk drive class. The third is fixed for floppy disks but varies among hard disks.

Settle time is the amount of time the disk drive waits after the recording heads have moved before the drive attempts to read or write information. Because of greater imprecisions in the floppy disk stepping mechanism, settle time usually applies only to floppy disk drives. The computer waits 20 ms for the heads to settle on 360K and 720K disks and 15 ms for 1.2M and 1.44M disks. Settle time usually applies to formatting or writing; settle time for reading is negligible. DOS retries the read operations if the recording heads are not yet settled.

Latency is the amount of time needed for the information on the track to move into the correct position. Because the sector underneath the disk drive head is random, latency is the statistically averaged time for one-half of a disk's rotation.

Because classes of disk drives rotate at a fixed speed, latency is constant among them. 360K diskettes rotate at 300 rpm. The average latency is 100 ms, one-half of a diskette's rotation. 720K, 1.44M, and 1.2M diskettes rotate at 360 rpm and have a latency of 89 ms. Most hard disks rotate at 3600 rpm. The average latency is 8.9 ms, one-half of a hard disk's rotation.

One difference between the latency of hard and floppy disk drives is waiting time. Latency does not include the waiting time for the disk to come up to the correct speed. Hard disks keep the platters spinning; floppy disk drives turn their motors off and on between operations, adding a time of 250 ms to 500 ms while waiting for the diskette to spin at the correct speed. If that time is taken into account, the time difference between the first floppy disk and hard disk operation is about 67 to 1.

2.6 Tip: Differences in seek times account for the differences in access times.

The variable component of access time is seek time. The terms are often confused. *Seek time* is the amount of time the recording heads take to move from one cylinder to another. *Track-to-track seek time* is the time the heads take to move between adjacent tracks. *Average seek time* is the average time the recording heads take to move from one random location to another. Both are rated in milliseconds.

The seek times of floppy disk drives vary little, with track-to-track seek times falling into the 3 to 6 ms range. Average seek time is seldom given for floppy disk drives because the disk drive heads move at a fixed, linear rate (3 to 6 ms per track). The mechanical imprecision of floppy disk drives precludes the use of a faster mechanism.

Most hard disks have track-to-track seek times of 3 to 6 ms, not much different from floppy disk drives. The average seek times for hard disks as a class, however, range between 18 and 100 ms. Because the head movement for average seek time is more than several hundred tracks, hard disks use a special trick, called *ramping*, to cover that distance.

After the hard disk heads start moving, the stepping mechanism accelerates (ramps up) the heads. The initial rate for moving the heads between the first two tracks is 6 ms. The rate quickens as the heads continue to move. Because of ramping, many hard disk drives have similar track-to-track seek times but different average seek times.

Track-to-track seek time is an important factor if the drive is transferring information between adjacent cylinders on the disk. As the user stores and removes information from the disk drive, information is spread over nonadjacent cylinders. The importance of track-to-track seek time decreases; average seek times (which translate into average access times) become more important.

2.7   Tip: Small differences in hard disk average seek times are significant.

Although average seek and access times are rated in milliseconds, the differences in times can be significant. Consider the difference between disk drives with 28 ms and 40 ms average seek times; the 22 ms difference may seem insignificant.

Assume, however, that both drives transfer information at 625K/second. By the time the 40 ms drive is ready to deliver information, the 28 ms drive delivers 11.25K of information. Multiply that 11.25K difference by hundreds of operations a day; the 22 ms difference becomes significant.

Although this example exaggerates the importance of average seek time, the minor differences are important. The most time-consuming housekeeping activity any disk drive performs is moving the recording heads between cylinders. The last operation you want your disk drive to perform is to move the recording heads.

Average seek time, like latency, settle time, and access time, has good news and bad news qualities. The bad news is that you cannot change the seek times, access times, latency, and settling times.

The good news is that you can speed up your disk drives. You can, for example, minimize moving the disk drive recording heads. The methods are discussed in Chapter 3 with the topics of fragmentation and disk performance. Another method is to ensure that the interleave factor your disk drive uses is correct. Interleave is the subject of the next set of tips.

Interleave

Interleave is the difference between the physical sectors and the logical sectors on a disk's track. The average transfer rate is a function of the average access time and the controller interface type. For hard disks, average access time is a function of latency and seek time. Because these factors are inherent to a disk drive, you exercise your control over them only when you decide which drive and computer to buy.

Average access time is also a function of interleave. Interleave is constant for floppy diskettes but variable for hard disks. The wrong interleave can seriously degrade your hard disk's performance. Fortunately, interleave for hard disks is a factor you can control.

If your disk drive was part of your original computer equipment, your interleave setting is probably correct. If you have changed the operating speed of your computer or changed or added a hard disk or controller card, the interleave of your disk drive may be incorrect.

To understand interleave, imagine an unusual merry-go-round. You are seated on a stationary horse at the side of the ride. Instead of horses, the merry-go-round has 17 prize-dispensers, numbered from 1 to 17, mounted on its platform.

The ride operator at your side will call out a starting dispenser number and the number of prizes to grab. You must grab the first prize from the starting dispenser, the second prize from the next highest numbered dispenser, and so on. Because the prizes are large, you can hold only one prize at a time. Before you can grab another prize, you must hand the preceding prize to the operator who will accumulate them for you.

As the game starts, the operator calls out the starting number two and three prizes. As dispenser two comes into reach, you grab the prize, hand it to the operator, and wait for dispenser three to come by. Dispenser three, however, has already passed. You must wait another turn of the merry-go-round before you can get the prize from dispenser three. The same holds true for dispenser four. As you hand off the prize from dispenser three, dispenser four has passed your reach.

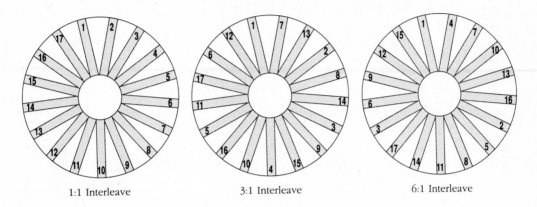

1:1 Interleave   3:1 Interleave   6:1 Interleave

Fig. 2.3. Examples of interleave.

The process is time-consuming. For every prize you grab, you must wait a full turn of the merry-go-round for the next prize. You cannot slow the merry-go-round, nor can you make the exchange between you and the operator faster.

The solution is not to change the merry-go-round but to change the numbering of the dispensers. The number of dispensers does not change; you change just the numbers you use to identify each dispenser.

If the dispensers are numbered correctly, you can grab a prize, hand the prize to the operator, turn, and have the next highest numbered dispenser at hand. You simply reach out again and grab the next prize. By the time you hand off the prize, the next correct dispenser comes into grasp.

If the numbering is not correct, you grab a prize, hand off, turn, and wait for the next dispenser. The length of the wait depends on the numbering scheme. The shortest wait is when the needed dispenser follows the dispenser at hand as soon as you turn back. The longest wait is when the needed dispenser has passed your grasp when you turn.

In this analogy, the merry-go-round is the disk platter. The dispensers are the disk's sectors. The prize is the data in each sector. The merry-go-round operator is a combination of the computer, DOS, and your programs. You are the disk's recording heads.

When a disk drive is physically formatted, the sectors on a disk's track are established one after the other. They are contiguous, but there is a gap between each sector. Each sector carries an identification number, which can be different from its physical position on the track.

The interleave factor is the relationship of physical sectors to logical (apparent) sectors (the identification number). Interleave is the number of physical sectors you must jump to get to the next logical sector (see fig. 2.3). If logical sectors 1 and 2 are adjacent (you jump one physical sector to reach the next logical sector), the interleave is 1:1 or 1.

If logical sectors 1 and 2 are two sectors apart (one sector resides between the two), the interleave factor is 2:1 or 2. IBM ATs have an interleave factor of 3, which means that two sectors are between each logical sector. IBM XTs use an interleave of 6, which means that five sectors are between each logical sector.

Remember that interleave is the physical "distance" needed to *reach* the next logical sector, not the number of physical sectors between logical sectors. The number of physical sectors between each logical sector is the interleave minus one.

The interleave factor also refers to the minimum number of revolutions the disk must make before the entire track is read. An interleave of 1 means that the entire track can be read in one revolution. An interleave factor of 3 means that the entire track can be read in 3 revolutions. Before assuming that an interleave of 1 is the best interleave, remember the merry-go-round example and read the next trap.

2.8 Trap: The wrong interleave setting can seriously degenerate your hard disk's performance.

Because a higher interleave means that the disk must spin more times before all data on the track can be read, you would normally assume that the best interleave is 1. The assumption is true for some computers but seriously flawed for others.

If the computer is as fast or faster than the disk drive, the interleave is set to 1. No delays are needed. The disk drive operates at its fastest speed.

If the hard disk delivers data faster than the computer absorbs information, however, a timing problem occurs. The correct prize dispenser is not in the right position. The disk drive must wait for the sector to revolve into position. You lose opportunities to move information at the highest rate if you must wait for the sectors.

If the drive delivers data too quickly, setting the interleave to a higher number gives the computer time to absorb the requested sector. When the computer is ready for the next sector, the sector is under the recording heads and ready to be moved.

2.9 Tip: The right interleave setting is a "mating" between your computer and disk drive.

Because of the variables, interleave is a "mating" game. There is no universal "best" interleave factor for all computers. Interleave must be determined on a case-by-case basis. The match-up of your computer type, the disk drive, operating system, and the operations you perform determine the best interleave.

Performance penalties are caused by an interleave set too low or too high. An interleave set one less than the optimum interleave causes the greatest performance penalty. You wait one full revolution for the sector to come into position. Although the time is rated in milliseconds, some arithmetic illustrates that the penalties do make a difference in performance.

Remember that most hard disks spin at 3600 revolutions per minute. The platter makes one revolution in 16.7 milliseconds. Assume the 625K/second transfer rate. Taking a full extra revolution to read a sector means losing the opportunity to transfer 10.5K. Your disk drive takes that one extra revolution per sector when the recording head just misses the sector.

Table 2.2, which quantifies the effect of interleave on disk drive performance, shows the effect of various interleaves on a Sperry IT (an AT clone) and the PS/2 Model 60. Both use 40M disk drives. For the Sperry, an interleave of 2 is best. For the PS/2, an interleave of 1 is best.

Table 2.2
Interleave Vs. Transfer Rate
The Sperry IT and PS/2 Model 60

| | Sperry IT 40MB | | PS/2 Model 60 40MB | |
| | Transfer | | Transfer | |
Interleave	Rate	Time	Rate	Time
1	28.3	75.0	256.2	8.3
2	254.5	8.3	169.7	12.5
3	169.7	12.5	169.7	12.5
4	127.3	16.7	127.7	16.6
5	101.8	20.9	102.1	20.8
6	85.0	25.0	84.8	25.0
7	72.9	29.2	72.9	29.2
8	63.7	33.3	63.7	33.3
9	56.6	37.5	56.6	37.5
10	51.0	41.6	51.0	41.7
11	46.4	45.8	46.4	45.8
12	42.5	50.0	42.5	50.0
13	39.2	54.2	39.2	54.2
14	36.4	58.3	36.4	58.3
15	34.0	62.5	34.0	62.5
16	31.0	66.7	31.9	66.7

Notice the worst interleave for the respective machines. For the Sperry, an interleave of 1 is the worst possible. For the PS/2, an interleave of 16 is the worst. The worst interleave is one "behind" the best. In the case of the PS/2, one behind is an interleave of 16. The 88% degeneration in speed shows the penalty for making an extra platter revolution for each sector read. The other interleaves show lesser penalties, ranging from 44% to 87% on the PS/2 and from 43% to 89% on the Sperry IT.

2.10 Tip: Buy and use a disk interleave tester if you have changed your computer's speed or installed third-party disk drives.

Most computer manufacturers set the interleave of the hard disk drives in their system. The setting is based on the type of disk drive, the type of drive interface, and the speed of the expansion slot bus. Because all these items affect the optimum interleave, changing any of them can change the best interleave for the disk drive.

When installing a third-party hard disk, don't assume that one interleave fits all. The different optimal interleaves for each type of computer are based on processor speed, interface and controller type, hard disk type, and operating system. If you have not altered your computer, you can use the interleave provided by the manufacturer for your computer (XT, AT, 386, and so on). If your computer is faster than the standard model (you are using a coprocessor board or have changed the clock speed that affects the expansion bus speed) or your drive manufacturer provides a vanilla interleave setting, you probably should test for the best interleave.

Several programs test for the best interleave for your disk drive. SpinRite® by Gibson Research and HOPTIMUM, part of the HTEST/HFORMAT package by Kolad Research (now marketed by Mace Software), are two examples. Both programs can test your disk drive for the optimal interleave and change the interleave setting.

Because using the wrong interleave can rob your disk drive of up to 80 percent of its performance, these programs are strongly recommended if you use a hard disk not provided by the computer's manufacturer. The programs are also recommended if you have changed any of the system performance aspects of your computer (such as resetting the computer's system clock or adding an accelerator board).

The programs work by reformatting your hard disk. Usually, interleave is established when the drive is physically formatted. When you physically format a disk, all previously recorded information is lost. SpinRite and HOPTIMUM, however, safely reformat the disk drive. Each program reads the entire track from the disk drive, reformats the track, restores the information, and then processes the next track. If no failures occur during the process (such as power loss to the computer), the process is totally safe.

Failures, however, are random and difficult to predict. For this reason, back up the hard disk before changing the interleave. Although the programs are reliable, they cannot recover from disasters. Although the amount of information lost may be small (one track's worth, from 8.5K to 17K), knowing which information was lost is difficult to trace. The best insurance against an abrupt termination and data loss is a current backup of the disk.

Disk Buffering

2.11   Tip: Some disk controller interfaces can increase disk performance or capacity.

Some, but definitely not all, hard disk controller cards offer additional performance or capacity. Performance can be boosted, for example, when the controller card offers full-track buffering. The controller card contains the necessary programming and RAM memory to hold a complete track's worth of information from the disk drive. The controller card, not the computer, handles the timing for the hard disk to read and write the track's worth of information. As a result, many disk operations are consolidated into a few disk accesses, boosting average performance 5 to 15 percent.

Also, some disk controllers pack more information into the same space. This technique, called *run-length limited encoding* or *RLL*, stores an additional 50 percent or more information in the same space. With more information per track, the disk recording heads step less, which results in greater performance.

If your disk controller does not handle RLL encoding, you can replace the controller or buy a new disk drive and controller. Adding RLL controllers onto disk drives not rated for RLL use is like using 720K floppies at 1.44M capacities: the process will work for some but not for others, and the process can fail unexpectedly.

If your disk controller does not handle full-track buffering, you have several choices: replace the controller with another that performs this task; use software that approximates this function; or ignore this aspect of disk performance. If your controller handles full-track buffering, you already have the benefits. You can, however, benefit more by using other items mentioned in Chapter 3, "Improving Disk Performance," especially if you don't have an intelligent controller card.

Protecting Floppy Disk Drives

The floppy disk drive's door, latch, ejector button, and faceplate are the most susceptible to damage from direct physical shock. Made of plastic, these items are the easiest to break. A broken faceplate, although aesthetically unpleasing, may still be mechanically usable. If any of the other parts break, however, the drive usually does not operate. Factory repair of these items is often more costly than replacing the disk drive.

Because it is susceptible to an indirect blow, the recording head mechanism can be damaged even more easily than the external parts of the drive. When the drive door is closed, the recording heads of an empty minifloppy disk drive touch each other. A shock applied to any part of the disk drive can bang the heads together.

A microfloppy's heads do not touch until a diskette is inserted. The force that causes the microfloppy's heads to bang together normally damages other parts of the disk drive. In addition, the arm that holds the recording heads on either type of drive can be broken or jarred out of its horizontal alignment. Again, replacing the disk drive may be cheaper than repairing it.

Considerable force, such as a direct forceful blow or a several foot drop, is required to damage the recording heads or other parts of the drive. Less force is required to disrupt an in-use disk drive, but the consequences can be more severe.

While the drive is in use, a strong shock can move the recording heads off track or away from the media. Because the media is flexible, little or no physical damage occurs to the media or recording heads. If it is reading or writing to the disk, DOS usually retries the operation so that no information is recorded improperly. However, the drive can write to the wrong part of the disk, causing data to be overwritten and lost files to be jumbled. The risk is small but potentially damaging.

2.12   Trick: If you ship the computer long distances or move the computer, place the cardboard protector or a junk diskette in the drive.

The recording heads of a minifloppy disk drive are the most vulnerable to physical shock because the heads barely touch each other when the door is closed. A severe shock to the disk drive causes the heads to bang against each other. Any material inserted between the heads will protect the disk drive.

You can use the original cardboard shipping protector or a junk diskette. Avoid using a vital diskette for this purpose. I have yet to lose a diskette by leaving it in a transported disk drive, but I don't like to take any chances of losing information.

You do not need to protect microfloppy drives in this manner. When no diskette is in the disk drive, the heads do not touch each other; therefore, placing a diskette into the drive is unnecessary. Also, a physical shock severe enough to damage the recording heads will damage other parts of the drive. An inserted diskette might absorb some of the shock but is unlikely to protect most of the drive.

2.13 Tip: Floppy disk drives are often more easily replaced than repaired.

Other than an occasional cleaning of the floppy disk drive heads, floppy disks require little maintenance. Given the competitive prices on floppy disk drives ($35 to $120, depending on the floppy drive type) and the expense of service to determine and fix a complex problem (at an average rate of $60 an hour), the standard operating procedure is to buy a new drive rather than repair the old drive.

There are exceptions to the rule. Three frequently broken but easily repairable items are spindle motor timing (adjustable with a screwdriver and a floppy drive timing test/maintenance program), the recording head alignment (also tunable, but which may require more expensive equipment), and placement or replacement of the band that connects the spindle motor to the spindle, which sometimes stretches or just falls off.

You can easily fix the motor timing and belt problems with the right tool and program. Head alignment requires an alignment diskette and a disk drive analyzer. Some programs turn your computer into the analyzer so that separate equipment may not be required.

Because many local computer repair services charge less than $50 to adjust a drive or provide preventive maintenance, you can have some problems inexpensively prevented or solved. But if the problem is severe, replacing the disk drive may be the less expensive alternative.

Protecting Hard Disk Drives

Stepper motors and voice coils are the two principal technologies used for positioning the recording heads of all disk drives. You need to know which type your disk drive uses so that you know which defensive measures to take.

Stepper motors move the heads in small increments called *steps*. Floppy disk drives use stepper motors exclusively. *Voice coils* use changes in a magnetic field to move the heads, a technology similar to that of audio

speakers. Voice coil drives also use a separate recording surface for the
servo information that positions the recording heads.

Most stepper motors have average seek times in the 40 ms to 100 ms
range, but the recent Seagate disk drive uses stepper motors that achieve a
28 ms average seek time. However, most voice-coil-based disk drives have
an average seek time in the 18 to 40 ms range. Voice-coil-based drives
offer superior performance.

Seek time, however, is only one of the differences between stepper motors
and voice coils. Voice coil disk drives are also more reliable than stepper-
motor disk drives. In the following tips, additional differences and
defensive measures for both types are examined.

Protecting Against Physical Shock

2.14   Trap: Physical shock is more dangerous to hard disks than to floppy disks.

As the old saying goes, it's not the fall but the sudden stop. That sudden
stop can happen in several ways. Of course, you expect damage to occur
from dropping a computer or disk drive from a height of several feet. But
that sudden stop can also occur from bumping or jarring your computer or
hard disk drive. In either case, you can ruin a hard disk drive, your data,
or both. Given the amount of information hard disks hold, the results can
be catastrophic.

Hard disk drives are more susceptible to physical damage than floppy
drives primarily because of their physical differences: the media's weight,
the media's rigidity, the media's spin rate, the weight of the recording
head, and aerodynamics. A floppy diskette is flexible and lightly massed,
spins at a lower rate, and has a low kinetic energy. The floppy recording
heads are larger and operate by touching the surface of the diskette.

The rigid hard disk platter is more heavily massed and spins at a rate 10
times faster than a floppy disk. The recording heads are light, and the
arms are aerodynamic. During operation, the air movement caused by the
rapidly spinning media lifts the recording heads off the platter. A gap of
thousandths of an inch separates the heads and platter.

A floppy diskette absorbs kinetic energy by flexing. Because the recording
heads are large, the energy transfer occurs over a large area. The state of
the drive, whether in use or at rest, does not matter. When a diskette is in

the disk drive (and the door or latch of minifloppy drives is closed), the head makes contact with the media.

A hard disk drive's heads make contact with the media in three situations. The first situation occurs when gravity overpowers the aerodynamic force as you power down the hard disk. As the disk slows, the aerodynamic force dissipates and the heads gently come to rest on the disk's surface.

The second situation occurs when kinetic energy overcomes the inertia of the recording heads, which are resting in a plane. The third situation arises when acceleration in an opposite plane overcomes the aerodynamic force. An external physical force provides the acceleration, such as a bump, drop, or jar. These last two situations are technically named *head crash*, and the results can be devastating.

While in use, hard disk drives are susceptible to movement and physical shock. The recording head floats over the disk drive, and if a shock forces the recording head into the drive, the media does not flex to absorb the shock. Instead, the energy is dissipated by friction, sending the smaller recording head away from the platter surface. In the process, the inflexible media and recording head, which is lighter but has a smaller area to absorb the shock, is scraped. Damaged recording heads, damaged media, or both often result. Data is lost, either because the media has been scraped or because tracks cannot be accessed by the damaged recording head.

While at rest, the hard disk drive is more stable. The heads do not receive the kinetic force of the spinning platters. Much more acceleration is required to lift and splatter the heads into the media.

Hard disks have two G ratings (a G is the force of the earth's gravity at sea level): one rating while in use and one while at rest. The in-use rating is typically half of the at-rest rating. Some drives have an in-use rating as low as 5 Gs; others have an in-use rating in the 30 Gs. The most common ratings range from 10 to 20 Gs in use and 20 to 40 Gs at rest.

Your drive can be damaged by sudden acceleration or deceleration. Sudden acceleration is difficult to achieve. Although humans black out at 5 Gs, humans can produce a G force that exceeds this rate by swiftly swinging an object on a rope. The more likely event is sudden deceleration. The 20 G force can be duplicated by dropping the disk drive from a distance of just over 3 feet onto a concrete floor. The same force can be duplicated by a 12-year-old's full-fisted punch.

Because knowing your disk drive's tolerance to shock is difficult to judge, treat the computer and disk drive with care. Casual, slight bumps and jars will not hurt a hard disk. Strong bumps, jars, and drops will destroy a hard disk.

Parking the Heads

2.15 Trap: Powering up the hard disk drive can adversely affect the recorded information.

Disk drive heads can accidentally record information in two situations. Both occur when the drive is first turned on.

When you turn on the disk drive, a minute surge of electricity can cause your drive heads to issue a magnetic pulse. Most disk drive manufacturers design damping circuitry for the drives to prevent this problem. The chance of a stray pulse is rare.

The other situation occurs when the disk drive heads have a weak latent magnetism. The latent magnetism accumulates with disk use, but is generally insignificant. During normal operation, the head is distant enough from the platter so that the latent magnetism of the recording heads has no effect. When the heads land on the platter, there is a small chance that the heads can inadvertently record information.

When the disk drive is first turned on, however, the disk heads are violently jerked sideways into random alignment, then into proper alignment. The movement is only within thousandths of an inch, but the heads rest on the not-yet-moving platter. The magnetic field is still weak, but the field now moves quickly, and the magnetic field is much closer to the platter; all of these factors increase the chance of a stray recording. The electronics of the disk drive usually, but not always, fail before the drive records stray matter.

The result can be a loss of one bit of information to several bits of information. If the loss is less than four bits, the drive normally can compensate for the error. If the affected bits are in a key disk housekeeping area or the result is larger than four bits, the result can be a bad sector. Develop a bad sector in a key DOS housekeeping area and the results can be disastrous.

2.16 Tip: If your hard disk drive does not park its heads automatically, run a parking program before turning off your system.

To prevent the hard disk drive heads from scraping the data area of the platter surface or making a stray recording, the heads should be retracted or extended to an unused area of the disk, called a *landing zone* or *parking zone*. The act of moving the heads to this zone is appropriately called *parking the heads*.

The disk drive heads can be parked at any time. The appropriate time to park the heads is before you move the drive or before you turn off the power.

Most hard disks in laptop computers automatically park their heads after 10 seconds of inactivity. Because laptop computers are more likely to suffer physical shock than stationary computers, the manufacturers protect the drive's data by keeping the heads off the data area as much as possible.

The same hard disks in laptops and many hard disks in other computers automatically park the disk heads when the drive is powered down. The auto-park mechanics are built into the recording head mechanism.

All drives that use voice-coil-driven recording arms automatically park the heads. Without power to the coil, the natural position for the drive heads is in the parking zone. To move the heads, power must be applied to the coil to counteract the pull into the landing zone. When the drive is powered down, the heads naturally seek the parking zone.

Few stepper-motor disk drives have auto-park features. Automatic parking adds to the price of the disk drive, and most stepper-motor disk drives are selected because they are less expensive.

If you are unsure whether your drive automatically parks its heads, you can perform a simple test. While the computer is idle, turn the power off and listen. A self-parking hard disk drive will produce a dull, but unique, "thunk" or "chonck." If you hear only the whining down of the platters, you must park the disk heads manually.

If your computer is stationary and at no risk from physical shock, the danger of physical damage is modest. Every time you power down your drive, there is a slight chance that the heads may nick the data surface. Unfortunately, the chance of a stray recording is slightly higher. Because some inexpensive disk drives seem to act as logical lightning rods, using parking programs is a good idea.

The greatest risk occurs when a stationary computer is struck or moved. If your computer is in a location where physical shock is probable, park the disk drive heads before you leave. If you move the system (including portable computers), park the disk drive heads before the computer is moved.

Several programs park the drive heads. Some are shareware or public-domain programs, such as TIMEPARK on CompuServe Information Service®. Others are provided with the computer, such as IBM's SHIPDISK on the XT or AT Diagnostic diskettes, or PARKHEAD on the PS/2 Reference diskettes. Some disk utilities packages, such as Gibson Research's SpinRite, also provide a head-parking program.

2.17 Trap: Some drives do not have a parking zone and some drives react violently with some disk-parking software.

Knowing whether a parking program is necessary for your hard disk is important. If you need such a program, you must choose the right type for your disk drive; ignorance in this area is dangerous.

Remember the following:

- All drives must be parked.
- If your drive doesn't park automatically, run a parking program.
- If you must run a parking program, be sure to match the program to the drive.

Some inexpensive hard disk drives do not provide a separate landing zone for the recording heads. Instead, the heads are parked on the last cylinder of the data area. Because IBM reserves this cylinder for diagnostic purposes, no user data is at risk.

Many disk-parking programs use this feature and send the head to this diagnostic cylinder. Some disk-parking programs use peculiarities in the controller interface disk drive and send the heads to a presumed safe zone. However, a poor mating between the parking program and the disk drive can force the heads beyond the data area, causing damage.

Normally, the disk drive controller protects the drive from potential damage. The Seagate 251 disk drive does not. The 251 is vulnerable to damage if a parking program attempts to force the heads beyond the normal data area. Although this is the only current disk drive reported to have this problem, be aware that other problem reports are possible.

A parking program is safe if the program handles the disk drive intelligently. If you use the hard disk provided with your computer, the parking program supplied with your computer is safe. If you use a third-party hard disk drive or parking software, check with either or both sources to be sure that the combination is acceptable. If in doubt, running the program is probably safe.

Reverse the advice if you are using a Seagate disk drive. If you have a Seagate, check with the third-party software publisher to see whether the parking program is safe for your drive. If in doubt, don't run the program. The risk of damage is too great.

If you have a voice coil disk drive, you do not need a head-parking program. Like some folklore cold remedies, running a parking program can't hurt your drive, but won't help either.

Using Batch Files for End-of-Day Tasks

2.18 Trick: You can partially automate end-of-day parking tasks by using a batch file.

If your disk drive does not park its heads automatically, you can ease the process of running a parking program by using a batch file. Run the batch file as your last operation before turning off the computer or leaving for the day. Several people use a shutdown batch file to run time-consuming or housekeeping tasks, such as a defragmenting program, a directory/FAT saver, or even CHKDSK.

There are a few tricks to this technique. First, copy the parking program to the disk. Then, create a new batch file or modify a current shutdown batch file to run the park program. A sample batch file called SHUTDOWN.BAT is shown in figure 2.4.

For convenience, both the parking program and shutdown batch file can be in a subdirectory on the DOS path. Both files can be on the hard disk or a floppy disk.

```
@ECHO OFF
CLS
ECHO  ┌──────────────────────────────────────────────────────────────┐
ECHO  │                                                              │
ECHO  │                 Preparing for System Shutdown                │
ECHO  │                                                              │
ECHO  ├──────────────────────────────────────────────────────────────┤
ECHO  │   Step 1: Check drive integrity with CHKDSK.                 │
ECHO  │                                                              │
ECHO  │   If any warning messages appear when asked to press any key to │
ECHO  │   continue, press Ctrl-Break. When the message Terminate Batch File │
ECHO  │   appears, press Y and then Enter, and contact the micro support │
ECHO  │   center immediately.                                        │
ECHO  │                                                              │
ECHO  │                                                              │
CHKDSK C:
PAUSE
CLS
ECHO  ┌──────────────────────────────────────────────────────────────┐
ECHO  │                 CHKDSK completed successfully!               │
ECHO  ├──────────────────────────────────────────────────────────────┤
ECHO  │                                                              │
ECHO  │   Step 2: Back up key files.                                 │
ECHO  │                                                              │
ECHO  │   Place the first backup diskette for the daily set into drive A:, │
ECHO  │   and then press any key to continue.                        │
ECHO  │                                                              │
ECHO  │                                                              │
PAUSE
BACKUP C:\KEYDIR\*.* A: /S /A
CLS
ECHO  ┌──────────────────────────────────────────────────────────────┐
ECHO  │                 Backup is complete!                          │
ECHO  ├──────────────────────────────────────────────────────────────┤
ECHO  │                                                              │
ECHO  │   Step 3: Park disk drive heads.                             │
ECHO  │                                                              │
ECHO  │   You may now remove the final backup diskette from the disk drive │
ECHO  │   while the disk drive's heads are parking.                  │
ECHO  │                                                              │
ECHO  │   When the red light on the hard disk goes out, you may turn off │
ECHO  │   the system safely.                                         │
ECHO  │                                                              │
ECHO  │                                                              │
ECHO  │   Good evening!                                              │
ECHO  │                                                              │
ECHO  │                                                              │
PARKHEAD C:
```

Fig. 2.4. SHUTDOWN.BAT.

2.19 Trap: If your parking program is in a shutdown batch file, run the parking program last.

A potential trap to this technique is the placement of the line that runs the parking program. If the batch file is on a hard disk, the line that runs the parking program must be the final line. If the batch file is on a floppy disk, the program must be the last operation to access the hard disk.

DOS reads a batch file one line at a time. If the batch file is hard-disk based, invoking the head-parking program on any but the final line is a waste. Unless the disk drive latches the heads into the parking zone (very few do), another hard disk access cancels the parking effect. For this reason, DOS automatically cancels the effect of parking when it accesses the next line of the batch file. If the batch file is diskette based, further use of the hard disk also cancels the effect of parking.

If you have two separate hard disk units and the batch file is on one of them, you must use two separate commands. The order of the commands is important. First park the hard disk that does not hold the batch file and parking program, and then park the hard disk with the batch file and parking program. This tip applies only when two hard disk units are involved, not a single hard disk with one or more partitions. (In this case, only one set of heads needs to be parked; because a multipartition hard disk is one physical disk, only one physical disk needs to be parked.)

Except when parking multiple disk drives, the location of the parking program is not important—you can run it from a floppy diskette or from your hard disk. The parking takes place after the parking program loads and runs. Running the parking program from the hard disk is safe.

To park multiple hard disks, place the parking program and the batch file on the same drive. First park the drive(s) not holding the parking program and batch file, and then park the drive holding the batch file and parking program.

3

Improving Disk Performance

Moving information within RAM memory takes less time than moving information between a disk and RAM. This statement underscores the philosophy of this chapter. Random memory access is rated in nanoseconds (10^{-6}, billionths of a second). Disk transfer rates are rated in milliseconds (10^{-3}, thousandths of a second). This threefold order of magnitude highlights the difference.

Given a choice, move information between memory locations rather than between the disk drive and memory. The effective performance difference between RAM and your disk drive ranges between 10 to 1 and 100 to 1.

You can use three methods to improve disk performance without changing the disk drive:

- Don't read information already in RAM and don't write information already on the disk drive
- Read or write a full track of information at a time
- Reduce disk access

A full track of disk information is read or written fastest when handled all at once, not in individual pieces. RAM disks, DOS's disk buffers, disk cachers, and some hard disk controller cards minimize disk access by holding information in RAM until a program requests the information. Disk cachers and some hard disk controllers read or write a full disk track in one operation, minimizing repeated access to the disk.

Each technique has its place in improving the performance of your computer. Because these techniques use and compete for RAM, the amount of available RAM may limit your use of these techniques. You must allocate RAM based on your use of the computer and the performance gain each technique can deliver.

In addition to these methods, you can use a defragmenter to increase performance. Defragmenters move files so that they are stored in contiguous sectors. This minimizes recording head movement, which means that information is transferred in the shortest possible time.

RAM Disks

RAM disks provide disk storage that is many times faster than accessing a physical disk drive. RAM disks are fragile because they are made of RAM. If you must restart DOS for any reason, such as a power loss, the data on the RAM disk usually is destroyed. Unless you use battery-protected RAM (an expensive solution), when your computer sneezes, your RAM disk is caught cold. This section reflects on this risk, offers tips on what type of files to place in a RAM disk, and gives methods for protecting RAM-disk data.

Placing Files in a RAM Disk

3.1 Tip: Use RAM disks to hold unchanging files, short-lived files, and frequently used files.

You should balance the risk of using RAM disks with the rewards. RAM disks offer outstanding performance benefits, but the contents of a RAM disk vanish whenever DOS is restarted. To balance the risks, you must decide whether you can easily replace the contents.

You can place nonchanging files, for example, on a RAM disk. The files are copied from a physical disk drive; therefore, if the RAM disk fails, the file still exists on the physical disk drive. No risk of losing the files is involved. Most program-related files do not change, or the changes are not meant to be permanent. In addition, some data files fit the nonchanging category—for example, the set of dictionary files for a spelling program. If a program doesn't write to the file, it is perfect for a RAM disk. All DOS external commands, batch files, and dBASE III® Plus command files are examples of nonchanging files.

Some changing files, on the other hand, involve a manageable risk. If the file has a short life, the risk is minimal. For example, many programs produce a temporary disk file to hold information that doesn't fit within DOS memory. When the program finishes, the temporary file is deleted automatically. The risk to the file is identical to the risk to the program.

Data files you heavily use and frequently change are most at risk in a RAM disk. For these types of files, you use a RAM disk to speed processing time but also place the file changes at constant risk. Impossible-to-reconstruct information does not belong on a RAM disk either. If you do place this information on a RAM disk, manage the consequences by copying periodically the RAM-disk based file to a physical disk. You should copy difficult-to-replace information frequently, every 15 minutes to 1 hour. As the difficulty to replace the information decreases, you can copy the file to a physical disk less frequently.

3.2 Tip: If RAM disk space is at a premium, use the RAM disk for frequently accessed files.

To use a file from a RAM disk, you must copy the file to the RAM disk. If space is tight, don't waste RAM disk space with programs or files you access only a few times a day.

Judge the best files to place on a RAM disk based on frequency of access (how much you touch the contents of the disk file), not the length of the file's use. Arguably, the two are often the same in database use (including accounting programs, which are disguised database programs). In some cases, the two are not the same.

For example, 1-2-3 is a massive program you may use most of the day. If you start 1-2-3 once in the morning, use it most of the day, and never load it again, you *use* the program frequently but *access* the program infrequently.

Programs that use overlays (additional program parts in a separate file) can be ideal for RAM disk use. AutoCAD® is a prime example. Each major function of AutoCAD is kept in an overlay file. As you execute the function, the program part responsible for the function is brought into memory from the disk drive. When the function is completed, the program piece is discarded. Because program overlays are frequently accessed, using a RAM disk can greatly speed performance.

3.3 Trick: Set the environmental variable TEMP or TMP to the drive name of the RAM disk.

Several programs use temporary files for holding partially processed information. Most programming-language compilers use temporary files; and file archivers, such as PKPAK, use a temporary file when adding or removing a file from an archive. Usually, the current disk drive holds the temporary file.

Most of these programs look for an environmental variable called TEMP or TMP, which holds a disk drive or drive and path name. If the variable exists, the program uses the disk drive and path specified by TEMP or TMP for the temporary files.

RAM disks are excellent for holding temporary files. To activate these programs automatically, use the following statements in your AUTOEXEC.BAT file:

SET TEMP=E:
SET TMP=E:

Substitute the name of your RAM disk drive if **E:** is not correct. The programs that utilize these variables can use the RAM disk for temporary files automatically.

Some programs, however, use different environmental variables to indicate the drive for temporary files. For example, PKPAK uses the variable name PKPAKTMP. Check the program's documentation for references to temporary files or the SET command. If you find that the reference and the variable name are different, add the appropriate SET command to your AUTOEXEC.BAT file.

If you later change the drive letter of the RAM disk or remove the RAM disk, change the appropriate SET commands as well. Some programs object to being told a RAM disk exists when the disk does not or when the given disk drive name does not exist.

3.4   Trick: If you use a floppy disk-based system, place COMMAND.COM on the RAM disk.

COMMAND.COM is the command interpreter for DOS. The memory used by COMMAND.COM can be freed for use by other programs. When this happens, COMMAND.COM must be reloaded from disk.

DOS looks at the COMSPEC variable, which states the file specification (full file name) for COMMAND.COM, and attempts to locate the file. If COMMAND.COM is found, DOS reloads the interpreter. If COMMAND.COM is not found, DOS demands that you insert a diskette that contains the command interpreter and press a key.

You have three choices to handle this situation:

- You can keep your DOS start-up diskette handy and insert it when DOS wants COMMAND.COM.

- You can put COMMAND.COM on your various program diskettes so that the disk in the start-up drive always has a copy of COMMAND.COM.
- You can copy COMMAND.COM to a RAM disk and tell DOS to use this copy.

For the last choice, you can use the following three lines from the floppy diskette-based AUTOEXEC.BAT file (assuming that the RAM disk is drive C:):

COPY COMMAND.COM C:
ATTRIB +R C:\\COMMAND.COM
SET COMSPEC=C:\\COMMAND.COM

The first line copies the command interpreter to the RAM disk, in this case, drive C. The second line sets the read-only attribute of the file. By setting the RAM disk version of the file to read-only, you don't destroy it when you issue an **ERASE C:** command (the way I normally clear all files on the RAM disk). The final command tells DOS where to find the interpreter. When DOS needs to reload COMMAND.COM, DOS goes to the RAM disk.

You can use this trick with a hard disk also (making sure that your drive references are correct), but the benefits are usually not worth the time nor disk space. Because you don't remove the hard disk, the start-up disk with COMMAND.COM is usually accessible. This trick is useful only if DOS reloads COMMAND.COM often and your hard disk is slow (as is the hard disk in an XT-class machine).

Protecting RAM-Disk Data

3.5 Tip: Copy important, changing files from a RAM disk to a physical disk before or just after you leave the program that uses the disk.

The number one item on my list of RAM-disk horror stories is forgetting to copy changes from the RAM disk to a physical disk before you turn off the computer or restart DOS. This *asleep at the switch* error strikes when you pop in and out of a program all day but don't make a permanent copy of the file. You forget that the current file is on the RAM disk, and you pull the plug.

The most practical solution is to discipline yourself to perform the task manually. When you leave the program, copy the file.

3.6   Trick: Use a batch file to automate copying files from a RAM disk to a physical disk.

You can automate saving a changed file from a RAM disk to the physical disk by using a batch file. The best solution depends on the program you use.

With my floppy disk-based laptop computer, I use a RAM disk to hold my edited files. Using a RAM disk conserves battery power, and the risk of losing power without warning is slim-to-nonexistent. I copy manually the files to the RAM disk, make it the current disk drive, and then invoke WordStar®. I have no physical disk drive activity other than accessing the program and its overlay files.

When I finish editing, I save the new copies to the floppy disk just after I leave WordStar. I make one exception: I run other programs that use the same data files (such as spell-checkers). If, however, I need to change data diskettes to work on other files, I still move the files from the RAM disk to a physical diskette before I change the diskettes.

Unfortunately, my self-discipline is not perfect. Once, I needed to clear my airline tray when the flight attendant brought dinner. Pressed by the interruption, I quickly saved the document and turned off the computer. The revision, which only existed on the RAM disk, was lost.

To solve this problem, I have a small batch file, called WSRAM.BAT, that automatically copies a file to the RAM disk, runs WordStar, and copies the file back when it leaves WordStar. To use the batch file, I type **WSRAM** followed by the name of the file to edit. Because DOS does not offer a method to specify a disk drive and path name, the file must be on the current disk drive and in the current directory.

WSRAM.BAT contains the following lines:

```
@ECHO OFF
REM
REM Batch file to copy a file from the current disk, run WordStar,
REM and copy the file back to the current disk.
REM
REM Test for a file name.
REM
IF not %1. == . goto gettemp
ECHO Usage: %0 filename
```

```
ECHO where filename is the name of the file to edit
GOTO end

REM
REM If you don't have an environmental variable named temp,
REM change the set temp= to the drive name of your RAM disk.
REM
:gettemp
IF %temp%. == . set temp=c:\
REM where c:\ is the name of the RAM disk

REM
REM If the named file doesn't exist, run WordStar with file name.
REM
IF exist %1 goto copyit
CALL ws %temp%%1
GOTO copyback

REM
REM If the file exists, copy it. If the copy exists, the operation was
REM successful. Run WordStar.
REM
:copyit
COPY %1 %temp% >nul
IF not exist %temp%%1 goto error
CALL ws %temp%%1

REM
REM Copy the file back.
REM
:copyback
COPY %temp%%1
GOTO end

REM
REM Couldn't copy the file to the RAM disk. Report the problem.
REM
:error
ECHO Couldn't copy the file to %temp%! Not running WordStar.

:end
```

Before you use the batch file, log onto the directory in which you want to copy files. When you type **WSRAM**, don't give a drive designator or path name in the command line.

The file demonstrates some interesting techniques, including some innovations of DOS V3.3 and later versions. The batch file requires the name of the file to edit, and **if not %1. == .** ensures that you give the name. (If you don't give a name, the batch file stops.) Then **%1.** translates to the file name and a period. Because this name does not match the single period on the other side of the double equal sign, the batch file proceeds.

The **%temp%** line demonstrates using environmental variables in a batch file. You use percent signs before and after the environmental variable names. DOS substitutes the contents of the variable for the name. On my laptop, my RAM disk is drive C. The line in my AUTOEXEC.BAT file is **set temp=c:**. Hence, **%temp%** becomes **C:**. For more information, see the environment section of Chapter 9 on advanced batch file techniques.

The batch file handles the major potential disaster—running out of space when you copy the file to the RAM disk. If this occurs, the batch file could fail to copy the file successfully and quit WordStar without saving a file; then COPY complains about a not-found file, although the current copy is intact. The worst case is not copying the file, accidentally putting a few keystrokes in the file, saving it, and then wiping out a good document on disk along with a junk document from the RAM disk.

The batch file avoids this disaster by checking for the file's existence on the RAM disk after the COPY operation. If COPY encounters insufficient disk space, COPY deletes the partial file. If the operation is unsuccessful, no trace of the file exists on the RAM disk. The batch file states the error and exits.

The batch file deliberately does not remove the data file from the RAM disk. Because DOS does not have a MOVE command (a command that copies a file and then deletes the original version), you must remove the file manually. Because there is no test to verify that the file was copied successfully, I use the safety play.

The only other major trick in this batch file is the CALL line. CALL is used like the GOSUB command of BASIC: it runs another batch file and returns. Without CALL, the second batch file does not return to the first.

You can use CALL with any executable file, not just with batch files. On my system, WS is WS.BAT, another batch file that does some setup work. In other cases, WS may be WS.EXE, the main WordStar program. By using CALL, this batch file can invoke a program or another batch file.

The WSRAM batch file is a prototype for any program that accepts the name of the data file from the command line. For clarity, the batch file uses blank lines and REM statements as comments, which you can omit. To use the batch file with a different program, simply change the **ws** in the CALL line to your program's or starting batch file's name. You should also change **WordStar** in the last ECHO line to the name of the program that the batch file runs and change the name of the RAM disk, if necessary.

This batch file has one unavoidable problem. With WordStar (and many other programs), I can edit and save one file and then edit another. The batch file copies the starting file, but not the additional files I work on before exiting WordStar. This batch file is oriented for using the program with only one data file and then exiting the program. Just remember to copy the file back before you lose it.

Using VDISK

3.7 Tip: DOS V3's VDISK can use extended memory. VDISK in V4 can also use expanded memory.

Although DOS does not use extended (XMA) memory directly, the RAM disk, VDISK, can use extended memory. Starting with PC DOS V4, VDISK can use expanded (EMS) memory also. If you have extended memory, such as the 384K on a PS/2 Model 50 or 60, VDISK is an ideal candidate for use of this extended memory.

The syntax for VDISK is shown in table 3.1. Only the /X:sectors parameter differs between V3 and V4. This parameter specifies that expanded memory should be used.

Table 3.1
VDISK Syntax

Syntax

DEVICE = *d:\path***VDISK.SYS** *bytes sec_size dir_entries /E:sector /X:sectors*

d:path is the drive and path name to VDISK.SYS.

bytes is the size of RAM disk in K, 1K to 4000K (16000K for DOS V4); 64K is the default size.

sec_size is the sector size, 128, 256, or 512 bytes per sector; 128 is the default.

dir_entries is the number of root directory entries; 64 is the default.

:sectors is the number of sectors to transfer at one time, 1 to 8; 8 is the default.

Switches

/E Use extended memory (XMA) for RAM disk data.

/X Use expanded memory (EMS) for RAM disk data, DOS V4 only.

3.8 Trap: Don't use IBM's VDISK.SYS /E with Microsoft's HIMEM.SYS or SMARTDRV.SYS.

Programs can use two methods to allocate extended memory on a 286-based computer:

- Allocate extended memory from the highest address available in the computer downward to the 1M point.
- Start at the 1M point and allocate memory upward to the highest extended memory available.

The two methods might coexist if each knew about the other. Unfortunately, the ROM BIOS of the Personal Computer AT does not provide a method of communicating who has what section of memory. Programs must look in extended memory for traces of other programs. The scheme is not infallible.

VDISK allocates extended memory upward from the 1M point. Using VDISK stops HIMEM.SYS from using the memory in the 1000K to 1064K range. This section of memory becomes unavailable to programs on 286-based systems that can use XMS memory and can add another 64K "conventional" memory. Also, SMARTDRV.SYS, Microsoft's disk cache, does not always function correctly with VDISK.

Because HIMEM.SYS, SMARTDRV.SYS, and RAMDRIVE.SYS (the Microsoft RAM disk software) are provided with Windows/286, and because Windows/286 is the leading application that uses this dual 64K extended/ conventional memory area, there is no reason to use VDISK.SYS. If you need HIMEM.SYS for Windows/286, you get SMARTDRV.SYS and RAMDRIVE.SYS with the package also. RAMDRIVE.SYS works slightly faster in extended memory than VDISK.SYS. For these reasons, retire VDISK.SYS and use RAMDRIVE.SYS exclusively.

Disk BUFFERS

Disk buffers (and disk cachers, which are covered in a later section of this chapter) are another form of using RAM as an extension of disk drive storage. RAM disks boost the performance of programs that use files stored on the RAM disk. Because disk buffers boost the performance of any program that uses *any* disk drive, you can use disk buffers with more programs than RAM disks.

The exact number of disk buffers you need depends on your computer, disk drive, and disk activity. Under DOS pre-V3.3, the default number of buffers (two for floppy disk-based systems, three for hard disk systems) was seldom adequate. Under DOS V3.3 and later versions, the default is usually adequate.

If you have a disk drive that holds more than 360K, DOS V3.3 and later starts with 3 buffers rather than 2. If the computer has more than 128K of RAM, DOS bumps the number to 5. If the system has more than 256K or 512K of RAM, DOS starts with 10 or 15 disk buffers, respectively. The next set of tips demonstrate that the new starting numbers are generally best.

3.9 Tip: Set the number of buffers somewhere between 15 to 25 for DOS V3.

Based on many tests run on a variety of machines, the best number of DOS disk buffers for DOS V3.0–V3.3 ranges between 15 and 25, with 15 usually yielding the best results.

Too few buffers invites slow disk operations. Remember that DOS keeps the FAT for each disk in disk buffers and uses the FAT when reading or writing all disk files. You need some extra disk buffers for DOS to be efficient when reading the FAT.

However, DOS V3 is not very efficient at managing disk buffers. Too many disk buffers slows performance. DOS performs a linear search, checking each buffer in order to see whether the requested information is already in a buffer. If the information is not in the first buffer, DOS moves to the second buffer, then the third, the fourth, and so on until all disk buffers have been searched. When recycling buffers, DOS uses the same linear search approach to recycle the least recently used buffer.

The search and recycling seems swift, but takes some processing time, which grows with additional buffers. For this reason, you want enough disk buffers to hold the FAT and frequently used parts of your files, but not so many buffers that DOS spends more time administering buffers than reading and writing information. Fifteen to 25 disk buffers are best, with 15 yielding the best general performance and 25 yielding slightly better performance if you use many database programs (including accounting applications).

With DOS V3.3 and later versions, the default value (15) works well; therefore, increasing or decreasing the number of BUFFERS is usually optional. With DOS versions before V3.3 (and systems with less than 512K), the default number of BUFFERS may result in poor performance; therefore, be sure to use a BUFFERS directive in your CONFIG.SYS.

This tip comes with an explicit disclaimer—the tip is based on a number of presumptions which may or may not be true for your computer. The tests conducted to determine the best number of buffers are based on reading and writing a 512K file both sequentially and randomly. The random test reads both one and two sectors' worth of information. These tests emulate normal computer activities, but your use of the computer may be exceptional.

If you have several large directories or large disk partitions, the ideal number of buffers may be greater. For example, one programmer reported that 60 disk buffers worked best with his 60M hard disk and 400-file subdirectory. If you have a large database that is accessed almost completely randomly and uses very short records, a larger number of buffers may be beneficial. (Remember that accounting applications are disguised database applications; the caution about more buffers may apply.)

The downside is that each disk buffer takes 532 bytes, about 1/2K, which comes from the 640K DOS memory. The default 15 buffers steal about 7 1/2K from your programs—a beneficial trade-off. Thirty buffers take 15K from your programs, and 30 or more buffers may be a problem if you are suffering from "RAM-cram" (too many TSRs and options competing for the same 640K).

Test your computer and your programs. Start with 15 disk buffers, run the system for several hours, change the buffers (add or subtract 5), restart DOS, and observe the results for several hours. Remember that the maximum number of BUFFERS for DOS V3 is 99, but considering performance and memory use, using 99 BUFFERS is of dubious benefit.

3.10   Tip: You can use more disk buffers with DOS V4 without affecting performance.

DOS V4 uses a different scheme for searching disk buffers. DOS keeps a separate index based on the disk and absolute sector that each disk buffer holds. When searching for information, DOS searches the index rather than each buffer. Because the search is many times faster than the DOS V3 method, you can use more disk buffers without a decrease in performance.

The number of buffers varies, but 15 to 25 is usually the best. For database applications, the optimum number may be greater. Remember that each buffer takes 532 bytes and can steal some DOS memory.

3.11   Tip: Improve disk performance by selecting the right look-ahead value when you use DOS V4's BUFFERS directive.

When a system program (cacher or device driver) reads or writes more disk sectors than requested, it is said to *look ahead*. For example, if a program requests sector 27, the cache reads sector 27, but also a number of additional sectors, from 2 to 8 more. If the program then requests sectors 28 through 35, they are already in the cache. At least 1 disk read is eliminated. If all 8 additional sectors are requested, up to 8 additional disk-read operations are eliminated. The time required to read 9 sectors at once is between one-fourth and one-half the time needed to read 9 sectors one at a time. The performance gain is significant.

If your programs sequentially read or write a file, using look-aheads dramatically improves disk performance. If a program performs random access, look-ahead may benefit or seriously degrade performance. If your program reads or writes more than one disk sector at a time randomly, the correct look-ahead value improves performance significantly. If the value is excessive, the overhead time can double or quadruple because many more sectors are read from the disk than are processed. The time spent reading the additional disk sectors is wasted.

The reference diskette that comes with PS/2 computers has a modest disk cacher called IBMCACHE.SYS, which can perform look-ahead. Starting with DOS V4, IBM has made the cacher part of DOS. The following shows the syntax for the DOS V4 BUFFERS directive:

BUFFERS = *sectors, look_ahead_sectors*

sectors is the number of DOS BUFFERS to establish. If BUFFERS is in DOS memory, this parameter is identical in DOS V3 and V4. *look_ahead_sectors* is the number of additional sectors that DOS reads when a new sector is requested. The value is any number from 1 through 8; IBMCACHE allowed values of 2, 4, or 8 only. Each look-ahead buffer takes 512 bytes of memory; normal buffers use 532 bytes. If you don't specify *look_ahead_sectors*, look-ahead reading is not enabled, and no additional memory is used.

The following directive sets up 15 buffers and 4 additional look-ahead buffers:

BUFFERS 15, 4

The correct value for the look-ahead buffers depends on your primary applications. If your programs do little random file work, four to eight is an ideal value. If you run accounting or other database programs, using a smaller value (one to three), or not using look-ahead buffers may be best.

Again, the best test is to try two look-ahead buffers, run your programs for several hours, up the value by one or two, restart DOS, and look at the change in performance. If it does not improve significantly, stop at the current value. If your performance degenerates, use a lower value.

3.12 Tip: You can place DOS V4 BUFFERS in EMS memory.

DOS V4's BUFFERS /X switch allows you to place disk buffers in EMS memory. Placing BUFFERS in expanded memory frees conventional memory for other uses. The new limit for disk buffers is 10,000. Because 10,000 disk buffers take just over 5.3M of EMS memory, the limit is more an intellectual curiosity than a practical limit.

Note some restrictions for using DOS V4 BUFFERS in EMS. First, you must have sufficient memory for the BUFFERS. Remember that each disk buffer takes 532 bytes and that each look-ahead buffer takes 512 bytes. If there is insufficient EMS memory, the number of BUFFERS is reduced to available EMS memory. If no EMS memory is available (either none free or none installed), no BUFFERS are installed.

Second, placing an equal amount of BUFFERS in EMS memory rather than in DOS memory results in slightly slower disk operations. The instructions for processing the EMS switching causes a degradation of about 4 percent on non-386 systems and about 1/2 percent on 386 systems. If you use enough buffers that large files are handled exclusively through disk buffers (exceeding the 99 DOS limit), the increased performance overcomes the slight degradation.

3.13 Trap: IBM PC DOS's BUFFERS /X and FASTOPEN /X work only with the XMA2EMS device driver.

PC DOS V4 has a significant problem with expanded memory: it can address expanded memory only if you use the XMA2EMS driver. The problem is that IBM dedicates a logical page of EMS to the BUFFERS /X command and an additional logical page to the FASTOPEN /X command. However, the only EMS device driver that can dedicate pages of memory in the fashion PC DOS V4 demands is XMA2EMS.SYS. Because XMA2EMS.SYS is written specifically for IBM memory expansion boards, you cannot use third-party expanded memory boards or EMS device driver software with PC DOS's BUFFERS /X command. With PS/2 Models 70 or 80, you must use the XMAEM.SYS with the XMA2EMS.SYS drivers.

With MS-DOS V4, you must have the appropriate device driver for your EMS memory board or 386-based computer. Microsoft and Intel resolved the problems of using expanded memory with DOS; they use a different scheme than IBM's PC DOS. The MS-DOS scheme works with any memory board and the board's LIM V4 driver. However, you may need new EMS device drivers to gain the desired performance in using EMS memory for DOS BUFFERS.

For more information on XMAEM.SYS and XMA2EMS.SYS, see Chapter 12 on device drivers.

3.14 Trap: Do not use BUFFERS /X or FASTOPEN /X with PC DOS V4.00. Avoid using BUFFERS /X and FASTOPEN /X with PC DOS V4.01 and certain programs.

IBM makes four presumptions when you use EMS memory for BUFFERS and FASTOPEN:

- The dedicated page for the option is always "visible" to DOS.
- No other program will access the same physical page through two or more logical handles (named EMS memory pages).

- No other program will demand that four page windows be available at one time.
- DOS need not save and restore the EMS page map.

The first three assumptions are occasionally fatal. The fourth was fixed in PC DOS V4.01. However, DOS V4.01 can corrupt the data of certain applications that use EMS memory, such as Paradox® and DESQview. Any program which presumes that multiple handles can access the same page of EMS memory (such as Paradox) or that four EMS page frames are available for use (such as DESQview) will not work when BUFFERS or FASTOPEN is used in expanded memory.

For these reasons, do not use BUFFERS /X or FASTOPEN /X with DOS V4.00 unless you are sure that other programs which use EMS memory for their data will not be corrupted. If programs are written to the LIM V3.2 specification, the programs are safe to use. If the program specifies that only LIM V4 should be used, check with the program's publisher before you use expanded memory for BUFFERS or FASTOPEN.

The preceding traps do not apply to MS-DOS V4, which uses a different method to handle BUFFERS and FASTOPEN in expanded memory.

FASTOPEN

FASTOPEN caches directory entries for files and subdirectories. The disk performance benefits you gain by using FASTOPEN can be one to several percent.

DOS always starts at the root directory to search for a file. If the file is in a subdirectory, DOS must search from the root through each subdirectory in the chain of directories until it locates the file. The directory search is part of loading or accessing any file.

3.15 Tip: Use FASTOPEN to buffer directory entries and speed directory searches.

To speed directory searches, use the FASTOPEN command. The following shows the syntax for FASTOPEN V3.3:

> **FASTOPEN d: = dir_entry ...**

The FASTOPEN command buffers directory entries on a disk drive-by-disk drive basis. **d:** is the name of the hard disk whose directory entries should be cached. **dir_entry** is the number of directory entries to be cached.

You may name additional disk drives in a single FASTOPEN command (the **...** in the command) or invoke FASTOPEN several times, specifying different disk drives each time. You may use FASTOPEN on a disk drive only once per DOS session, and you cannot change the value for directory entries after you have given the command.

For example, the following command uses 200 directory entries for drive C and 100 for drive D:

> **FASTOPEN C: = 200 D: = 100**

Or you can separate this command as follows:

> **FASTOPEN C: = 200**
> **FASTOPEN D: = 100**

The absolute minimum value for **dir_entry** is equal to the deepest subdirectory level, starting the count with the subdirectory of the root. If your deepest subdirectory level is five (you have a subdirectory such as C:\DIR1\DIR2\DIR3\DIR4\DIR5), the minimum value is five. Because FASTOPEN recycles directory entries, a value that barely covers the deepest subdirectory entries is of little help.

The maximum value for **dir_entry** for all disk drives is 999. You can use 999 for one drive or distribute 999 directory entries among all hard disk drives. There is, however, a point of diminishing returns. Each directory entry takes 35 bytes. The maximum (999 entries) takes about 35K. If you have the memory to spare, more entries are better than less. However, too many entries can waste memory.

3.16 Tip: Use FASTOPEN to speed the disk access of fragmented files.

A major improvement in FASTOPEN V4 is the capability to cache the starting and ending cluster of each noncontiguous portion of a file. This feature improves performance when you work with large, fragmented files. (Fragmentation is discussed in a later section of this chapter.) In effect, FASTOPEN caches the file's FAT entries.

Instead of returning to the FAT every time a section of the file must be read, FASTOPEN buffers the location of the file. For each file, FASTOPEN keeps a table of entries, called a *fragment table*, which holds the starting and ending cluster number of the fragment. When you use the file, DOS uses the fragment table rather than the FAT to track the file.

Under certain conditions, the process of using a fragment table is noticeably faster than simply using the FAT. The files must be large (more than 300K) and have at least 5 separate fragments of any size. Also, sufficient space in the fragment table must be available.

The following shows the syntax for FASTOPEN V4:

*dc\pathc***FASTOPEN** *d:=***dir_entry** *or d:=***(dir_entry, frag_entry)** ... **/X**

dir_entry is the number of directory entries to cache for the named hard disk drive. You can give additional disk drive names on the same line, but you can use FASTOPEN only once for each disk drive. The restriction of 999 directory entries for all FASTOPEN commands applies.

The new information is **frag_entry**, the number of *fragment entries* (called "continuous space buffers" in the DOS manual), for the drive. If **frag_entry** is omitted, DOS does not use the fragment table. Like **dir_entry**, the total number of fragment entries for all disk drives cannot exceed 999. Unlike directory entries, each fragment entry uses 16 bytes rather than 35 bytes.

When you give the number of fragment entries, you must enclose dir_entry and frag_entry for a drive in parentheses and use a comma to separate the two. You can give one of the two values, such as **(100,)** for 100 directory entries and no fragment entries, or **(,100)** for no directory caching and 100 fragment entries.

The following command uses 100 directory entries and 200 fragment entries for drive C, and just 100 directory entries for drive D:

FASTOPEN C: = (100, 200) D: = 100

If you want to place the cache in expanded memory, add the /X switch. For example, the following command places all FASTOPEN cache data in expanded memory:

FASTOPEN C: = (100, 200) D: = 100 /X

3.17   Tip: Use about 25 to 50 directory entries and twice as many fragment buffers per 10M of disk space.

Twenty-five to 50 is an average number of directory entries, but no number is best for everyone. Start with about 25 directory entries for 10M of disk space and then experiment. Also try twice the number of directory entries for fragment entries.

If you have several levels of directories or many files in a directory, use 50 directory entries rather than 25. If you have fewer large files, use one-and-one-half the number of the directory entries for fragment entries.

Using too small a number with FASTOPEN is wasteful because the directory entries or fragment entries are recycled too quickly. As with any cache, the benefit comes when you use a file the second time. The directory entry or fragment information is already held by FASTOPEN. If the information has been flushed, FASTOPEN is useless.

Using too large a number of entries does not slow performance, but can rob your programs of conventional memory. If your programs are sluggish because too little RAM is free, reduce the number of directory or fragment buffers.

Quantifying the benefits of a particular FASTOPEN directory-entry setting is difficult because separating the directory search time from reading or writing the file is difficult. Normally, programs search *and* read parts of a file. Giving the DIR command several times on different directories will give some notion of the speed of directory searches. However, the speed of the screen can slow the DIR display. The time may be more accurate if you are using a sweep program, such as WHERE.COM.

You must access a large file to appreciate the benefit of a FASTOPEN fragment setting. The program that accesses the file may take more time processing than actually reading the file.

Don't hesitate to experiment with the FASTOPEN command. Try various settings, restart the system, and observe the results.

3.18 Tip: Use the /X switch to place FASTOPEN V4's buffers in expanded memory.

An advantage of FASTOPEN V4 over FASTOPEN V3 is that you can use the /X switch to place FASTOPEN's cache in expanded memory. This frees conventional memory for other uses. If you do not give the /X switch, conventional memory is used for the directory or cluster cache.

For IBM PC DOS V4 only, logical page 254 is used for the cache. You must have XMA2EMS.SYS installed, and if you use a 386-based system, you must have XMAEM.SYS installed also. If you set any EMS pages when you invoke XMA2EMS, you must also set page 254. In addition, when the cache is placed in expanded memory, the cache cannot exceed 16K. Traps 3.13 and 3.14 contain additional cautions about using FASTOPEN /X.

3.19   Trap: You can use only about 460 directory entries or about 225 directory and 450 fragment entries if you use expanded memory and PC DOS V4.

If you use expanded memory, the FASTOPEN cache must reside within one 16K EMS page. Each directory entry takes 35 bytes; each file fragment entry takes 16 bytes. If you plan to use expanded memory, you may need to ignore the advice in Tip 3.17.

3.20   Trap: Do not use FASTOPEN with some directory renamers.

FASTOPEN keeps the name and location of directory entries, including subdirectories. Some directory renamers, in order to work with DOS V2, bypass the normal DOS renaming routine. If FASTOPEN is active and you rename a directory with these programs, you can access the files in the subdirectory using either name until the previous name is pushed out of the cache. Unfortunately, if you attempt to remove the previous directory name, you wipe out the subdirectory. Fortunately, most current directory renaming programs are safe.

3.21   Trap: Do not use FASTOPEN with a defragmenter or certain disk tools.

Using a defragmenter with FASTOPEN is also an invitation to disaster. When a defragmenter moves files, FASTOPEN's cache is not updated. The problem comes when you attempt to use the disk after the defragmenter is finished. Files appear as nonsense, and writing to the disk is writing to a random, unrelated file. If you use a defragmenter with FASTOPEN active, immediately restart DOS after the defragmenter is finished. Failure to follow this caution will cause a loss of files. The best solution is to deactivate FASTOPEN.

Certain disk tools that perform a surface scan can be fooled by FASTOPEN. The result is that unnecessary sectors are marked as bad. For this reason, restart DOS and do not run FASTOPEN if you need to run a disk test program.

Disk Cachers

Disk cachers are brethren to DOS's disk buffers and the FASTOPEN command. Just as RAM disks are faster than physical disk drives, DOS disk buffers and FASTOPEN compare to disk cachers as motor scooters compare to Ferarris.

All cachers perform the same main function—minimizing access to the disk drive. Each cacher holds information that was read from the disk drive. The initial advantage to disk cachers is that cachers can have a larger cache area than DOS V3 buffers. With DOS V4 allowing up to 10,000 buffers in expanded memory (meaning a cache size of 5M), the advantage of cache size is trimmed. However, some cachers can use 8M to 32M, a cache size almost beyond comprehension.

(Don't discount the feature. I am aware of 4 commercial installations that use 300M+ disk drives and 16M cache sizes that are outperforming their companies' minicomputers.)

Unlike DOS BUFFERS or FASTOPEN, all commercial and some noncommercial disk cachers can use expanded or extended memory. While almost any cacher is better than none, the biggest benefits come with larger cache sizes. Because you need some DOS memory to run your programs, using a cache size larger than 256K in conventional memory is difficult.

If you want the best performance (although you do sacrifice speed), place it in expanded or extended memory. If, however, the cache is sufficiently large, the speed disadvantage is negated in favor of the overall improved performance.

Disk cachers differ in their use of expanded and extended memory, and in other features as well. A representative sampling of disk cachers includes Golden Bow Vcache™, Multisoft's PC-Kwik and Super PC-Kwik Disk Accelerator™ (PC-Kwik is bundled with several third-party computer systems), Microsoft SMARTDRV (bundled with all versions of Microsoft Windows), and Software Master's FLASH. Prices range from free (included with the computer or a software package) to $79. The next few tips cover some of the differences between cachers and describe what to look for in a disk cacher.

3.22   Tip: If many of your programs read or write information sequentially, use a cacher with track buffering.

The benefits of track buffering depend on the programs you use. Spreadsheet and word processing programs will benefit; some accounting and database applications may benefit. The benefits of the feature are greater incrementally for floppy disks than hard disks. However, the benefits to hard disk users are great.

Some cachers perform track buffering—the entire disk track is read or written at once. Although DOS V4 look-ahead buffers can read up to 9 sectors at once (one track's worth for 360K and 720K floppies), all cachers with track buffering will read or write the entire track (15 to 32 sectors, depending on disk type). If the file operation is sequential, such as loading spreadsheets or documents, track buffers speed disk operations significantly.

As with the look-ahead DOS buffers, if the file operation is random and less than a track is read or written, track buffering can be a small liability. If the entire file fits in the cache and the entire file is eventually accessed, track buffering is still a benefit. Choose cachers with which you can control track reading separately from track writing. Also, prefer cachers where these features can be turned off and on at the command line.

3.23   Tip: Use cachers that prevent unneeded disk writes.

Preventing unneeded disk writes is an important feature for all users. Some disk cachers look at all requests to send information to the disk and determine whether the request is required. For example, a program reads four sectors of information but alters only the first and second sectors. The program then requests that all four sectors be written to the disk.

An intelligent cacher looks at the write request, notices that all four sectors are in the cache, recognizes that only two sectors are changed, and writes only the first and second sectors. The unchanged third and fourth sectors are not written. Because disk writing takes longer than disk reading, cachers that suppress unnecessary disk writes can yield significant speed.

3.24   Tip: If you frequently use a small set of important data files, use a cacher with a definable priority list.

If you use many different files but only a few key data files frequently, a definable priority list is an important feature. If the cache supports a priority list, you can tell the cache to keep key files in the cacher, regardless of other activity. As the cache area fills, the cacher recycles space by disregarding the longest unused portions. As you use different files, the previous information on the file is flushed from the cache.

The priority list allows you to specify which files to keep in the cache. Use this feature if you have several frequently used program or data files you want to keep in the cacher. Instead of wasting cache space with information that may not be needed, you can manually keep the information that frequently changes. You will get better performance because the cache will hold the frequently used information.

3.25 Tip: If you use large files or many files at once on hard disks, a cache with delayed writes is helpful.

The delayed-write feature is most important for those who use large files or who use many files at one time on large hard disks. There is an element of manageable risk to delayed writes.

The delayed-write feature can be compared to elevator service in a large building with many floors. Elevators run in one of two principal modes: peak or rush-hour mode, and random or service-on-demand mode.

Peak or rush-hour mode runs each elevator from the bottom floor to the top floor and back, picking up and dropping off passengers at each floor. Because requests come from almost every floor, running the elevator from bottom to top and back makes sense.

During random, or service on-demand mode, the elevator sits idle until service is requested. Then the elevator moves to the requester's floor, picking up additional passengers on the way, and moving to the requested floors. After all requests are serviced, the elevator sits idle, either at its current location or after returning to a central location (such as the first floor).

Variations on random-use mode come when the elevator attempts to service the most requests in the smallest possible time. The elevator controller examines floors currently requesting service and considers historical information (which floors have had the most traffic during this time period). For example, the controller notices one call request from the 20th floor, but also notices requests for the 5th through 9th floors. Priority usually goes to the bunch, in this case the 5th through 9th floors. To ensure that the waiting passenger gets a ride, most intelligent elevator controllers override the "maximum-passenger" bias after a time limit.

Disk drive caching operations can be compared to random-mode elevator service. Disk drive I/O requests are bunched. On a single-user, single-task system, only writing is bunched. Because the computer cannot work further without finishing the read request, the read requests must be handled immediately. (Because the elevator seeking is different when using multiple elevators, both reads and writes are bunched on multiprogram or multiuser systems.)

The cacher examines the write requests and determines how far the heads need to move from the current cylinder and how many requests are clustered around the locations. The closest group is written first and then the next closest groups until all information is written. If read requests intervene, each read request is serviced, the head position noted, and a new write schedule is produced. Whenever the information is delayed past a given deadline, the cache writes this information immediately to the disk.

The benefit of the delayed-write feature is that disk-head movement is minimized. Because moving the disk drive heads is the second biggest time delay in writing information (verifying the information is the longest), delayed writes can boost disk performance.

Note that some risks are involved with delayed disk writes. Until the write is completed, the unwritten portion can be lost if the system locks up or if power is lost. Most cachers with delayed writes use a time limit of 1 to 10 seconds—within acceptable risk standards. Also, cachers that have this feature can be instructed to disable the delayed writes.

You usually can use delayed writes safely. A delay time of three to five seconds is safe because the chance of losing the system during an arbitrary three-to-five-second period is very small. However, if your information is absolutely critical and the information is written frequently, do not use delayed writes.

3.26   Trick: If you use a disk cacher, use between 4 and 11 DOS BUFFERS and don't use FASTOPEN.

A disk cacher works better than DOS's BUFFERS and FASTOPEN. You don't need the FASTOPEN command, and you can reduce the number of disk buffers without impeding performance.

The exact number of buffers to use varies among cachers, but is about the same between versions of DOS. When I tested a number of cachers, most worked best with 4 to 7 disk buffers; one worked best at 9 to 11. Start with BUFFERS = 4. If this seems slightly sluggish, increase the buffers by 1 or 2 at a time.

Defragmenters

The phenomenon of *fragmentation* occurs when files are not stored on contiguous disk sectors (see fig. 3.1). As files and subdirectories (which are a form of files) are added, extended, and deleted from disks, fragmentation increases.

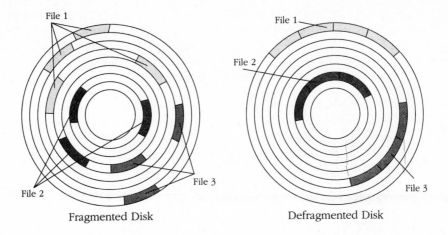

Fragmented Disk   Defragmented Disk

Fig. 3.1. Disk fragmentation.

To understand fragmentation, recall how DOS stores files on a disk. When the disk is empty, DOS places the first new file on the first available cluster. If the file must occupy more than one cluster, DOS uses the next adjacent clusters to hold the file. DOS places the next added file on contiguous clusters, starting directly after the first file. As you add new files, DOS places them after the immediately preceding file and on contiguous clusters. The advantage of this system is that recording head movement is minimized, which means that information is transferred in the shortest possible time.

The problem occurs when a file must be extended or when disk space is reused. When a file is extended, the chances of DOS placing the added clusters in contiguous sectors to the established file are small if other files have been stored.

DOS still works on a fragmented disk and the data remains intact, but your disk operations slow down. As more files are stored in different sections of the disk, the overhead of moving the disk drive heads increases.

The effect of fragmentation is awesome: it can add 50 to 200 percent or more overhead time to the use of the disk. This means that your disk operations can take 1 1/2 to 4 times longer because of fragmentation. To negate the speed degradation from fragmentation completely, you must make all files and subdirectories contiguous.

The limited size of floppy diskettes causes fragmentation to start more quickly than on hard disks. Floppy disks already operate slowly, and fragmentation further reduces the performance. To defragment a diskette and store files contiguously, copy all files to an empty floppy diskette. (Do not use DISKCOPY to copy these files.)

For a nonremovable disk, one method of packing (defragmenting) files is to back up the disk. Then you either delete all files and restart DOS, or reformat the disk. As the final step, you restore all files. The process is lengthy. A faster method is to use a defragger, a program that writes the files and subdirectories into contiguous spaces.

3.27   Tip: Use a disk defragger frequently.

Disk fragmentation can increase the time taken by disk operations significantly. For this reason, serious hard disk-based computer users should have a disk defragger in their DOS tool chest. Disk defraggers can regain the speed lost to fragmentation.

Most disk defragmenters, nicknamed *defraggers*, work the same way. Each examines the entire disk directory and FAT and notes which files are fragmented. The defragger next moves the files on the disk so that they are stored in contiguous sectors, and then updates the FAT.

The defragging process is like toppling dominoes. To make one file contiguous, the defraggers often must move other files. For this reason, the process is usually run on a complete partition rather than on a set of subdirectories.

Disk defraggers, like disk cachers, have a variety of features, modes of operation, and prices. Some defraggers are part of a disk utility package; others are independent. Examples of disk defraggers include Vopt™ from Golden Bow Systems, SD (Speed Disk) of the Norton Advanced Utilities, COMPRESS of the Mace Utilities, FASTTRAX from Bridgeway Publishing Company, and DOG (a public domain disk defragger).

3.28   Tip: When you select a defragger, remember that the speed of the defragger does not necessarily indicate its thoroughness.

The most important differences among defraggers are the way files are defragmented and the way free space is handled. Most defraggers let you choose operating time versus better results. The slower the cacher works, the more defragmentation is performed. In many cases, a slower time yields the best results.

For example, some defraggers have a fast mode. The defragger takes less time by consolidating the files, but it does not store them in one contiguous section. Some files may be stored in two or three fragments, but all sectors within the fragments are contiguous. If you have only a few fragmented files, the fast mode can produce good results.

Defraggers that have an intermediate mode make all files contiguous, but the free space on the disk may be split into several pieces. Intermediate mode works well if you run the defragger frequently or if you do not add many files or several large files that overflow from one free disk space to another.

Other defraggers have a high mode. In high mode, defraggers make files contiguous and consolidate the free space into one section at the end of the disk. You should use high mode the first time you run the defragger on a disk and each time you rerun it if you don't use the defragger often. If a defragger does not offer a selectable mode, the default mode is usually a form of intermediate or high mode.

Some defraggers do even more analysis and move files onto the start of cylinders. This feature is helpful for many files, particularly for moderately sized files that can fit on an entire cylinder (files that range from about 42K to about 112K, depending on the hard disk). After the defragger moves files to the cylinder, DOS can read the entire file without moving the recording heads again.

The defragger FASTTRAX has another useful feature: you can specify which files should be kept together. You can use this feature to reduce future defragmenting if you move unchanging program files to the front and continually changing data files to the back of the disk. You also can use this feature to keep related files together, sacrificing some latter fragmentation for better initial performance with programs that use many data files. Because you can run the defragger at any time, both options have appeal.

Also, look for defraggers that can operate from a batch file. As you will see in a later tip, defraggers that you can operate unattended have advantages.

3.29 Tip: Depending on your computer use, run a defragger between once a week and once a month.

How often you use a defragger should depend on how quickly your disk fragments. Defraggers take between 8 to 15 minutes per 10 megabytes of files. The exact time varies among defraggers, the mode of defragmenting, the number of files on the disk, and how badly the files are fragmented. For this reason, you should not perform defragging every day, particularly on large disk drives.

If you create and delete many small files, your files probably fragment quickly. If you have several very large files to which you frequently add information (every day or two), the large files fragment quickly. If less than 20 percent of your disk space is free, your files are fragmenting frequently.

If you are a frequent fragmenter, run the defragger weekly. Over a period of one week, the loss of performance is not great, but the more files you add, extend, or delete, the greater the effect of fragmentation. If you use your computer less often, running the defragger every two to four weeks is adequate. Running the program more often is a waste of time.

If you can run your defragger when the computer is normally idle (such as at night or during the lunch hour), run the defragger as often as you want. Because the computer is not doing other productive work, running the defragger during these times makes sense.

3.30 Tip: To speed defragmentation, have as much free RAM and free disk space as possible and delete unneeded files.

Most defraggers use RAM to act as a buffer while moving files. With more RAM free, the defragger can work faster. Even more important is free disk space. Most defraggers move files from one section of the disk to another but do not delete the old file until the new file is created. Having as much free disk space as possible means that the defragger can work faster.

To free disk space, remove unneeded files from your disk. Because I rarely use my word processing .BAK files after I finish an editing session, I often delete them before running a defragger. I also delete any temporary files that I used with I/O redirection. By deleting absolutely unneeded files, I have more free disk space, and the defragger has fewer files to process.

3.31 Trap: Back up your disk before running a defragger; otherwise, you can lose files.

Most defraggers work with copies of the files on the disk and are fairly safe programs. However, using a defragger involves a small element of risk because it works behind DOS's back to accomplish its magic.

If the computer loses power or DOS locks up, the file being moved could be lost. Usually, the original copy is intact or the lost file ends up as a set of orphaned clusters, which you can recover with **CHKDSK /F**. The file could be corrupted (a small chance), but generally the problem is isolated to just one file.

A greater disaster can strike if the defragger goes astray (possible, but very unlikely) or if the computer locks up while the FAT is being updated. If the FAT is corrupted, you lose information that can be recovered only by restoring the files from a backup copy (or using the "needle-in-the-haystack" file-recovery approach). A corrupted FAT is a disaster, but not having a current backup is a greater disaster.

Another disaster can happen when you run a defragger with FASTOPEN active. See Trap 3.21 for additional information.

I have run defraggers many times on many systems and have not had a single problem. I know that my systems are reliable, and I know that the chance of power failures is slim. I also know that running a defragger on a disk without a current backup is a calculated risk, a tad too large for my tastes. Before you run a defragger, make sure that your backup is current.

3.32 Tip: Use the defragger as an end-of-day, end-of-week, or end-of-month batch file procedure.

Because defragmenting is time-consuming, it is best done when you can leave the computer unattended. Assuming that the disk has a current backup, you can run the defragger from a batch file. If you have multiple partitions or multiple hard disks, running the defragger from a batch file is exceptionally useful. You can run the program twice by simply starting the batch file.

To use this method, the defragger must accept its arguments from the command line and not just from a menu. You can use all the defraggers listed in Tip 3.27 in "batch mode." Simply add the appropriate lines to a batch file called EOD.BAT (end of day), EOW.BAT (end of week), or EOM.BAT (end of month) to run the defragger once per hard disk or once per disk partition. If the defragger offers several modes, use the most thorough defragmenting mode.

3.33 Tip: If you use FASTOPEN and a batch file to run the defragger, include a program to restart DOS as the last line of the batch file.

If you use FASTOPEN, restart DOS after you run the defragger. If you use a batch file to run the defragger, make defragmenting the last steps of the batch file. You also can include a program such as WARMBOOT (a public domain program that restarts DOS as if you pressed Ctrl-Alt-Del) as the last line of the batch file.

However, you cannot use a hard disk parking program with WARMBOOT in this batch file. If WARMBOOT runs before the parking program, the parking program does not run (the batch file execution ends when DOS restarts). If the parking program runs, WARMBOOT is loaded from the hard disk, and the effects of the parking program are canceled.

You can use three solutions. The first alternative is to restart the system without FASTOPEN and run the defragger. Then your end-of-period batch file does not need to restart DOS.

Another option is to place and run the end-of-period batch file with WARMBOOT on a floppy diskette. Because the hard disk is not accessed again after you run the head-parker, you can restart DOS easily.

As a third alternative, you can run the batch file and parking program from the hard disk, but return the next day and restart the computer manually. I prefer the solutions in the order they are given.

4

Formatting Disks and Diskettes

You perform two basic, yet different, types of formatting on a disk. One type, *physical* or *low-level formatting*, establishes the tracks and sectors of the disk; the other type, *logical* or *high-level formatting*, establishes housekeeping areas for the operating system to use.

Physical formatting establishes the guard areas around each sector for each track of the disk and marks the identification number for each track and sector (which includes the interleave factor discussed in Chapter 2). Physical formatting also sets up error-checking and correcting information, and other housekeeping information.

With DOS, logical formatting determines how the operating system uses the physical information. This formatting includes writing the start-up (boot) sector and establishing the file allocation table and root directory of the disk. As a convenience, the logical formatting program (DOS's FORMAT) can write parts of the operating system to the disk.

For hard disks, another step intervenes between physical and logical formatting. The additional step establishes the partitions of the disk drive. Because FORMAT logically formats, but cannot physically format a hard disk, you can recover from the logical formatting of a hard disk if you have the right tools and follow some precautions.

FORMAT both physically and logically formats floppy diskettes. After you run FORMAT on a floppy diskette, any information previously recorded is destroyed.

This chapter covers using FORMAT and establishing partitions. The chapter discusses formatting diskettes also.

Using the FORMAT Command

This section gives you tips, tricks, and traps on using the FORMAT command on hard disks and floppy diskettes. Specifically, the text covers suggestions for using switches, assigning volume labels, and unformatting a hard disk.

4.1 Trap: Always give a disk drive name with the FORMAT command; otherwise, you may format the wrong disk.

The FORMAT command's operation has changed with each version of DOS V3. Before V3.3, FORMAT used the current disk drive if you did not give a disk drive name. If the current disk drive was the hard disk, you could format it inadvertently. Starting with DOS V3.0, DOS gave an emphatic warning message. Too many people committed an "asleep at the switch" error (continued with the formatting anyway) and formatted their hard disks.

FORMAT V3.3 and later versions insist that you specify a disk drive name (don't forget to include the colon). If you forget, FORMAT V3.3 displays the following message:

    Drive letter must be specified

FORMAT V4 displays the following message:

    Required parameter missing

In both cases, FORMAT aborts unless you specify the drive. To avoid formatting the wrong disk or diskette, make sure that the drive name is correct.

Using FORMAT's Switches

Table 4.1 lists the switches you can use with FORMAT. You cannot use some combinations of switches, nor can you use some switches with certain disk drives.

4.2 Tip: When you format the primary partition of the hard disk, use the /S and /V switches. When you format extended partitions, use just /V.

To start DOS from the active partition of the hard disk, you must place the system files on the hard disk. Use the /S switch to copy the IO.SYS, DOS.SYS, and COMMAND.COM files.

Table 4.1
FORMAT Switches

Switch	Use
* /1	Formats 1 side
* /4	Formats double-sided, double-density, 360K disks
* /8	Formats 8 sectors per track (DOS V1) disks
* /B	Formats 8 sectors per track, single-sided; reserves space for the DOS start-up files but does not place DOS on the disk
/B	When formatting a hard disk with DOS V4 only, reserves the space for the DOS start-up files but does not place DOS on the disk
* /F:size	Formats a *floppy diskette* with a given *size*; works with DOS V4 only
/N:nn	Formats nn *number* of sectors per track (1 to 99)
/S	Places the *start-up* operating system files on the disk (IBMBIO.COM and IBMDOS.COM for PC DOS; IO.SYS and MSDOS.SYS for MS-DOS; COMMAND.COM for both)
/T:ttt	Formats ttt number of *tracks* or cylinders (1 to 999)
/V	Places a *volume* label on the disk
/V:name	Places the *volume* label *name* on the disk; works with DOS V4 only

*Designates commands you can use with diskettes only

Because you can't start DOS from an extended partition, you don't need the two start-up files and probably won't need COMMAND.COM. Therefore, don't use the /S switch when you format the additional hard disk drives.

You do want the volume label on each hard disk, however. Volume labels are added insurance against inadvertent formatting. Before formatting any nonremovable disk, FORMAT V3.3 and later versions check for the presence of a volume label. If the disk is labeled, you must enter the volume label. The extra work in entering the volume label can prevent up to 512M of data from becoming instant history.

4.3 Trap: Don't use FORMAT's /1 or /8 switches with hard disks.

The /1 and /8 switches are valid only with 360K disk drives. The /1 switch creates a single-sided minifloppy diskette; the /8 switch creates an 8-sector (DOS V1 compatible) minifloppy diskette. These switches work only with minifloppy (5 1/4-inch) 360K diskettes. You cannot use these switches to format a 1-sided or 8-sectored high-capacity (1.2M) minifloppy diskette or any microfloppy diskette (720K or 1.44M).

4.4   Tip: Use the /B switch to reserve space for DOS.

The /B switch formats a diskette and reserves space for DOS, but does not place the operating system on the disk. You can use this switch when you need to send diskettes to others but do not want to put DOS on the diskette.

With DOS V3.3, /B worked only with diskettes. Starting with DOS V4, the switch works with hard disks as well. However, you do not need to use this switch on a hard disk because users rarely ship hard disk drives to other users.

4.5   Trap: Don't use /N:ss or /T:ttt with hard disks.

The /N and /T switches are designed to be used with any capacity diskettes, but not with hard disks. FORMAT displays an error message if you try to format a hard disk with /N or /T.

The /N switch sets the *number* of sectors per track. The /T switch sets the number of *tracks* (or cylinders). DOS's standard for hard disks is 17 or 32 sectors per track and all available tracks or cylinders. Unless you have a compelling reason, don't use either switch when formatting a hard disk. These switches shortchange the capacity of your hard disk (if you use a lesser number of sectors or tracks) or may result in sending information to the bit-bucket (if you use more sectors or tracks). In addition, DOS V4's /F switch makes using /N and /T unnecessary.

Because FORMAT only logically formats a hard disk, you can tell white lies to DOS for those drives that have RLL controllers. You give the command a different logical number of tracks or sectors than the disk physically has. Don't, however, use these switches unless the hard disk or interface-card manufacturer instructs you to use them.

4.6   Tip: Don't use /S with /B; don't use /8 with /V.

Some contradictory combinations that FORMAT bans are /S with /B ("put DOS on the disk but don't put DOS on the disk"), and /8 with /V (8-sector diskettes are DOS V1 diskettes, which do not work with volume labels).

4.7 Tip: If you use FORMAT /S, make the boot drive the current drive or have on hand a diskette that contains the system files.

When you use the /S switch, DOS looks for the system files by searching for COMMAND.COM. DOS first looks at the COMSPEC environmental variable. If it finds COMSPEC, DOS tries to load COMMAND.COM from this location and loads the two other system files from the root directory of the disk. If this method fails, DOS asks for the start-up diskette.

If DOS doesn't find the COMSPEC variable, it searches the root directory of the current disk for all three start-up files. If this method fails, DOS asks for the start-up diskette. If this occurs, ensure that the start-up drive is the current disk drive, have available a diskette with the two start-up files and COMMAND.COM available, or have COMSPEC set to your hard disk. (See the tips on environmental variables in Chapter 9 for more information about COMSPEC.)

4.8 Trap: If you change the names of the start-up files, change the boot sector of the disk; otherwise, DOS will not start from the disk.

This trap is for the technical user. Only the bootstrap loader and FORMAT.COM need to know the names of the IO.SYS and DOS.SYS start-up files. The bootstrap loader searches the root directory of the disk for the two names (which are stored at the end of the loader); it then loads the two files into memory. When you use the /S switch, FORMAT.COM searches the disk for these files.

If you change the names of the start-up files (the IO.SYS and DOS.SYS files) in the root directory of the disk, you must make the changes in the boot sector of the disk as well; otherwise, DOS will not start from the disk. You also must change the names of the system files in FORMAT.COM or set aside a DOS diskette that contains the system files with the correct names.

4.9 Trick: Use the /H switch to silence the initial FORMAT V3.3 message and request.

When you give the **FORMAT /H** command, FORMAT starts immediately to format the indicated disk; it does not display a message prompting you to insert the correct diskette. The in-progress message (current cylinder and side being formatted), space summary, and request to format another diskette still appear.

Before you start FORMAT with /H, be sure that the correct diskette is in the indicated drive. Also, if you answer Y (for Yes) to format another diskette, make sure that the diskette to be formatted is already in the disk drive. Remember that FORMAT immediately starts formatting when you answer the question. (This trick applies to formatting hard disks also.)

4.10   Trick: You can suppress FORMAT V4 messages by using the /BACKUP, /SELECT, or /AUTOTEST switches.

FORMAT V4 does not use the /H switch but adds the /BACKUP, /SELECT, and /AUTOTEST switches. As with /H, the initial message for inserting the correct diskette and pressing Enter is suppressed when you use these switches. The in-progress message (percentage of disk formatted) is displayed.

/BACKUP requests a volume label, displays the disk statistics, and asks whether you want to format another diskette. /SELECT requests a volume label and then exits. /AUTOTEST exits without requesting a volume label or displaying any other message. The previous cautions about FORMAT /H also pertain to these switches. (This trick applies to formatting diskettes also.)

Using Volume Labels

More flexible than file names, volume labels can have 11 characters in sequence. File names can have no more than 8 characters in a root name; the extension can have 3 characters. Volume labels can contain spaces; file names cannot. You can create meaningful volume labels, such as **PRIMARY DSK** or **1-2-3 DATA**.

4.11   Tip: To place a volume label on a disk, use the /V (V3.3) or /V:name (V4) switch.

FORMAT V3.3 and earlier versions do not automatically request a volume label. To give one, you must use the /V switch; then after formatting is complete, FORMAT requests a volume label. Type the name and press Enter. If you press Enter without giving a name, no volume label is used.

FORMAT V4 automatically prompts you for a volume name. To specify the name and skip the prompt, you can use the **/V:name** switch. **name** is the volume label that each formatted disk receives.

If you use the **/V:name** command, all disks formatted during this run of FORMAT receive the same volume label. If you want to use different

volume labels on diskettes, do not use the **/V:name** switch. When you are
prompted for a volume label, you can specify the name.

4.12   Trap: Don't use a period as the ninth character of a volume label.

Be aware of one peculiarity of volume labels: If you use a period in the
ninth position, DOS may interpret the label as a file name. Depending on
the operation, DOS may try to "load" or "execute" the volume label.

4.13   Trick: If you need to format a hard disk that has a volume label, run a CHKDSK or DIR command to see the volume label.

To format a hard disk that has a volume label, you must remember the
volume label. Just before running FORMAT, run either CHKDSK or DIR;
either command displays the volume label. CHKDSK runs through the
entire directory structure before producing results, which is a
disadvantage. If the list of files is long, the volume label scrolls off the top
of the screen when you use DIR, which is another disadvantage. In this
case, use Ctrl-Break or Ctrl-C to halt DIR and keep the line with the
volume label line on-screen.

4.14   Tip: If you assign a volume label when you format, you can use the directory entry to determine the date and time of formatting.

A volume label is a root directory entry. The entry holds the date and time
the label was created. If the label hasn't been changed, you can use this
entry to determine the date and time of formatting.

DOS pre-V4 and V4 differ slightly in their use of volume labels. DOS V4
also writes the volume label into the boot sector. The change allows DOS
to deliver the volume label quickly so that you don't have to run a
program that wades through the root directory.

4.15   Trick: To protect a hard disk from unintentional formatting, use a volume label with a hidden character or lowercase character.

To help prevent the accidental (and occasionally deliberate) formatting of
a hard disk with DOS V3.3 and later versions, use a hidden character or
lowercase character in the volume label. You can perform the hidden
character trick with DOS; you need a third-party program to use lowercase
characters.

For the hidden character (which is also useful with file names), use the
ASCII 255 (FF hex) character. This character, which is viewed as a unique
character by DOS, appears as a space on-screen. If you embed this

character in a volume label, FORMAT will not reformat the hard disk when you enter the incorrect volume label (without the hidden character).

You enter the hidden character by holding down the Alt key, typing **255** on the numeric keypad, and then releasing the Alt key. The cursor moves left as if you have typed a space. The best way to use this technique is to add the 255 character either where a space would normally appear or at the end of the volume label. For example, you can type the following sequence when FORMAT requests a volume label:

> **DOS<255>DISK<255>**

An ASCII 255 character is placed between the **S** in DOS and **D** in DISK and after the **K** in DISK. (The **<255>** designates the Alt-255 sequence.)

The second trick is to use lowercase characters in the volume label. FORMAT automatically converts lowercase letters to uppercase letters in volume labels. If you enter a volume label that contains lowercase characters, FORMAT transforms the characters to uppercase, compares the transformed volume label to the real volume label, notices the difference (FORMAT is literal when comparing characters), informs you that the entered volume label is incorrect, and stops. Until you change the volume label by using a non-DOS utility or disk-sector editor, the disk cannot be reformatted.

For example, I entered **DOS Disk** to VL (from Norton Utilities™) as the new volume label for drive C:. I then tried to run FORMAT, which requested the volume label. When I entered **DOS Disk** again, FORMAT transformed the label into **DOS DISK** and rejected the entered label as incorrect.

Note that both methods offer limited protection. The next trick explains why and introduces another method of protection.

4.16   Trick: For protection, set the volume label to read-only.

Be aware that using a bizarre volume label has one shortcoming. Because you can use the DOS LABEL command to replace the label, you easily can delete any volume label. A casual user could remove the volume label and undo the protection.

To protect the volume label further, use a disk-sector editor to set the read-only attribute. The normal attribute value for a volume label is 08 hex; the attribute of a read-only volume label is 09 hex. After you change the read-only attribute, you cannot delete or change the volume label without using a disk-sector editor to undo the change. Neither DOS's LABEL nor Norton's VL commands will work.

You can change other file attributes (except the subdirectory attribute) without adverse effects. You also can set the hidden or system attributes of the volume label. However, setting either does not inhibit the display of the volume label.

A knowledgeable person with malicious intent can undo the change. (For that matter, such a person simply could delete key files.) Just as locks keep the honest person honest, this scheme prevents the casual to experienced user from destroying your hard work, but does not prevent an all-out assault by a knowledgeable person with the right tools.

Unformatting a Hard Disk

4.17   Tip: You can unformat a hard disk if you have the right program and take the right precautions.

No versions of DOS's FORMAT can perform physical, or low-level formatting, for a hard disk. FORMAT performs only logical, or high-level formatting. DOS rewrites the disk's partition record (which tells the computer how the disk is divided and what system uses which part), boot record, directory, and file allocation table. DOS also tests whether each sector in the partition can be read and marks out any unusable sectors. (Some bad sectors can spill through this test because it is not exhaustive.)

When you use FORMAT on a floppy diskette, all data is destroyed. When you use FORMAT on a hard disk, however, the directory and file allocation table are destroyed, but the data is left intact. Retrieving the data manually is possible but impractical. It's like separating one pound of sand from one pound of salt after thoroughly mixing both together; you can do it with patience and the right tools, but it's cheaper to start over again with an unmixed pound of salt and sand.

4.18   Trap: You cannot recover from some versions of FORMAT.

Some MS-DOS versions of FORMAT provide better security and more extensive testing of the entire hard disk than others. These FORMAT versions write a pattern of data into each sector of the disk and then read the sector. If your FORMAT version performs this test, you have a greater chance of detecting disk errors, a zero chance of someone stealing erased information from the disk, and a zero chance of recovering after an accidental format.

Lethal FORMAT programs include AT&T® and Boroughs DOS V2.1, COMPAQ DOS V2.1 through V3.2, and Wyse DOS V3.21. If you format with these versions of DOS, forget about recovering. Use the hard disk format program provided with the Mace Utilities® instead, or use a newer version of DOS.

Using DOS Partitions and FDISK

Until a new hard disk is physically formatted and partitioned, it is unusable. DOS's FDISK does the partitioning; however, DOS does not provide a program for the physical formatting of a hard disk. For that, you need an outside program.

With DOS V3.3, partitions are the only way you can use a hard disk drive that is larger than 32M. With COMPAQ DOS V3.31, PC DOS V4, or MS-DOS V4, on the other hand, make partitions discretionary; a single partition can be up to 512M or 1024M, respectively. If you make the transition between DOS V3.3 and DOS V4, you can choose to maintain your current partition size, or you can change the partitions. If you are starting with DOS V4, you may want to reconsider your partitioning after you read the information in this section. There is no universal "best" way to partition a hard disk. Solid arguments can be made for any partition setup.

FDISK is the DOS-provided program that manipulates partition information on a hard disk. FDISK is responsible for creating the master boot record (which holds the partition information), creating the primary DOS partitions (abbreviated **PRI**) and the extended DOS partitions (abbreviated **EXT**), and creating logical volumes in the extended partitions. FDISK also marks which partition should be used to start the computer. For DOS users, the primary partition should be marked as the *active* partition (the startable partition).

You run FDISK after a low-level format program and before DOS's FORMAT. Note that certain disk drive manufacturers provide their own partitioning software. If you use one of those disk drives, use the provided program—do not use FDISK.

Creating Partitions

4.19 Tip: A primary partition has one logical drive. An extended partition can have several logical drives.

DOS V3.3 and later versions use three types of hard disk partitions: primary, extended, and logical volume. The differences are not important when you use the hard disk, but are important when you set up the hard disk or when you perform some manual repair operations.

Although every hard disk can have four disk partitions, DOS pre-V3.3 recognized natively only one type of partition—a single DOS partition. Because DOS could not use a logical disk drive larger than 32M, you could not use a large hard disk drive without help.

Many computer manufacturers and third-party software developers provide alternatives that circumvent the 32M limit. The details of the schemes vary between implementations of DOS and third-party hard-disk partition managers. The popular scheme is to partition the disk into one DOS partition and additional partitions. A device driver allows DOS to recognize the additional disk partitions as additional DOS partitions.

DOS V3.3 and later versions use the same basic scheme with some differences. DOS V3.3 and later recognize two types of partitions—a primary and an extended DOS partition. The device driver that recognizes the additional partition is built into DOS. The slight variation is that you can divide the extended partition further.

Most hard disks have a primary partition. (DOS starts only from a primary partition.) For this reason, you cannot create an extended partition on a single hard disk drive system without first creating a primary partition. DOS views the primary partition as a single disk drive; the entire primary partition is addressed by a single DOS disk drive letter. Unlike primary partitions, DOS can view an extended partition as several disk drives. You divide the physical disk into a primary partition and an optional extended partition to circumvent the 32M limit of DOS.

The extended partition acts like a hard disk. You can subdivide that partition into 1 to 21 different *logical volumes* (a term new to DOS V3.3). Logical volumes are similar to additional disk partitions. Each logical volume is a separate logical disk drive and is assigned its own disk drive letter.

With this new scheme, you can use disk drives as large as 704M with DOS pre-V3.31. For DOS V3.31 and V4, the logical volume scheme allows DOS to use multigigabyte hard disk drives, CD-ROMs, and other optical disks.

4.20 Tip: You must create partitions and logical volumes in ascending order.

When you create partitions with FDISK on the first hard disk, you must create the primary partition first, and then you can create an extended partition. With most implementations of DOS (true of PC DOS), you must follow the same order with additional hard disks.

After you create the extended partition under any DOS version, you must create the logical volumes in ascending order. For example, the primary partition on the first hard disk is drive C:, and the first logical volume in the extended partition is drive D:. If space is available, you can create additional logical volumes, assigning each an ascending disk drive letter.

When you run FDISK on a new hard disk (and after low-level formatting), follow these steps:

> ***Step 1:*** *Create a primary DOS partition.*
>
> ***Step 2:*** *Mark the primary partition as the active partition.*
>
> ***Step 3:*** *Create an extended partition, if you want.*
>
> ***Step 4:*** *If you create an extended partition, create one or more logical DOS drives in the extended partition.*

Before you actually run FDISK, you should plan your partition sizes and note the information in the next tip.

4.21 Tip: For FDISK V3.3 and earlier, use cylinders when you give sizes. For FDISK V4, use percentages of disk space.

FDISK V4 differs from earlier versions of FDISK. When you establish partitions or logical volumes with FDISK pre-V4, you give the starting and ending cylinders for the partition or volume. With FDISK V4, you give percentages of disk space for each partition or volume, and FDISK calculates the appropriate starting and ending cylinder.

FDISK pre-V4 is somewhat more complex and intimidating to use. If you use a different setup (other than the default), you must perform some manual calculations. The default setup makes each partition or logical volume up to 32M and assigns the remaining space to another partition or volume.

If you want something else (for example, 2 equal-sized partitions on a 40M disk), you need to find how much space each cylinder holds—this amount varies between hard disk drives. Most hard disks use 8.5K per track (17 sectors), although some ESDI or RLL hard disks use 12.5K (25 sectors) or 16K (32 sectors) per track. Multiply the amount each cylinder holds by the number of recording surfaces to determine the amount of storage per cylinder. Then divide the desired partition or volume size by that figure, and use the resulting number of cylinders with FDISK.

Partitions and volumes must start and end on cylinder boundaries, starting on sector 1 and ending on the last sector. The primary partition can begin on a side other than 0 and can share the cylinder that holds the master boot record. (The boot record occupies the first sector of the first side of the first cylinder of the hard disk.) The extended partition starts on side 0, but that side holds the boot record for the first logical drive. All logical volumes follow this pattern (side 0 of the cylinder holds the boot record; side 1 starts the logical volume itself).

FDISK V4 simplifies the partitioning process. The default setup for FDISK is to make one primary partition the size of the disk drive. If you want a different setup, you specify what percentage of disk space for each partition or volume; FDISK does the remaining work. However, this simplified approach has a minor disadvantage, discussed in a later tip on the primary partition.

4.22   Tip: You may need to tell white lies to FDISK for some ESDI and RLL controllers.

When you set up partitions, FDISK requires the starting and ending cylinder numbers. Because of a limitation in the ROM BIOS and DOS, the computer normally cannot use disk drives with more than 1,024 cylinders. Some disk drive controller boards work around this limit by disguising the disk drive. The controller boards make the computer think that the drive has fewer than 1,024 cylinders, but has more sides or sectors per track than the drive actually has. Only the disk controller board knows that it is performing *sector translation*.

When you set up a third-party disk drive and controller with FDISK, check the documentation for the correct values to use with FDISK. The documentation may recommend that you use a different number of cylinders to create a given size of disk partition. In that case, you may need to tell a white lie to FDISK by giving a logically correct, but physically inaccurate number of cylinders.

Using Partitions

4.23   **Tip: To decide how to establish and use partitions, study the types of programs you use and the way you use them.**

Partitions are like subdirectories. The best guidelines for establishing and using partitions and subdirectories are the types of programs you use and the way you use them. You should know the following basics about your programs:

- Do your programs load into memory completely or do they use overlays or other program files extensively?
- What are the size and number of the data files your programs use?
- How do you use the programs and the computer?

The first factor is whether your program loads into memory completely or whether it uses overlays or other program files extensively. For example, 1-2-3 is a one-shot loading program organized into several independent sections that can be loaded separately. When you use the 1-2-3 or PrintGraph sections, the entire portion of the program loads into memory; 1-2-3 or PrintGraph returns to the disk for program parts only when you switch between sections.

WordStar and dBASE®, on the other hand, use overlays; the entire program does not load into memory. When a program piece is needed, these programs load the overlays into memory. WordStar uses overlays moderately; the program loads the pieces only on certain infrequent operations. Because most of its applications use many separately loaded command files, dBASE III Plus is an extreme example of a program that uses both overlays and program files. dBASE is almost as disk intensive in using its program files as it is in using data files.

The second factor refers to the size and number of data files your programs use. The extremes include accounting or database applications on one side and word processing programs on the other. Accounting or database applications usually have only a few data files (a few to several dozen), but the files can be large, from 100K to 10M+. Word processing applications usually have many small files (scores to hundreds of 2K to 10K files, and some files as large as 100K).

The third and final aspect is how you use the programs and the computer. This aspect concerns convenience. Is working with one partition or several partitions more convenient?

When planning partitions, know that no one scheme is right for everyone and that every partitioning setup has pros and cons. In some cases, several or smaller partitions worker better; in other cases, one or several large partitions work well. Use your programs, the programs' capabilities, and your files as a guide for planning partitions.

4.24　Trap: Once you make a partition larger than 32M, DOS V3.3 and earlier versions cannot use your hard disk.

If you divide your disk to use the larger-than-32M partitions, DOS V3.3 cannot use the disk because it cannot use the large partitions.

If your software operates with DOS V3.31 or DOS V4, you don't need to worry about earlier versions of DOS. If some of your software does not work with DOS V3.31 or DOS V4, you will need to update the software, continue using your current version of DOS and wait until the update becomes available (if not currently available), or set up your system so that you can use either version of DOS. If you must use either version of DOS, do not use partitions larger than 32M.

Planning Partitions on File Size

4.25　Tip: If you have many small files, use an 18M to 32M partition for DOS V3, 18M to 64M for COMPAQ DOS V3.31, and 18M to 128M for DOS V4.

Partitions of less than 18M use a cluster size of 4K, not 2K. DOS V4 shifts to 4K clusters on partitions over 128K; COMPAQ DOS V3.31 shifts to 4K clusters at 64M. If you have many small files, too much space is wasted because of the larger clusters.

4.26　Tip: If your files are large, select a partition that uses larger cluster sizes.

DOS allocates space and moves through large files marginally faster when a larger cluster size is used. For accounting or database applications with large data files (in the hundreds of K or more), the larger cluster sizes are helpful.

COMPAQ DOS V3.31 and DOS V4 users might consider increasing the partition size to use the larger cluster sizes (greater than 64M for DOS V3.31 and greater than 128M for DOS V4). However, other factors can outweigh the marginal increase in speed gained by working with larger clusters.

Planning Partitions on Disk Speed

4.27　Tip: Use multiple partitions to reduce average seek time.

Seagate Technology specifies the average seek time for its 40M disk drives. If the drive is a single 40M partition, the average seek time is 40 ms. If the drive is divided into two 20M partitions, the average seek time is 28 ms.

When the activity is isolated to one-half of the disk drive, the mathematical average distance is cut by half. Therefore, the seek time is lower. No matter how many logical disk drives are on the physical disk drive, however, the disk has only one set of recording heads. If your programs continuously flip between logical disk drives, the disk heads move over the entire drive surface. The average seek time reverts to 40 ms.

If you can organize your files so that only one logical disk drive is used, the disk heads stay within the partition, and you use the faster access time. Also, if the running program does not use another disk drive frequently, the multiple partition approach can be faster.

4.28　Tip: Isolate fragmentation and improve performance by using one partition for frequently changing files.

If you delete and add files frequently, you subject your drive to fragmentation. Files are not stored in contiguous sectors; therefore, performance slows as the disk heads must make extra moves to read a file.

If you use one partition for unchanging program files and a second partition for data files on the second logical disk drive, only the second logical drive will suffer increased fragmentation and slower performance. Your programs load quickly, but they still run slower as fragmentation increases.

Don't make the data partition too small. The worst effects of fragmentation can happen sooner on a small logical drive than on a large logical drive. As you delete and add files, less continuous free space at the end of the disk is available. As this space is consumed, empty spaces at the front of the disk are used. When DOS starts recycling the entire partition looking for free room, your files become more scattered, and performance slows.

The entire argument of fragmentation is moot if you use a defragmenting program periodically. Defragmenters move files so that they are contiguous. Chapter 3 on disk performance discusses defragmenters.

4.29 Tip: Some disk-wide operations are faster because they use more than one partition. Other disk-wide operations are more convenient because they use only one partition.

Some operations that affect an entire partition can be faster or more convenient when they use only one partition; other operations can be faster or more convenient when they use more than one partition. The issue depends partially on processing time and the number of times you need to issue a command.

Sweep programs search a set of directories or the entire disk for files. The FF program from the Norton Utilities, which searches an entire drive for a file name, works on one disk at a time. If you are looking for a file, you must issue one FF command for each disk drive until you find the file. In this case, one large partition is easier to use.

Conversely, using FF once on one large partition may be slower than using FF on separate drives. Some versions of FF continue to search for a file until all subdirectories have been searched. With smaller partitions, the search is faster because fewer files and smaller partitions are searched.

The DOS commands BACKUP and RESTORE also balance convenience with performance. You use BACKUP and RESTORE once for each disk drive. If you have one large disk drive, you run BACKUP and RESTORE only once. If you have more than one disk drive, you run the commands once for each drive. Because the amount of information processed by the program is the same, the running time of BACKUP or RESTORE is the same.

Other convenience factors can dictate partition sizes. Ward Christensen, the author of the XMODEM communications protocol, has a 72M hard disk divided into four 17M to 19M partitions. He performs four primary tasks with his system: program development, communications, desktop publishing, and database applications. The programs and data files for each task fit completely on one partition.

Christensen prefers this setup, however, for an even more important reason: the tape drive he uses for backup holds only 17M. He can place all backup files for an entire partition on one tape. Because tape backup is one of the "coffee break" tasks (get a cup or an entire pot of coffee while the computer works, depending on the task time), tape backup is more convenient on the partition-by-partition basis.

Disk defragmenters, which require 15 minutes to several hours to finish their work, can fall into the same category. Because the computer is unusable while the program runs, this task demands no attention from the user. Most people run their defragmenters at night. If you can run the defragmenter from a batch file, you don't care how many partitions are defragmented. You place one command for each drive in the batch file.

If the defragmenter requires attention at the beginning or end of its operation, you cannot run it from a batch file. In that case, running the program once on a one-partition drive defragments all files. Two partitions require two runs of the program. Therefore, the one-partition operation is more convenient.

Deleting Partitions

4.30   Tip: You must delete partitions and volumes in descending order.

When you delete partitions or logical volumes, you must use the reverse order of their creation. You must delete the last logical volume first, and then the next to the last logical volume, and so on, until you delete all logical volumes. After you delete all logical volumes, you can delete the extended partition. After you delete the extended partition, you can delete the primary partition.

4.31   Tip: You can delete the last volume or partition without affecting earlier volumes or partitions.

If you want to resize your partitions or logical volumes, you must first delete and then re-create them. If you update from DOS V3.3 to DOS V4 and want to take advantage of the larger partitions available with DOS V4, you probably will need to back up, repartition, format, and restore all your files. Most users will want to enlarge the first disk drive (drive C:). Because this process takes space from the extended partition, all partitions are affected.

If you want to change only the volumes in the extended partition, this tip applies to you. When you delete volumes or partitions, remember that you must use the reverse order and that the extended partition cannot be deleted until all logical volumes are deleted. You can delete safely each "last" volume or partition, however, without affecting earlier volumes or partitions. If you have three logical volumes, for example, you can delete the last two and create a larger volume from the two without affecting the first logical volume or primary partition.

4.32 Trap: You normally cannot recover a partition or volume deleted by FDISK.

When FDISK deletes a logical volume, the pointer to that area in the previous volume is zeroed. When you delete the partition, the record that holds the information on the partition is zeroed in the master boot record. If you have a disk-sector editor and some knowledge of the partition information, you can restore the appropriate entries and re-create the partitions or volumes without destroying the information held in the partitions or volumes.

FDISK, however, is destructive. When FDISK creates a partition or volume, the area that will hold the boot record, FAT, and root directory for the partition or volume is zeroed by FDISK. This means that you cannot delete a partition or volume with FDISK and then immediately re-create the partition or volume with the same information without losing data. After you run FDISK to reestablish the partition information, the previous FAT and root directory are destroyed.

Usually, FDISK's destructiveness is not a problem. FDISK has several strongly worded warnings about data being destroyed. Heed these warnings. Do not run FDISK unless you are partitioning a new drive, or repartitioning a previously used drive and you have backed up all useful information. When repartitioning, you must use FORMAT to reestablish a new FAT and root directory anyway. (The old FAT and directories are invalid because the disk layout has changed.) Make a habit of backing up the drive before you run FDISK.

FDISK's destructiveness is a problem in one circumstance—when the master boot record has been destroyed. A stray write to the first sector of the disk or a bad sector that develops in the master boot record can cause this problem. In the latter case, you must low-level format the first track of the hard disk to cure the problem. In either case, you must restore the master boot record to use the disk.

Unless you have taken precautions (such as using a FAT saver or disk-sector editor to save the information), running FDISK destroys the FATs and root directories of the disk. Recovering from this problem is more difficult than recovering from most other errors because FDISK has zeroed both the FAT and starting directory. To take precautions, see the section on FAT savers in Chapter 15 on troubleshooting.

4.33   Trick: To minimize the chance of destroying the master boot record, start the primary partition on cylinder 1.

If you use DOS V3.31 and earlier, you can specify the starting cylinder for the primary partition. (FDISK V4 does not offer this option.) Use cylinder 1 rather than cylinder 0. Although this trick wastes one cylinder's worth of disk storage, consider the following reason.

Chapter 2 explained that certain hard disks inadvertently write information when the disk is powered up. This problem strikes mainly stepper-motor-based hard disks, which do not park their heads. Because the most frequently used part of the disk is the part that holds the FAT and root directory, this area is the most likely spot for the heads to come to rest.

If the heads rest where the FAT and root directory are kept for the primary disk partition, the heads are resting on cylinder 0. Cylinder 0 also holds the master boot record. If the recording head inadvertently writes to cylinder 0, the master boot record (that holds the partition information) will probably be affected. If a stray disk write also reaches the cylinder with the FAT and root directory, the partition table can be similarly affected. If the partition information is lost, rerunning FDISK to restore the partition destroys previous information.

To minimize the chance of the head resting on the master boot record, start the primary partition on the next cylinder. If the heads rest on the FAT or root directory on cylinder 1, you incur little risk of damaging cylinder 0. If the master boot record is on a different cylinder, the chance of a stray write affecting the FAT, root directory, and master boot record is almost zero. The wasted disk space will be well spent on preventing the loss of the master boot record.

Note that this trick applies mainly to stepper-motor disk drives-disk drives that do not park their heads. If you park your disk heads every time you turn off the computer, you need not pay attention to this trick. The recording heads on your system will rest in the parking zone, safely away from the master boot record. However, the stray write is still a problem. Because the chance of the stray write is very small, this trick is not essential but can ensure a more robust disk drive.

Using FDISK with Other Operating Systems

4.34   Trap: You cannot use DOS's FDISK to alter non-DOS partitions.

DOS's FDISK can create or delete its own partitions or logical volumes; however, FDISK respects the logical walls between itself and other operating systems. If you use more than one operating system (other than OS/2) on your hard disk, you cannot use DOS's FDISK to create or delete the partitions owned by other operating systems. You must use the partitioning program (usually also called FDISK) provided with the other operating system.

4.35 **Trick: Use a disk-sector editor to allow PC DOS V4 to recognize an MS-DOS disk.**

By checking the boot record in each partition, IBM PC DOS V4 protects itself from working with hard disks it may not know correctly. The 4th through 12th bytes (bytes 3–B) make up the 8-character OEM name. For PC DOS V4 to recognize the drive, the first 3 characters must read **IBM**; IBM is usually followed by a space and then a version number (such as **3.3** or **4.0**).

If you are using MS-DOS V3 and attempting to use PC DOS V4, you may receive a message about an invalid drive when you try to access the disk. The previous OEM name for most MS-DOS computers is **MSDOS 3x** (where the **x** is the second digit in the version number, such as **3** for MS-DOS V3.3). To correct the problem, use a disk-sector editor on the boot record of each partition and change the OEM name to **IBM 4.0**. If you change the record before you use INSTALL, PC DOS V4 should recognize the disk drive and INSTALL will work correctly.

Performing Low-Level Formatting

Low-level formatting establishes the physical housekeeping information on a disk: the guard areas around the sectors, the identification numbers for sectors, the error checking information areas, and the interleave factor. This formatting differs from the logical housekeeping areas established by DOS.

FORMAT does not physically format a hard disk. You must use another program. In the case of an IBM XT, work-alike, or some disk controller boards, the formatting program is located in the ROM on the disk controller board. For the PC AT, PS/2 family, and close clones, you must use a separate format program not provided with DOS.

The program usually is available in a special diagnostics package sold by the computer manufacturer, provided with third-party disk drives, or sold through third-party software houses. For example, the IBM advanced diagnostics packages for the PC family members include the physical format program. Priam provides a formatting program with its drives. Paul Mace Software publishes a hard disk format and test utility package called HTEST/FORMAT.

If you use an IBM PS/2 computer, a low-level format routine is provided on the Reference Diskette. To locate the program, start the computer with the reference diskette, get to the main menu by pressing Enter when the IBM logo appears, and then press Ctrl-A. The advanced diagnostics menu appears, which displays the option to low-level format the disk.

In most cases, the computer manufacturer or dealer physically formats the disk drive before you purchase the system. If you must reformat the hard disk, you may need a physical format program.

4.36   Trick: If you are not sure whether your controller has a built-in format routine, use DEBUG.

If you use a PC XT or similar computer, the format routine is in the ROM of the disk controller board. If you use a PC AT or PS/2, the format routine is not in ROM. And if you use a third-party disk controller, the format routine may or may not be in ROM. Usually, the documentation for the controller board states whether the routine is in ROM. If you are not sure, you can use DEBUG for a quick check.

Start DEBUG and then type **U C800:5**. C800 is the usual segment address for the disk controller board ROM. The formatting routine is normally located at location 5 within the ROM. If the first line of DEBUG shows **JMP** followed by a two- or four-hexadecimal digit number, ROM probably contains the format routine. If you see nonsense or if the first or next few lines do not contain **JMP**, the routine probably is not in ROM. In that case, you need an outside program for formatting.

If your format routine is in ROM, you normally execute the routine by typing **G=C800:5**. Be exceptionally cautious in experimenting. The format routine usually asks for an interleave value or for confirmation that your intent is to format the disk. Because low-level formatting is destructive, never unleash this operation on a disk that contains useful information.

4.37   Tip: Some drives demands special low-level formatting programs.

Disks that demand special low-level formatting programs use a controller-type not supported by most third-party programs, or the disks perform special bad-sector remapping or other forms of sector translations. For example, disk drives from Priam use the last cylinder of the disk for sector-translation information. Most low-level format programs will destroy the factory-installed information on this track.

Most manufacturers state in their documentation whether a special format program is needed. Most manufacturers also provide the program.

4.38   Tip: Never tell lies to a low-level format program.

You must give the low-level format program the correct characteristics of the disk drive. If you give the incorrect number of heads, sectors, or cylinders, the results are arbitrary and seldom desirable. The entire disk will not be formatted or will be formatted incorrectly. DOS's reaction to the disk seldom will be correct.

This does not mean that you cannot format only parts of the disk. Almost all physical format programs allow you to "spot" format just a track or several cylinders of the disk. This spot formatting is useful for certain manual disk repairs.

4.39   Tip: Expect physical formatting to take about 5 to 30 minutes per 10M.

Physically formatting a disk drive is time-consuming; the physical format process takes about 5 to 10 minutes for each 10 megabytes of disk space. Also, most programs simultaneously perform extensive tests for disk drive errors. Including the testing time, the process can take up to 30 minutes per 10M.

Run the physical format process on a new disk drive at the beginning of the day or overnight. If you run the program during the day, run it using a low level of testing (most programs can set the number of times the entire disk is tested); then run the hard disk test program overnight. If you are formatting overnight, run the program at its highest level of testing. Remember that most drives do contain a few errors; seeing a few bad tracks should be not astonishing.

If you are physically formatting a previously used drive, use a moderate testing level. Because few new bad tracks should develop, you do not need extensive testing. If many bad tracks show during the testing phase, something is wrong with the drive or controller; you need a service call.

Formatting Diskettes

Formatting a floppy diskette is an irreversible process. FORMAT performs a physical, or low-level format, that destroys all information previously recorded on the diskette. Once the diskette is reformatted, the previous information is lost.

4.40   Tip: If you don't know whether the diskette contains any data, use the DIR command on the diskette before you format it.

Use the DIR command to make sure that the diskette you are about to FORMAT is blank. If no files appear, you can reformat immediately. If a list of files appears, check the list and decide whether you should save any files. If no useful files appear, you can reformat the diskette.

If the list appears as gibberish or you get a DOS disk error message (`General failure` is a common message), the disk is probably not formatted and does not contain useful information. However, in three exceptions the diskette may still hold useful information.

The first exception occurs when you use two different operating systems, such as DOS and XENIX®, and the diskette contains information that was stored under a different operating system. (DOS and OS/2 users need not worry; OS/2 V1.x diskettes are compatible with DOS.) Because the key housekeeping information or diskette formats of each system are different, DOS sees the directory as gibberish or cannot read the key sectors of the diskette.

The second exception occurs with programs that format and record information on the diskette differently than DOS—for example, Fifth Generation's FASTBACK™ backup program. FASTBACK gets some of its speed by using a unique disk format. However, DOS cannot read this information; if you try, you usually receive the `General Failure` error message.

The third exception occurs with a hidden file (or hidden subdirectory with files) that does not appear in a directory listing. If you are unaware of the file and format the diskette, the file is lost. Some copy protection schemes use hidden files.

The three exceptions are rare, but formatting the wrong diskette is devastating. The solution is to label every diskette. With the label intact, you should be able to identify whether a diskette is fair game for FORMAT.

4.41   Trick: For extra safety, consider using the Mace Utilities FORMAT-F program, which does not destroy diskettes.

The Mace Utilities FORMAT-F program tests each track of the floppy diskette to see whether the track requires formatting. If the track is correct, FORMAT-F moves to the next track. FORMAT-F marks all files on the disk as erased, but the directory and file allocation tables are left intact. If you immediately run the Mace Recover program, you can recover your files.

4.42 Tip: Unless you are making a bootable program diskette, do not use FORMAT's /S switch.

The size of the DOS start-up files grows with each new version of DOS. The start-up files include IBMBIO.COM, IBMDOS.COM, and COMMAND.COM for PC DOS; and IO.SYS, MSDOS.SYS, and COMMAND.COM for MS-DOS. The size of these three DOS V3.3 start-up files is approximately 77K; the size of DOS V4 start-up files is about 105K.

Because you need to maximize the space on the diskettes, do not place the start-up files on the diskette. Use FORMAT /S only on diskettes that will be used to start DOS.

For my floppy-based portable computer, I usually place DOS only on the main program diskettes. I then can start DOS conveniently from these diskettes. The other program and data diskettes cannot start DOS, but omitting these files saves diskette space.

4.43 Trick: Place COMMAND.COM on a nonbootable program diskette if the program is likely to use all available DOS memory.

You may want to place a copy of COMMAND.COM on the program diskette. When a program requests all available memory from DOS, the transient portion of COMMAND.COM is clobbered. When you exit the program, DOS must reload COMMAND.COM from the disk, and the following message is displayed:

```
Insert a diskette with \COMMAND.COM
and strike any key to continue
```

The program has requested all available RAM; COMMAND.COM has been freed and must be reloaded from the disk. You can insert a DOS bootable diskette in the drive, strike a key, and then change diskettes again. To avoid changing diskettes, simply place COMMAND.COM on the diskette which will be in the start-up disk drive. When DOS needs to reload COMMAND.COM, the command interpreter is already on the diskette.

4.44 Trap: Some pre-V3.2 DOS diskettes do not have the proper disk-parameter block; using these diskettes causes the system to hang.

You place the diskette into the disk drive, run a directory of the diskette, and your system locks up. A warm boot won't restart the computer; you must turn off and on the system to regain control. You have encountered the infamous "death disk," so named by Barry Simon of Ctrl-Alt Associates.

This problem doesn't happen with diskettes formatted with PC DOS, but it has occurred with other implementations of DOS, usually V2.0 or V2.1. The errant FORMAT programs from these implementations either do not write or do not write correctly the disk-parameter block to the boot sector of the diskette.

When DOS V3.2 or later tries to read the diskette, it reads the errant boot sector, usually finds a 0 for the number of disk heads, and promptly generates an illegal CPU instruction. The drive light stays on, a message is displayed, or both. The result is a locked-up system.

Two factors make the problem difficult. First, DOS hangs on the first access of the diskette (loading a program from or running DIR or CHKDSK on the diskette). This means that any activity, even reading the directory, locks up the computer. The second factor is that the diskette will work correctly with previous versions of DOS but causes current versions to lock up.

You can use one of two techniques to solve the problem. You can format a diskette with the current DOS version, restart the computer using DOS V3.1 or earlier versions, and then copy the files from the original diskette to the newly formatted diskette.

Or you can use a disk-sector editor, such as IBM's Disk Repair, which bypasses DOS and directly reads the boot sector from the diskette. (The disk-sector editor program from the Norton Utilities does not work in this case.) You then can edit the errant disk-parameter block to the correct values. You can read the boot sector from a working diskette of the same capacity and then write the boot sector to the diskette. Unless you are comfortable with disk-sector editors, however, you shouldn't use this approach.

4.45   Trap: If FORMAT V3.3 reports a Bad Track 0, the diskette is not necessarily unusable.

If FORMAT reports that a disk has a bad track 0, the disk may be unusable. You may, however, have encountered a FORMAT bug instead.

The problem occurs when you change your CONFIG.SYS or TSRs frequently. FORMAT worked correctly before, but does not work now. The problem is not what you are doing, but rather, a bug in FORMAT.

FORMAT is position-sensitive in memory. If FORMAT loads into memory at the wrong spot, it attempts to cross a magical 64K segment boundary, gets confused, and reports the bad track 0.

The cure is to load FORMAT into another spot in memory. First, run CHKDSK to see the amount of free memory. Then either use more or less memory by adding or removing a TSR or loading a copy or two of COMMAND.COM (use **COMMAND** once or twice). Check the free memory again and then rerun FORMAT. If the message is the same, the disk is bad. If FORMAT works, you know that you must free or occupy some memory to use FORMAT with your current setup.

4.46 Trap: You cannot format some 1.2M diskettes at 360K.

The 1.2M disk drive differs from the 360K drive in several ways. The 1.2M drive records 15 512-byte sectors in the same space that a 360K disk drive records 9 512-byte sectors. (The 1.2M disk drive also records 80 tracks in the space that the 360K drive records 40 tracks.)

Ostrand is the unit of measure for recording flux (bits of information) changes on a diskette. The 1.2M diskette is rated at 800 Ostrands; the 360K diskette is rated at 300 Ostrands. Because a 1.2M diskette can record 2 2/3 as many flux changes as 360K diskettes, the 1.2M diskette can hold more information.

If you try to format 1.2M diskettes by using the /4 switch or /F:360 switches (360K capacity), FORMAT reports that track 0 is bad. The diskettes are unusable, yet they format correctly at their 1.2M rating. The problem is seemingly random. Some 1.2M diskettes work at either capacity, yet another diskette from the same box won't. Why does a diskette withstand the strenuous formatting at the 1.2M capability but not the casual formatting at the 360K capability?

The problem is called *reduced write current*. The 1.2M disk drive uses a higher current level to record 1.2M diskettes and a lower current level to record 360K diskettes. When using the lower current level, the disk drive does not use a high enough magnetic field to affect some 1.2M diskettes.

If you get an error message that a 1.2M diskette cannot be formatted on a 360K disk drive or use the /4 switch on a 1.2M disk drive, either use 360K (double-sided, double-density rated) diskettes or try a different 1.2M diskette.

4.47 Trap: If you format 360K diskettes on a 1.2M disk drive, the diskettes seldom work on 360K disk drives; 360K diskettes written on a 1.2M disk drive sometimes work.

Remember that a 1.2M disk drive records a track that is less than half the size of a 360K disk drive's track. For this reason, some 360K disk drives cannot read reliably a diskette written by a 1.2M disk drive. The problem is consistent for any particular 360K disk drive. If the 360K disk drive cannot read a diskette written on a particular 1.2M disk drive, the disk drive will not read any diskettes written by a 1.2M disk drive. On the other hand, some 360K disk drives can read any 360K diskettes written by any 1.2M disk drive. Because the 1.2M drive formats tracks of smaller width than the normal 360K track, most 360K disk drives produce read errors when you attempt to use these diskettes.

You must test the 360K disk drive to see whether the drive can read diskettes written by a 1.2M disk drive. Don't, however, bother to format a 360K diskette on a 1.2M disk drive. The resulting diskette works fine on the 1.2M disk drive but is useless on the 360K disk drive. If you must format a 360K diskette, use the 360K disk drive.

4.48 Tip: If you need to produce 360K diskettes on an AT, use a 360K drive or a special program.

The 360K problem has two solutions. The first solution, installing a 360K disk drive, is inexpensive ($60 to $120) and relatively easy to implement. However, if you are out of disk-drive slot space in the AT or want a software-only solution, Microbridge Computer International's CPYAT2PC ($40) can format and copy 360K diskettes in a 1.2M disk drive.

CPYAT2PC has two programs: a diskette formatter and a copy program. The program performs its magic by writing the 360K diskette with 80 tracks rather than the usual 40 tracks and by recording each 360K track "twice." What would be tracks 0 and 1 on a 1.2M diskette become track 0 on the 360K diskette; tracks 2 and 3 for a 1.2M diskette become track 1 on the 360K diskette; and so on for all 80 tracks. The double copying allows the wider 360K disk drive head to locate the information more reliably.

If you use CPYAT2PC's formatting program on a 1.2M drive, you must use CPYAT2PC's copy program for file copying. The product is reliable but slow. The double recording doubles the time to format or copy. If you need to produce a number of 360K diskettes on your AT, installing a 360K disk drive is more effective.

4.49   Tip: To format a 720K diskette on a 1.44M disk drive, use the command FORMAT /N:9 (V3.3) or FORMAT /F:720 (V4).

Producing 360K diskettes on a 1.2M disk drive is a problem because the two types of drives differ in the thickness of their respective recording bands (the diskettes have a different number of tracks). Although 720K and 1.44M diskettes use a different number of sectors, they have the same number of tracks. Therefore, you should have no problem producing 720K diskettes on a 1.44M disk drive.

Because the number of tracks is the same, give FORMAT with the /N (number of sectors) switch (DOS V3.3 and later) or the /F (format size) switch (DOS V4). No other switch is needed. Use **FORMAT /N:9** for DOS V3.3 and **FORMAT /F:720** for DOS V4.

If you can format 1.44M diskettes but have problems producing 720K diskettes, see the tips on DRIVPARM and DRIVER.SYS in Chapter 12.

4.50   Trick: Use FORMAT V4's /F switch for formatting different-sized diskettes.

Instead of remembering the number of tracks and sectors for each type of diskette, you can use the FORMAT V4's /F switch. This switch makes formatting different-size diskettes easy.

The following shows the syntax for the /F switch:

   /F:size

size is the capacity of the diskette. You can choose almost any conceivable numbering system (either in kilobytes or megabytes for higher capacity diskettes). The arguments that /F accepts are the following:

160K	180K	320K	360K	720K	1.2M	1.44M
160	180	320	360	720	1.2	1.44
160K	180K	320K	360K	720K	1.2M	1.44M
160KB	180KB	320KB	360KB	720KB	1.2MB	1.44MB
					1220	1440
					1220K	1440K
					1220KB	1440KB

For instance, for a 360K diskette, you can specify 360, 360K, or 360KB. For a 1.2M diskette, you can specify 1.2, 1.2M, 1.2MB, 1220, 1220K, or 1220KB.

However, remember that you must give a size. Also, don't bother to use the /F switch with a hard disk; the /F switch is a floppy-only switch.

5

Using and Protecting Your Diskettes

Although hard disks are the major form of disk storage for most computers, floppy disk storage endures. The fragile, changeable diskette is used to transport programs and data between machines and to back up nonremovable storage systems. On some machines, diskette storage is the only form of storage.

The first two parts of this chapter are devoted to the mechanics of diskette use: labeling, storage, and duplicating. This chapter includes a discussion of DISKCOPY, the diskette carbon-copy command of DOS.

The last part of this chapter concerns traveling with a computer. The tips, tricks, and traps in that section cover circumstances unique to using a portable, transportable, or laptop computer.

Handling Diskettes

More diskettes are ruined from logical damage than from physical damage, and most data dies from inadvertent operations. In order, the frequent causes of diskette data loss include the following:

- Inadvertent operations
- Logical damage
- Physical damage

The largest killer of diskettes and data is inadvertent operations, such as formatting the wrong diskette, unleashing the wrong erase command, and overwriting the wrong file during a COPY command. Chapter 7 on files discusses ways to avoid these problems.

Logical damage occurs when the logical structure of the diskette is damaged—primarily the diskette's directory and file allocation table. Causes range from malfunctioning disk drives, to flawed programs, to turning off the computer while writing to a disk drive. Chapter 14 provides tips, tricks, and traps to avoid and repair logical damage.

Physical damage is caused by normal diskette wear and poor diskette handling. A track on a diskette can be read or written more than one billion times before physical wear flaws the diskette. The spin life of a diskette (the amount of time that a disk drive actually reads or writes information on the diskette) is several years. Usually the information on the diskette is obsolete before the diskette wears out.

Poor handling ruins more diskettes than wear. Common causes of physical damage include accidental spills and contamination, diskette bending, extreme heat, stray magnetic fields, and misplaced diskettes. You can solve most of these problems with proper handling practices—the subject of this section.

5.1   Trap: Using the wrong kind of diskette can ruin information.

Buy and use the diskettes rated for your disk drive. If you have double-sided disk drives (almost all computers do), buy double-sided diskettes. If you have 1.2M or 1.44M disk drives, use 1.2M or 1.44M diskettes (rated HC for high capacity or HD for high density). The manufacturer certifies that the diskettes you buy are correctly rated as indicated on the box.

Using 720K diskettes at 1.44M capacity or 360K diskettes at 1.2M capacity invites disaster. This practice is comparable to writing business records on flash paper and then storing the records next to a sparking furnace. The diskette may work at the higher capacity, but can suddenly produce errors. Buy and use the right diskettes for your disk drive. (The bargain-brand bulk diskettes are as reliable as most name brands.)

5.2   Tip: Label every diskette.

Diskettes are like rabbits: they all look alike and multiply quickly. Trying to find one particular diskette in a group of 50 or more identical, unlabeled diskettes is frustrating and time-consuming.

Depending on your style of operation, label each diskette after you format it, or just before or just after you first use it. If you format a few diskettes at a time, label them after formatting. Because you probably format when you need a diskette, you know what you will place on it. Make an identifying label and place the label on the diskette. The best practice is to write on the label and then place it on the diskette. If a label is already on a minifloppy diskette, be sure to avoid writing on the label with a hard instrument; using a felt-tipped marker is best.

If you format diskettes a boxful at a time, use some system that identifies the diskettes as formatted. Put a blank label on each diskette or a sticker on the box. If you place the DOS start-up files or COMMAND.COM on a diskette, write on the lower portion of the label the version of DOS, such as DOS V3.3. Use the upper portion of the label to indicate the diskette contents.

5.3   Trick: Use colored labels or diskettes and write identifying information on each label.

Finding the right diskette when 12 identical diskettes have identical labels is almost like not labeling diskettes at all. Locating the right diskette is easiest when you use colored labels, use colored diskettes, and write significant, easily remembered information on each label.

For example, you can use a particular color of label or diskette for a specific program. You can use yellow labels for all word processing files, blue for all spreadsheet files, and red for all DOS and utility programs. Or you can use colors to classify the type of files, such as blue for data files, red for program files, green for auxiliary programs, and yellow for backup diskettes.

Because you may easily forget your color-coding scheme, consider the most important trick for labeling diskettes: use a standard, meaningful naming pattern. Most diskette labels have little space for writing. Therefore, short, standard information is important.

For program diskettes, write the program name and version number, class of program (such as start-up, main, or auxiliary), and DOS version (if DOS start-up files or COMMAND.COM are included on the diskette). Examples of meaningful label information include **1-2-3 R3.0 Programs, DOS V4.0**; and **WordStar R5 Programs, DOS V3.3**. If you use more than one computer, include the machine or DOS brand. I usually put the program name and version on the top line, purpose or type of diskette in the center, and DOS and machine information last, as in the following example:

| WordStar 5 |
| Start-Up |
| PC DOS V4.0 |

In one glance, I have all the information I need.

For data diskettes, include the type or purpose of the files, name of the program that uses the files, version number of the program (if the format of the data files changes between versions), and other distinguishing information, such as the date the diskette was formatted or first used. The following examples illustrate model labels for data diskettes:

| Sales Projections |
| Excel V2.01 |
| 02/01/89 |

| Sales Projections Worksheets |
| 02/01/89 |

Each label gives significant, easily remembered information. Both identify the information on the diskette; both use a date, which helps you identify the diskette if more than one has the same name. If you use just one spreadsheet program, the key word *Worksheets* on the second label identifies the program. If you use more than one spreadsheet program, identify the program as on the first label.

One final trick: Write *Backup* on the lower right side of a program or data backup diskette. (I use a different technique for diskettes used to back up a hard disk; that technique is explained in Chapter 10 on backup.)

5.4   Trap: Don't keep diskettes in hot cars.

Diskettes, which are made of plastic, are thermal sensitive and are damaged by extreme heat. Keep diskettes in the range of 50 to 124 degrees Fahrenheit or 10 to 52 degrees Celsius.

When a diskette is hot, the jacket and the diskette can warp. When either diskette part warps, the diskette does not spin freely; the disk drive cannot read the information reliably; and you lose the information contained on the diskette. On a sunny day, don't leave your diskettes in the car or trunk.

This problem strikes mainly in the late spring, summer, and early fall when the sun is most potent. The infrared heat created by sunlight can raise the ambient temperature in a car to 135 degrees Fahrenheit (58 degrees Celsius). Direct sunlight can cause the dashboard and steering wheel to approach 170 degrees Fahrenheit (62 degrees Celsius). If the ambient temperature crosses the red line, only diskettes located in cool spots (under a car seat or in some protective box or stack) survive. Diskettes left in direct sunlight will convert infrared energy to heat and are a lost cause.

Note that the minifloppy jacket warps at a lower temperature than the microfloppy shell. Microfloppy diskettes, because of the better thermal protection offered by the hard shell, are more resistant to heat damage. The diskette inside, however, can "bake" if it is left in the sun too long.

Dark-colored diskette jackets are more sensitive to sunlight than light-colored jackets. The white envelopes for minifloppies offer some protection. But because envelopes do not protect the top of the diskettes, they still remain vulnerable to sunlight.

5.5 Trap: Don't use cold diskettes.

Cold temperatures do not damage diskettes, but do affect their use. If your diskettes have been left in the cold (in a car, room, or case outdoors), let the diskettes warm up to their operating temperature before you use them.

When a diskette is cold, it shrinks. As a diskette shrinks, the narrow bands (tracks) that hold the information move slightly. When you use a cold diskette, the disk drive moves the recording heads to the correct track, but the track you want to read is in a different location. The disk drive cannot read or write information correctly, and previous information and new information recorded on the diskette cannot be retrieved.

You cannot read or write to a cold diskette. When DOS tries to read a cold diskette, a read error may be displayed. No information is lost; you simply cannot read the information currently. Writing to a cold diskette invites disaster. At best, DOS complains about not being able to write to the diskette. At worst, DOS writes information that can never be read again.

The cold temperatures affect 720K, 1.2M, and 1.44M diskettes more than 360K diskettes. The first three diskettes use information recorded at 96 tracks per inch; 360K diskettes are recorded at 48 tracks per inch. To obtain the higher track-per-inch densities, the information is recorded in a narrower band. Therefore, even a small movement in the location of the tracks on 720K, 1.2M, and 1.44M diskettes leads to problems.

To expedite the recovery from frostbite, separate the diskettes from each other. You can speed the recovery of minifloppy diskettes by removing each diskette from its envelope and waving the diskette. Air moves around the media to warm the diskette. You might rotate the media once or twice by placing your fingers inside the centering ring and turning the diskette.

Microfloppy diskettes can be warmed quicker using another technique. Hold the shutter open between your thumb and forefinger and wave the diskette. Because less of the media is exposed through the shutter, the process may take longer. You also can open the shutter and blow on the exposed media. Be sure that your mouth is dry when you try this technique.

5.6   Trap: Keep diskettes away from magnetic fields.

You know to keep magnets away from diskettes. But what about keeping your diskettes away from telephones, video monitors, pencil sharpeners, fans, soldering irons, and your telephone? Any item that uses electricity generates a magnetic field. The magnetic field of some items has the potential to "clean" your diskettes and ruin precious information. The most offensive objects are transformers and electric motors, which generate strong magnetic fields.

Stronger magnetic fields affect media more than weaker fields. Magnetic fields weaken geometrically with distance. Finally, magnetic media is subject to harm only when the media is moved through the magnetic field or when the magnetic field is moved. When the flux lines (magnetic flow) of the field and the media are stationary, there is no danger.

Generally, electronic items that use little electricity generate weak magnetic fields and are not harmful to your diskettes. Most items among home and office equipment fall into this category because they have very small or well-shielded motors and transformers. You can use and store diskettes near these items for extended periods of time (months or years) without any risk, or with negligible risk.

Be cautious of home and office equipment with stronger magnetic fields. This list includes telephones, microwave ovens, video monitors, and televisions. The latter two contain more potential harm than the former two.

You can use and store safely diskettes next to this equipment for moderate periods of time, from several days to several weeks. Ideally, keep your diskettes away from these items as much as practical. Avoid putting diskettes on the top or near the back of a monitor or television where the magnetic fields are strongest. For safe, long-term storage, keep the distance between the media and offender one foot or more.

Electric items that consume more electricity generate stronger magnetic fields and are more dangerous to your diskettes. Appliances with unshielded or poorly shielded transformers and motors, particularly AC (alternating current) motors, are potential killers. The stronger the motor or transformer, the greater your aversion should be. The list of potential killers include air conditioners, power drills, and power saws. Treat the motors in these items as magnetic plague carriers. Use and store media one foot or more from stronger motors.

Electric motors are a double threat. When not in use, the metal bar magnets encased in many office and household motors are not high-risk threats. Simply avoid storing diskettes within one foot of these unused motors. However, be wary of motors with ratings into the high teens or more (such as large-scale air conditioning motors). The bar magnetics are stronger and a three-foot or greater storage distance is recommended.

In-use motors are more threatening. Remember that a moving magnetic field, not a stationary field, is deadly. Magnetic fields generated by AC motors reverse at a rate of 50 to 60 times a second and "move" when the fields expand and contract (which happens when you turn the power on and off). Depending on the horsepower of the motor, you may need a distance of several feet or more for safe use and storage of magnetic media.

The largest desktop diskette killer, other than spilled soft drinks, is the mundane electric pencil sharpener. The magnetic field in this device is not particular strong, but the field is volatile. Although you don't move the sharpener, its magnetic field moves each time you start and stop its motor. The frequently expanding and collapsing magnetic field does the damage. Avoid using a pencil sharpener within one foot of your diskettes and don't store diskettes next to a frequently used pencil sharpener.

5.7   Tip: Keep a comfortable amount of free space on working diskettes.

Programs that generate temporary files for your data are ungracious about full diskettes. You can lose your current work if your program runs out of disk space. Periodically run CHKDSK or DIR on your working diskette to see how much space is left. If the diskette is nearly full, use another diskette or erase unneeded files.

5.8   Tip: Always keep a formatted diskette or two on hand.

Suppose that you are working with a program and you need to store information on a diskette; but the diskette runs out of room. If you don't have another formatted diskette, you may be unable to format one without abandoning your work.

You must have formatted disks ready, for example, when you use BACKUP. Unless you use the /F switch (for DOS V3.3) or use DOS V4, BACKUP expects only formatted diskettes. When you run out of diskettes, you must stop BACKUP to format more diskettes. Another problem occurs when you save a 1-2-3 worksheet on a diskette with insufficient room. When you save a worksheet, 1-2-3 deletes the previous version. If the worksheet has grown and 1-2-3 cannot store the new version, you must save the file to another formatted diskette or abandon the new version. To avoid these situations, keep a couple of formatted diskettes on hand.

5.9   Tip: Back up important diskettes frequently. Back up other diskettes on an as-needed basis.

All magnetic media "dies." Diskettes and hard disks are vulnerable to inadvertent operations (such as erasing the wrong file) and logical damage (from electronic problems). Chapter 10 discusses backing up hard disks; this section offers advice for backing up diskettes. Diskettes are more vulnerable to physical damage and wear than hard disks. You must be sure to back up important diskettes.

The backup schedule you follow depends on the type of system you use and the work you do. If you keep and back up the working files on your hard disk, you must back up only frequently used program diskettes and data diskettes. If you use a floppy-based system, all your data is on diskettes. In that case, you must back up all data diskettes and some program diskettes.

Use the following questions to judge which diskettes to back up:

- Can you re-create the information on the diskette?
- How difficult will re-creating the information on the diskette be?
- How long will re-creating the information on the diskette take?

The key to backing up diskettes is assessing the difficulty of re-creating the information on each diskette. If you cannot re-create the information, back up the diskette. If you can re-create the information, decide whether re-creating the diskette takes longer than backing it up. If the effort and time to re-create the information is greater than the effort and time to back up, back up the diskette.

Data diskettes that often change require frequent backup. If you work with vital files or files that cannot be recovered, back up frequently—daily or every couple of days. If you can recover your work within a couple of hours, back up the data diskette every couple of days to couple of weeks. Every third day, back up information that is difficult to recover; every couple of weeks, back up information that you can recover easily.

Unless you make extensive configuration changes to program diskettes, those diskettes do not require frequent backup. In most cases, one backup copy of your operating program diskettes may be all you need. Generally, you should back up a program diskette after you make modifications. Because working program diskettes don't change that often, your backup of those diskettes will be infrequent.

The next section describes how to use DISKCOPY to back up diskettes. DISKCOPY, however, is not the only way to back up diskettes. If only one or a few files change, you can use COPY or XCOPY to transfer the files to other diskettes.

Using DISKCOPY

The tips, tricks, and traps in this section are about the DISKCOPY command. This command is used only for copying floppy diskettes. DISKCOPY reads the source drive first, fills available memory with as much information as possible, and then begins copying to the destination diskette.

5.10 **Tip: When you use DISKCOPY with two floppy disk drives, watch the diskette lights; if the wrong disk drive lights first, eject the diskette or open the drive door immediately.**

A common mistake when using DISKCOPY is to reverse the source and destination disk drives. You might, for example, either mistype the command or put the wrong diskette into the disk drive. Then the destination diskette is copied over the source diskette, resulting in disaster.

When you press the key to start the copying process, watch which disk drive lights first. DISKCOPY uses this lighted drive as the source. If the wrong disk drive is used, eject the source diskette or open its disk drive door immediately. The procedure does not harm your diskettes or disk drive. DISKCOPY stops and gives an error message; you then can quit and issue the right command.

Quick reflexes in ejecting the diskette or opening the drive door are essential. If you wait too long, DISKCOPY finishes reading the source diskette and starts copying to the destination diskette. You have 10 seconds to 1 minute to notice the problem, depending on the amount of free RAM. If DISKCOPY starts writing to the wrong destination diskette, you lose information. Moreover, the information you lose in the first part of the diskette contains the directory and file allocation table. Even if DISKCOPY does not clobber your data, retrieving the data intact is like finding a needle in a haystack.

Don't use Ctrl-C or Ctrl-Break in this circumstance because DISKCOPY doesn't check the keyboard immediately for the abort-program sequence unless DOS's BREAK setting is on. Because you want DISKCOPY to stop *now*, eject the diskette or open the floppy disk drive door.

5.11   Tip: When you perform DISKCOPY, write-protect the source diskette for added protection.

Reversing the source and destination disk drives is the most common two-drive DISKCOPY mistake. Reversing the source and destination diskettes when you insert them in the disk drive is the most common one-drive DISKCOPY mistake.

With a single drive, you usually exchange diskettes two to eight times during the DISKCOPY procedure. Losing your concentration and inserting the wrong diskette isn't difficult. An easy technique to protect the source diskette is to slide the write-protect tab up for a microfloppy diskette or cover the write-protect notch on a minifloppy diskette. If you reverse the diskettes accidentally, DISKCOPY stops when it encounters the write-protected diskette. When you finish copying the diskettes, reverse the write-protect tab or uncover the write-protect notch so that you can write information to the diskette.

I use this tip only on source diskettes that are absolutely irreplaceable. Generally, I am cautious about getting the right source diskette into the disk drive, and I use the next tip.

5.12   Tip: When you perform a single-drive DISKCOPY, keep the diskette not currently in the drive in an easily identifiable spot.

Because a DISKCOPY operation ties up the computer for a period of time, you might take a break to make a phone call, have a conversation, or perform a short bit of other work. You easily can get distracted and forget which diskette is which in the copying process. When DISKCOPY stops and prompts you to change diskettes, you need to remember which diskette to insert.

Generally, I segregate the other diskette by keeping it in my hand or on top of the computer. If I am distracted and then notice that DISKCOPY is requesting a change of diskettes, I know which diskette to pop into the drive. I remove the diskette from the drive, insert the other diskette, and put the first diskette where the other diskette resided. I continue my work until DISKCOPY prompts me again.

5.13   Tip: If the current drive is a hard disk or you have two dissimilar floppy disk drives, give two disk drive names for DISKCOPY.

What source and destination disk drive names you must use with DISKCOPY depends on the version of DOS and the type of current disk drive. Earlier versions of DOS allowed you to give one disk drive name if the current drive was the hard disk, as in the following example:

> C>**DISKCOPY A:**

This command was acceptable to earlier versions of DISKCOPY, but is not acceptable with current versions. DISKCOPY in DOS V3, for example, rejects using a hard disk or a RAM disk as the source or destination. For DOS V3.3 and later, if the current disk drive is not a floppy disk drive (the current drive is a hard disk or a RAM disk), you must give a source and destination disk drive name. If you fail to give both names, DOS responds with the following message:

> Invalid drive specification
> Specified disk drive does not exist,
> or is nonremovable

5.14   Tip: If the current drive is the only floppy disk drive used for DISKCOPY, you can omit the source and destination disk drive names.

DISKCOPY, by the rule of currents, uses the current disk drive for the source and destination. If the correct floppy disk drive is the current drive, you can perform a single disk drive DISKCOPY by typing **DISKCOPY**.

If you prefer, you also can supply the source disk drive when the correct floppy disk drive is the current drive. In that case, DISKCOPY uses the current drive as the omitted destination disk drive. With the following commands, DISKCOPY uses the named disk drive as the source disk drive

(drive A: and B:, respectively) and then uses the current disk drive (drive A: and B:, respectively) as the destination disk drive:

A>DISKCOPY A:

B>DISKCOPY B:

Using these commands on a single disk drive is optional; you can accomplish the same operation by simply typing **DISKCOPY**.

5.15 Tip: If you are not copying the diskette in the current disk drive, always give the source and destination disk drive names to DISKCOPY.

Be sure to include both the source and destination disk drive names whenever you are not copying the diskette in the current disk drive. Including both names is particularly important when your computer has more than one floppy disk drive and you want to perform a single disk drive DISKCOPY in a drive that is not the current drive.

Suppose, for example, that you omit the destination disk drive name, as in the following example:

A>DISKCOPY B:

DISKCOPY responds with the following message:

```
Insert SOURCE diskette in drive B:
Insert TARGET diskette in drive A:
```

In this case, DISKCOPY assumes that two different disk drives should be used. Here DISKCOPY uses the named disk drive (B:) as the source drive. Because the destination name is omitted, DISKCOPY uses the current disk drive (A:) for the destination.

When you notice this mistake, use Ctrl-C or Ctrl-Break to exit DISKCOPY. Then start again and give a source and destination disk drive name. If you proceed with the DISKCOPY, the wrong diskette becomes the destination diskette, and the data on this diskette can be lost before DOS recognizes the error.

5.16 Trap: When you copy between microfloppy and minifloppy disk drives, don't count on DISKCOPY to behave rationally.

Using DISKCOPY to copy mini- to microfloppy diskettes or micro- to minifloppy diskettes has varied results. Experiments with several versions of DOS on several different machines reveal that under some conditions, DOS does not recognize disk drive mismatches.

For example, DISKCOPY produced a usable copy of a 360K diskette on both a 720K and a 1.44M microfloppy drive. When copying a 1.44M microfloppy diskette to a 1.2M or 360K minifloppy disk drive, however, DISKCOPY generally issued an error message and stopped, but not with all versions of DOS V3.3.

Attempting to copy other combinations of diskettes (such as a 720K to 1.2M) yielded similar results. DISKCOPY copied correctly the first 40 tracks and then gave write errors for the remaining tracks. In each case, the previous contents of the destination diskette were lost.

5.17　Tip: You can use DISKCOPY safely for a 720K diskette on a 1.44M drive.

As you may recall, a 720K diskette is half of a 1.44M diskette. The major difference between a 720K and a 1.44M diskette is that a 720K diskette uses 9 sectors per track; a 1.44M diskette uses 18 sectors per track. The number of tracks the disk drive uses is the same. Because the tracks are the same, a 1.44M disk drive has no problem handling 720K diskettes. You can safely read, write, format, and DISKCOPY 720K diskettes on 1.44M disk drives.

5.18　Tip: Before you use DISKCOPY for a 360K diskette on a 1.2M disk drive, first format the diskette on a 360K disk drive.

Although 720K diskettes are reliably produced on a 1.44M disk drive, you cannot reliably format a 360K diskette on a 1.2M disk drive. Instead, you must format on a 360K disk drive any 360K diskette you plan to use on a 360K disk drive. (If you will use the 360K diskette only on the 1.2M that copied the diskette, this caution does not apply. You do not encounter a problem reading a 360K diskette formatted or written by the same 1.2M disk drive.)

If DISKCOPY encounters a destination diskette that is not formatted identically to the source diskette, DISKCOPY formats the destination diskette—an action you want to avoid. If you must use DISKCOPY for a 360K diskette on a 1.2M disk drive, make sure that the destination diskette is already formatted as a 360K diskette. If the diskette is new, run FORMAT with a 360K disk drive. This gives the diskette a fighting chance to be used on other 360K disk drives.

5.19 Trap: Don't use DISKCOPY's /1 switch.

DISKCOPY reads the source diskette and knows the number of tracks and sides to copy. When DISKCOPY encounters a single-sided diskette, DISKCOPY knows automatically to copy just one side. The /1 switch is unnecessary.

Using the /1 switch when you copy a double-sided diskette is a mistake. Most DOS pre-V3.2 DISKCOPY programs ignore the switch and still copy both sides of the diskette. Other DISKCOPY versions copy the single side, and you end up with only half the information on the diskette.

Keep in mind the sequence DOS uses to write information on a disk. DOS first writes to side 1, track or cylinder 0. When this tracks fills, DOS switches sides or cylinders and continues writing information. If your files occupy both sides of a diskette, you literally copy a portion of each file, not half the number of files. Using /1 when you copy a double-sided diskette is folly. The resulting copy is always unusable directly.

5.20 Tip: Don't DISKCOPY a diskette with bad sectors unless you need an exact copy of the diskette; use COPY instead.

Detected bad sectors on a diskette are marked as in-use in the diskette's file allocation table. The detection and subsequent marking can come when formatting the diskette or when using the RECOVER command. As DISKCOPY duplicates the diskette, the source diskette's file allocation table is duplicated, along with the bad-sector markings.

Good sectors on the destination diskette that correspond with bad sectors on the source diskette are marked as bad, and good diskette space is wasted on the destination diskette. You may lose as little as 5K to 9K, depending on the type of diskette. If you have more bad sectors on the source diskette, you lose more available space.

To avoid wasting diskette space, COPY the files from the diskette with bad sectors. Only the files are copied, not the bad sectors, and no space is wasted on the destination diskette.

Suppose that you need an exact duplicate of the original diskette—for example, you must run RECOVER on a complete disk, not on a file. To produce a copy of an original diskette, warts and all, you need to DISKCOPY a diskette with bad sectors. Because you might want to return to the original diskette if something goes wrong, you should use DISKCOPY.

Traveling with a Computer

My laptop computer, a Toshiba 1100 Plus, has kept me both sane and
productive while I travel. In fact, this book was written while I was visiting
15 states and 3 countries and flying over 20 more states and 5 other
countries. If you travel with your computer, you will find the tips, tricks,
and traps in this section helpful.

5.21   Tip: When you travel, always have on hand a bootable diskette.

Always have at least one bootable diskette available for your computer.
Preferably, have handy a configured version of your DOS start-up diskette.

On an overnight train trip, I took a new COMPAQ Portable II™, which I
received two days before the trip. I frantically configured the COMPAQ,
and then copied files from my workhorse machine to the COMPAQ. On
the train, I started using programs copied from my workhorse computer.
(The COMPAQ II is AC powered, but the sleeping compartments on all
trains worldwide have power outlets.)

The first time I used my text editor program, it malfunctioned. I realized
immediately that the AUTOEXEC.BAT file did not contain the proper
environmental variables (via the SET command); therefore, I added the
proper variables and started DOS again. Because I used too many SET
commands, DOS complained about running out of environment space. To
increase the size of the environment, I needed to use the CONFIG.SYS
SHELL directive with the /E switch.

The CONFIG.SYS file I had copied from my workhorse machine was
almost identical to the COMPAQ's except for the following line:

    SHELL = C:\BIN\COMMAND.COM C:\BIN /E:860 /P

This directive tells DOS to load COMMAND.COM and set up an
environment size of 860 bytes, and tells the command interpreter to stay
resident. I copied this version over the old version of CONFIG.SYS, started
my computer again, and received the following message:

    `Bad or missing command interpreter`

On my workhorse computer, I kept COMMAND.COM in \BIN. On this
computer, COMMAND.COM was in the root directory; therefore, DOS
would not start.

I searched frantically for a bootable diskette and realized that I had not packed one. Although no work was lost and no files were harmed, I was frozen out of the computer until I could find a bootable diskette. Needless to say, the odds of finding anyone on that train with a bootable DOS diskette were quite slim.

Remember that a relatively minor incident (erasing the wrong file, changing your start-up files, or a software or hardware glitch) can prevent your computer from starting from the hard disk. In your office or home, you simply reach for a DOS diskette to start the computer, copy or edit the needed files, start the computer again, and continue. If you don't have a bootable diskette when you are away from your base, you may not be able to run your computer.

This advice is particularly important for those whose traveling machines use a heavily customized version of MS-DOS. If your machine cannot use IBM's PC DOS, you need your own version of DOS. The places to where you travel may not have the copy of DOS that you need to start your machine. Also while microfloppies are widely used, some companies and friends still use minifloppy diskettes only. Your friends with minifloppy-based machines may not be able to rescue you.

5.22 Tip: When you travel by airplane, hand-carry your computer or ship it in a suitable container.

I have checked my COMPAQ as baggage many times on several airlines and never had a scratch—except once. On one trip, I watched my COMPAQ come down the airport baggage carousel with its keyboard (with several keys missing) resting on top of the case. When I turned on the unit at the hotel, the computer smoked.

The airline paid for the repair and told me several facts of which I was unaware. Checked baggage must be rugged enough to survive a five-foot fall onto a concrete floor. Anything not able to survive this test must be tagged as fragile, and the airline still does not assume liability for damage. Although portables are rugged, no portable is rated to withstand a five-foot drop. The traveling bags for these units do not provide enough padding for such a drastic physical shock.

If you have a laptop or portable, carry the unit on the plane. If you must ship the unit, pack it in an airline case or in the computer's original carton. Either provides the essential protection your unit needs in case of an accident.

5.23 **Trap: Airport X-ray and walk-through metal detectors in the United States and Canada generally will not damage your diskettes or hard disk. When you travel outside the United States and Canada, however, you should ask for hand inspection of any carry-on diskettes.**

The key to knowing when to hand inspect disks is the X-ray machine's ISO rating for photographic film. ISO (International Standards Organization) ratings cover the light (and X-ray) sensitivity of the film. Slow film, which yields rich colors and grainless pictures, is less susceptible to X rays and has a low ISO number ranging from 16 to 200. High-speed film, good in low-light situations, is more susceptible to X rays. These films have a higher ISO number, ranging from 400 to 3200 or 6400.

Most X-ray machines will fog film that has an ISO number above 1000. Some domestic machines, which have stronger X rays and subsequent magnetic fields, will damage ISO 400 rated film. However, machines that will fog film rated at less than ISO 400 are hazards to your disks.

The trend at many airports is to label the machine with its ISO number. If the number is less than 400, ask for hand inspection. If the machine is unlabeled, ask the security guard for the machine's ISO rating. If the answer is 400 or higher, feel comfortable in placing the computer or diskettes on the conveyer. If the answer is "I don't know" or a number lower than 400, ask for hand inspection. Most American and Canadian X-ray machines are rated at 400 or higher and are safe. However, don't make that assumption in other countries. Ask. And don't make the assumption when treating yourself to a supersonic Concorde flight; those machines will magnetically whammy your media.

All walk-through metal detectors do not generate a field strong enough to damage diskettes. You can safely carry diskettes through these. However, carrying more than a couple microfloppy diskettes on your person in one pocket can cause you embarrassment. The metal shutter on the diskettes can trigger the detector and a red face.

Avoid hand-held metal detectors used in many foreign countries and in some locations in the United States. Because the hand-held units are waved over your person at a close distance, the magnetic field from these units can wipe out diskettes or a fixed disk. Ask the guard to hand inspect the computer or diskettes.

A travel tip is to put any carry-on diskettes in an easily opened case or box. The carry-on computer should be in an easily opened travel case, not a sealed box. Assume that everything will be opened and inspected carefully. Assume also that the guards will ask you to start your computer. Plan for a slight delay for the inspection. I put my carry-on film in transparent film holders so that the security guards can easily see the contents. If you make the process of examination easier for the guards, you will clear security faster.

5.24   Tip: When you travel with a laptop or portable computer, operate your computer at a comfortable temperature.

Just as diskettes are sensitive to cold and heat, your computer has an acceptable temperature range for operation—typically 55 to 95 degrees Fahrenheit or 18 to 28 degrees Celsius. You can let your computer get colder or warmer than the operating range; however, let your computer warm up or cool down to these temperatures before you use the machine.

Because the circuits in the system are temperature sensitive, cold or hot systems can malfunction. Hard disk drives, the most temperature-intolerant part of computers, will not start or may act erratically. At best, the system may not start; at worst, files are destroyed.

Your computer can easily catch cold in the fall, winter, or spring if you leave it in the trunk of your car or inside your car on a cold day. If you must use the machine immediately, transport the computer inside the car, not the trunk. If abandoning your car for more than one hour on cold days, take the computer with you. If you will have an hour or more before you will use the system, however, don't worry. One hour at room temperature is sufficient time for your system to warm up.

Your machine can easily get steamed up during the spring, summer, or fall if you leave it in the back seat of the car or in the trunk during a hot, sunny day. You can perform the same ill feat by leaving the computer in front of a window with sunlight pouring through. Just as black-enveloped diskettes are more susceptible to infrared heat, so are black-cased computers. To keep the system comfortable, place your computer out of sunlight.

If your system gets too warm, let it cool down to 90 degrees Fahrenheit or 28 degrees Celsius before using the system. This ensures that your computer will operate properly.

5.25 Tip: Carry a floppy diskette "emergency" kit when you travel.

Forgetting to take a bootable diskette is a problem if you cannot start the computer from a hard disk. However, all computer travelers may face another problem, recovering from other types of errors on the road. If you forget to pack an emergency tool kit that contains your error recovery programs, you may be stuck for a remedy.

When you travel, always pack a diskette or two containing copies of your favorite setup programs, disk utilities, unerase programs, and diagnostics. Also pack a new extra formatted diskette (even if you use a hard disk). When a problem strikes at the office or at home, you simply reach for the appropriate program or diskette and correct the problem. When you travel, you must have the same ability; otherwise, work will be lost. For example, inadvertently erasing the wrong file is easy. Without an unerase program, your work is halted. By including your unerase programs or disk-sector editors, the problem is corrected quickly and you remain productive.

PART II

Controlling Your Hard Disk

Includes

Managing Subdirectories

Managing Files

Creating and Using Batch Files

Using Advanced Batch File Techniques

Backing Up and Restoring Your Hard Disk

6

Managing Subdirectories

People often use individual floppy diskettes to organize files. Ten to 50 files organize easily on a floppy diskette. One thousand to several thousand files, which most hard disks can hold easily, don't organize as simply. When you use a hard disk, change your mind-set slightly and view subdirectories as nonremovable floppy diskettes.

The need to establish and use subdirectories effectively cannot be overemphasized. The number of files that the root directory can hold has a strict limit. DOS refuses stubbornly to exceed 64 or 112 files on a floppy diskette and 512 files in the root directory on most hard disks.

Other compelling reasons exist for maintaining organized subdirectories. First, keeping track of files in a long directory listing can become difficult. In addition, selective operations, such as copying and deleting files, are more difficult in large directories. Finally, an inadvertent operation (such as using the wrong file name for an ERASE command) has more potential harm in a large subdirectory than in a small one. You must divide and conquer.

This chapter provides tips, tricks, and traps for organizing subdirectories: naming them, structuring them according to the programs you use, installing programs within them, and storing DOS and its utilities within them. The chapter also gives you tips for manipulating subdirectories with PATH, APPEND, and SUBST.

Organizing Subdirectories

You can choose from two primary ways to subdivide files—divide by application program or divide by purpose. Most systems use a hybrid of the two. The specific way you should divide files into subdirectories depends on four factors: your programs, how you use those programs, the non-DOS tools you have, and your operating style. Each factor, discussed in this chapter, affects the others.

6.1   Tip: Keep the number of files in a subdirectory to a minimum.

Consider the first of two basic tips for organizing subdirectories: Keep as few files as possible in each subdirectory. This advice is important for several reasons.

As a directory grows, the housekeeping tasks (listing, copying, deleting, and moving) and program maintenance tasks become more complex. For each screenful of directory listings you must wade through, your disk operations become less efficient.

Performance can diminish as a subdirectory gets larger. If the subdirectory becomes fragmented, DOS must thrash the disk heads to read the directory. Keep in mind that DOS reads the directory whenever a file is written or read (including when the file is run).

Note that the "magic" number for subdirectory sizes is a multiple of a disk cluster. Depending on the cluster size (1K or 2K for floppy diskettes; 2K, 4K, or 8K for hard disks), each subdirectory cluster holds 32, 64, 128, or 256 files, respectively. Because most hard disk users have 2K or 4K clusters, the magic number of directory entries is 64 or 128. However, because all subdirectories have 2 set entries (. and ..), the magic number becomes 62 or 126.

If you extend a subdirectory and cross one of these magic boundaries, the subdirectory becomes fragmented, and performance penalties result. If you copy all files into the subdirectory at one time and the boundary is crossed, the subdirectory may or may not become fragmented. Fragmentation depends on the exact status of the disk. (Fragmentation is discussed in Chapter 3; that chapter also deals with defragmenters, the cure for subdirectory and file fragmentation.)

6.2   Tip: Use short, easily typed names for subdirectory names.

The second basic tip for using subdirectories is to keep subdirectory names short and memorable. Short names offer convenience; long subdirectory names are laborious to type. Cryptic subdirectory names are difficult to remember and challenging for the best typist to key quickly. Shortening names past the point of comprehension can be self-defeating. Memorable names simplify the process.

Using systematic names within each subdirectory further helps you keep your hard disk organized. The eight characters in the root name are usually enough to identify a subdirectory. (Using an extension in a subdirectory's name is dubious.) The files within the subdirectory or the chain of directory names also can help in identification. Anyone can guess the purpose of a subdirectory called SHEETS in a directory called 1-2-3 or EXCEL, or guess the contents of a subdirectory containing all .WK1 files.

Naming Subdirectories

6.3 Trap: You cannot use directly a path or full file name larger than 63 characters.

One final reason for shortening subdirectory names is rooted in DOS. DOS has a general limit of 63 characters in any full path or full file name. Although 63 characters seems spacious, you easily can brush against this limit.

Each path character in the name uses one of the 63 characters. A disk drive name, if given, takes another 2 characters. The file name, the space eater, can use up to 12 characters (8 for the root, 3 for the extension, and 1 for the separating period). Using a "full" file name, you have at most 48 characters for the subdirectory names. If the subdirectories have long names and are deeply nested, you may be unable to issue the name needed to operate on a file or subdirectory. If you use the worst case (full drive and file name, and each subdirectory using 12 characters plus 1 for the path character), you can use only 3 subdirectory names in a full file specification.

You can use the SUBST command, in a trick discussed later in this chapter, to handle long path names.

6.4 Tip: Avoid having a subdirectory with the same root name as a file in that directory.

This tip minimizes confusion. Although DOS works correctly when you have a file such as WS5.xxx in the current WS5 subdirectory, the result from unusual operations can be puzzling.

You cannot have a subdirectory and a file with the exact same name in the same directory. DOS gives an error message when you try to create the later arrival (creating the file if the subdirectory existed or making the subdirectory if the file existed). After checking the directory, the error is apparent.

More puzzlement comes when a subdirectory has the same root name as an executable file (.COM, .EXE, and .BAT) in the same directory. Almost all operations work as expected. DOS won't run, open, or write to the subdirectory, nor try to use the file as a subdirectory. The puzzlement comes when copying; some programs may become confused whether to copy the single file, the files in the subdirectory, or both. Simply avoid the practice.

6.5   Tip: When you include the path character first, DOS starts at the top.

The dual use of the path character confuses even intermediate users. The trick is in the first character of the path name. If the path character (\) is the first character of the path name, DOS starts at the topmost directory, the root directory. In all other cases, the path character is used to separate subdirectory names from each other and subdirectory names from the file name.

If the path does not start with a path character, the movement starts with the current directory. Instead of the movement being absolute (from the root directory), the movement is relative (from the current directory). Specifying the wrong path by omitting the backslash (and starting in the current directory) or adding a leading backslash (and starting at the root) is the major cause of **File not found** messages.

The separation of the subdirectory and file name has one exception. When the path is a single backslash character, the path is the root directory. The name **\CONFIG.SYS** specifies that CONFIG.SYS is in the root directory of the disk. The name **A:\AUTOEXEC.BAT** specifies that AUTOEXEC.BAT is in the root directory of drive A:.

Structuring Subdirectories

6.6   Tip: You can change your subdirectory structure with little to modest work.

Fortunately, subdirectory organization is fluid. You do not need to get the organization right on the first attempt. You can change the organization by creating, renaming, or deleting subdirectories; or moving files into other subdirectories.

To make the task of organizing subdirectories easy, you need some outside programs. Specifically, you need two features that DOS lacks: a move facility (a program that copies and erases files, or simply moves the directory entry from one subdirectory to another) and a facility to rename subdirectories. Chapter 7 discusses move programs.

DOS has internal functions that can move directory entries from one subdirectory to another and that can rename subdirectories. The command interpreter (COMMAND.COM), however, does not allow you to use these facilities directly. This fact is unfortunate for the advanced user, but fortunate for the newcomer.

6.7 Tip: Make all needed subdirectories before you copy files.

So that the subdirectories you will use are placed closer physically on the disk, make them before you copy files into them. In this way, the subdirectories will be close to the front of the disk and the file allocation table. When traversing the subdirectory tree, the disk heads move less, and the subdirectories are read faster. This trick works best on newly formatted disks.

This performance tip comes with a warning: The tip backfires when the subdirectories become fragmented. Fragmentation occurs when you copy one more than the magic number of files into the subdirectory. When this happens, the performance of the affected subdirectory and all subsequent subdirectories in the tree is reduced slightly.

6.8 Tip: Place only subdirectories and absolutely vital start-up files in the root directory of the start-up hard disk.

Cluttering the root directory, the starting directory of the disk, with unneeded files increases search time and confusion. The root directory is your initial roadmap to the disk. If the directory listing of the root is more than one screenful, the listing is probably too long. If the file does not absolutely need to be in the root directory, move the file! You will keep the master roadmap uncluttered and help preserve the performance of your system.

Two DOS files must reside in the root directory of the start-up disk: IO.SYS and DOS.SYS. (These file names may differ slightly depending on what version of DOS you are using.) These files are hidden from normal directory searches. Two optional files that also must be located in the root directory are CONFIG.SYS and AUTOEXEC.BAT. COMMAND.COM is a toss-up. If you use the SHELL directive, you can move COMMAND.COM to the directory that holds DOS. Most people, however, prefer to keep COMMAND.COM in the root directory.

Keep device drivers and other start-up files out of the root directory. You can place these files in another subdirectory and let the PATH command handle running them. Accede to any program that stubbornly demands its files to be placed in the root directory (and then stubbornly demand that the publisher change the program).

6.9   Tip: Make subdirectory trees wider rather than deeper.

When creating subdirectory trees, making more subdirectories on the same level is preferable to making deeper subdirectories. The reasoning relates back to two fundamental tips: short path names are more convenient and faster to use.

Knowing Your Programs

6.10   Tip: Know how well your programs use subdirectories.

You need not be a programmer to know how your programs operate. A little knowledge of key facets of the program can make the difference between inconvenience and disaster.

When you organize your programs into subdirectories, knowing each of your programs is helpful. You should find out the answers to some key questions. Does your program know where its program files are kept? How easily can you change subdirectories while using the program?

These questions affect where you place the program and data files. If the program does not understand subdirectories, either you must put the program and data files into one subdirectory and operate from it, or you must depend on a little DOS trickery (the APPEND command, discussed later in this chapter).

Today, most multifile programs allow you to place the program files in any subdirectory. The programs search the path for the start-up program and subsequently used program files, examine an environmental variable for the appropriate subdirectories, or install into the main program file the name of the subdirectory that holds the other program files. You can use programs that work like this while operating in any subdirectory. (For a discussion of environmental variables, see Chapter 9.)

You next need to consider how well your program supports subdirectories for data files. If you can change subdirectories easily while using the program, arranging files by purpose rather than by application program makes sense. If the program is stubborn or clumsy about retrieving a file from a subdirectory, you may find that the easier approach is to exit the program, change subdirectories using a command line editor or subdirectory switcher, and start the program again.

Grouping programs by purpose rather than by application (if you can switch subdirectories easily) works best with programs that generate many unrelated files, such as word processors or text editors. I find this capability useful when I am working on several projects at one time. My files related to a book go into one subdirectory; my files for an article go into another subdirectory; my source code files for programming fit into their own subdirectories; and so on.

You might organize your subdirectories so that operations you perform frequently are made easier. For example, consider a common word processing operation—reading blocks of text from one file into the current document. If you must exit the program, copy the file from its current directory, and then restart the program, the word processor or text editor is heading for electronic oblivion quickly. The same applies when writing blocks of text. You shouldn't have to copy the block unnecessarily—write the block, exit the word processing program, and then move the file.

I am biased toward programs that install the drive and subdirectory name into the main file or that use an environmental variable. This capability allows you to keep the program files in their own subdirectory. I then copy the main program file or use a batch file in a PATHed subdirectory to run the program.

The segregated approach works well for program maintenance. To perform maintenance on the program, I move to the subdirectory and run the maintenance program. Because most publishers use the name INSTALL for the installation/modification program, using the wrong INSTALL to manipulate an unrelated program presents a problem. By keeping the maintenance programs with the main program, you avoid inadvertent name clashes.

For programs such as spreadsheets, being able to run the program from anywhere is helpful but not required. Most spreadsheet programs allow you to change subdirectories rapidly or to specify the subdirectory when naming the data file. In this case, running from the subdirectory that holds the program files makes sense. The data subdirectories "swing from" (are subdirectories of) the program directory.

For dedicated database applications, such as accounting, running from the program's subdirectory is the only way to use the program. Dedicated database programs use a fixed set of files. Because so many files are affected, the flexibility of being about to select the subdirectory that holds the files is lost. However, as the next trap explains, you should keep the program files separated from the data files.

Organizing Your Program and Data Files

6.11 Trap: Avoid putting data files in the same subdirectory with program files.

Keep your program files separated from your data files. You copy and delete data files more frequently than program files. If you unleash the wrong delete command on a subdirectory that holds your program and data files, you compound the error and may lose both sets of files.

6.12 Tip: When data files work with one application only, organize the files in subdirectories of the application; when data files can be used by more than one application program, organize the data files by project or use.

The classic question in organizing data files is what files go into which subdirectory and where should the subdirectory be located? Consider the following possibilities.

You can organize files by application. You place the program itself in a level-one subdirectory, a subdirectory of the root, and the data files in level-two subdirectories operated from that subdirectory. When you have a sufficient number of data files, you create another level-two subdirectory and move the files from this subdirectory into others. Figure 6.1 shows an example of this organization.

The second possibility is to organize files by projects. Place each major application program in its own subdirectory and place files related to one project in another level-one subdirectory. When the number of files are sufficient, create level-two subdirectories and disburse the files among the new subdirectories. Figure 6.2 illustrates this organization.

The third way to organize your subdirectories borrows the best of the first two methods. You place major applications in their own level-one subdirectory and files that work with only one application in a level-two subdirectory of the application subdirectory. Files that work with several programs are organized by project and placed in their own level-one subdirectories. As data subdirectories grow large, create level-two subdirectories and disburse files into these subdirectories. Figure 6.3 shows a sample structure that typifies managing your subdirectories effectively.

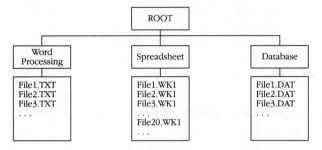

Fig. 6.1. Files organized by application.

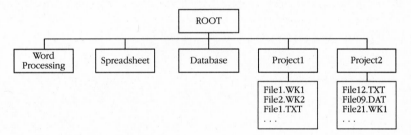

Fig. 6.2. Files organized by projects.

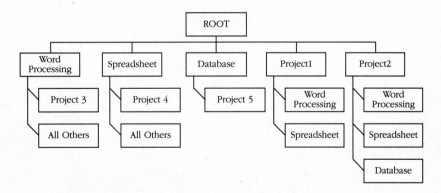

Fig. 6.3. Effective management of subdirectories.

Note one final part of this hybrid philosophy: depart from this organizational scheme anytime the departure makes sense. An example is figure 6.4, which shows the organization for desktop publishing projects. Although data files are used principally by the desktop publishing software, the system uses too many files to fit conveniently in one subdirectory. The program itself is placed in two subdirectories: TYPESET and VENTURA. Although the data files fit best by project, the large number of data files makes using one subdirectory inconvenient. The files, therefore, are subdivided further by file type (text, chapters, articles, and images).

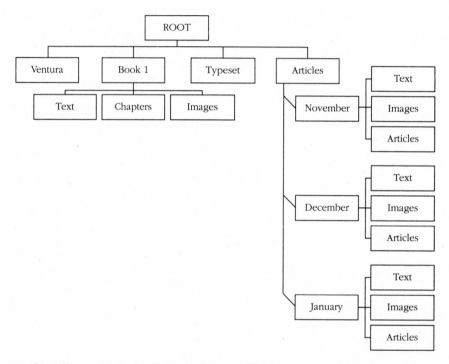

Fig. 6.4. A file organizational scheme for desktop publishing.

An organizational scheme geared for programming, another possibility, is shown in figure 6.5. The program files (for the C program) are kept in a level-two subdirectory; the data files (PROJECT1, PROJECT2, and so on) are placed in other level-two subdirectories. Moving the programming language files to their own subdirectory keeps this level-one subdirectory uncluttered.

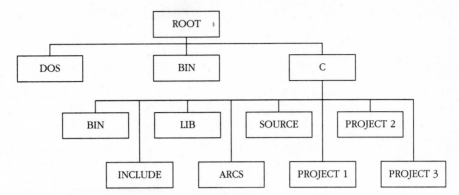

Fig. 6.5. A file organizational scheme for programming.

Use the organizational scheme that best fits the application and project. As mentioned in an earlier tip, subdirectory reorganization requires only modest work if you have the right tools.

6.13 Tip: A convenient organization may sometimes make larger subdirectories desirable.

Sometimes the best organization fits all files into one subdirectory. In that case, put the related files into one subdirectory. If the number of files is unwieldy, however, create additional subdirectories and move files. Keep in mind that copying files usually increases fragmentation; therefore, moving files is preferable to copying them.

6.14 Tip: Check your program's documentation to determine whether parts of the program must be in a PATHed subdirectory or a subdirectory specified with SET.

Application programs sometimes consist of a multitude of different files. Some programs use the technique of installing the "home" subdirectory for the files into the main program; some use an environmental variable to specify where the files are kept. This variable may apply to both program and data files.

Check your program's documentation or provided installation program. If the program can use an environmental variable, place the appropriate one with the subdirectory in your AUTOEXEC.BAT file. Alternatively, you can use a batch file that sets this variable when you run the program.

One overly popular environmental variable used by some programs is PATH. Because you want a short directory search (this idea is discussed later in this chapter), avoid using this feature, if possible. Cluttering the PATH with unneeded subdirectories and a multitude of files reduces the performance of the search. If required, use a batch file to set the PATH temporarily, run the program, and then restore the original PATH. The technique for this switching is explained in Chapter 9 on batch files.

Installing Programs

6.15   Tip: When you install programs, avoid copying files you don't need.

Most installation programs are fairly effective in copying the files you need. However, some installers and many installing batch files go overboard and copy too many extraneous files. In addition, when the installation instructions state, "Put the floppy diskette in drive A: and type COPY A:*.* C:", be wary. Considering that some application programs use ten to twelve 360K diskettes (four megabytes of files!), wasting disk space for unnecessary files or expanding subdirectories past the point of comprehension makes little sense.

Unfortunately, you may not be able to determine immediately which files you need and which files you can leave on the diskettes. Use your common sense. Instead of copying the tutorial files to your hard disk, for instance, run the tutorial from the floppy diskettes or remove the tutorial after you complete the course. If the program includes device drivers for equipment you don't have, such as a Hercules driver for a VGA-based system, either do not copy those files or erase them from the hard disk.

If the installer only copies files to the disk, don't keep the installer on disk. If the installer configures the software, however, consider keeping it. I usually eliminate the installer from the hard disk only after a few weeks of using the application program, if at all. I might reconfigure the program several times before I am satisfied. If I plan on reconfiguring after three weeks or more, I simply leave the installer on the hard disk for convenience.

If you can't prejudge what you will need, copy the files into a separate subdirectory tree. You can move and eliminate the unnecessary files later.

Storing DOS and DOS Utilities

6.16 Tip: Put DOS in its own subdirectory to simplify updating.

I have vacillated on this issue for several years. My original thoughts were that DOS and common programs could be mixed into one PATHed subdirectory. I now admit the error of my ways. After updating hard disks through seven versions of DOS (DOS V2.1, V2.11, V3.0, V3.1, V3.2, V3.3, V4.0) and six maintenance releases, I have come to the conclusion stated in the tip: put DOS in its own subdirectory to simplify updating.

The straw that broke the camel's back was my need to run two versions of DOS on the same system. This need forced the segregation of the DOS-provided files from the other files. Two of my systems have subdirectories called DOS33 and DOS40. One system boots into DOS V3.3, the other into DOS V4. By inserting the appropriate floppy diskette, however, I can boot either version of the operating system.

6.17 Tip: Put your commonly used DOS tools and utilities in their own subdirectory.

Having a master subdirectory that holds your commonly used utility software makes sense. Because many utility programs consist of one or a couple of files, grouping these files into one directory makes operations easier.

Almost all hard disks have this utility subdirectory under one of two names: \BIN or \UTIL. \BIN, a term held over from UNIX, is the common bin for holding system and utility software. Which name you use is not important; using a subdirectory for this purpose is. In this book, I use the name \BIN for the utility subdirectory. Change \BIN to \UTIL if you use \UTIL instead.

If you acquire a major utility package, such as the Mace Utilities or Norton Utilities, you may find that the \BIN subdirectory contains too many files. In these cases, make a subdirectory within the \BIN subdirectory and put the utility package files in that new subdirectory. If you frequently use the utility, add that subdirectory to the PATH.

Opinions are divided concerning what to do with batch files that run programs. I place these in the \BIN subdirectory so that DOS will not be required to search an additional subdirectory, and therefore the search will be speedier. Others argue justifiably that these batch files should be placed in their own PATHed subdirectory called \BATCH. In this case, the \BIN subdirectory is kept smaller, reducing fragmentation and speeding the search for files in this subdirectory. Both arguments are valid.

Manipulating Subdirectories

This section shows you how to manipulate subdirectories with the PATH, APPEND, and SUBST commands. The first tips, tricks, and traps help you make the most of the PATH and APPEND commands to run programs and find files. The later tips discuss how to use the SUBST command to trick programs that do not accept path names into using subdirectories, and to shorten path names and circumvent the 127-character command line limit.

Using PATH and APPEND

6.18   Tip: Use PATH to run programs; use APPEND to allow running programs to find their files.

The PATH command works when you run a program from the command line. DOS searches the given directory path for the program files. While a program runs, however, PATH usually falls by the wayside. If your programs do not know how to use subdirectories, you need a PATH-like command for data files. If you use DOS pre-V3.2, you need a program such as SDA Associates FilePath©. DOS V3.2 or later includes APPEND, the path command for data files.

Referring to APPEND as a data file PATH command is a slight misnomer. Normally you think of APPEND as allowing a program to find its files in any subdirectory. The files can be data files or additional program files. APPEND allows programs to load and run other program files, not just to find data files. The slight techno-blur between calling these data or program files, however, does not affect the use of APPEND.

6.19   Tip: Some programs use the PATH for data files.

As mentioned earlier, some programs use PATH to find their data files. I dislike this feature because it needlessly lengthens the PATH. Check your program's documentation for information about this "malfunction." If this technique cannot be avoided, follow the advice given earlier: Use a batch file to set the PATH temporarily, run the program, and then restore the original PATH. (This technique is demonstrated in Chapter 9 on batch files.)

6.20 Trap: Errors in the search path for PATH or APPEND are not detected until the path is used.

When you give the PATH or APPEND commands, DOS does not check for an error in the search path name; DOS detects the error only when the PATH is used. If DOS detects an invalid subdirectory name (the path name is misspelled or does not exist), DOS simply skips the name and proceeds to the next subdirectory name. For APPEND only, DOS ends the search if the path is on a not-ready disk drive.

Under DOS V3.2 and later, DOS does not even mention that something is wrong with the search path for PATH or APPEND. The only effect you will notice is a problem when a file that should be found is not found.

Check the spelling of each subdirectory name. Make sure that each path is separated by a semicolon and that no spaces appear between the first character in the first path name through the last character in the last path name.

6.21 Tip: Trick older programs into using subdirectories for data files with APPEND.

Some older programs (still useful, but not yet revised), do not understand path names. These programs force you to place all program and data files into one subdirectory and run from this subdirectory.

As mentioned, you needed a non-DOS program to trick programs into using separate subdirectories with versions of DOS prior to V3.1. Programs such as FilePath or the public domain DPATH tricked programs into finding their data files the same way DOS finds program files with the PATH. Starting with DOS V3.1, the SUBST command (discussed later in this chapter) expanded the capability but did not solve the problem. Starting with DOS V3.2, a data path program, APPEND, became a part of DOS.

APPEND is similar conceptually to the PATH command, but APPEND works with any file, not just executable program files. You can use APPEND, like the other data path programs, to trick programs into finding their program overlays or data files in a different subdirectory. You can use APPEND to run recalcitrant programs from any subdirectory.

APPEND is a terminate-and-stay-resident program. You can give the drive and path name for the command the first time you run it if APPEND is not on the PATH. After APPEND is loaded, it becomes an internal command; you thereafter do not need to give a drive and path name.

You can establish, change, or display the APPEND path. To establish or change the APPEND path, type the APPEND path as in the PATH command. To display the APPEND path, type **APPEND**. Type **APPEND ;** to deactivate APPEND.

The syntax for APPEND, shown in table 6.1, is slightly different between APPEND in DOS V3.3 and in DOS V4. In DOS V3.3, you must give the /X switch when APPEND first runs. DOS V4 allows the /X switch at any time and adds the ON/OFF setting for /X and a new function, /PATH. These switches and the /E switch are discussed in later tips.

6.22   Tip: To examine or change the APPEND path with SET, use the /E switch.

If you give the /E switch the first time you run APPEND, the switch places the path in the environmental variable APPEND. Programs can examine this variable, and you can display or change it with the SET command.

The primary reason to use the /E switch is so that another program can use the APPEND variable. Another reason is so that you can see both the PATH and APPEND paths (as well as 11 other environmental variables) when you type **SET**. You also may use the switch if you need a search path that exceeds 127 characters; this lengthy path is possible if you use an environmental variable editor. Because you can display and change the APPEND path with APPEND, using the /E switch has little other use.

Be aware that the /E switch must be given the first time you use APPEND and that you cannot include any path names when you use /E. You must issue APPEND a second time to establish the search path if you use /E.

6.23   Tip: The /X switch differs between APPEND in DOS V3.3 and in DOS V4.

Although the effects of the switches between APPEND in DOS V3.3 and DOS V4 are not identical, the positive results are the same. The DOS V3.3 /X switch controls whether APPEND intercepts and processes programs that use the DOS function calls for FIND FIRST (DOS V1 compatible), SEARCH FIRST (DOS V2 compatible), and EXEC (execute file). If you don't give the /X switch, programs that search the directory rather than attempt to open or use the file fail. If you give the switch, the programs can find the file. Unlike in DOS V4, the /X switch must be given when you first invoke APPEND in DOS V3.3.

APPEND in DOS V4 drops the support of processing FIND FIRST and SEARCH FIRST. In general, most programs will not miss the loss. To

Table 6.1
APPEND Syntax

	DOS V4	DOS V3.3
Syntax		
	*dc:patbc*APPEND /E /X:*setting* /PATH:*setting* or *dc:patbc*APPEND *d1:patb1;d2:patb2;...* /X:*setting* /PATH:*setting*	*dc:patbc*APPEND /X /E or *dc:patbc*APPEND *d1:patb1;d2:patb2;...*
	dc:patbc is the drive and path name to APPEND (given only the first time APPEND is run).	Same as V4
	d1:patb1, d2:patb2, and ... are the names of subdirectories holding the files to be searched. Semicolons separate path names; spaces are not allowed.	Same as V4
	setting is either ON or OFF.	
Switches		
/E	Places the APPEND path in the environment. /E may be given only the first time APPEND runs.	Same as V4
/X	Allows programs to find and run executable files (.COM, .EXE, and .BAT) using the EXEC facility.	Allows programs that use the DOS SEARCH FIRST, FIND FIRST, and EXEC facilities to find files. The /X switch may be given only the first time APPEND runs.
/X:ON	Same as /X	
/X:OFF	Prevents programs from finding and running executable files via APPEND. The default mode.	
/PATH:ON	Allows APPEND to process any file request regardless of whether a drive and path name is given with the file name. The default mode.	
/PATH:OFF	Prevents APPEND from processing any file request if a drive or path name is given with a file name.	

handle menu programs (which need the EXEC capability), use the DOS V4 /X switch. The /X switch under DOS V4 controls whether executable files are found in the data file search. If you turn on /X (with /X or /X:ON), APPEND finds any .COM, .EXE, or .BAT files in the search path. The /X:OFF switch turns off this facility.

The /X facility should be turned on for programs, such as older menu programs, that must execute other programs; otherwise, the switch is best left off. The default action for APPEND in DOS V4 is /X:OFF. As stated, any of the three DOS V4 /X switches may be given at any time.

6.24   Trap: Don't back up when APPEND's /X in DOS V3.3 is active.

APPEND's /X switch in DOS V3.3 has some interesting side effects. If you use DOS V3.3, try this experiment. Type **APPEND /X** followed by **APPEND C:\BIN;C:**. Put an empty formatted diskette into drive A: and type **DIR A:**. Your eyes do not deceive you—you see the subdirectory of C:\BIN.

APPEND's processing of SEARCH FIRST is also unusual. If a specified drive is empty (no files are found), APPEND starts using the search path. In this case, APPEND uses the first search directory (BIN). Now consider any file backup software that searches the subdirectory. APPEND /X fools these programs when empty subdirectories are found. You will suddenly be backing up far more files than you have on the disk. Before backing up, type **APPEND ;** or start DOS again to deactivate APPEND.

The trap does not apply to APPEND in DOS V4, which does not process the SEARCH FIRST commands. However, using APPEND in DOS V4 with backup software is dubious. Kill APPEND before running any backup software.

6.25   Tip: To stop APPEND in DOS V4 from tricking a program if a drive or path name is given, use /PATH:OFF.

APPEND in DOS V4 has an added /PATH switch. The command starts with /PATH:ON, meaning that DOS searches for a file even if the file name has a drive or path name. If you give /PATH:OFF, APPEND does not process a file name that has a drive or path name included. APPEND in DOS V3.3 would not process file names that had subdirectory names, but would process files that had drive names.

To the see effect of /PATH, type the command **APPEND C:\ /PATH:ON**, move to a directory other than the root, and then issue each of the following commands, in turn:

TYPE AUTOEXEC.BAT
TYPE C:AUTOEXEC.BAT
TYPE C:\BIN\AUTOEXEC.BAT

In all three cases, DOS types the contents of AUTOEXEC.BAT. Now type
APPEND /PATH:OFF and repeat the three commands. DOS types
AUTOEXEC.BAT for the first command and gives a **File not found** for the
latter commands. When you give the /PATH:OFF command, APPEND does
not process this file if you include a drive or path name.

If you don't want APPEND to be active after trying this test, either type
APPEND ; or start DOS again.

6.26 Trap: If you save a file found with APPEND, the original file is not updated.

Your programs may find their files in any location with APPEND; however,
when programs write files, APPEND does not trick those programs. The
files are always written to the current directory, resulting in two copies of
the file—the original file in its original directory and the new copy in the
current directory. If this happens, you may need to replace the original file
with the updated version manually.

6.27 Tip: Prioritize the subdirectories you give to PATH and APPEND.

When you run a program or batch file, DOS follows a set procedure to
locate the file to run. If you include a path name, DOS searches the
specified directory for a .COM, .EXE, or .BAT file (in this order) with the
given root name. If the file is not found, DOS gives the error message **Bad
command or file name**.

If you don't specify a path to the program or batch file, DOS searches the
current directory for the file. If the file is not found, DOS searches each
subdirectory specified in the PATH command in the order the subdirectories appear. If the file is found, DOS runs the file. If all subdirectories are
exhausted, DOS gives an error message and quits. This path search occurs
whenever you run a command without a path name; DOS still searches
the PATH if you give a disk drive name.

For APPEND, DOS searches the current subdirectory first and then the
subdirectories given to APPEND in their order of appearance. Unlike
PATH, APPEND in DOS V4 searches for files regardless of a path name.

This search occurs unless you give the /PATH:OFF switch; then the command does not process a file with a path name. Note that APPEND in DOS V3.3 does not search if a path name is included with the file name.

Because DOS searches the subdirectories in the order you specify them, prioritize the subdirectories to minimize the search time. Include the subdirectory that holds the most frequently used programs first, then the subdirectory with the next most frequently used programs, and so on. Give the subdirectory that holds the most frequently used files to APPEND first, and so on, following the pattern for PATH. The search time will be reduced, and your system will run more quickly.

6.28   Tip: Keep search paths as short as possible.

The reason for a shortened search path to PATH or APPEND is threefold. First, DOS has a 127-character limit on command lines. You need exceptional methods to create a search PATH or APPEND longer than 127 characters. Second, as the number of files that can be run increases, you easily can run the wrong program. Third, too many subdirectories and files in the PATH or APPEND search path burden the directory search. DOS slows significantly when searching for the executable file if the PATH is too long. DOS slows when trying to locate or open the file if the APPEND path is too long.

Frequently, you can avoid a long path name. You can add subdirectories temporarily to PATH or APPEND using the batch file technique discussed in Chapter 9. If you absolutely need a long search path name for PATH, see the tips on environmental variables in Chapter 9 on batch files or on SUBST later in this chapter. If you need a long APPEND search string, either use SUBST or give APPEND /E and use the tips for extended environment strings.

6.29   Tip: Always give drive names with subdirectory names in the search path.

If you don't give disk drive names in the search path to PATH or APPEND, DOS searches for files within the specified subdirectories on the current disk drive. When operating from drive C: on a hard disk-based system or from drive A: on a floppy disk-based system, the lack of a drive name works fine. As soon as you change the current disk drive, however, DOS cannot find the subdirectories because they exist on another disk drive.

Give drive names with the path names; then you can change current disk drives and always have DOS find the file. This capability makes using PATH, APPEND, and the computer easier.

Using SUBST

6.30 Trick: Use SUBST to shorten path names.

SUBST (which stands for substitute) is a command that plays with the logical structure of the disk drive. SUBST creates pseudo disk drives that are actually subdirectories of another disk. When you give the substituted disk drive name, DOS actually uses the indicated subdirectory. Normally, you use SUBST to trick programs that do not accept path names into using subdirectories.

SUBST has a second use: it can shorten path names and circumvent the 127-character command line limit. By using the pseudo disk drive letters instead of the physical path names, you can create search path names for PATH or APPEND which translate into paths that are hundreds of characters long.

To use the trick, issue the appropriate LASTDRIVE directive in your CONFIG.SYS file so that you have enough logical drive letters to use. Then issue the SUBST commands to shorten any long (or not so long) subdirectory path name. Finally, use the disk drive letters instead of the drive path name in the PATH or APPEND command.

For example, you can shorten the following 128-character PATH statement to well under the 127-character limit:

PATH=C:\DOS33;C:\BIN;C:\BIN\MISC;C:\BIN\NORTON;C:\;
    D:\WORD;D:\WORD\STYLE;D:\WINDOWS;
    D:\DBASE;D:\DBASE\ACCOUNT\PROG;C:\C\ECO\BIN

To shorten the statement, use the following commands:

SUBST F: C:\DOS33
SUBST G: C:\BIN\MISC
SUBST H: C:\BIN\NORTON
SUBST I: D:\WORD
SUBST J: D:\WORD\STYLE
SUBST K: D:\WINDOWS
SUBST L: D:\DBASE
SUBST M: D:\DBASE\ACCOUNT\PROG
SUBST N: D:\C\ECO\BIN
PATH=F:\;G:\;H:\;C:\;I:\;J:\;K:\;L:\;M:\;N:

Or, if you just want to shorten the path slightly and avoid using so many SUBST commands, use the following commands:

SUBST F: D:\WORD

SUBST G: D:\DBASE

PATH=C:\DOS33;C:\BIN;C:\BIN\MISC;C:\BIN\NORTON;C:\;F:\;
F:STYLE;D:\WINDOWS;G:\;G:ACCOUNT\PROG;C:\C\ECO\BIN

In this case, you can reduce the common parts of the path names (D:\WORD and D:\DBASE). Actually, you can give one SUBST command (SUBST F: D:\DBASE\ACCOUNT\PROG) and substitute F: in the PATH to put the search name under the 127-character limit.

Again, this method is useful when any path name exceeds the 63-character limit. If the file FULLNAME.TXT is in a directory called C:\SUBDIR1\SUBDIR2\...\SUBDIR8, consider the following command:

SUBST F:
C:\SUBDIR1\SUBDIR2\SUBDIR3\SUBDIR4\SUBDIR5\SUBDIR6\SUBDIR7

This command allows the following reference to work:

F:\SUBDIR8\FULLNAME.TXT

Apply this trick in emergency situations only. Only a few valid reasons exist for a path name to exceed 63 characters or a search path name to exceed 127 characters. You should rethink your subdirectory organization if this happens. Remember that long PATH and APPEND paths can bog down performance.

7

Managing Files

Most DOS command-line activity relates to files: naming, copying, moving, and erasing files. This chapter covers these frequent activities as they relate to single files and groups of files.

The first part of the chapter offers tips, tricks, and traps concerning file names and using the file attributes maintained by DOS for each file. The later part of the chapter discusses file operations: erasing files, moving files, copying files, renaming files, and replacing files. A vital troubleshooting topic, unerasing files, is also covered in this section.

Naming Files

This section of the chapter offers tips, tricks, and traps about naming files. Among the tips are those that show you how to standardize file-name extensions, use device names, use numeric characters within file names, and include an unprintable character in a file name.

7.1 Tip: Use standardized file-name extensions, but know when to violate this tip.

Although you can give a file name any extension, some operations are easier if you use a standardized extension. With standardized file names, you can identify files easier, and you can use a wild-card name to copy, move, or delete related files.

You don't need to type a file-name extension when you load or save a 1-2-3 worksheet or BASIC program. These programs automatically add the extensions .WK1 or .BAS. In some cases, you must use a certain extension. For example, DOS requires batch files to have the extension .BAT and executable program files to have the extension .COM or .EXE.

If a program does not require a certain extension or make using a particular extension easier, focus on giving common extensions to related files. You can assign file extensions, such as those listed in table 7.1, based on the file's content or use. For example, you can use the extension .LET for letters or .DOC for documents. Note: Using standard extensions allows users of the DOS V4 visual shell to invoke automatically a program and pass to it the standard-named file. For example, .DOC files could trigger a word processor.

Table 7.1
Common File Name Extensions

Extension	Common Use	Extension	Common Use
.ARC	Archive (compressed) file	.MAP	Program linker map file
.ASC	ASCII text file	.MEU	Menu file (DOS visual shell and SELECT)
.ASM	Assembler source file		
.BAK	Backup file	.MNU	Menu file
.BAS	BASIC program file	.MOS	Mouse driver file (DOS visual shell)
.BAT	Batch file		
.BIN	Binary program file	.MSG	Program message file
.C	C source file	.NDX	Index file
.CBL	COBOL source file	.OBJ	Intermediate object code (program) file
.CFG	Program configuration information	.OLD	Alternative extension for a backup file
.CNF	Program configuration information	.OVL	Program overlay file
		.OVR	Program overlay file
.COM	Command (program) file	.PAS	Pascal source file
.CPI	Code page information file (DOS)	.PAK	Packed (archive) file
.DAT	Data file	.PCX	PC Paintbrush® graphics file
.DBF	Database file (dBASE)	.PIF	Program information file (Windows)
.DCT	Dictionary file		
.DEV	Program device driver file	.PRO	Profile (configuration) file (DOS GRAPHICS)
.DIC	Dictionary file		
.DOC	Document (text) file	.PRN	Program listing for printing
.DRV	Program device driver file	.PS	PostScript® program file
.DTA	Data file	.SAV	Alternative extension for a backup file
.EXE	Executable (program) file		
.FNT	Font file	.SYS	System or device driver file
.IDX	Index file (Q&A™)	.TST	Test file
.IMG	GEM™ image (graphics) file	.TMP	Temporary file
.HLP	Help file	.TXT	Text file
.KEY	Keyboard macro file	.$xx	Temporary file (or incorrectly stored file)
.LET	Letter file		
.LST	Listing of a program file	.WK1	Worksheet file (1-2-3, Release 2)
.LIB	Program library file	.WKS	Alternative extension for a worksheet file
.MAC	Keyboard macro file		

Violate this tip whenever using a standard extension name does not make sense—for example, if the file is unique (doesn't fit any category). In this case, be creative but use an extension that is easy to remember.

Another good time to violate this tip is when you need to protect a file temporarily. Suppose, for example, that you want to copy all files with a .LST extension to another directory. However, two files on the source, FAST.LST and FAR.LST, also exist on the destination. The destination's copy of FAST.LST is the more current copy.

If you use a version of DOS before V3.2, the common alternative is to issue several COPY commands so that FAST.LST is not copied. This approach can be tedious if you have many files. My preferred alternative is to RENAME FAST.LST to something such as FAST.TSL (or FAST.ORG, or even change the root name to FASTORG.LST), issue the **COPY *.LST \NEWDIR** command, then **DEL FAST.LST**, and finally change the name of my renamed file back to FAST.LST. (The best alternative is to use XCOPY /P to query which files should be copied or use a copy program that asks whether existing files should be overwritten.)

I also use this technique when I'm unsure of the results of changing a file. I copy the file, keeping the root name but using a nonstandard extension (such as .KAB for backup files, .TST for test files, or .ORG for original files). I edit or change the file, and then I test the new file. If the new file doesn't work, I still have the original file.

All techniques mentioned here also work by changing a file's root name. I prefer changing the root name only if one or two files are involved and a single wild-card name can be used to rename the file's name to the temporary name and back.

7.2 Trap: If you use a device name as the root name of a file, DOS will use the device instead of the disk-based file.

Using one of DOS's 12 device names as the root name of a file causes DOS to use the device and not a disk-based file (see table 7.2). The result ranges from comical to serious.

For example, a logical name for a text file involved in printing is PRN.TXT. Unfortunately, using this name causes DOS and your programs to write or read information from the system printer, not from a file named PRN.TXT. When you use the root name PRN—a device name—DOS ignores the extension and immediately attempts to use the system printer.

Table 7.2
DOS Devices

Name	Description
CON:	System *console* (keyboard and display); an input and output device
LPTx:	*Line printer* (parallel) ports, numbered 1 through 3; an output-only device
COMx:	Serial *communications* ports, numbered 1 through 4; an input and output device
PRN	System *printer*, usually the same as LPT1:; an output-only device
AUX	System *auxiliary* port, usually the same as COM1:; an input and output device
NUL	*Null* (nonexistent) device; an input and output device

The results of using PRN.TXT depend on what you are attempting to accomplish. If you are trying to write information to a file, the information is written to the printer instead. If you are trying to read information from a file, no information is read. Because PRN is an output-only device, most programs simply get an end-of-file signal from DOS and continue. However, if your program requires input before continuing, the program will wait forever, and you will need to press Ctrl-C or Ctrl-Break, or possibly reset to free the computer.

7.3 Tip: If you use numeric characters in a file name to number more than 9 associated files, add a leading 0 to the numbers.

Suppose that you "number" your files to keep track of their order. For example, the root name of the chapters of a book can start with the common name **CHAP**, followed by a chapter number. For the extension, you use **.TXT**. For instance, you name the first chapter of the book **CHAP1.TXT**; the fourth chapter, **CHAP4.TXT**; the ninth chapter, **CHAP9.TXT**; and so on.

The system works well until you write the 10th chapter. You assign this file the name **CHAP10.TXT**. Sorting the directory that contains these file names produces the following list:

```
CHAP1.TXT
CHAP10.TXT
CHAP4.TXT
CHAP9.TXT
```

In this list, Chapter 10 comes before Chapter 4. Because the "numbering" starts at the fifth position in the file names, and both CHAP1.TXT and CHAP10.TXT have a 1 in the fifth position, these files are listed before Chapters 4 and 9.

To sort file names correctly, add a leading zero as a placeholder. When you add a leading 0 to the files with numbers less than 10, the new names for the chapters become CHAP01.TXT, CHAP04.TXT, and CHAP09.TXT. The chapters numbered under 10 have a 0 in the fifth position. In a sort, the program places these chapters before those 10 and above, which have a 1 or higher number in the fifth position.

7.4   Trick: If you need a quick printout, use a device name to send the information directly to the printer.

DOS's casualness about devices and files has an excellent side effect. Instead of saving pieces of information into a file and then printing the file, you can "save" to the printer. When the program asks for the name of the file to hold the output, answer with PRN or LPT1. Rather than storing the information in a disk-based file, DOS sends the information to the printer.

This trick has some limitations. Although you can use this method with many programs, the trick does not work with all programs—WordStar, for example. WordStar first checks for the existence of the file before writing to it. When DOS affirms that the "file" does exist, WordStar then attempts to rename or delete the file. DOS denies the request, and WordStar displays a message stating that the file is protected.

The trick also does not work with the output of all types of programs. Saving to the printer works best with programs that store files as ASCII text. If your program stores information in a compressed or encoded format, the printer may interpret the encoded or compressed codes as printer commands. In these cases, the printer prints nonsense.

7.5   Trick: Instead of sending the output of a program directly to a printer, send the output to a disk-based file.

This trick is the inverse of the preceding trick. In this case, you use a file name to capture the output of a program into a disk-based file rather than send the output directly to a printer. If your program accepts a device name, you usually can substitute a file name. Instead of printing to the printer, the program prints to a disk-based file.

I admit that this trick is seldom usable. Most programs "install" the device for printing, and you cannot change dynamically the output device. Most programs do not allow a long name for a device and check that you have given a device name. Therefore, your options for using a file rather than a device name are limited.

7.6   Trick: Use an unprintable character to protect a file.

Although you cannot use most control characters in a file name, DOS allows one unprintable character—ASCII 255 (FF hex), the ASCII Delete character with the eighth bit turned on. You can type this character by holding down the Alt key, typing **255** on the numeric keypad, and then releasing the Alt key. The cursor moves, but no character appears.

This character appears only as a blank space on-screen. By using one or two of these characters in the root or extension, a person cannot see the correct file name and cannot type it to open the file. In essence, the file is protected from casual use.

You can test this trick by typing the following commands, which create a text file. For the **<255>**, hold down the Alt key, type **255**, and then release the Alt key. Press Enter after each line.

> **COPY CON TEST<255>.TXT**
> **This is a test**

To complete the file, press F6. Now try each of these commands, in turn:

> **DIR TEST*.***
> **TYPE TEST<255>.TXT**
> **TYPE TEST.TXT**
> **DEL TEST.TXT**
> **DEL TEST<255>.TXT**

The file name should appear in the directory list after you type the first command. Notice that the **<255>** does not appear in the name. The second and fifth commands work as usual; the third and fourth commands invoke a **File not found** message from DOS.

Caution: The protection is not foolproof. As you notice from the first command, the correct wild-card file name catches the file. For instance, **DEL TEST*.*** deletes the file. **RENAME T*.* TEST.*** changes the file's name. Moreover, some programs, such as WordStar Release 4, offer a menu selection of appropriate files in a directory. If the file name appears with the DIR command, the user can select the file without any trouble.

If you want further protection, set the hidden, read-only, or system attributes for the file, as described in the next section of this chapter. Keep in mind also that anyone with a disk-sector editor can examine the directory, see the correct file name, and change the name (or reverse the attributes). Using an invisible character is protection against only inadvertent or casual operations.

Using File Attributes

DOS currently maintains six unique settings or directory attributes for each file. Four attributes actually concern files; the remaining two attributes cover subdirectories and volume labels. Table 7.3 lists all six attributes. This chapter covers some general tips, tricks, and traps concerning attributes. Chapter 10 on backup and the section on copying files in this chapter also cover attributes.

Table 7.3
DOS File Attributes

Attribute name	Directory value (hex)	Description
Normal	00	A file without any other attribute set
Read-only	01	A file that may be read, but cannot be altered or erased
Hidden	02	A file hidden from view during normal directory searches
System	04	A file used by the operating system
Volume label	08	An electronic label for the disk
Subdirectory	10	Not a file, but a directory holding additional information about other files
Archive	20	A file that has been created or changed

7.7 Tip: Use a third-party program to set the system or hidden attributes.

DOS ATTRIB, a powerful program, can set the archive and read-only attribute of any file or files and, starting with DOS V3.3, can "sweep" through a set of subdirectories (look forward through all subdirectories). ATTRIB, however, cannot set the system or hidden attributes. You need an outside program, such as the Norton Utilities FA™ (File Attribute) program or SDA Associates SDACHMD© (short for Change Mode), to do this trickery. If you plan on using the hidden or system attributes, obtain a program that can set these attributes.

Although you can use a disk-sector editor to set these bits, using attribute setters is preferable. Mistakes using a disk-sector editor have significant ramifications. On the other hand, you can reverse most mistakes made using an attribute setter by running the program again.

7.8   Tip: To protect a file from being erased or changed, set the file's read-only attribute.

The primary use of the read-only attribute is to protect files from being erased or changed. As the name implies, information may be read from the file. If the file is a program, the file may be executed. However, DOS protects the file from erasure and protects the contents from change.

7.9   Tip: The only files that should be marked read-only are files that never change or seldom change.

Although any file can be marked read-only, you should limit your use of this attribute. The practical use for the read-only attribute is to protect files that never or seldom change.

The problem with applying read-only protection *carte blanche* to all files is that you cannot change or delete a file without reversing the read-only protection. For each read-only file, you must turn off the read-only attribute manually every time you must alter or delete the file, then turn the attribute back on manually after altering the file. These two additional steps are impractical operationally for files that are constantly changing.

DOS uses two start-up files, which vary depending on your system. PC DOS uses IBMBIO.COM and IBMDOS.COM. MS-DOS generally uses IO.SYS and MS-DOS.SYS. These start-up files qualify in the "never change" category. Marked as read-only, these files cannot be altered or erased. The effects of changing or erasing the two start-up files is usually profound (and frequently negative). The results range from DOS not starting properly to DOS operations going awry.

The files holding the program instructions for most major applications also qualify as "never changed." You can protect these files from accidental erasure by using the read-only attribute. Because deleting part of a program can be annoying or even quite problematic, you should protect these files from accidental erasure if the same directory holding the program files also holds data files.

Examples of "seldom changed" files are configuration information files, which are altered when you install a program or change some of the features of the program. In some cases, the file is separate (for example, 123.CNF for 1-2-3). In other cases, the main program itself is altered (WS.EXE for WordStar). Because configuration is an infrequent operation, you can protect the file by turning on the read-only attribute. When you are ready to reconfigure the program, set the attribute off, make and test the changes, and then turn on the attribute again afterward.

7.10   Trap: The read-only attribute protects only read-only files.

Some versions of DOS prior to V3.2 had a useful quirk. The ERASE command didn't work when you tried to delete a read-only file. This quirk was useful for protecting entire subdirectories from an inadvertent DEL *.* command. If you set the read-only attribute of the first file in the directory listing, ERASE *.* (or DEL *.*) stopped when you tried to delete the first file. This setup protected the entire subdirectory, but still allowed you to erase individual files. Unfortunately (or fortunately), this quirk did not appear in all versions of DOS V3.0 and V3.1 and disappeared completely in DOS V3.2.

Do not depend on this quirk if you use DOS V3.0 or V3.1. When you move to a different version of DOS, you lose this protection.

7.11   Trap: The protection from the read-only attribute does not extend to the file name.

DOS's read-only attribute protects the existence of a file (the file cannot be erased) and the contents of a file (the contents cannot be changed). You can, however, rename a read-only file. Because some programs, such as word processors, rename files when they produce automatic backups, the result can be annoying time bombs.

An example of quirk-plus-program-equals-time-bomb is read-only text files and WordStar Release 3. (WordStar Release 4 and later handles read-only files intelligently.)

When you save a new version of a file, WordStar Release 3 creates a backup copy. The program follows this internal procedure:

1. The program saves the current version under a temporary name.
2. If a .BAK (backup) file already exists, WordStar deletes the previous .BAK file.

3. If a previous version exists, that version becomes the current backup file; the program changes that file's extension to .BAK.

4. The program renames the temporary file to the file's original name.

Exacerbating the problem is that WordStar Release 3 does not check whether the renaming or deleting process is successful. The program simply assumes that the file is renamed or deleted.

Suppose that you have two files: LETTERS.DOC (the current revision of the file) and LETTERS.BAK (the backup file created when the current revision was saved). When the program saves the next revision of LETTERS.DOC, WordStar Release 3 follows these steps:

1. Saves the new version of LETTERS.DOC in a temporary file.

2. Deletes the previous LETTERS.BAK.

3. Renames the previous LETTERS.DOC to LETTERS.BAK.

4. Renames the temporary file to LETTERS.DOC.

What happens if LETTERS.DOC is marked read-only? The first time all goes well. WordStar successfully deletes the previous LETTERS.BAK, renames the previous LETTERS.DOC to LETTERS.BAK, and renames the new revision in the temporary file to LETTERS.DOC.

Luck runs out for the next revision. When WordStar attempts to save a new version of LETTERS.DOC, the previous LETTERS.BAK cannot be deleted (the file is marked read-only). WordStar cannot successfully rename the old LETTERS.DOC to LETTERS.BAK nor rename the temporary file to LETTERS.DOC. When attempting to edit the file again, the program re-creates the temporary file, and the recent revision is lost.

Notice that the time bomb does not explode when the read-only file is renamed; the problem occurs when you try to edit the document the second time. The results are puzzling. You don't receive a message about failing to delete a read-only file; your edits seem to be dispatched to the bit-bucket.

The latter versions of WordStar cure this problem intelligently, calling a read-only document "protected." You can view, but not change or save, a protected document—solving the delayed read-only bomb. However, other programs that swap files by renaming (such as many text editors and other word processors) may not be as intelligent.

7.12   Trap: When you copy a file, attributes are not maintained.

When you rename a file, the file attributes are not affected. When you copy a file, however, the DOS attributes are not maintained. DOS views the copy of the file as unique. The hidden, read-only, or system attributes are cleared, and the copy of the file loses the protection of these attributes.

The archive attribute of the copy is turned on regardless of the status of the attribute on the source file. By definition, the archive attribute represents a file that has been created or changed since the last "backup." (This statement is not always correct because XCOPY, ATTRIB, and other attribute-setting programs can clear the bit.) The archive bit, therefore, is set for any file that is copied.

7.13   Tip: To protect a file from being copied, erased, or renamed, use the hidden attribute.

The hidden attribute hides files from normal directory searches. A normal directory search produces the names of files that do *not* have the hidden, system, subdirectory, or volume label attribute set. In other words, only normal files appear in a normal directory search. (The archive attribute does not affect a file's normalcy.) Because most DOS commands use the normal directory search for files, hidden files gain some protection.

Hidden files are protected from the directory commands DIR, CHKDSK, and TREE. COPY and XCOPY cannot copy a hidden file; using these commands results in a File not found error. COPY and XCOPY cannot copy to a hidden file; the result is a File creation error. Because ERASE and RENAME cannot find hidden files, these commands cannot erase or rename hidden files.

7.14   Trick: You can run hidden .COM, .EXE, and .BAT files as you do other files; most programs can use hidden files.

The DOS hidden file attribute controls whether the file appears in a directory listing. If the hidden attribute is turned on, the file is hidden from normal directory searches.

Folklore expounds how knowing someone's or something's name gives you power over that person or thing. The same is true for hidden files. The hidden attribute does not control whether you can run or use the file, and does not affect DOS running a program or batch file. Programs that specifically request the file by name still have access to the file.

To run a hidden file, you type its root name as you would with any file. DOS finds, loads, and executes the .COM, .EXE, or .BAT file normally. To use a hidden file within a program, you simply give the correct file name.

The trick of using hidden files is useful for protecting files from casual users. If the user does not know the exact name, the file will not be found.

Obviously, you can undo the protection by using an extended DIR command to find the name. For example, you could use SDA Associates extended directory program (SDADIR©) or the Norton Utilities FA (File Attribute) command. After the magic is discovered (the correct name), the user has power over the file.

This trick is also of little use for hiding commonly known files, particularly when the file is in a PATHed or APPENDed directory. PATH and APPEND still find the file. Don't try to hide commands such as FORMAT, for example, if the subdirectory holding FORMAT is still on the PATH. Typing **format** still invokes the command.

Be careful when saving new versions of the hidden file. Most programs do not maintain the hidden attribute. The old version may keep the hidden attribute, but the new version will not.

7.15   Trick: To stop a program from being run from the command line, use the system attribute.

The system attribute has a special meaning to DOS. When the system attribute is set, the file is hidden and cannot be run from the command line. The only way a system file can be executed is by another program loading and executing the file.

The trick has some limitations. Flipping on and off the system attribute each time is tedious. Although the process could be handled through a batch file, the batch file then could be discovered and the method exposed.

Performing File Operations

The remainder of this chapter discusses the file-based operations of erasing, moving, copying, concatenating, and renaming files. The discussion on unerasing files also covers many troubleshooting tips on handling the problem of when the wrong file is erased. Also covered in this section of the chapter is information on the REPLACE command, useful when updating to a new version of any program, including DOS.

Erasing Files

7.16 Tip: Before you use ERASE with a wild-card file name, test the wild-card file name with DIR.

Using a wild-card file name with assurance with any DEL or extended ERASE command is an invitation to problems. You easily can specify too many files to be erased. To be absolutely sure which files will be deleted by the wild-card name, use the name first with DIR and check the file list. If the wrong file(s) show up, change the wild-card name or issue separate deletion commands for each file.

Don't depend on using a file uneraser. If you discover the mistake too late, another file may overwrite the data on the disk, and the information will be lost. Even if you discover your error right away, the file may not be recoverable. This phenomenon is explained later in this chapter.

7.17 Tip: Be careful with programs that issue sweeping ERASE commands.

Several timesaving programs, such as SDA Associates SDADEL©, can search the subdirectories of a disk for files to delete. One command can find and delete all files on the disk with a similar name, such as .BAK (backup) files, regardless of the subdirectory. You need not search each directory, find the files, give the DEL *.BAK command, and continue the search.

These programs are examples of grabbing the tiger by the tail. The same speed and power applied to ridding the disk of all useless files might be applied to useful files. If you use the wrong file name with ERASE, you delete the wrong files, but only in one directory. Unleash the super-ERASE command in the root directory with the wrong file name and the sweep switch on, and you lose all or almost all files that match the name on the disk.

Don't let advanced-user syndrome strike. When the **Are You Sure** prompt is displayed (SDADEL issues this query whenever you use a wild-card name), take a second and check the file name. I *once* confused a **SDADEL *.BAK /T** (/T is SDA's sweep subdirectory switch) with **SDADEL *.BAT**. I also inadvertently *once* used **SDADEL *.* /T**. (You don't make these mistakes more than once.) I needed about 10 minutes with Norton's

UNERASE to fix the first one. And I caught the second mistake within a few seconds, pressed Ctrl-Break, and recovered within 15 minutes.

I still use these super-erase programs, and I encourage others to use them. Be cautious, however, with wild-card names. I was lucky in both cases; you may not be.

7.18   Tip: Although ERASE in DOS V4.0 handles selective erasing, you need a third-party program to erase selective files under DOS V3.3.

One wonderful addition to DOS V4.0 is ERASE's /P switch. Like all other DOS-provided programs, the /P switch tells ERASE to pause and display a prompt. You therefore can erase files selectively without giving many separate ERASE commands. When you use the /P switch, ERASE presents each file matching the name and asks **Delete (Y/N)?**. Answer Y to delete the file, N to skip the file. If you answer Y, the file is deleted immediately.

You can use any file name with ERASE V4.0 (including *.*). If you use *.* with /P, ERASE skips the message **All files in directory will be deleted!** and the **Are you sure** confirmation. Therefore, be careful when answering Yes or No to each **Delete (Y/N)?** prompt. Because you must press Enter after each answer, you always have the chance to change your mind.

If you have used a wild-card file name to delete the files you want and the list contains more files, halt ERASE by pressing Ctrl-Break or Ctrl-C. Ending ERASE prematurely does not restore the files already erased nor harm any other files.

ERASE in DOS V3.3 and earlier does not have a prompt command. To display prompts, you need to use an outside program such as SDA Associates SDADEL. These programs are excellent timesaving conveniences for any DOS user. Also, you won't abandon the programs when moving to DOS V4. Although ERASE in DOS V4 has query, that version of DOS does not sweep subdirectories. You can continue to use sweeping programs such as SDADEL with DOS V4.

Unerasing Files

7.19   Tip: Obtain and use an unerase program.

When DOS erases a file, the file is not removed from the disk. The first character in the file's directory entry is marked with an E5 hex (229 decimal); and the FAT entries that marked the file's location are cleared to zeros, thereby freeing the disk space. The directory entry and the contents of the file remain on disk until the entry or the space is reused.

You therefore can recover erased files. You need to follow a couple steps to make unerasing successful. The most crucial step (unless you enjoy the tedium and risk of playing with the directory and FAT directly) is to use an unerase program.

Several unerase programs are included with utility sets such as the Mace Utilities, the Norton Utilities, and PC-Tools™. All users should have one of these programs. The chance of deleting a file inadvertently is great. If you haven't already erased the wrong file, you *will.* Before disaster strikes, have one of these tools on-hand. The entire price of a disk utility set can be repaid through the first use of one of these unerase programs.

Another step to successful unerasing of files is to provide the first character of the erased file name. Because DOS replaces the first character with a σ, you need to provide a character to the unerase program. Don't be afraid to use the wrong character. After you successfully unerase the file, you can rename it.

7.20 Trap: The moment you discover that you have erased the wrong file, store no more files!

As soon as you erase any file inadvertently, store no more files. Also, do not copy to the disk, or move or remove any other files from the disk. To have the best chance of unerasing the file, you must not write any more information to the disk. If the directory entry that holds the file is reused, the file is probably lost. If the clusters that previously held the file are reused, part of the file is lost. If you fail to heed this advice, your chances of complete recovery are diminished. (Unfortunately, discovering the inadvertent erasure too late has the same effect.)

You can read information safely from the disk. Therefore, you can copy files *from* the disk and use any command or program that does not *write* to the disk. Do not run any program that creates temporary files, as most text editors or word processors do. Running such programs increases the chance of the directory entry and now-free clusters being reused.

The advice about not deleting more files is not absolutely critical, but is important. For each additional file you erase, you have one more file you must wade past using the unerase program. If you don't erase any more files, unerasing is more convenient. However, the more crucial aspect is that each additional erased file increases the chance of botching the recovery. The trap on fragmented files presented later in this chapter explains why erasing more files can be detrimental.

7.21 **Trap: If you erase a file inadvertently while you are working with a program, you may lose some of your work if you are not deliberate in your next actions.**

You end up between a rock and a hard place when you are working within a program and erase the wrong file. You are faced with the possibility of losing past work (the erased file) or current work.

(This is the reason why I save any pending work before using a program's file erasing features. If I botch the erasing, I can abandon the program without losing work. Of course, this approach does not work if the reason I am erasing the file is because of a lack of free space.)

In cases where work can be lost, I stop my work, call time-out, and consider my possibilities. My first thoughts concern how I can best salvage the current work while giving priority to the old work. Reconstructing the current work, which is fresher in my mind than the past work, is easier. If facing the difficult choice—losing one or the other—I'd rather lose the current than the past.

The situation, however, is seldom this bleak. Usually, you can write the work-in-progress to a floppy diskette or another disk drive, and then abandon the work. This approach works when discrete files can be saved, such as word processing documents or spreadsheets. Because the entire spreadsheet is in memory, you can save the file to another disk. (I always avoid creating a spreadsheet that exceeds the storage capacity of a floppy diskette for this reason.) For word processing documents, I mark just the changed areas as a block and write the block to the other disk. If I move too far into the document, the word processors I use extend their temporary files, which decreases the chance of recovering the files intact. (This is a case where knowing how your program works is essential.)

If you are in a multifile application (an accounting or similar database application), gracefully attempt to leave the program. Aborting the program with any information to be written to the disk may transfigure the database into an unusable state.

After you have left the program, you can unerase or restore the correct file(s), merge or reconstruct the current work, and hopefully praise yourself for handling well the recovery from your error.

7.22 Trap: If the erased file is fragmented, you may not be able to unerase the file completely.

When erasing a file, DOS marks the file's clusters in the FAT as free. The unerase program uses logical detective work to restore the file from these free clusters. From the file's directory entry, the program finds the starting cluster for the file and then follows the adjacent clusters that are marked as free. When the disk space represented by these clusters equals or exceeds the file's size as stored in the directory entry, the uneraser marks the clusters again and restores the directory entry.

The key is the trail of free clusters. If the number of adjacent free clusters is not sufficient, you must hunt manually for the remainder of the file. Otherwise, you will recover only part of the file.

Another trap in recovering fragmented files is that the now-free adjacent space may have been part of another file. This trap is encountered particularly when several files are deleted at once. The unerase program assumes that the free space was part of the file and gathers up the adjacent clusters. The wrong information leaks into the file without warning.

For this reason, running a defragmenter periodically not only improves your system's performance, but also helps your chance of recovering unerased files intact. The defragmenter puts the files in adjacent clusters and thereby gives you the best chance of recovering the file fully with minimum work. When running the defragmenter, avoid options that do not fully defragment all files. Don't worry about the free space becoming contiguous; concentrate on making the file completely contiguous.

If you are forced into a manual hunt, keep in mind that most unerase programs which double as disk-sector editors (such as the Norton Utilities' main program, NU®) have both a semiautomated and a completely manual mode. Either mode may be required for a manual recovery.

The manual hunt is less painful if you know the contents of the file. For example, when the last bytes in the fragment of an ASCII text file are **dis** and you know that the word is either **discuss** or **discover**, you can use a disk editor to search for the **cuss** or **cover**. If these appear as the first bytes of the file and the cluster is not marked in use, you've found the missing part.

If the file is a non-ASCII data file, manual recovery is possible, but difficult. Reconstructing the file using the backup files may be easier. If the erased file is a program file, be cautious. Test the program carefully. Even an automated recovery that appears flawless may not be. Suppose, for example, that during the recovery, a data file is mistaken for a program file. The results of running a program that interprets arbitrary data as computer instructions is bound to be either puzzling, amusing, or disastrous, and never what you expected.

Note one final side benefit (or side curse) of running a defragmenter: Some programs automatically compress or include an option to compress directory entries. During compression, these programs move valid directory entries to the top of the list and move deleted entries to the bottom or turn the entries to zeros. (DOS stops searching a directory when an entry contains all zeros.) The program removes entries for previously deleted files, and this nails the coffin shut on recovering a file that was erased before you ran the defragmenter.

7.23   Trick: If you are unsure which version of a file to unerase, first view all the choices and then choose the version using the date/time stamp and file size.

When several erased files have the same name, you may not know which file to unerase. For example, text-editing operations often delete an old version of a document as the program saves a new version—producing more than one version of the same document. Many versions of a file may exist in the same directory without directory entries being recycled.

When you delete a file, DOS destroys the first character of the file's root name. If the names of two or more files vary by only the first character, you can become confused about how many files should be unerased.

Before you unerase files, first view the list of files you might possibly recover. When you have deleted several files inadvertently, you might want to write down the choices by hand or print-screen the options. After you have the complete list of unerase candidates, use the file date and time, and the file size as clues. The file with the most recent date is usually the correct file.

Although the date is an excellent clue, sometimes following that lead can lead you astray. When you copy a file, for example, the destination file retains the same date and time as the source file. If you have copied to a directory a file that has the same name as a previously erased file, the later file may be the file to unerase. In this case, use the second clue—the file size. Knowing the approximate size of the file helps you decide which file to unerase.

If your computer does not set the system date and time on start-up, the file size may be your *only* clue. Don't be afraid to unerase the wrong file. If you do, simply erase the file again; then unerase another likely candidate. However, be careful if you are using a program that creates temporary files; don't view the file with any program that writes to the disk.

7.24 **Tip: Unerase your most valuable files and the ones you are sure are correct first; then unerase those you are not sure of.**

Unerasing files can require extensive work if you have a fragmented disk or a full directory, or if you have unleashed a super-erase program on many directories. You might, for example, unerase an invalid file (whose clusters were already used by another file), which should remain erased. The useless file's clusters are marked in use, and the unerase program reports that the file (a different file from the one you requested) cannot be unerased successfully.

This message does not always mean that the wrong file has been unerased. You will find that the unerase program reports this message for several files and that those files have been overwritten. However, if you are sure that the file can be unerased successfully and you get this report, you have unerased at least one wrong file.

When you know that a file should be recoverable, but it is not, you know that you have goofed. In this case, erase the files again, reexamine the file lists, and start unerasing once more. Usually, you will need to make several passes with the uneraser. Your top priority should be to unerase the files that you know are absolutely correct—the ones that you remember existed in the directory before the inadvertent erasure and that do not have multiple directory entries by the same name. Also, give the highest priority to the files that are the most difficult to replace.

When making multiple passes, give the files with the largest sizes a slightly higher priority than smaller files. Unerasing larger files locks up more clusters. If a mistake is made or the file is fragmented, restoring the large files first will reveal problems faster than unerasing smaller files first.

After you have recovered the known files, start probing the not-so-well-known files. At this point, abandon the larger-file-first attitude; getting more files unerased correctly is more important.

If multiple directories were affected, move back and forth between the directories, applying the same rules. Restore the known files first from all directories; then return for the marginal files. Stop frequently, examine the contents of files (where possible), and continue. When you are left with files that might conflict, don't be afraid to erase a conflicting file again and unerase another. Near the end of the procedure, you may need to experiment.

Remember that unerasing files on an unfragmented disk is much easier than unerasing files on a fragmented disk. Frequent defragmenting helps. Again, don't trust any file until you are sure that the file's content is correct. Be especially suspicious of program files in which you may have had problems when unerasing. Do not destroy your most recent backup of the files until you verify all files. You may need the old copies if something goes wrong.

Keep in mind also that you have other options for restoring files. You may reach a point at which restoring files from your backup copies or reconstructing files from the original program diskettes or backup disk is faster and requires less work than unerasing.

7.25 Trick: Sort your directory periodically to make unerasing easier.

Use a program such as the Norton Utilities DS (Directory Sort) to sort the directory when you are unerasing multiple files. An orderly directory makes identifying the correct files to unerase easier. The deleted entries appear at the bottom of the list, out of the way of the search. When you encounter multiple entries by the same name, you can find the correct entry easier.

If you have not saved new versions of a file, the directory entries appear in their original sorted order. Conversely, if you have saved a new version of the file, the out-of-order entry will probably be correct.

For this trick, a new version of a file means that another copy of the file with the same name was generated to replace the previous copy. If you are simply extending a randomly accessed file, the directory entry does not move. Most database and accounting programs do not move the file. Most other programs, which read or write a file sequentially, do generate new files as each version is saved. (Again, know your programs.)

Moving Files

7.26 Trick: Obtain and use a move utility.

A move utility copies a file and then "erases" the original file. Move utilities have three advantages. First, they are more convenient to use than

COPY and ERASE because one command replaces two operations
(copying, then erasing the file). Second, move utilities are safer than
copying and then erasing a file with a batch file; the deletion does not
happen until the file is copied successfully. Finally, unlike the COPY and
ERASE commands, move programs typically leave a testable exit code that
can be used by an IF ERRORLEVEL line in a batch file (see Chapter 8).

Many move programs are available in the public domain—most following
the syntax and form of the original UNIX™ mv command. Almost all these
programs accept wild-card file names and can move all files in one
subdirectory to another. Some allow you to move selected files; only one
or two let you move a complete subdirectory branch (the starting
subdirectory and all subsequent subdirectories).

Interestingly, the move programs seldom need physically to copy the file.
The programs copy the file only if you are moving the file across disk
drives. If you are moving the file from one subdirectory to another on the
same disk drive under DOS V3 and later, the internal RENAME service (a
function call, not the RENAME command) takes the directory entry for the
file from the source directory and establishes the entry in the destination
subdirectory. The file itself does not move. Because the file is not copied,
the move operation is quick, and further file fragmentation does not occur.

If disk space is tight, room may not be available to hold two copies of the
same file (the source file, which is deleted after the copy is successful, and
the destination file). In this case, using a move program not only makes
copying many files faster and easier, but also makes moving files possible.

Although DOS V4 does not offer a move command, the visual shell of
DOS V4 does have a move option. The option, located in the File
System—File menu, can move the selected files from one directory to
another disk or directory. (Ignore the help message for PC DOS V4; the
option does move *all* selected files.)

Copying Files

7.27   Trap: Copying one file over another destroys the overwritten file.

When you copy files, unlike when you delete files, DOS usually recycles
the directory entry immediately, and you have little chance of recovering
the directory entry and the old file's data. Be careful when copying files.
Inadvertently overwriting one file with a completely different file makes
the previous file history.

7.28   Tip: Before you use COPY with a wild-card file name, test the wild-card file name with DIR.

If you are unsure whether you will overwrite the wrong files, use the DIR command with the wild card on the source disk or directory and on the destination disk or directory. If the wrong files appear in the list, change the names, issue separate COPY commands, rename files, or use a copy program with a query capability (such as XCOPY).

7.29   Tip: To copy files between diskettes on the same disk drive, use XCOPY rather than COPY.

The COPY command copies files one at a time. The program reads the source file and then copies the file to the destination. If the file size exceeds the available memory, the program makes several passes to copy the file. XCOPY attempts to read into memory as many files from the source as possible. When available memory fills, XCOPY then copies the files to the destination.

You will note a dramatic difference between COPY and XCOPY when you copy files between diskettes on the same disk drive. When you use COPY, plan on changing diskettes at least twice for each file—once when reading the source file and once when reading the destination file. On higher-capacity diskettes, if the file is larger than free memory, plan on another set of changes.

When you use XCOPY, you don't need to change disks until the available memory is filled. This method reduces the number of disk swaps needed to copy the files. The only limitation is the amount of free memory. Depending on the type of diskette, the number of files, and the amount of free memory, XCOPY is 2 to 20 times faster than COPY on the same disk drive.

Remember that you must use two different disk drive letters when you copy on a single disk drive. The commands **COPY B: B:** and **XCOPY B: B:** do not work; you get the error message File cannot be copied onto itself. On a single drive system, you must use **XCOPY A: B:** to copy on drive A:. If you have two dissimilar floppy disk drives, you must establish a separate logical disk drive using **DRIVER.SYS** and use the logical drive letter. (For more information, see Chapter 12 on device drivers.)

7.30   Tip: To copy files between diskettes, use the hard disk or a RAM disk.

When you copy several files between diskettes, first copy the files to an empty subdirectory on the hard disk or RAM disk. Then copy the files from the hard disk or RAM disk to the second disk. Finally, delete the files from the directory on the hard disk or RAM disk.

Although this tip takes three steps, it is easier and faster than using COPY or XCOPY on two diskettes using the same drive. The trick is also faster than using COPY or XCOPY between two floppy disk drives.

The tip works because the single floppy disk controller in most computers works with one disk drive at a time. DOS starts the disk drive motor, waits up to one-half second for the motor to come up to speed, and then starts reading or writing. When DOS switches drives, the motor on the other drive turns off. These half-second delays (which happen each time DOS switches drives, at least twice for each file) plus the lower data transfer rate of the floppy disk drive make copying between diskettes slow.

The hard disk or RAM disk, on the other hand, is always on-line and ready. The data is transferred as fast as possible from the floppy diskette to the hard disk or RAM disk with no delay. The floppy disk drive does not have a chance to turn off. When copying the files to the floppy diskette, the limitation is the speed of the floppy disk drive, not the hard disk or RAM disk. The net result is that the double copy-and-erase operation can take less than half the time that a floppy-to-floppy transfer takes.

To copy files between diskettes in this way, you must have enough space on your hard disk or RAM disk to hold the files. I maintain an excess of RAM—my RAM disk can hold 1.2M—for this specific purpose. For copying that exceeds the capacity of the hard disk or RAM disk, I keep an empty directory called \TMP, whose specific purpose is to hold temporary files. Having this "spare" directory makes copying and deleting files easy.

Verifying Copies

7.31   Tip: Don't use the /V switch if you run a disk cacher.

When you use COPY's or XCOPY's /V switch to request that DOS verify copied files, DOS rereads key information just written to the disk. If the information does not agree with what DOS has written, DOS gives the write error message, signifying that the copy is incorrect.

If a disk cacher is active and you use the /V switch, DOS rereads the information. However, the information DOS reads comes from the cacher's memory, not from the physical disk. In other words, using the /V switch (or turning VERIFY ON) with a cacher active is futile. The cacher inhibits DOS from rereading the information on the disk.

If you are unsure about the integrity of your copy, temporarily disable the cacher, and then run COPY or XCOPY /V. After the copy is complete, turn on the cacher again.

7.32 Tip: Use COMP or FC with critical files rather than /V.

In the thousands of diskettes and hundreds of thousands of files I've copied, I have received less than a dozen random verify errors. I have abandoned using the /V switch customarily. I believe the practice to be safe.

You should verify your copied files under two conditions: when the copy must be absolutely correct, such as when making distribution diskettes; and when the only copy of the file will exist on this diskette. In these cases, using /V is not enough because a minute probability exists that DOS's verification will not catch an error. For these cases, use a file comparer such as COMP or FC (File Compare). Most versions of DOS include COMP; some versions include FC instead. (I prefer to use my version of FC from MS-DOS V2.1 rather than the current version of COMP.)

To copy a file and compare the copy to the original, first turn off your cacher, if you use one. (If you can turn off your cacher for only a disk drive, use this feature to disable caching the destination disk drive.) Second, issue the COPY command. If you use COMP, type **COMP**, press F3, and then press Enter. (F3 is the special-function key that recalls the remainder of the previous line.) If you use FC, type **FC** and then execute the following sequence:

    \<Del>

    \<Del>

    \<F3>

With either COMP or FC, the files are compared. If you get even one error message, the copy is bad; make the copy again and recompare.

This technique works, with some modification, with XCOPY. The problem comes when you use the /S (subdirectory search) switch. COMP nor FC compares files in more than one set of directories at a time. You need to issue a COMP or FC command for each set of corresponding source and destination subdirectories.

A good example of when you want verification of correct copies is when your disk drive gives an unusual number of errors. If you get read or write errors on two or more diskettes within a week, and the diskettes worked correctly before, your drive has a problem. In this case, verify nearly everything.

If the problem lies with your hard disk, run a disk test program immediately. You can replace floppy diskettes easily and disk drives at a modest cost. The amount of lost information is disagreeable, but not as catastrophic as the amount of information that can be lost if your hard disk has errors.

Using XCOPY

7.33   Tip: Use XCOPY to copy files from more than one subdirectory.

Unlike COPY, XCOPY can traverse a subdirectory tree to copy files. If you need to copy files from more than one subdirectory in the same tree, a single XCOPY /S command may do the job.

When you specify the /S switch, XCOPY examines the current or specified directory for files that match the source file name. After finding these files, XCOPY searches the subdirectories of the source directory for matching files and makes copies of these matching files.

Files are deposited in parallel subdirectories in the destination. The files found in the starting source subdirectory are placed in the starting destination directory. The files found in subdirectories of the source are copied, and the copies are placed in identical subdirectories of the destination. If the appropriate subdirectory does not exist on the destination, the subdirectory is created.

In essence, a copy of the subdirectory structure of the source (without the starting source directory name) is duplicated on the destination. The starting source directory name is not duplicated because the files from the starting directory are copied to the specified or current directory of the destination. The names of all other subdirectories are duplicated if the subdirectory did not exist before the XCOPY command was issued.

There is one exception. If the destination subdirectory is empty (no matching files are found in the parallel source subdirectory), a parallel subdirectory is created only if you use the /E (empty) switch. If you want an exact parallel subdirectory tree on the destination, use the /E switch. If you do not want to create empty subdirectories, omit the /E switch.

Use the /E switch when you will later copy files from the source to the destination and you want to maintain the parallel directory tree. Omit the /E switch when you don't want to waste the disk cluster that the empty subdirectory would occupy.

7.34 Tip: Use XCOPY's /A, /M, /D, and /P switches to select files for copying.

Another advantage of XCOPY over COPY is that XCOPY can copy selective files (/A, /M, or /D), selected files (/P), or both. You can use almost any combination of switches in the same command.

To select a set of files based on a date, use the /D (date) switch. The switch in the form of */D:date* selects files whose directory date is the same or later than the specified *date*. The exact form of the *date* generally is *mm-dd-yy* for United States users, but may vary depending on the country code.

To select files based on the archive attribute, use the /A or /M switch. Either switch selects files whose archive bit is on (the file has been created or modified since the last program that turns off the archive switch was run). The difference is that the /M switch turns off the archive bit; /A does not reset the attribute. Use /M when the archive attribute should be turned off; for example, BACKUP /M or XCOPY /M should skip this file. Use /A when the bit should remain on; for instance, you want to back up this file with BACKUP or XCOPY /M or /A later.

To select files based on a file name, use the /P (prompt) switch. When you give the /P switch, XCOPY queries whether the file should be copied. Responding Y copies the file; pressing N skips the file. As expected, if you also use the /D switch, the program skips files whose date don't match the criteria.

You can use any combination of switches in the same XCOPY command (including /S, /E, and /W switches). You cannot, of course, use the nonsensical combination of /M and /A.

The four switches (/A, /M, /D, and /P) are useful when you want to copy selected files. The /A, /M, and /D switches are most useful as a mini-backup command, when only the more recent files or files not yet backed up should be copied. (See Chapter 10 on backup for more information.)

The /P switch is useful when you want to copy several files, when no single wild-card name picks the files you want to copy, and when only a few files need to be skipped with a given wild-card name. If you want to exclude many files, issuing separate COPY or XCOPY commands may be faster than using the /P switch. However, the combination of a /D, or a /D with an /M or /A switch might exclude enough files to make the /P switch faster.

7.35 Trick: Use ATTRIB and XCOPY when you must copy more files than one diskette can hold.

COPY and XCOPY are somewhat ungracious about full destination diskettes. Both programs abort when the destination diskette fills. If you don't have a super-COPY command such as PCOPY, Norm Patiquin's shareware copy program, you can work around this problem by using the archive attribute maintained for each file.

If you don't know whether you will fill a single destination diskette, determine the wild-card file name (or names) you must use with XCOPY. Running a super-DIR command such as SDADIR, which totals file sizes, helps.

If you will overflow the diskette, issue the following command:

> **ATTRIB +A** *filename*

In this command, *filename* is the exact source file name you will use with XCOPY. If you must issue more than one XCOPY command, issue one ATTRIB command for each name you will use. If you plan to use the /S switch, add it to the end of the ATTRIB command(s).

Now issue the appropriate XCOPY command with the /M switch. XCOPY starts copying files. When the destination diskette fills, XCOPY stops. Put a new diskette in the destination drive and issue the same command again. XCOPY skips those files that were copied (the reason for setting the archive attribute and using the /M switch). Repeat the exact command each time XCOPY stops and displays the full diskette message. When XCOPY ends without the message, you have the copies you want.

If you determine that you need to use another file name to copy the files, issue another XCOPY command with the next file name and continue using the /M switch. Repeat this process until you have copied all the files.

Note one flaw to this trick: You cannot copy a file that is larger than the destination diskette. Because COPY and XCOPY cannot handle this task, use BACKUP instead.

7.36   Tip: To copy files on a diskette-based system, use XCOPY /W.

XCOPY is an external command that must be loaded into memory. The command starts reading source files immediately when the command is issued. On a floppy disk-based system, this procedure can lead to an awkward situation. You must have a diskette with XCOPY in the drive to start the program. If the diskette with XCOPY is not in the source or destination diskette, you either must exchange diskettes quickly or use the /W switch.

The /W switch causes XCOPY to pause and prompt you for the diskette(s). Insert the correct diskette(s) and press any key to start the copying process. Using the /W switch is easier than changing a source or destination diskette quickly on a floppy-based system.

7.37   Tip: For speed and versatility, use a copy program such as PCOPY.

I have two quibbles with XCOPY. When you use the /P switch, XCOPY copies each file as soon as the Y response is received. In addition, XCOPY stops when it encounters a full destination diskette.

I prefer a program such as PCOPY, which caches all the responses and then starts copying the files. Using this program, you can select the files you want and then step back as PCOPY runs. Because PCOPY also handles full destination diskettes, you need to pay attention only when PCOPY needs another formatted diskette. You insert the diskette and press Enter; PCOPY continues.

Because PCOPY is more powerful and has many other selection capabilities, I use PCOPY more than XCOPY. PCOPY also can test a wild-card file name (show what files will be copied), traverse a subdirectory, copy files between certain files (based on where the file appears in the directory), and copy system and hidden files. Although you may not need to use the program often, PCOPY is indispensable for certain copying procedures.

PCOPY does not handle a file larger than the destination directory, but this limitation is not a problem. You can use BACKUP in that case.

Copying between Devices

7.38 Trick: Use COPY CON *filename* to capture text to a file quickly.

COPY is a general-purpose command. Unlike XCOPY, COPY can copy between any DOS device, including the console, the printer, and even the communications port. One of the novel uses of COPY is to capture keystrokes into a disk file. This technique is demonstrated several places in this book. The syntax for this quick file-creation procedure is **COPY CON *filename*,** where *filename* is a full file name (which can include a drive and path name).

When you use COPY CON, keep in mind the following tips:

- The only message comes at the end. You don't get any prompts.
- You can use any of the DOS editing keys while entering a line. Once you press Enter, however, the line cannot be recalled for editing.
- If you notice a mistake after entering a line, continue entering lines and later use a text editor on the errant line(s). An alternative method for correcting short files is to cancel the file creation by pressing Ctrl-Break or Ctrl-C and then starting over.
- When you finish typing the text for the file, press F6 or Ctrl-Z, and then press Enter. The message 1 file(s) copied appears.
- Press F6 at only the start of a line to end the entry of a file.

COPY CON is excellent for text files that have a few lines. You can enter almost any character into the file except Escape (which cancels the line), null (ASCII 0), Backspace (ASCII 8), Ctrl-Z (ASCII 26 or 1A hex), or Delete (ASCII 127 or 7F hex). If you need to enter these characters, use a text editor.

I don't recommend COPY CON for files that exceed 8 to 10 lines unless your typing is good. If you make a mistake and have to correct it with the text editor, the speed advantage offered by COPY CON is lost.

7.39 Trick: Add text to the end of a file by using COPY *filename* + CON *filename*.

Another trick performed with COPY CON is adding more lines to the end of a file. The syntax, which uses a plus sign (+) as the concatenation operator, is **COPY *filename* + CON *filename*,** where *filename* is the full name of the file to which text should be added.

After you press Enter, DOS copies the named file "in place" and allows you to enter more lines. The same rules and tricks that apply to COPY CON apply also to this procedure.

You receive two messages. COPY first displays the name of the copied file and then the name **CON** on the next line; this is your signal to enter lines. When you press F6 and Enter, you receive the message **2 file(s) copied**.

This trick is excellent for adding text to a previously established text file. Using this trick to add to a nontext file is dubious.

Caution: Do not reverse *filename* with **CON**. Typing
COPY CON + *filename filename* destroys the original *filename*.

7.40   Tip: Use COPY for printing ASCII text files quickly.

Because COPY accepts almost any device name, you can use COPY rather than invoke PRINT or a similar program to print a file on the printer. Use **COPY *filename printer***, where *filename* is the full name of the file and *printer* is the name of the DOS device to which the printer is attached. This technique is handy for printing short files or sending PostScript program files to the printer (something a Macintosh cannot do).

For the device name, you usually choose **PRN** (a synonym for LPT1). If your printer is connected to another device, such as LPT2 or LPT3, or COM1 through COM4, give this name instead. (If the printer is connected to a serial port, make sure that you use the appropriate MODE command, **MODE LPT1 = COMx**.)

Be judicious in what you print. Non-ASCII text may not appear on the printout or may drive your printer into a state of electronic babbling. Also, no form feeds are issued automatically at the end of a file or between files (when you use a wild-card file name). If you use concatenation, use the /B switch as in the following command:

COPY FILE1+FILE2 /B PRN

7.41   Trap: COPY COMx does not replace communication programs.

Although COPY can work between devices, using COPY to send a file through the communication port to another system is ill-advised. First, the traditional DOS services for handling communication is slow. Information is dropped into the bit-bucket if operating at even 1200 baud. Second, DOS does not do any communications protocols other than parity checking. The popular file transfer protocols, such as XMODEM, YMODEM, and KERMIT, are beyond DOS. If you need to communicate through the serial port to a modem, use a communication program.

Concatenating Files

7.42   Trap: If the source files are specified by a wild-card name and the destination is a nonexistent directory, the source files are concatenated into a destination file.

You may encounter problems if you issue a COPY command with a wild-card source file name and only a subdirectory name (with or without a disk drive name) for the destination. If the subdirectory exists, DOS copies the files to the subdirectory. For example, the command **COPY C:\BIN\FILES TEST** copies all files from the subdirectory C:\BIN\FILES to the subdirectory called TEST on the current disk and directory. The problem arises if TEST does not exist as a subdirectory of the current subdirectory and the current disk. In this case, DOS concatenates all source files into a single destination file. The result is a huge file called TEST in the current directory on the current disk that contains all the source files.

If you haven't deleted the source files, you can correct this error. Simply delete the concatenated file and reissue the COPY command with the correct destination directory name. The moral to this trap is to check that the files are copied successfully before deleting the source files.

7.43   Trap: For DOS V3.3, do not use wild-card names when concatenating files.

DOS V3.3 has a slippery random bug. If you use a wild-card source file name when concatenating files, random Ctrl-Zs are introduced into the destination file. Because Ctrl-Z is the end-of-file marker, you cannot use the resulting file with most DOS programs.

The bug is slippery because the Ctrl-Zs appear without a pattern. The number and size of the files have no apparent relationship to when or how many Ctrl-Zs will be introduced into the source file.

If you need to concatenate files with COPY, use nonwild-card names for each source file. This procedure works correctly.

7.44   Trap: If you concatenate files to a source file, you first must name the source file; otherwise, the source file is lost.

A concatenating operation that is fraught with pitfalls is summing files (appending other files to a preestablished file). Essentially, the destination file is one of the source files. Either you give no explicit destination file, or the named destination file is also a source file.

COPY looks at each source file name. If the source name matches the destination name, the program does not copy the file (because you are adding other files to this file). Before copying, COPY produces an error message that the contents are lost. If the destination file is the first source file, the message is incorrect. However, in all other cases, the message is correct, and the current contents of the file are lost before the copy is made.

This problem arises when you use wild cards in the source file name. COPY concatenates the matching files as it encounters the names in the directory. For example, consider the following listing:

```
LARGE.LST
LARGE.PRN
SCANNER.LST
SETTER.LST
TRANS.LST
XSET.PRN
```

Using the command **COPY *.LST + *.PRN ALL.LST** works (provided that the DOS V3.3 Ctrl-Z bug is not encountered). The command **COPY *.LST LARGE.LST** also works. The command **COPY *.LST + LARGE.PRN LARGE.PRN** destroys the previous contents of LARGE.PRN; the command **COPY *.LST SCANNER.LST** destroys the contents of SCANNER.LST before the process is complete.

If you are unsure, either use explicit file names and have the destination file as the first named file, or use a unique name for the destination file. Either procedure works.

7.45   Trick: Use a null character to prevent two lines from being joined when concatenating files.

When you concatenate files, the last line of one file and the first line of the next file may become one line because of the position of the end-of-file character. Note the following files:

FILEA.TXT	*FILEB.TXT*
FILEA LINE 1	FILEB LINE 1
FILEA LINE 2	FILEB LINE 2
FILEA LINE 3^Z	FILEB LINE 3
	^Z

Notice that the end-of-file character for FILEA.TXT follows the third line. The end-of-file character for FILEB.TXT, however, is on a line by itself. In this case, the end-of-file character follows a carriage return. When you concatenate the two files by typing **COPY FILEA.TXT+FILEB.TXT FILEC.TXT**, the resulting FILEC.TXT is as follows:

```
FILEA LINE 1
FILEA LINE 2
FILEA LINE 3FILEB LINE 1
FILEB LINE 2
FILEB LINE 3
^Z
```

If, however, you type **COPY FILEB.TXT+FILEA.TXT FILEC.TXT**, the resulting FILEC.TXT is as follows:

```
FILEB LINE 1
FILEB LINE 2
FILEB LINE 3
FILEA LINE 1
FILEA LINE 2
FILEA LINE 3^Z
```

To prevent the files from joining lines, insert a null character (^@). Press function key F7; ^@ appears on-screen. The following batch file illustrates the use of the null character:

```
ECHO  OFF
CLS
ECHO  ^@  >>  FILEA.TXT
COPY  FILEA.TXT+FILEB.TXT  FILEC.TXT
```

The resulting FILEC.TXT is as follows:

```
FILEA LINE 1
FILEA LINE 2
FILEA LINE 3
FILEB LINE 1
FILEB LINE 2
FILEB LINE 3
^Z
```

Renaming Files

7.46 Tip: When you rename a file, don't give a drive or path name with the new file name.

If you include a drive or path name in the new file name, RENAME delivers a syntax error. Keep in mind that DOS gets the drive and path name from the previous file name. Note: DOS pre-V3.2 ignored a drive or path in the new file name; DOS V3.2 and later gives an error message.

7.47 Trick: Use wild cards in the original name to designate what files to rename; use wild cards in the new name to designate what characters to keep.

When you use wild-card file names with RENAME, be aware that wild cards are different conceptually for the original and new name. For the original or source file name, wild cards select the files to rename. In the new (or destination) file name, wild cards form what characters to keep from the original name. The minor difference can be slightly confusing.

The command **RENAME *.TEX *.TXT**, for example, renames all files that have the extension .TEX. The file extensions are changed to .TXT; the root names stay the same. The command **RENAME CHAP??.TEX *.TXT** selects all files that start with CHAP, have up to two additional characters in the root name, and have an extension of .TEX. RENAME changes the extension of the selected files to .TXT. Note one difference between the two examples: any file with a .TEX extension is selected with the first command; only files starting with CHAP and having no more than two additional characters are selected in the second.

7.48 Trick: Use XCOPY /P to change garbled file names; use DEL /P or a super-erase program to delete files with garbled names.

When a file has a nonsense name, something has affected the directory holding the file. To repair the directory, usually the technique of choice is to use a disk-sector editor. This task is both tedious and fraught with hazards for the newcomer. You can affect some repairs, however, without a disk-sector editor.

If the FAT is intact and only the file names have been altered, you can restore the original names or delete now-useless files. The trick is in using a wild-card name and a query function. You generally give the file name

. with the query switch (/P), skip the files you do not want to affect, and then copy or delete the files with the garbled names.

To rename files by copying, use the form **XCOPY** *.* *file* **/P**, where *file* is the unambiguous new name. You can use about any name you want, including single letter names such as A or T. As XCOPY presents each file, answer N until XCOPY displays a file you cannot rename normally. Answer Y, let XCOPY copy the file to the new name, and then exit XCOPY immediately. Examine the file, determine whether the file is useful, and then change the new file name to the original file name. Afterward, use **DEL /P** or a different super-erase program to delete the original file.

Because you cannot have two files with the same unambiguous destination name, you can restore only one file at a time. Each time you copy a file, you must exit XCOPY. To restore another file, you must reinvoke XCOPY. Although the task can be somewhat tedious, it is fairly painless if you don't want to edit the directory itself.

Unless you know that a file contains nonsense, rename the file rather than delete it. You always can delete the file later. If you suspect that the disk has further damage, use XCOPY to copy all the files to another disk. (Copying files to the same damaged disk would cause further havoc with the new files.)

Replacing Files

7.49 Tip: When you update DOS or any major application program, use REPLACE to update and copy selective files.

REPLACE is helpful when updating DOS or any major application program, from dBASE to 1-2-3. Depending on the directory setup of the source and destination, one or two REPLACE commands can update and add all the required files. The syntax for the REPLACE command is given in table 7.4.

REPLACE is a super-COPY command that, almost effortlessly, can add new files to a single subdirectory or update all files in a subdirectory tree. REPLACE has two functions that differ from XCOPY. REPLACE's actions are governed basically by whether file names match on the source and destination; this feature is the basic strength of REPLACE. Also, REPLACE reads the source files from one subdirectory only, but can update (but not add) files to many subdirectories.

Table 7.4
REPLACE Syntax

Syntax

d:path**REPLACE** source_name destination_name /P /W /R /U /S /A

source_name is the drive, path, and file name
(**d:path\\filename.ext**) of the source files. Wild cards are allowed,
and only the root name is mandatory.

destination name is the drive and path name (**d:path**) of the target.
The drive name is mandatory, and a file name is not allowed.

Switches

/P   *Prompts* (queries) whether each file on the destination should
be updated (when the /A switch is not given), or whether each
nonmatching file from the source should be added (when the /A
switch is given).

/W   *Waits* for a keystroke before starting, allowing a diskette change
before the file names are read.

/R   Updates matching files on the target that are marked *read-only*.

/S   Searches all subsequent *subdirectories* on the target for matching
files to update.

/U   *Updates* matching files on the target that have an earlier date
and time than the source files.

/A   *Adds* files from the source that do not match files on the
destination. (This switch cannot be used with the /S or /U
switches.)

REPLACE operates by first accumulating the names of the files in the
source directory that match the given source file name. Then REPLACE
reads the names of the files in the target directory and performs a literal
file-name-by-file-name comparison. When updating files (without using
the /A switch), REPLACE copies from the source to the destination all files
that have matching names. When adding files (using the /A switch),
REPLACE copies from the source to the destination all files that do not
have matching names.

The /S switch tells REPLACE to sweep through all subdirectories on the
destination disk only, not the source disk, and to hunt and replace all files
that match the source files. The /S switch is useful if all files to be replaced

are in a single directory tree, and most useful if all source files are in a single subdirectory.

If the source and destination files are properly organized, you can update a major application by running REPLACE twice. You give the REPLACE command without the /A switch to update existing files in the target directory. If the "replaceable" files are in one subdirectory chain, use the /S switch to hunt and update all matching files. After the older files are replaced, repeat the REPLACE command with the /A switch to add new files to the target directory. By reading only one source subdirectory per run, you usually will run REPLACE twice for each source subdirectory—once to update existing files and once to add new files.

REPLACE offers two additional controls to restrict the files for updating or adding files: /P and /U. The /P switch works when updating or adding files and tells REPLACE to query whether a file should be updated or added. You respond by pressing Y (Yes) or N (No). This switch gives you selective control over the update/addition operation and is useful when you need to preserve some of the existing files or when you do not want all new files to be placed in one directory.

The /U switch works only when updating files. This switch forces REPLACE to update only those files on the target that have an older file date and time than the matching files on the source. Use the /U switch when only out-of-date files should be updated.

The /U switch is more similar to BACKUP's date-time switches than to XCOPY's /D switch. REPLACE works with the file's date *and* time, and is similar to using BACKUP's /D and /T switches together. XCOPY's /D switch works with the file's date only.

When updating files marked read-only on the target, use the /R switch. This switch forces REPLACE to overwrite read-only files. However, REPLACE does not preserve the read-only attribute on the new file. If the updated file should be marked read-only, you must set the read-only attribute manually.

REPLACE's /W switch is identical to XCOPY's /W switch. /W tells REPLACE to wait for a key press before reading the source file names. Use this switch if the files you are updating or adding are on a floppy diskette.

A powerful and versatile command, REPLACE performs some functions that COPY and XCOPY cannot. However, REPLACE is not always the appropriate or best command to use. The traps that follow explain why.

7.50   Trap: REPLACE is not useful for installing all programs.

REPLACE does not find hidden or system files in the source directory, nor replace these files on the target disk. If you are installing a program that has any hidden or system files in either location, REPLACE will not work fully. For example, you can use REPLACE to update DOS, but not to copy the system files. You still must run SYS manually to make a bootable DOS disk.

In cases where the application provides an installation program or batch file, use it instead of REPLACE. The installer may perform tests, configure the program file or start-up files, copy only required files, or distribute files into certain subdirectories. REPLACE cannot replicate the work performed by *all* installation programs or batch files.

If you are knowledgeable about the installation procedure, you may be able to replicate it with REPLACE. Because most installation programs and batch files have the required sophistication to install the application in the subdirectories you want, however, you may not need to install the program manually. You need to perform the same steps manually only if the installer does not work.

7.51   Tip: Consider using other commands with, or instead of, REPLACE.

REPLACE is not always the most convenient command to use. REPLACE processes only one source directory at a time. If the source files are in several subdirectories or on several diskettes, you must run REPLACE once to update files from each source subdirectory and once to add files from each source subdirectory. You also multiply the number of REPLACE runs needed if the source files are in different subdirectory chains. If the source files must be added to several different subdirectories, you further increase the runs of REPLACE.

COPY, XCOPY, and a move utility may work faster than using REPLACE, or using REPLACE exclusively. Instead of using REPLACE only, you may find that a faster approach (depending on the setup of the source and destination) is to copy all the files via REPLACE, COPY, or XCOPY from the source to a single destination subdirectory, then distribute the files among the various destination directories using COPY or a move utility. Generally, if the updated or added files should be placed into different subdirectory trees, using COPY or XCOPY and then moving the files is faster.

7.52 Trap: Be cautious when you use REPLACE /S or you may lose an unrelated file.

The first lesson I learned when using REPLACE is don't unleash REPLACE on an entire disk. I used REPLACE to update DOS V3.1 to V3.2. My DOS program files were in one subdirectory off the root; the device driver files were in a different subdirectory off the root. I used the command **REPLACE A:*.* C:\ /S**. REPLACE did exactly as I requested: it replaced all the DOS files on the entire hard disk.

I had a program called SORT.EXE in a subdirectory segregated from the DOS files. This SORT.EXE could handle comma-delimited files, exclude or include records, and perform its function much better than the DOS-provided program. REPLACE overwrote this file with the pale DOS SORT.EXE.

REPLACE chooses files for updating based on the root and extension name only, not the file's contents. If unrelated files have matching names on the source and destination, the existing file on the destination is overwritten. Without a backup copy, the file is lost.

When you use REPLACE /S, use the most restrictive source path name as possible. If you are unsure whether unrelated files can be replaced, use a super-DIR command to list all files in the potential subdirectories and compare this list against the source files. Alternatively, use the /P switch and don't update any files of which you are unsure. After you have checked the files, run REPLACE /U /P again.

8

Creating and Using Batch Files

A *batch file* is file of readable text that contains a series of DOS or batch commands. Batch files, which have an extension of .BAT, are stored in a subdirectory on your PATH and executed from the DOS prompt when you type the root name of the file.

Understanding and using batch files can speed and ease many tedious computer tasks. This chapter, which discusses the basics of batch file construction and use, contains tips, tricks, and traps on using the special batch subcommands and on making batch file execution even faster and more convenient.

Batch File Basics

A batch file provides a shortcut for executing one or many DOS commands. When you type just the name of a batch file, the file executes each line as if you had entered the line from the keyboard.

Batch files are extremely convenient and useful tools that can automate long or repetitive instructions. The chance of mistyping a command is reduced, and long tasks can be started and left unattended. This section covers the basics of batch file construction and use.

Using Batch Files To Execute Commands

8.1 Tip: Use batch files for "quick-and-dirty" projects.

Often you have a choice between using a program to do a task or using a batch file. Given the choice, use a batch file for one-shot work or for short work. Use a program when DOS does not provide a good solution or when speed is essential.

Moving a file (copying a file, and then erasing it) is one instance when batch files do not work best. For example, a batch file that copies and then erases a file would look like the following:

COPY %1 %2

DEL %1

This batch file copies the files designated by %1 to whatever is specified by %2. Although this batch file is quick, it is far from ideal for checking bugs and errors. If anything goes wrong, the DEL %1 command is still executed and the files are deleted. Following are two possible solutions to this problem:

COPY %1 %2

IF EXIST %2\%1 DEL %1

and

COPY %1 %2

IF EXIST %2 DEL %1

The first solution works only if the second parameter is a subdirectory name. The second solution works only if a full file specification is given both times—for example, when you are copying the file and when you are renaming the copy, as in the following statement:

COPY MYFILE.TXT \WORDS\NEWFILE.TXT

No single batch file can perform this sequential task, and using the wrong batch file could even erase files. The solution is to use a program that moves files. (Another reason for using a program is that DOS can move a file's directory entry internally without moving the file. Only a program can access this DOS system function.)

When speed is important, programs execute faster than batch files. Que's book *Managing Your Hard Disk*, 2nd Edition, shows a complete menu system that includes batch files and one outside program (ANSWER.COM, which is used to get input from the keyboard). The system is an excellent example of batch file construction. But given the difference between a batch file menu system and the visual shell of DOS V4, the batch system looks pale. The batch file approach is too fragile and too slow. More information on running programs from batch files is found in Chapter 9, "Using Advanced Batch File Techniques."

Placing Batch Files on a RAM Disk

8.2   Trick: To speed the performance of batch files, put frequently used batch files on a RAM disk.

DOS reads batch files one line at a time. The process is slow. To speed the performance of batch files, you need to decrease the time DOS spends reading the file. Do this by placing frequently used batch files on a RAM disk, which reads much faster than a hard disk or floppy disk.

You can make the procedure even faster by including the drive and path name of the RAM disk in your PATH command. You can then run the batch file without giving a drive or directory name.

Using Subcommands within Batch Files

You can use any valid DOS command in a batch file. DOS also provides a handful of special commands for dealing with batch files: the batch subcommands. The batch file subcommands and their functions are listed in table 8.1.

Table 8.1
Batch File Subcommands

Command	Function
@	Suppresses the display of a line on-screen (DOS V3.3 and later)
CALL	Invokes one batch file from another and then returns to the original batch file (DOS V3.3 and later)
ECHO	Used with redirection to create batch files, data files, and programs, or to add lines to such files; used with piping to send commands directly to BASIC and other utilities; turns on and off the display of batch commands and displays a message on-screen

Command	Function
FOR..IN..DO	Instructs DOS to repeat the same command many times with different data
GOTO	Bypasses parts of a batch file by jumping to the line after the label; creates "loops" within a batch file
IF	Tests conditions in batch files; enables conditional execution of a command
PAUSE	Halts processing until a key is pressed; optionally displays a message
REM	A remark statement inside the batch file; DOS displays the comment or remark but does not execute the remark
SHIFT	Processes a list of operands in succession; shifts the command line parameters one parameter to the left

This section focuses on these commands, which form the foundation of a thorough understanding of batch file techniques.

Using SHIFT and Loops

8.3 Tip: SHIFT gives you access to more than nine replaceable parameters and provides looping features with parameters.

The heart of one type of looping structure in batch files is the SHIFT instruction, which shifts all parameters forward. The value of %2 thus becomes that of %1; %3 becomes %2, and so on. If more than 9 parameters exist, the excess parameters are not available until shifted into the range of %1 through %9.

The 10th parameter cannot be referenced in the batch file because the expression %10 is not recognized; %10 is interpreted as %1 followed by the digit 0. For example, if %1 is EXE, %15 is interpreted as EXE5. If %1 is HERE, %10 is interpreted as HEREO. After SHIFT, however, the tenth parameter becomes the 9th and can be referenced as %9; similarly, the original 11th parameter becomes %9 after a second SHIFT, and so on.

Although SHIFT's capability to deal with more than nine parameters is important, the real advantage is that you can use SHIFT to process any number of parameters (less than nine or more than nine) in a batch file by using a loop. Each repetition of the loop processes the next parameter.

In many cases, the number of parameters varies each time the batch file is invoked. You use SHIFT when you must perform an operation on a series of arguments, one after another; the same processing thus applies to every parameter.

8.4 Trick: Use a loop for repetitive processing.

If you often copy files from your hard disk to a diskette, but you copy different files each time, you can use a batch file similar to the following, CTD.BAT (copy to diskette):

```
ECHO OFF
CLS
:LOOP
COPY %1 A:
SHIFT
IF NOT %1.==. GOTO LOOP
```

To execute the batch file, you type the following:

CTD MASM.EXE LINK.EXE SCREEN.ASM

Because %1 is the value of MASM.EXE (at the outset), the COPY command on its first execution becomes the following:

`COPY MASM.EXE A:`

The command copies MASM.EXE to drive A:. SHIFT then causes LINK.EXE to become %1 (and SCREEN.ASM %2). IF tells DOS to go back to :LOOP. %1 still has a value (it is now LINK.EXE).

COPY is executed again and becomes the following:

`COPY LINK.EXE A:`

This command copies the second file. SHIFT is again executed, and %1 becomes SCREEN.ASM. GOTO returns to :LOOP, and the last file is copied. SHIFT is then executed a third time, causing %1 to have no value (the value of %1 should be that of the original fourth parameter, which does not exist.) IF next tests whether %1 has a value. Because that condition fails, GOTO is not performed, and DOS proceeds to the next line, which is the end of the batch file.

With this batch file, you can type **CTD** followed by any number of file names (even more than nine); all will be copied. Note that %1 is the only parameter reference used; every parameter becomes %1 when its turn comes. The action of the batch file does not depend on the number of parameters.

You can use this technique with individual file names and with wild-card characters. For example, consider the following command:

CTD *.TXT LETTER.DOC FILE*.LET

The command copies all files with a .TXT extension, the file LETTER.DOC, and all files that include FILE in the root and .LET as the extension to drive A:.

8.5   Trick: Use a loop and SHIFT when the number of replaceable parameters in a batch file may vary.

You can construct a batch file that uses one replaceable parameter. The following batch file, MOVE.BAT, is an example:

```
ECHO OFF
CLS
IF %1. == . GOTO END
IF %2. == . GOTO END
IF NOT EXIST %1 GOTO END
COPY %1 %2
DEL %1
:END
```

MOVE.BAT works well with one file or a group of files (when a wild-card character is used in the file name). For example, the command **MOVE *.TXT A:** copies all files with a .TXT extension to drive A: and then deletes the source files that have the .TXT extension. To copy all .TXT files to drive A: and all .DOC files to C:\DATA\DOCU, however, you must run the batch file twice. Instead, you can use the following revised batch file, which uses SHIFT to provide more than the fixed number of parameters.

```
ECHO OFF
CLS
:LOOP
IF %1. == . GOTO END
IF %2. == . GOTO END
IF NOT EXIST %1 GOTO END
COPY %1 %2
DEL %1
SHIFT
SHIFT
```

GOTO LOOP

:END

With this revision, you can type the following command:

MOVE *.TXT A: *.DOC C:\DATA\DOCU

You execute the batch file only once, but in effect, the batch file runs twice because of the loop.

Remember that this batch file can delete the source file even if the file is not copied successfully.

Using the ECHO and REM Subcommands

8.6 Trick: Use ECHO to show comments on-screen; use REM for batch file comments to yourself.

ECHO "echoes" a line by displaying on-screen the comment after ECHO. REM shows remarks. If ECHO OFF is given in the batch file, however, all REM statements are not displayed.

The common technique is to use @ECHO OFF as the first line of the batch file, and then use ECHO statements for on-screen prompts or messages. Because REMs are suppressed when ECHO is off, you can use REM for comments to yourself on how your batch file works. If the batch file is complicated, the REM statements will be excellent guideposts if you need to change the batch file weeks or months later.

8.7 Trick: Use @CTTY NUL to quiet a batch file completely.

ECHO OFF turns off the display of lines that execute in the batch file. The **> NUL** redirection quiets a program's output by redirecting it to the NUL device. Error messages written to the standard error device (the video display), however, are displayed.

You can use the CTTY command to silence completely any part of or the entire batch file. Inserting the command **@CTTY NUL** informs DOS to use the NUL device as the system console. All output, including error messages, is sent to the "bit bucket."

To restore the system to its normal state (to restore the CON device to the keyboard and video display), use the command **@CTTY CON** before your batch file terminates. If you do not, you cannot type commands, and you need to restart DOS in order to regain control of the computer.

Keep in mind that this trick redirects all output from the program executed in the batch file. Any error messages are lost. The trick also inhibits input from the keyboard. You cannot use CTTY NUL during the sections of the batch file that require user intervention. You can use CTTY NUL and CTTY CON several times in the batch file, but the console cannot be changed when error messages must be seen or some ASK-type program is needed.

8.8 Tip: The replaceable command line parameter (%0 through %9) can be used with ECHO and REM statements.

You can use any of the 10 replaceable parameters in your ECHO or REM lines. For example, one such use is with error messages, as in the following message:

ECHO %0: I cannot find the file %1!

This line echoes the name used to invoke the batch file for %0 (which includes a drive and path name, if given) and the name of the expected file, %1. Such messages are used to point out problems and to suggest corrective actions. You are not left in the dark about why the batch file failed.

8.9 Trick: You can put text into an ASCII file by using the ECHO command.

You can use either of the following commands to put text into an ASCII file:

ECHO *message* > *filename*

or

ECHO *message* >> *filename*

This trick is most useful when you are building batch files from within batch files. More information on using the redirection symbols in an ECHO statement to put text into a file is found in Chapter 9.

8.10 Trick: You can use EDLIN or certain other text editors to give ANSI.SYS commands in batch files with ECHO.

One of the problems with ANSI.SYS and DOS is that each ANSI command starts with the Escape character (1b hexadecimal or 27 decimal.) Unfortunately, DOS immediately interprets the Escape as a cancel-line sequence. You cannot type an Escape character directly into a text file using the COPY CON technique or indirectly using the Alt-keypad number technique. Holding down the Alt key and pressing 2 and then 7 on the keypad generates an Escape character. DOS snags the character before it gets into the file.

To get around this problem, use a text editor (such as BRIEF™ or EDLIN) or a word processor (such as WordStar) in the nondocument or programmer's mode. Both techniques enable you to enter the Escape character when you create the batch file. You can then create an ECHO statement such as the following, which changes screen colors:

ECHO ^[[34;43m

By saving this line in a batch file, you can execute the batch file. With EDLIN, the key combination Ctrl-V followed by the character [creates an Escape character. In WordStar, you enter Ctrl-P and then press the Esc key. As the batch file executes, the escape sequence is echoed to the screen and intercepted by ANSI. The screen colors are then changed. See Chapter 13, "Customizing the Video Screen and Keyboard," for more information on ANSI.SYS.

8.11 Trick: Use the command ECHO Y | DEL *.* to prevent DOS from confirming that you want to delete all files in a directory.

ECHO can be used to pass any string to another command. The form **ECHO Y** sends to standard output a **Y** (for Yes) followed by a carriage return. By piping the output to DEL, the prompt Are you sure is answered immediately.

This trick should be used with extreme care. When I showed this trick to a friend, I managed to unleash the DEL command on the wrong directory. Having the right unerase program made the recovery a one-minute task. The caution applies whether or not you have an unerase program handy.

Using the IF Subcommand

8.12 Tip: Use two equal signs with the batch file IF subcommand for string comparisons.

This is more a reminder than a tip. The batch IF is not a BASIC IF. BASIC uses one equal sign for an equality test.

8.13 Trap: The only ELSE to an IF subcommand is the next line in the batch file.

The batch IF subcommand is like BASIC's IF...THEN. If the test is true, the batch file executes the rest of the line. If the test is not true, the file ignores the line and proceeds to the next. The only ELSE to the command is the drop to the next line.

8.14   Trap: Avoid empty parameters when using IF.

When you write a batch file, avoid empty parameters. Consider the following batch file, TEST.BAT:

ECHO OFF

CLS

IF %1 == TEST ECHO The batch file worked.

If you type **TEST TEST** and press Enter, the following line is echoed to the screen:

```
The batch file worked.
```

Because TEST was the parameter, the batch file interprets the line as follows:

```
IF TEST == TEST ECHO The batch file worked.
```

If you type **TEST QUE**, nothing is echoed to the screen; the batch file instead interprets the command as follows:

```
IF QUE == TEST ECHO The batch file worked.
```

If you type only **TEST** and press Enter, the batch file interprets the command as the following:

```
IF == TEST ECHO The batch file worked.
```

You receive a **SYNTAX ERROR** message; nothing is echoed on-screen.

You will have fewer problems if you rephrase the IF test to the following:

IF TEST == %1 ECHO The batch file worked.

Even though no parameter is typed, there is a null-string right before ECHO. A *null-string* is a character whose value is nothing. The test is invalid, but an error may not occur.

To completely avoid the invalid test, simply add a character to each side of the equation. For example, consider the following modified batch file:

ECHO OFF

CLS

IF TEST. == %1. ECHO The batch file worked.

Notice the addition of a period after TEST and after %1. If you now type **TEST TEST** and press Enter, the batch file interprets the line as follows:

```
IF TEST. == TEST. ECHO The batch file worked.
```

The phrase is echoed. If you omit the parameter, the batch file interprets the line as follows:

```
IF TEST. == . ECHO The batch file worked.
```

Nothing is echoed to the screen; no error is reported. It is good practice to always add the period to both sides of the equation to prevent errors.

8.15   Tip: Test for the opposite of a condition and use GOTO if the test is true.

You may find it easier to test for the opposite condition and use GOTO if the test is true. A hypothetical example might be to test for the first command line parameter that is equal to "A." The test could be written in a batch file as follows:

IF %1 == A GOTO PASSED
<statements to handle a failed test>
GOTO END
:PASSED
<statements to handle a successful test>
:END

The opposite way might be to jump if the opposite condition is true, as in the following batch file:

IF NOT %1 == A GOTO FAILED
<statements to handle %1 == A>
GOTO END
:FAILED
<statements to handle %1 <> A>
:END

8.16   Tip: Check for empty parameters in the first part of the batch file.

Based on the last two tips, the "up-front" testing for empty parameters is apparent. If your batch file depends on a parameter, test for the parameter in the first few lines of the batch file. If the test shows an empty parameter, give an error message and jump to the end. When a mistake is made, you avoid the delay as DOS executes nonessential lines from the batch file.

The two possible constructions to use are an IF NOT test to jump around the error message or an IF test to jump to the error handling lines. My preference is the IF NOT technique as shown in this file:

```
@ECHO OFF
IF NOT %1. == . GOTO GOOD:
ECHO %0: You did not give a file name to copy.
ECHO    Please try again.
GOTO END
:GOOD
<remaining statements for the batch file>
:END
```

8.17 Trick: Although DOS does not test directories directly, you can trick DOS by using an IF EXIST sequence.

IF EXIST works with files, not drives or subdirectories. You can, however, test to see whether a subdirectory exists with the following sequence:

```
IF EXIST %1\A GOTO EXIST
ECHO TEST >%1\A
IF EXIST %1\A GOTO EXIST2
ECHO Sorry, the directory %1 does not exist
GOTO DONE
:EXIST2
DEL %1\A
:EXIST
ECHO The directory %1 does exist
:DONE
```

This batch file fragment tests for a subdirectory by trying to create a file in the %1 subdirectory. If the subdirectory does not exist, a file cannot be created by the ECHO command.

The trickery of testing for the presence of a subdirectory is in the first three lines. If a file named **A** exists in the named subdirectory (the first command line parameter), the batch file immediately jumps to the EXIST label. If the file does not exist (single letter file names are rare), the batch file attempts to create the file in the named subdirectory. If the creation is successful, the third line jumps to the EXIST2 label, where the file is deleted. Because the file at this point does not exist, the test in the third line falls through to the error message and jumps to the end.

8.18   Trap: You cannot use IF ERRORLEVEL with any DOS internal commands.

An annoying aspect of DOS is that DOS does not set an exit code (ERRORLEVEL) when any of its internal commands are used. This means that you cannot test for successful or unsuccessful completion of commands such as COPY, DATE, TIME, and MKDIR. If such a command is built into COMMAND.COM, IF ERRORLEVEL is worthless.

8.19   Tip: Test for ERRORLEVEL from the highest number to the lowest.

One of the traps of IF ERRORLEVEL is that ERRORLEVEL matches an exit code equal to or greater than the specified ERRORLEVEL. For example, the statement **IF ERRORLEVEL 1** is true if the exit code is 1 or more. The statement **IF ERRORLEVEL 0** is always true if the program produces an exit code.

To check for multiple exit codes, test the numbers in order from the highest to the lowest. For example, to test for the powers of 2 for an exit code, the technique is as follows:

```
IF ERRORLEVEL 128 GOTO 128
IF ERRORLEVEL 64 GOTO 64
IF ERRORLEVEL 32 GOTO 32
IF ERRORLEVEL 16 GOTO 16
IF ERRORLEVEL 8 GOTO 8
IF ERRORLEVEL 4 GOTO 4
IF ERRORLEVEL 2 GOTO 2
IF ERRORLEVEL 1 GOTO 1
GOTO 0
:128
<handler for 128>
GOTO END
:64
<handler for 64>
GOTO END
:32
<rest of handlers for 32 to 0>
:END
```

Watch out if you reverse the order. The statement **IF ERRORLEVEL 1** would match 1, 2, 4, 8, . . . 128. In other words, the statement matches all values but 0.

Using the FOR..IN..DO Subcommand

8.20 Trick: To use wild-card file names with DOS commands that do not recognize wild cards, use FOR..IN..DO.

For DOS commands that do not expand wild-card file names, use FOR..IN..DO. For example, you can use the following batch file, TYPER.BAT, to TYPE more than one file:

FOR %%d IN (%1 %2 %3 %4 %5) DO TYPE %%d

You execute this batch file by giving the name **TYPER** and the wild-card name of the files you want to type, such as **TYPER *.TXT** or **TYPER *.TXT *.ASM**.

8.21 Trick: Instead of writing a batch file, use FOR..IN..DO at the command line.

FOR..IN..DO is one of a few batch commands that can be used meaningfully at the command line. When you use the command at the command line, however, use a single percent sign for the replaceable parameter, not two (as you do in a batch file). For example, you can issue a command that does the same work as TYPER.BAT by entering the following at the command line:

FOR %d IN (*.TXT) DO TYPE %d

Only the number of percent signs changes; no other part of the command changes. Notice in particular that you still need both the parentheses around the argument list and the word DO.

8.22 Trick: Use FOR..IN..DO to execute multiple commands.

This technique saves time and is more useful at the command line than within a batch file. Put the single word commands for your batch file into a single FOR..IN..DO line. The extra speed comes because DOS does not reread the batch file each time.

Consider, for example, the following batch file:

CLS
C:
CD
DATE
TIME
\DOS\CHKDSK
VER

Using FOR..IN..DO, you can rewrite these commands in a single statement, as follows:

> **FOR %%d IN (CLS C: CD\ DATE TIME \DOS\CHKDSK VER) DO %%d**

Another alternative is to execute a similar statement from the command line:

> **FOR %d IN (CLS C: CD\ DATE TIME \DOS\CHKDSK VER) DO %d**

This bit of trickery is not always practical within a batch file. You cannot, for example, execute a FOR..IN..DO command if the parameters must be separated from the command by a delimiter, such as a space or a comma. For example, **DEL *.BAK** does not work; DOS views DEL and *.BAK as separate words and attempts to execute DEL and then *.BAK. **CD** works, but **CDD:** (for **CD D:**) does not. If the starting character of a path is the backslash, a space is not necessary between the internal DOS command and the path. If the leading character is not a backslash, a space is needed and the command cannot be used.

8.23 Tip: You can use any typeable string with FOR..IN..DO.

Don't limit the argument list given to FOR..IN..DO to file names. Any typeable string can be used. For example, to check whether %1 is a valid floppy disk name, you can use the following construction:

> **FOR %%d IN (A: a: B: b:) DO IF %1 == %%d GOTO OKAY**
> **GOTO BADDRIVE**

In this example, FOR..IN..DO processes the first parameter (%1) against each word in the argument list, which is made up of floppy disk drive names. If an argument matches, the file jumps to the OKAY label. If none of the arguments from the list matches, the batch file jumps to the BADDRIVE label.

8.24 Trick: Use IF and FOR..IN..DO to search two directories for duplicate files.

You can create a batch file that produces a list of files with duplicate names. There are two restrictions:

- Your current directory must be one of the two directories to be compared.
- You must give the name of the second directory to be compared.

The following batch file, DUPS.BAT, produces a list of files with duplicate names.

@ECHO OFF
FOR %%d IN (*.*) DO IF EXIST %1\\%%d ECHO %%d

You enter the command **DUPS**; the list of duplicate files appears on-screen.

8.25   Trap: FOR..IN..DO is the only subcommand that cannot be nested.

You cannot use two FOR..IN..DO subcommands on the same line. Nor can you use two DOS commands on the same batch file line. As shown by the examples, you can use more than one batch file subcommand on a line, such as IF..GOTO, FOR..IN..DO..IF..GOTO, or even FOR..IN..DO..IF..IF..GOTO. There are few uses for multiple IF statements, and using any other subcommand ends the batch file line's execution. However, the possibilities exist.

Using the GOTO Subcommand

8.26   Tip: If you get a Label not found message, check to see that the target line starts with a colon.

A frequent mistake made with labels is omitting the colon at the start of the line intended for the GOTO jump statement. You may forget the colon or put the colon at the end of the label. The first time you run the batch file, DOS gives a Label not found error message and halts the batch file. Although you can use a text editor to correct the problem by inserting a colon at the beginning of the label line, remembering to put the colon on the label line when you create the line is easier.

8.27   Tip: DOS uses only the first eight characters in a label name.

Although labels can be any length, remember that DOS uses only the first eight characters. START_DOS and START_DISK are different labels; START_DOS and START_DOSDISK are not. The comparison stops at the O of DOS. If you use both in a batch file, the first of the two labels always will be executed.

Using the CALL Subcommand and COMMAND/C

8.28   Trick: If you use a DOS version earlier than V3.3, you can approximate the CALL subcommand with COMMAND /C.

DOS versions before V3.3 do not contain a command that performs a GOSUB to another batch file. Under these versions of DOS, batch file execution is one-way, from the first batch file to the second. The second batch file does not return to the first.

With the CALL subcommand of DOS V3.3 and later versions, you can make a batch file run another batch file and then return control to the first batch file. You can approximate the same function by using COMMAND /C. The /C string switch tells COMMAND to run the information in the string as if it were typed from the keyboard. After executing the string, COMMAND exits and returns control to the program or batch file that invoked COMMAND.

If you use DOS V3.3 or later to call BATCH2.BAT from BATCH1.BAT, the sequence is as follows:

CALL BATCH2

For DOS V3.2 and earlier, the sequence is as follows:

COMMAND /C BATCH2

9

Using Advanced Batch File Techniques

This chapter explores advanced batch file techniques. The tips, tricks, and traps are designed to help you utilize the more powerful batch file commands. You learn techniques of redirection and methods for using the environment. Ways to run programs from batch files and the use of the AUTOEXEC.BAT file are also explored.

Redirecting Input and Output

You use the redirection (>) or the redirection/append (>>) symbols to create or add to a file. The redirection symbol is used to send what normally goes to the screen to a file of a given name. For example, the command **DIR > DIRLIST.TXT** sends the contents of the current directory to a file called **DIRLIST.TXT**. The command creates the file **DIRLIST.TXT** if it does not exist. If the file exists, it is replaced with the new file.

You can also assemble a file that contains listings of more than one directory. You first use the single redirection symbol, followed by the double-redirection symbol. The double-redirection symbol adds to an existing file. The following sequence redirects, then appends:

DIR > DIRLIST.TXT
DIR \DOS >> DIRLIST.TXT
DIR \WP >> DIRLIST.TXT

The first line creates a file called **DIRLIST.TXT**, which contains a list of files in the current directory. The second and third lines add to the file **DIRLIST.TXT**. Each line adds the list of files from the **\DOS** and **\WP** directories, respectively.

The tips, tricks, and traps in this section cover ways to use these redirection techniques with and within batch files.

Using Redirection To Modify Batch Files

9.1 Trick: You can easily add to a batch file by using ECHO and redirection.

The ECHO command is intended to display messages from a batch file by sending to the screen the character string that follows the ECHO command, excluding the space that separates the string from the command. For example, consider the following command:

ECHO Hello, World!

The command displays the message **Hello, World!** on-screen.

If an ECHO command contains the redirection symbol > on the command line after the string, the string is sent to a file by the given name. With the double-redirection symbol >>, the string can be appended to a file.

To add a command to a batch file, you normally must use some type of text editor to modify the batch file. However, you can append a command to a file.

The following batch file is called COPYMORE.BAT:

```
ECHO OFF
CLS
FOR %%f IN (%1 %2 %3 %4) DO COPY %%f A:
```

To add to COPYMORE.BAT one line that deletes the files that are copied, you enter the following command:

ECHO FOR %%f IN (%1 %2 %3 %4) DO DEL %%f >> COPYMORE.BAT

COPYMORE.BAT now consists of four lines. The batch file was modified easily, and you did not need a text editor for the process.

9.2 Trap: You cannot double redirect a statement.

You can use redirection to send a directory listing to a file by typing the following command:

DIR >FILES.LOG

You cannot, however, redirect a statement made with ECHO to a file. For example, consider the next command:

ECHO DIR >FILES.LOG >TEMP.BAT

The command redirects DIR to a file, FILES.LOG. In fact, >TEMP.BAT is completely ignored. You cannot use two of the same redirection symbols in the same file.

You must use the pipe characters carefully, as well. The following command uses the pipe character correctly:

DIR | SORT > DIRSORT.TXT

You cannot, however, create a batch file by typing the following command because the pipe character intercedes:

ECHO DIR | SORT > DIRSORT.BAT

Using Redirection within Batch Files

9.3   Tip: You may use IF testing in a batch file to determine which type of redirection to use.

To keep track of changes in files in a particular subdirectory or on a certain diskette, you can use redirection. The following command redirects the output of the directory command from the screen to the file DIRLIST.TXT:

DIR > DIRLIST.TXT

You may, however, prefer to use a batch file such as the following, LIST.BAT, to accomplish the same thing:

```
ECHO OFF
CLS
IF %1. == y. GOTO NEWLIST
IF %1. == Y. GOTO NEWLIST
DIR >> DIRLIST.TXT
GOTO END
:NEWLIST
DIR > DIRLIST.TXT
ECHO NEW LIST CREATED.
:END
```

If you type **LIST** to start the batch file but do not give a parameter, one of two things happens. If **DIRLIST.TXT** does not exist in the current directory, it is created. If **DIRLIST.TXT** does exist, the current directory is appended to the end of the file. As you continue to work on the file, you can refer back to the stages of the file in the directory.

If you type **LIST** to start the batch file and include **y** or **Y** as the parameter, a new file named DIRLIST.TXT is created, possibly overwriting a previous DIRLIST.TXT file. This can be handy if you want to track a new set of files in the current directory.

You can also use this principle with other batch files in order to regulate the use of the redirection symbols > and >>.

9.4   Trap: Don't bother redirecting the input or output of a batch file.

You cannot redirect the input or output of an entire batch file. You must redirect the input or output of each line of a batch file. For example, the command **TYPER > MYFILE** does not work. You must add the > MYFILE to the FOR..IN..DO line to make redirection work. (See Chapter 8 for the complete text of TYPER.BAT.)

9.5   Trap: You cannot use the %%d argument of FOR..IN..DO with input redirection.

The %%d argument does not work because DOS processes the I/O redirection before replacing the arguments in the FOR..IN..DO. For example, a MORER.BAT file that followed the same structure of TYPER.BAT (discussed in the preceding trap) does not work.

Consider another example:

FOR %%d IN (%1 %2 %3 %4 %5) DO MORE < %%d

This batch file tells MORE to get its input from a file called **%d**, which is not what is intended.

The solution is to use two batch files: one file to expand names and call the second file, and a second file to hold the command line parameter that does the work. The batch files might look like the following:

MORER.BAT
FOR %%d IN (%1 %2 %3 %4 %5) DO CALL MORER2 %%d

and

MORER2.BAT
MORE < %1

This solution is not elegant, but it works. If you have a version of DOS before V3.3, use **COMMAND /C** in place of the word **CALL**.

9.6   Trap: Use >> rather than > when redirecting output with FOR..IN..DO.

There is a subtle difference in the use of >> and > because redirection is run with each iteration for the FOR..IN..DO command, not after all iterations. Consider the following command:

FOR %%d IN (*.TXT) DO TYPE %%d > ALLFILES

After the command runs, ALLFILES contains only the typed contents of the last file that matches *.TXT. DOS runs the command following DO once for each matching file. Everything after the DO is run as if typed from the keyboard, including the redirection. Each time DOS runs TYPE, the redirection is reapplied but not continued (although the redirection does not appear if ECHO is ON). In the example, the ALLFILES file is destroyed for each run, and a new file is created.

If you want to place the entire redirected output from a FOR..IN..DO run into one file, you must use the >> symbol, as in the following command:

FOR %%d IN (*.TXT) DO TYPE %%d >> ALLFILES

9.7   Trick: To use a redirection character as text within an ECHO or REM statement under DOS V4, enclose the character in double quotation marks.

If you use a redirection character (>, >>, <, or |) in an ECHO or REM statement under any DOS version, DOS activates I/O redirection. Consider the following statement:

ECHO Type DIR > PRN to list the files to the printer

This line prints to the printer the following line (which is explained later in this trick):

Type DIR   to list the files to the printer

As with many ill-fated command or batch file lines, the results from the first example are undesirable, but logical. As the first step of processing command lines, DOS grabs the I/O redirection. In the example, DOS grabs the > PRN before the remainder of the line is executed; the > PRN literally disappears. The double space between the **DIR** and **to** comes from the space after the **DIR** and the space before the **to** of the original command.

With DOS V4, however, you can print the redirection characters within an ECHO or REM statement by enclosing the character within a string inside double quotation marks. Although the > *must* be within double quotation marks, other characters also can be within the quotation marks. Consider, for example, this revision of an earlier example:

ECHO Type DIR ">" PRN to list the files to the printer

This statement results in the following line:

Type DIR ">" PRN to list the files to the printer

This line is close, but not exactly what you should type. You might instead create the following line:

ECHO Type "DIR > PRN" to list the files to the printer

The result, which follows, is closer to what you should type.

Type "DIR > PRN" to list the files to the printer

Keep in mind that this example works only with DOS V4. The example does *not* work with DOS V3.3 and earlier versions.

Using Redirection with DATE and TIME

9.8 Trick: Redirect DATE and TIME with a CR file to avoid answering the date and time.

Many users put the DATE and TIME commands in their AUTOEXEC.BAT files to ensure the current date and time upon start-up. Because most computers (except for PCs and XTs) have a fairly accurate clock-calendar, you may want to see the date and time, but you usually don't need to reset them.

The solution is to create a file with a single carriage return. Use the following technique: type **COPY CON CR**; then press Ctrl-M (a carriage return); press the F6 function key, and then press Enter. The screen displays a message that tells you one file is being copied.

Use the file with DATE and TIME, as in the following example:

DATE < CR
TIME < CR

DATE and TIME display the current date and time, and DOS gives DATE and TIME the single carriage return.

Remember that CR is a data file. If you move the file from your root directory or from your current directory, you must add the path to the name of the file so that DOS can find the file.

Using EDLIN in Batch Files

9.9 Trick: EDLIN can receive its input from a redirected file.

EDLIN, the text editor included with DOS, may not be as powerful as third-party text editors and word processing programs, but it is handy for "on-the-fly" text editing of batch files and other ASCII files. One advantage of EDLIN is that the input it receives can also be redirected from a file rather than just from the keyboard.

For example, the command **EDLIN MAKE.BAT < MODI.INP** starts EDLIN and loads MAKE.BAT for editing. The characters from MODI.INP are redirected to EDLIN so that MODI.INP types the sequence rather than the user.

An important rule of thumb is that MODI.INP must contain *every* keystroke that you normally type from the keyboard. If, for example, you update a batch file in which line 10 is deleted, and a label at line 3 is inserted, MODI.INP looks like the following:

```
10d
3i
:NEWLABEL
^Z
e
```

When an EDLIN command is on a line by itself, it is understood that a carriage return is included at the end of the line; the carriage return serves as the Enter key that you manually press while editing with EDLIN. Notice that the ^Z is needed to exit EDLIN's Insert mode.

Because redirecting input to EDLIN requires the extra steps of creating a file that contains the needed keystrokes, a one-time editing session with EDLIN in this manner is useless. If, however, you repeatedly edit the same text file (perhaps one that is used on many different computers), redirection saves keystrokes.

9.10 Trick: Using a batch file can make redirecting input to EDLIN less of a chore.

A batch file can automate the sequence of the preceding trick, which demonstrates how to redirect input to EDLIN from a file. The following batch file, ED.BAT, eliminates the step that creates the input file called MODI.INP:

```
ECHO OFF
CLS
IF EXIST MODI.INP DEL MODI.INP
SET EDITFILE=%1
SHIFT
:LOOP
ECHO %1 >> MODI.INP
SHIFT
IF NOT %1. == . GOTO LOOP
EDLIN %EDITFILE% < MODI.INP
SET EDITFILE=
```

To use this batch file, type the following command:

ED MAKE.BAT 10d 3i :NEWLABEL ^Z e

ED is the name of the batch file; MAKE.BAT is the file to edit; the rest of the line contains the commands mentioned in the preceding trick. Notice that the ^Z is actually a Ctrl-Z, which causes EDLIN to leave Insert mode.

If MODI.INP exists, it is erased. The first parameter, which must be the file to edit, is assigned to the environmental variable EDITFILE. SHIFT removes the file name from the command line and makes the next parameter become the first. This new first parameter (10d) is echoed to MODI.INP. Because the file had been erased, it is now created by the double redirection symbol (>>). SHIFT takes place again to make 3i the first parameter. The batch file then tests to see whether a first parameter exists. If so, the batch file changes back to the label LOOP where the first parameter is appended to MODI.INP. If, however, no more parameters exist, the file represented by %EDITFILE% is edited, using the commands in MODI.INP. Finally, the variable EDITFILE is erased.

9.11 Trick: You may pipe commands to EDLIN.

Piping, which is similar to redirection, can be used to send commands to EDLIN from a source other than typed commands. Piping takes the output of one program and pushes it into the input of another. Redirection, on the other hand, takes the output of a program and pushes it into a text file or device name. Conversely, redirection can also take the input from a text file or divide and put it into a program. With redirection, however, a file must be created that contains the commands that you normally type in

EDLIN. If the editing job is a one-time, "on-the-fly" job, it is a waste of time to create the file and redirect the file into EDLIN.

The pipe character is the vertical bar, |, that shares the key with the backslash on most keyboards. Using a pipe causes the output of one command to become the input of another. For example, typing the command **ECHO 10de | EDLIN MAKE.BAT** normally causes **10de** to echo to the screen. Because of the pipe character, however, **10de** is passed to the next command, which starts EDLIN and edits MAKE.BAT. Line 10 is deleted and MAKE.BAT is saved.

Using Advanced Redirection Techniques

9.12   Tip: Use redirection to invoke a file under a batch file.

You can invoke a file under a batch file in either of two ways:

- Call the file as a subroutine batch file (using CALL or COMMAND /C).
- Call the file as redirected input to a secondary command processor.

In either case, the difference in the way the file is being read can produce some useful effects.

The GOTO command is bypassed any time the file is being redirected to a secondary command processor and not being processed as a true batch file. The EXIT command, on the other hand, is ignored when encountered by the primary command processor. When it is encountered in the secondary command processor, however, EXIT causes the secondary command processor to be abandoned along with any processes under the secondary command processor. Execution returns to the primary command processor, as well as whatever process is going on under the primary command processor.

Table 9.1 illustrates the differences in interpretation of commands depending on whether the file is being executed by the batch file processor (AS BATCH) or by a secondary command processor (AS INPUT). A check (✔) means that the command works normally; no check means that the command works in a special way or is ignored.

Table 9.1
Command Interpretation in Batch Files

	AS BATCH	AS INPUT	
GOTO	✔		Note 1
IF EXIST	✔	✔	
IF ERRORLEVEL	✔	✔	
IF (string)	✔		Note 2
%1, %2, etc.	✔		
%F, etc. (in FOR)	✔	✔	Note 3
%.....% (in environ.)	✔		
Double %%	✔		
SET	✔		Note 4
EXIT	✔*	✔	Note 5
PAUSE	✔		
FOR	✔	✔	
CALL	✔	✔	Note 6
SHIFT	✔		
REM	✔	✔	
ECHO	✔	✔	
Redirection	✔	✔	
Direct invocation of another batch file	✔		

Note 1. Because GOTO is ignored when read as input, it is useful as a conditional jump. GOTO is also useful as a conditional termination of the file if you include GOTO END with the label END undefined. (Labels in a file being read as input produce a **Bad command or filename** message.)

Note 2. Any IF test, in which one testing is done for %0 (the name of the file) is always false when the file is read as input, rather than being called as a subroutine.

Note 3. The percentage signs for the variable in a FOR..IN..DO command must be in a pair (%%f) when used as a batch file but only individually (%f) when read as input.

Note 4. Environmental variables must be SET under the primary command processor if you want the variable to still exist when the process is finished.

Note 5. If the file is being read by a secondary command processor, any EXIT command encountered causes an immediate return to the primary command processor.

* EXIT, however, will work if the batch file is operating from a second command interpreter (if it is out of a SHELL).

Note 6. CALL is used to call another batch file and then return to the original batch file.

9.13 Trick: Redirect commands as input to a secondary command processor.

This trick demonstrates a method to speed up batch file execution. The trick does not work with any batch file that uses parameters from the command line (or from the environment), nor with batch files that contain GOTO commands. The file must contain EXIT as the last command that returns control to the first command processor.

You use this trick to redirect input to the secondary copy of COMMAND.COM. As an example, consider the following file, ROUTINE.INP, which looks like a batch file but meets the preceding restrictions.

```
CD\DATA\DOC
ECHO COPYING FILES
FOR %F IN (*.LTR *.MMO *.DOC) DO COPY %F A:
ECHO DELETING .BAK'S
IF EXIST *.BAK DEL *.BAK
CD\
EXIT
```

You can then can type the following command:

```
COMMAND  <  ROUTINE.INP
```

The file may run faster because it is not being read from the disk one line at a time like a batch file. ROUTINE.INP is not being interpreted by the batch file processor, but as a series of regular DOS command lines, just as if you were typing them.

Several batch file routines work with this technique; others do not. Following is a list of restrictions:

- % signs are not resolved except in the FOR statement. You cannot "pull in" any environment variables, nor can you include parameters on the command line.
- The FOR command works as usual, but remember not to use double % signs as you normally would in a batch file; ROUTINE.INP is not a true batch file. Likewise, CALL works, but is unnecessary unless it is in a FOR statement.
- Because the file is being processed sequentially, each line is executed once only. No labels, jumps, loops, or GOTOs can be used.
- ECHO works and can be used with redirection to create or add to the file. REM also works and can be used to display escape sequences.

- Because the keyboard is inoperative while this file is running, don't try to use PAUSE.
- The IF EXIST and IF ERRORLEVEL commands work. IF (string) and SHIFT have no possible use without parameters.
- Ctrl-Break will neither terminate the file's execution nor cause a return to the primary command processor. Ctrl-Break will terminate the command in progress, but execution will continue with the next command.
- Don't set ECHO OFF in such a file; you will want to see what is happening in case something goes wrong.
- Remember to specify the file's extension; to avoid confusion, do not use .BAT.
- Variables placed in the environment by SET commands in ROUTINE.INP will not exist when the file finishes running; the secondary COMMAND.COM has its own copy of the environment and does not change the original environment.

9.14   Trap: The file must end with an EXIT command.

If you do not include the EXIT command at the end of ROUTINE.INP, the computer will lock up. The EXIT command is necessary so that the file will return to the primary COMMAND.COM; the secondary COMMAND.COM does not look for input from the keyboard.

9.15   Tip: Change the PROMPT whenever you use COMMAND.

Unless you are executing a single command with the /C switch, it is a good idea to change the prompt. If you usually use the default prompt ng, which appears as C> or A>, begin the file with **PROMPT Sng**. The prompt will then appear as SC>; the S will remind you that you are using the secondary command processor. When the prompt changes back to C>, you know that the processor has EXITed.

9.16   Tip: Use several techniques to provide keyboard input to the file.

Be sure to include the responses with any commands that require keyboard input; ROUTINE.INP tries to read them from the file. If they are not there, you could be in trouble. For example, be careful with commands such as CHKDSK that might ask:

    27 lost clusters found in 4 chains.
    Convert lost chains to files (Y/N)?

Because there is no way to type the answer, you must reboot. If, however, you want a particular program to go to the keyboard for input, you can include < CON on the line that invokes that program; < CON supersedes the disk redirection for that program. The technique's success depends on the particular program and whether ANSI.SYS is installed. If the technique doesn't work with BASIC, you can use the OPEN "KYBD:" statement in the following program.

```
10 OPEN "KYBD:" FOR INPUT AS #1
20 PRINT "TYPE YOUR NAME."
30 INPUT #1, A$
40 PRINT A$
50 CLOSE
60 SYSTEM
```

OPEN "KYBD:" opens the keyboard for input or output.

If the file contains any calls to BASIC or other utilities, they will look to the next line(s) of that same file for any input; they will not accept anything from the keyboard. You can call them "on-the-fly" if their input is included in the file.

9.17 Trick: Run a BASIC program directly from a batch file.

You may have written utility or novelty programs in BASIC. It is likely, then, that you have a batch file that calls BASIC, then loads and runs the program. Rather than deal with two files, you may find it easier to deal with just one.

The following batch file uses the same technique of starting a secondary command processor and redirecting the batch file to take over the keyboard as did the preceding batch file. Notice, however, that a line-numbered BASIC program is part of the batch file. When BASIC loads, redirection causes the program to by "typed" and then run. When the program is finished, BASIC returns control to the secondary command processor. In turn, the secondary command processor is exited, and control is given back to the batch file, which ends execution.

```
ECHO OFF
GOTO PREP
ECHO ON
BASIC
1    OPEN "SCRN:" FOR OUTPUT AS #1
10   LET B$=" "
20   FOR T=1 TO 27
30   READ A$
40   LET B$=B$+A$
```

```
50    LOCATE 2,(80-LEN(B$))/2
60    PRINT #1,B$
70    NEXT T
80    CLOSE:END
90    DATA W,e,l,c,o,m,e," "
100   DATA t,o," ",t,h,e," ",W,o,r,l,d," "
110   DATA o,f," ",D,O,S
RUN
SYSTEM
EXIT
:PREP
COMMAND < ROOT.BAT > NUL
```

This trick works with either EDLIN or DEBUG by replacing the line to start BASIC, as well as the BASIC commands, with a line to start EDLIN or DEBUG and their respective commands.

Using the Environment

DOS maintains an area in RAM called the *environment*. The environment is a safe haven for text. Information can be stored in the environment and later used by programs. Many programs use the safe haven of the environment to hold start-up or operational information. The environment also can hold information used by batch files. This section considers several aspects of using the environment in batch files.

Expanding Environment Space

9.18 Trap: Running batch files can cause you to run out of environment space.

From the command line, you can issue a series of SETs that make the environment grow to its 32K limit. When DOS runs a batch file, however, the growth is halted immediately. To save memory space, DOS reduces the size of the environment to the default limit (127, 168, or the value used in the SHELL directive) or to the current environment size plus 16 bytes, whichever is greater.

The decrease in size means that when you run a batch file which adds information to the environment, the batch file can bump against the limit of environment space. The result is the infamous **Out of environment** space message. When the batch file ends, so does the limit. From the command line, you can insert more information into the environment.

The trap also applies to programs: while a program runs, growth is limited. DOS reduces required memory space by passing a copy of the environment to the program, which is up to 16 bytes larger than the space currently used in the environment. This means that if you have used 200 bytes out of the 800 you have allocated with the /E switch, your program gets a 208-byte copy of the environment. All in-use variables are in the copy, but the copy's growth is limited.

A trick to get around the problem in versions of DOS after V3.3 is to use the SHELL directive and load COMMAND.COM with a sufficiently large value for the /E switch.

9.19   Trick: To expand environment space, use the SHELL command.

DOS starts with a limited environment size. The default limit is 168 bytes for DOS V3.3 and later, and 127 for all previous versions. At the command line, you can expand the environment up to the limit of 32,767 bytes. If a TSR (terminate-and-stay-resident) program is loaded, however, the environment is frozen to the default limit or the current size, whichever is greater.

If you need a larger environment, use the SHELL directive of CONFIG.SYS to load COMMAND.COM and expand the environment size. The general form of the directive is as follows:

SHELL = *d:\path* **COMMAND.COM** *d:\path* **/E:***size* **/P**

/E:*size* is the switch to set the environment space. For DOS V3.2 and later, *size* is the number of bytes for the environment. Because DOS allocates memory based on 16-byte paragraphs, *size* should be an even multiple of 16; otherwise, DOS rounds up to the next multiple of 16.

If you use DOS V3.1, *size* is the number of 16-byte paragraphs, not the number of bytes. To calculate *size*, take the environment size in bytes you want to use, divide by 16, and round up. Also, in DOS V3.1, size must be greater than 10 (160 bytes) and less than 63 (992 bytes). DOS V3.1 ignores **/E:***size* settings outside this range and defaults to 128 bytes.

The amount of environment is dictated by your programs. The minimum size is 256 bytes if you use few environmental variables. If you have many programs that use environmental variables, 320 to 800 bytes is an average upper limit.

/P, the other switch to COMMAND, directs COMMAND to become permanent.

Caution: If you forget this switch, COMMAND.COM loads, executes, and then exits immediately, leaving the system locked up!

The first parameter after the equal sign is the full file name of COMMAND.COM, including the full drive and path name. This parameter specifies where DOS.SYS will find and load COMMAND.COM. If this parameter is incorrect, DOS.SYS issues the Bad or Missing Command Interpreter error message, and your system stops.

The second parameter (**d:\path**) automatically sets the COMSPEC environmental variable, which DOS uses to reload (not initially load) COMMAND.COM. Although the DOS manuals may be confusing on this point, COMSPEC is set when the second parameter is used with COMMAND.COM. (SHELL itself does not set COMSPEC; COMMAND.COM does.)

Although the two parameters can be different, this approach is risky. A RAM disk user, for example, can give the following command (which assumes that the RAM disk is drive E:):

SHELL = C:\COMMAND.COM E:\ /E:512 /P

If COMMAND.COM is not copied to E:\ before DOS attempts to reload COMMAND, however, the system may lock up. My suggestion is to have the drive and subdirectory agree for the first two parameters, copy COMMAND.COM to the other drive or directory (E:), and then set COMSPEC afterward. The last two operations can be part of the AUTOEXEC.BAT file.

Staying within Environmental Variable Limits

9.20 Trap: You cannot use PATHs or other environmental variables larger than 122 or 120 characters.

Without outside help, you cannot create a PATH longer than 122 characters. Other environmental variables have a limit of 120 characters.

Remember that DOS has a 127-character limit for the command line. You cannot type a line longer than 127 characters, nor include an expansion larger than 127 characters. When you set the PATH with the PATH command, the limit is 122 characters. In this case, 5 characters are used by the word PATH and the following equal sign or space.

When you use other environmental variables or SET to establish the PATH, the word SET, the following space, and the equal sign use 6 characters. The name of the variable plus the environmental string, therefore, cannot exceed 121 characters. Because the variable name requires at least 1 character, the string is limited to 120 characters. For PATH, the actual limit is 118 characters.

Several outside programs can surpass the 127-character limit. Two of these programs are ENVED, a shareware program by Robert Scott Ladd, and BATUTIL, by Barry Simon and Robert Wilson. With both programs, you use a larger variable. A few programs, however, object to a long environmental variable. If your programs use environmental variables and mysteriously malfunction, the problem may be that your program expects the 127-character limit to be enforced. In that case, either use smaller variables or update the program.

Conserving Environment Space

9.21 **Tip: Do not use a space between the variable name, equal sign, and string.**

Consider the following two statements:

SET PATH=C:\DOS;C:\BIN;C:
SET PATH = C:\DOS;C:\BIN;C:

The difference between these statements is the spacing. Using the second statement, DOS stores the spaces between the variable name and the equal sign, and between the equal sign and the characters after it. DOS therefore carries two extra spaces as baggage. Although two bytes are not much when you have 640K of memory, many environmental variables using two extra bytes each can eat away your environment space.

The other problem with the second statement is apparent when you try to release an environmental variable. Try this experiment. First type **SET TEST = TEST**. Then type **SET** to display the environment strings. Next, attempt to release the string by typing **SET TEST=**. Try **SET** again to look at the environment strings. TEST still exists. To clear the variable, you must type **SET TEST =**. Be sure to leave a single space before the equal sign.

9.22 Tip: Conserve environment space by deleting temporary variables after their use.

Environment space is usually tight, and DOS is not efficient in reallocating it. If you often create temporary environmental variables, you can conserve space by killing the variables after you are finished with them. Suppose, for example, that you use the following as a temporary variable:

SET OLDVAR=C:\BIN\OVERLAY;C:\WORDS\ARTICLES

After you finish using OLDVAR, issue the follow command:

SET OLDVAR=

This second SET command frees the space used by OLDVAR so that you can use other environmental variables.

9.23 Trick: To save memory space, place all APPEND, PATH, PROMPT, and SET statements after the lines that load TSRs.

When you run a program, DOS gives the program a copy of the environment. The copy is also given to any TSR (terminate-and-stay-resident) programs such as SideKick or the DOS MODE and PRINT commands. Most TSRs do not use the information in the environment, nor release their copy of the environment. Memory is therefore trapped until the TSR is removed or until DOS is restarted.

The size of the problem depends on the size of the environment. If you fill the default 168 bytes and use 5 TSRs, you waste 840 bytes. If you use more TSRs and have a larger environment, you waste more memory. If you use fewer or no TSRs or have a smaller environment, you waste little or no space.

When you use any DOS function that places information into the environment before you run TSRs, you trap environment space. By placing any environment-setting statements after most or all TSRs, you maximize your memory.

Five DOS commands place information into the environment:

DOS Command	Environment Function
COMMAND.COM	Inserts the COMSPEC variable
PATH	Inserts the PATH variable
APPEND /E	Inserts the APPEND variable only if /E is used
PROMPT	Inserts the PROMPT variable
SET	Inserts whatever variable is named

In your AUTOEXEC.BAT, place these statements after all TSRs.

I run a large environment of 800 bytes, of which 430 bytes are typically used. (I run 800 bytes because I often add additional environmental variables during my DOS sessions.) My AUTOEXEC.BAT follows what I considered to be good practice. Here is the skeleton for the file, which shows the effect of statement ordering in an AUTOEXEC.BAT:

```
@ECHO OFF
PATH=C:\DOS33;C:\BIN;C:\BIN\MISC;C:\
SET BFLAGS=–i120pr –mCDV
SET BHELP=C:\BRIEF\HELP
<more set statements>
APPEND C:\BIN\OVR;C:\WORDS\SPELL\LEX
FLASH 736 /M=A
<more TSRs loaded here>
PROMPT $p$_yes,Chris? $
```

Free memory = 467,136

The PATH statement is first, followed by a series of SETs. All TSRs are run, and finally the system prompt is set. The following shows the new order. When I reversed the order to put the TSRs first and the other lines last, my free memory grew by about 2,200 bytes!

```
@ECHO OFF
C:\DOS33\APPEND C:\BIN\OVR;C:\WORDS\SPELL\LEX
C:\BIN\FLASH 736 /M=A
<more TSRs loaded here>
PATH=C:\DOS33;C:\BIN;C:\BIN\MISC;C:\
SET BFLAGS=–i120pr –mCDV
SET BHELP=C:\BRIEF\HELP
<more set statements>
PROMPT $p$_yes,Chris? $
```

Free memory = 469,344

Notice that full names for each program (drive, path, and program root name) are given in the second AUTOEXEC.BAT file. Because the PATH statement is after the TSRs, you must add path names and/or drive names to the program names. If you don't mind wasting some memory, you can place the PATH statement at the top of your AUTOEXEC.BAT file and omit the path names in each command. Because the PATH statement is generally less than 128 characters, the most memory you waste is the size of the COMSPEC variable plus the size of the PATH.

Using Environmental Variables within Batch Files

9.24 Trick: You can use the contents of an environmental variable by using %name%.

This trick works only within a batch file. The **%*name*%** causes DOS to use the contents of *name*, not the word *%name%*. You can add information to an environment string within a batch file by using the following form:

SET NAME= %*name*%ADDED STRING

Use the standard SET syntax and the same environmental variable name surrounded by the percent signs, immediately followed by the new information to add. Remember that spaces are significant. If you use a space between the **%*name*%** and the **ADDED STRING**, the space is inserted into the string. For PATH and APPEND, this added space is a mistake.

9.25 Trick: Use a batch file to issue commands that contain references to your environmental variables.

When you work with applications software, you may use four or more data files at a time. If you use a hard disk, you may want to copy these files to floppy disks or to another subdirectory on your hard disk for safekeeping. Using the COPY command for this task becomes quite tedious.

You can, however, create a shortcut by storing the names of these files in the environment. For example, you can type

SET FILES=C:\DOC\CHAP1.DOC C:\DOC\CHAP2.DOCC:\CHRT\GRAPH.PIC

You then can create a batch file similar to the following:

ECHO OFF
CLS
FOR %%f IN(%FILES%) DO COPY %%f A:

Notice the use of the environmental variable **FILES**. If you place this variable within percent signs, the batch file uses the contents of the variable, rather than the variable itself. As the batch file operates, the third line reads:

FOR %%f IN (C:\DOC\CHAP1.DOC C:\DOC\CHAP2.DOC C:\CHRT\GRAPH.PIC) DO COPY %%f A:

When you change the group of data files, simply change the SET statement.

9.26 Trick: You can place special characters in the environment for use in a batch file.

You sometimes need access to a character while in a batch file. Certain characters, however, are not easily accessed because they have a special meaning to DOS. You can assign these characters to environmental variables and indirectly access them in a batch file.

Following are the important characters to keep in the environment:

- The delimiters: space, comma (,), semicolon (;), equal sign (=), backspace, tab, percent symbol (%), and quotation mark (")
- The redirection symbols: > < |
- Miscellaneous characters: End-of-File (^Z), Break, Escape, Plate, carriage return, line feed, substitute space (#255)

Most of these characters cannot be typed directly into the environment; their presence prevents the SET command from being correctly interpreted. For example, typing **SET TO=>** produces a file creation error message.

Several characters, including the comma and the at symbol (@), can be entered directly into the environment, but because you need a program to make the other entries, you can use the same program to put in all the characters at once.

The substitute space is never treated as a special character, so you cannot use the space directly wherever you need it. When it is used in a batch file, it looks like a plain space, so the fact that it is really a substitute space will not be obvious and it is easy to forget.

You can assign names for the characters to be entered into the environment. The following is a list of my names for the characters that will be entered into the environment:

Name	ASCII value	Character
COMMA	44	,
SEMI	59	;
EQU	61	=
CR	13	Carriage return
LF	10	Line feed
BSP	8	Backspace
TAB	9	Tab
PCT	37	%
QUO	34	"
FROM	60	<
TO	62	>
PIPE	124	|
SPC	32	Space
SUB	255	Substitute space
EOF	26	End of File (^Z)
ESC	27	Escape
BRK	3	Break
DEL	127	Plate

The null character (ASCII value 0) is the only character that cannot be entered into the environment. The null character becomes whatever the environment uses as its delimiter. Whatever falls between two successive nulls is taken as one environment string. The string, in turn, is then divided at the first = sign found in it; everything to the left of the = sign is taken as the variable name, and everything to the right is the contents of the name.

The value (the right side of the equal sign) may be any character except the null. The value may even begin or end with delimiters. Delimiters are not considered as separate entities from the contents of the delimiters when in the environment. The contents of an environmental variable is a single value, no matter which characters it contains. In the following line, the spaces are the delimiters:

SET VAR=THIS IS A TEST

The phrase **THIS IS A TEST** is therefore not considered four words, but one value.

After being set, however, the one value may be used for individual words, as in the case of a FOR..IN..DO statement.

9.27   Trick: Use an end-of-file character to prevent error messages when the batch file deletes or renames itself.

A batch file that erases itself causes few problems: at worst, an error message and the inconvenience of pressing Ctrl-Break to get out of the still-in-effect batch file. But there is a way to tell DOS: "This is the last line of this batch file, so just execute it and stop. Don't come back and look for the batch file again." You simply add the end-of-file character that is stored in the environment to the line that does the deleting. An example is the following batch file:

> .
>
> .*<batch file commands>*
>
> .
>
> **DEL RUN.BAT %EOF%**

%EOF% represents the end-of-file character (^Z) in the environment.

Running Programs with Batch Files

One of my favorite tricks is using batch files to run programs. I use this technique with many programs, including 1-2-3 and WordStar. This section covers the use of batch files to run programs and special uses of the AUTOEXEC.BAT file.

9.28   Trick: To set up and run a program, use a batch file stored in a directory on the DOS search path.

The general form of each batch file has three parts:

> 1. Setup commands
> 2. Program commands
> 3. Cleanup commands

The setup commands change directories or set any environmental variables, PATHs, or APPENDs. The program commands invoke a program and supply parameters for programs that accept information from the command line. The cleanup commands restore any environmental variables and return to the preceding directory.

A simple example is my one-line WordStar 4 batch file:

> **C:\WORDS\WS4\WS %1**

This simple file runs WordStar from its subdirectory, \WORDS\WS4, and optionally opens a file for editing.

The following example is my LIGHT.BAT file, which runs Borland's Turbo
Lightning™:

```
CD > \TMPDIR
CD \BORLAND\LIGHT
MKDIR E:\DICTS
COPY DISK.DIC E:\DICTS
COPY THES.DIC E:\DICTS
LIGHT
CWD <\TMPDIR
DEL \TMPDIR
```

Many of the Borland resident programs demand that you run each
program from the directory that holds the program files in order to make
the help facility work. The trick to this batch file is to change to the
directory that holds Turbo Lightning, do the work, and then get back to
the subdirectory from which you came (the subdirectory you were in
before running LIGHT.BAT).

The first line in the batch file uses I/O redirection to place the current
directory in a root directory file called TMPDIR. The second line changes
to the Turbo Lightning subdirectory. The third line creates a subdirectory
in drive E: (a RAM disk) to hold the Turbo Lightning dictionary and
thesaurus files. The fourth and fifth lines copy the files to the RAM disk.
The sixth line starts Turbo Lightning. After a trick in the seventh line, the
eighth line deletes the \TMPDIR file.

The trick to the batch file is in line seven. You use the program called
CWD, short for **C**hange **W**orking **D**irectory. With this program, before you
change the directory, you save it with the following command:

```
CD > \TMPDIR
```

This command redirects the output of **CD** to the file **\TMPDIR**. You
need the CWD program because you cannot redirect the input of DOS's
CHDIR command (COMMAND.COM ignores the redirection).

I wrote a version of CWD in the C language. The program simply checks
the command line for a drive and path name. If a name is found, CWD
changes to the current directory of the named drive. If no name is found,
CWD gets a line from standard input and changes to that directory. By
getting the name from standard input, the program can redirect the input,
and CWD can do its magic.

You can write the same program in BASIC. The three-line CWD program is shown below.

```
10 INPUT A$
20 CHDIR A$
30 SYSTEM
```

If you use interpretive BASIC, change the seventh line of the batch file to the following:

BASIC \BIN\CWD <\TMPDIR

Then place CWD.BAS in your BIN subdirectory. If you place CWD.BAS in a different subdirectory, change \BIN to the new subdirectory name.

Caution: The batch file assumes that you are operating from the same drive as Turbo Lightning. Because DOS maintains a current directory for each disk drive, CD changes the current directory but not the current drive.

9.29 Trick: Use the %name% feature to change the DOS path temporarily; then restore the original PATH.

I use this trick with Microsoft® Windows and Word, and with MicroPro WordStar 5. The sequence is to put the current PATH string into an environmental variable, add or substitute the additional path, and then restore the old path.

My normal path is **C:\DOS;C:\BIN;C:\BIN\MISC;C:**. To use Microsoft Word from any subdirectory, however, the subdirectory that holds Word must be on the DOS path. Here are the lines from my WORD.BAT file:

SET OLDPATH=%PATH%
SET PATH=%PATH%;D:\WORD
WORD %1
SET PATH=%OLDPATH%
SET OLDPATH=

The first line creates a variable called OLDPATH, which holds the current DOS path. The second line assigns to PATH the current path plus D:\WORD. Be sure to place the semicolon (;) between the final % and D, but do not place any spaces between the = and the final letter in the new path (PATH allows neither). The third line invokes Word with an optional file name. The fourth line restores the old path, and the fifth line removes the OLDPATH variable from the environment.

A program, such as WORD.EXE, may need to have its subdirectory on the DOS PATH whenever you execute the program. At all other times, the PATH should not include this subdirectory.

9.30   Trick: Let a batch file pass parameters to a programming language using the environment.

Normally, you pass parameters to a program on the command line. For example, DISKCOPY allows for two parameters: the source and destination parameters. With the following command, **DISKCOPY A: B:**, **DISKCOPY** is the program to start, **A:** is the first parameter and **B:** is the second.

You can also, however, use a batch file to pass parameters. The following batch file, ROOT.BAT, processes the square root of a number. The number is the parameter. To invoke the batch file, type **ROOT** followed by the argument (for example, **ROOT 73**).

```
ECHO OFF
CLS
GOTO PREP
BASIC
PRINT SQR(VAL(ENVIRON$("ARG")))
SYSTEM
EXIT
:PREP
SET ARG=%1
COMMAND < ROOT.BAT
SET ARG=
```

ROOT.BAT is written in BASIC. Assume that you type **ROOT 73** at the command line and press Enter.

After ECHO is off and the screen is cleared, GOTO causes execution to switch to **:PREP**. The argument, %1 (in this example, **73**), is placed in the environment as **ARG**. The batch file then invokes a secondary command processor, redirecting ROOT.BAT as the input of commands to execute.

The secondary COMMAND.COM treats the file as a series of commands rather than as a batch file. DOS carries out these commands one at a time, as if you were typing them. Special batch commands, such as GOTO, are ignored, so the next line starts BASIC.

Even though BASIC has started, input redirection continues with the next line. This line is the PRINT command of BASIC, which displays characters on-screen. In this case, the PRINT command displays the answer, the square root of 73.

Notice that BASIC has a provision to work with environmental variables with the ENVIRON$("ARG"). 73 is thus taken from the environment and changes from a string (from text to a value). The square root is then determined and the answer is displayed on-screen. Next, BASIC reads the SYSTEM command which exits BASIC and returns to DOS (to the secondary COMMAND.COM).

The EXIT command causes the secondary COMMAND.COM to be abandoned, and control is returned to the primary COMMAND.COM. The batch file execution resumes with the line after `COMMAND < ROOT.BAT`. The environmental variable is deleted, and the batch file ends.

9.31 Tip: Use GOTO to consolidate batch files that run programs.

If you have many small batch files, you sacrifice disk space. Any file occupies at least one cluster. Depending on your disk or partition size, the minimum disk space used by a file is 1K to 8K, regardless of the file size.

You can consolidate several batch files into one larger batch file by using the technique shown in the RUN.BAT file that follows. Simply add two labels (one in uppercase and one in lowercase) in front of the batch file instructions to execute. Then add a **GOTO END** line after the statements. Finally, enter the command **RUN *LABEL*** to execute the batch file. (Caution: If the ***LABEL*** does not exist, DOS give a Label Not Found message and the batch file ends.

```
@ECHO OFF
IF NOT %1. == . GOTO JUMP
ECHO Please specify the name of the program to run.
ECHO Example: run ws
GOTO END
:JUMP
GOTO %1
:light
:LIGHT
CD >\TMP\TMP.BAT
CD \BORLAND\LIGHT
COPY DISK.DIC E:
COPY THES.DIC E:
LIGHT
CWD <\TMP\TMP.BAT
```

```
DEL \TMP\TMP.BAT
:spell
:SPELL
SET LEX= C:\SPELL\DICTS
C:\WORDS\SPELL\SPELL %1
SET LEX=
GOTO END
:ws
:WS
C:\WORDS\WS4\WS %1
GOTO END:
:vp
:VP
D:
CD D:\VENTURA
COPY PERMVP.PS LPT1 /B
DRVRMRGR VP %1 /S=SD_EGAH5.EGA/M=22/O=E:
GOTO END
:END
```

The drawback to this approach is that DOS reads batch files one line at a time. The combined batch file executes more slowly than separate batch files.

9.32   Trick: Set an environmental variable equal to a program's return code.

Putting into the environment the return code that you get back from a program is sometimes useful. Test the return code with the IF ERRORLEVEL command (even though the information it conveys doesn't necessarily represent an error). The code can be isolated through any kind of loop—including the automatic loop created by the FOR statement.

IF ERRORLEVEL n represents a condition that is true if the return code is equal to or greater than **n**. Consider the following command:

IF ERRORLEVEL 2 GOTO ALTRTN

The command jumps to ALTRTN if the return code is 2 or more, but not if it is 1 or 0. The next command shows the converse:

IF NOT ERRORLEVEL 2 GOTO ALTRTN

The command jumps only if the return code is 1 or 0.

You can make a return code the value of any variable you establish for the purpose. If 5 is the highest return code the program uses, you include the following line immediately after the line that invokes the program.

FOR %%R IN (0 1 2 3 4 5) DO IF ERRORLEVEL %%R SET RESULT=%%R

For example, if on a particular occasion the return code is 3, the first iteration of the command sets **RESULT=0** because ERRORLEVEL is equal to or greater than 0. Similarly, the next three repetitions set it successively to 1, 2, and 3. The final two repetitions, however, will not set it to 4 or 5, because ERRORLEVEL is not equal to or greater than those values. Therefore, 3 becomes the final value of RESULT.

Return codes up to 255 are possible, but because programs rarely use more than 6 or 8 return codes, the loop takes only a short time to complete.

Remember that including 0 in the FOR-parameter list is not necessary. IF ERRORLEVEL 0 is not a condition; it is always true; all possible return codes are equal to or greater than 0.

If, however, 0 is omitted from the list and the return code is 0, no SET commands are executed. Any previous value of RESULT that may have been in the environment remains there to confuse your batch file; if there was no value, the name RESULT will not be there when your batch file looks for it.

Getting the Date and Time into Environmental Variables

9.33 Trick: You can get the date or time into an environmental variable using either of two sets of batch files.

To solve the problem of how to get the DATE into an environmental variable without using outside programs, two individuals created batch files as solutions. The solutions are excellent examples of batch file gymnastics. The first example was created by Barry Simon, professor at the California Institute of Technology and contributing editor to the *Washington PC Users Group* newsletter and *PC Magazine*. The second example was created by David Frier of Logical Software, Inc., a Washington, D.C., area consulting firm. Barry Simon's approach uses only batch files. David Frier's approach shows an innovative use of EDLIN, the DOS line editor.

Barry Simon's approach uses two existing batch files and a third batch file that is created dynamically. The first batch file can have any valid batch file name. The name of the second batch file, SILLY.BAT, is created by the first batch file and can be modified. The third batch file must be called CURRENT.BAT. The three batch files follow:

ECHO THIS IS SILLY | MORE | DATE >SILLY.BAT
SILLY

and

SET DATE=%4

To understand the gymnastics, remember that DATE needs a carriage return. Using **ECHO THIS IS SILLY** is just a way to pump some characters into MORE (any single printable character could have been used for **THIS IS SILLY**). MORE appends a carriage return to the output. The output is shuffled to DATE, which demands a carriage return; this explains the strange construction of the entire first line. The output of DATE is sent to a file called SILLY.BAT. The last line of the first batch file invokes SILLY.BAT.

To understand the second phase of the gymnastics, consider the output of DATE. On my machine, the contents of SILLY.BAT was as follows:

Current date is Sat 12-17-1988
Enter new date (mm-dd-yy):

When SILLY.BAT runs, DOS interprets the first line as a command. The command is to run something (a program or batch file) called CURRENT. Because DOS runs the CURRENT.BAT file, control is transferred one-way from SILLY.BAT to CURRENT.BAT. The second line of SILLY.BAT (`Enter new date`) never executes.

CURRENT.BAT uses the fourth parameter in the line and places it into the environmental variable DATE. The result is an environmental variable called DATE with the contents of `12-17-1988`.

David Frier's example uses three existing files: a batch file called DATER.BAT, a CR file that holds a single carriage return, and an EDLIN script file called EDDATE. Following are the contents of DATER.BAT:

DATE <CR > STAMP.BAT
TIME <CR >> STAMP.BAT
EDLIN STAMP.BAT < EDDATE > NUL
STAMP

DATER.BAT runs the DATE and TIME commands and redirects the output to a file called STAMP.BAT. The **<CR** forces a carriage return for the DATE and TIME commands.

The DATER file then runs EDLIN. A notable feature of EDLIN is using an established text file for scripting EDLIN commands. EDLIN accepts commands from standard input, which means that EDLIN can be directed by keystrokes to get its commands from a script (standard ASCII) file. The EDDATE file is used to script EDLIN to perform certain edits to STAMP.BAT.

To create EDDATE, type the following command at the DOS prompt. (Note: EDLIN should always be in your path for this example to work.)

EDLIN EDDATE

EDLIN responds with the following prompt:

*

Following are the commands (in bold) used to create EDDATE; the prompts are included as references. Type the lines in the following sequence and finish each line with Enter. The <> sequences denote keys you should press (the F3, F6, or Del keys) rather than typing the signs and letters.

***i**

> **2d**
> **3d**
> **1,2rCurrent** *<F6>***set boot**
> **1,2r is** *<F6>***=**
> **1i**
> **@ECHO OFF**
> *<space><F6>*
> **e**
> **<F6>**

***7**

> **^Z**
> *<DEL><F3>^Z*

***e**

Notice that when you press <F6>, the ^Z character appears on-screen. I have filled in the ^Zs in their respective places for your reference.

The EDDATE file first deletes the lines that ask for the date or time, then replaces the **Current** sequence with set boot, a space, is, and a space followed by =. The EDDATE file then inserts the line for setting ECHO to off, ends the insertion of lines, and then ends EDLIN, which saves the new version of STAMP.BAT.

Because this batch file places variables into the environment, you may want to increase the amount of space that DOS sets aside for the environment. You can increase the amount by placing the following line into your CONFIG.SYS file and rebooting.

SHELL=C:\DOS\COMMAND.COM /E:800/P

This command increases the environment table to its maximum of 800 bytes.

The result, after successfully rebooting and running the DATER batch file, is two environmental variables named BOOTDATE and BOOTTIME. My display showed the variables as follows:

```
BOOTDATE=Sun 12-18-1988
BOOTTIME=12:46:11.92
```

Both approaches work and are excellent examples of the gymnastics you can perform using batch files and redirection. If you need more flexibility, a utility such as BATKIT or a full-function command-line utility such as CED or PCED works faster and better.

Finding the Location of the Environment in Memory

9.34 Tip: Use DEBUG to find the location of your environment in memory.

Your environment's location depends on how much memory is occupied by the other items that are located in front of it in memory (see fig. 9.1). A list of the first 10 areas in memory follows; notice that the environment is number 8:

1. Interrupt vectors
2. BIOS data areas
3. BIOS routines
4. DOS Routines
5. DOS data areas
6. Device Drivers

7. COMMAND.COM (resident portion)
8. Environment
9. Program memory
10. Other (transient portion of COMMAND.COM, ROM, BIOS, and other RAM/ROM)

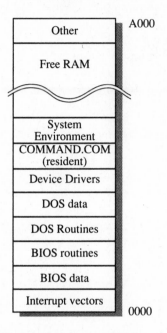

Fig. 9.1. Memory map of DOS.

Areas 1, 2, 3, 4, and 7 are fixed in size for any given version of DOS on any one machine; area 2 does not vary in size depending on the version of DOS. The system configuration area, 5, varies in size and contains customized instructions for your CONFIG.SYS file: the number of input/output buffers, device drivers, and file control blocks.

Whenever you change your CONFIG.SYS file or change to a different version of DOS, the location of your environment in memory changes as well. If knowing the location of your environment is important, use this procedure again to find the memory location of your environment.

To look for the environment, include one or more strings, such as SET THIS=THAT, that you will easily recognize in a dump and that are not likely to occur anywhere else in memory. For example, you can type **SET THIS=THAT** at the DOS prompt, and then call DEBUG and enter a search command similar to the following:

S 0:0 FFFF "THIS=THAT"

DEBUG searches the first block of memory (block 0) from its first byte (byte 0) to its last byte (byte FFFF) looking for the string **"THIS=THAT"**. Remember that DEBUG is itself a program and has its own copy of the environment. Only the program environment and the master environment (which you are looking for) will contain the string **"THIS=THAT"**.

The string you are searching for may be in memory at one or more locations, simply because you typed it twice—once to put it in the environment and once in the search command. The string may therefore be in input buffers or in other areas where DOS and DEBUG hold commands while processing them.

DEBUG responds to the search command by printing the addresses in memory of all occurrences of the string in block 0. The addresses will look like **0000:3B74** or **0000:C2A6**. The segment address precedes the colon: **0000** for block 0; **1000** for block 1 (the 2nd block); **2000** for block 2; and so on up to 9000 for block 9 (the 10th and last block). Following the colon is the offset address, the number of the particular byte at which the string begins. Write down the addresses.

You next choose one of the addresses and issue a dump command similar to the following:

D 0:5E90

Use an address about 50 or 60 bytes before the address of the string so that you are dumping the contents of memory in the neighborhood of the string, both before and after it. If you do not find the rest of the environment there (COMSPEC, PATH, and whatever else it contains), you have found a spurious occurrence of the string, not the real environment. In that case, try another address. When you do find the entire environment in one place, remember that this is only one of two such locations. You have found the master environment only if the environment is the first one that is found in memory, the one at the lowest address.

If you search through block 0 of memory and you still have not found the environment, search the next block (block 1) by typing

S 1000:0 FFFF "THIS=THAT"

To know whether to start searching in block 0 or 1, determine how much memory is occupied by drivers and buffers. If 64K of memory is being used by drivers and buffers, one entire block is occupied. In that case, you should search in the second block (block 1) from the start.

When you find the master environment, you want to find the beginning of the environment (the first string) rather than the address of your string. Its location always appears at the beginning of a line in the dump—that is, at a byte whose offset address is a multiple of 16 (the display is 16 bytes to a line). Notice also that the line immediately preceding always begins with the letter M; there is always an M in memory exactly 16 bytes before the beginning of the environment. If that M is not there, you have not found the master environment.

When you find the string, look at the far left of that line (the line following the M, which is the first line of the actual environment). At the far left, separated by a colon, will be the segment and offset that represent the address of the master environment. Write down those two numbers and keep them in a safe place; those numbers determine the location at which your program must place the environment characters whenever you are using the CONFIG.SYS file and the current version of DOS. You will need those two numbers when you write the program. Figure 9.2 is an example of the dump I created.

```
0000:CCE0   00 01 00 00 00 00 00 D2-00 00 00 FF FF FF FF FF    ...............
0000:CCF0   FF FF FF FF FF FF FF FF-FF FF FF FF FF FF FF 43    ...............C
0000:CD00   3A 5C 41 55 54 4F 45 58-45 43 2E 42 41 54 00 00    :\AUTOEXEC.BAT..
0000:CD10   4D FA 0B 40 00 00 00 00-00 00 00 00 00 00 00 00    M..@............
0000:CD20   43 4F 4D 53 50 45 43 3D-43 3A 5C 43 4F 4D 4D 41    COMSPEC=C:\COMMA
0000:CD30   4E 44 2E 43 4F 4D 00 43-4F 4D 4D 41 3D 2C 00 53    ND.COM.COMMA=,.S
0000:CD40   45 4D 49 3D 3B 00 45 51-55 3D 3D 00 46 52 4F 4D    EMI=;.EQU==.FROM
0000:CD50   3D 3C 00 54 4F 3D 3E 00-50 49 50 45 3D 7C 00 53    =<.TO=>.PIPE=|.S
0000:CD60   50 43 3D 20 00 53 55 42-3D FF 00 45 4F 46 3D 1A    PC= .SUB=..EOF=.
0000:CD70   00 45 53 43 3D 1B 00 42-52 4B 3D 03 00 44 45 4C    .ESC=..BRK=..DEL
0000:CD80   3D 7F 00 50 41 54 48 3D-43 3A 5C 42 3B 43 3A 5C    =..PATH=C:\B;C:\
0000:CD90   4F 3B 43 3A 5C 55 3B 43-3A 5C 44 3B 43 3A 5C 00    O;C:\U;C:\D;C:\.
0000:CDA0   50 52 4F 4D 50 54 3D 24-6E 10 24 65 00 53 43 52    PROMPT=$n.$e.SCR
0000:CDB0   4E 3D 38 30 20 4C 37 00-00 00 74 FE CD 20 B4 65    N=80 L7...t.. .e
0000:CDC0   B0 02 BA FF FF BB FF FF-B9 05 00 BF 03 0C CD 21    ...............!
0000:CDD0   BA 6F 16 B1 04 D3 EA 8C-C8 03 C2 A3 58 16 A1 16    .o.........X...
```

Fig. 9.2. A screen dump that shows the master environment.

The environment begins at 0000:CD20. Note the address at the left on the fifth line of the dump. Note also that at the right on the same line, the environment begins with the COMSPEC parameter, followed by my characters, plus several other items, including the PATH. Notice the M at offset CD10, just 16 bytes before the environment begins.

Setting the Environment with Programs

9.35 Trick: Use a program to find your environment and place variables into the environment.

Before you set the environment, you must have enough environment space. You can do this by adding the following line to your CONFIG.SYS file:

SHELL C:\COMMAND.COM C:\COMMAND.COM /P/E:1104

The command assumes that you boot from a hard disk, drive C:, and that your COMMAND.COM file is in the root directory of the hard disk. The environment is set to 1104 bytes—ample space for your PATH, PROMPT, and COMSPEC statements as well as the variables to be created. The SHELL directive is discussed later in this chapter.

Two programs, VECTOENV.COM and ENVCHARS.COM, work together to find your environment and then place the variables in the environment. The two programs, which are created through DEBUG, can be entered in one of two ways. With the first method, you start DEBUG and then type all the keystrokes listed in the program. (Do not include the notes.) *<Enter>* means to press Enter only.

Another method is to create two ASCII files. Each file should contain the keystrokes for each program (name them VECTOENV.INP and ENVCHARS.INP, respectively). Then use redirection with DEBUG as in the following:

DEBUG < VECTOENV.INP

DEBUG < ENVCHARS.INP

The following is VECTOENV.COM, a program that finds the environment and points an interrupt vector to it. The environment can then be found by ENVCHARS and by other programs. Either call DEBUG and then enter the program or create a text file consisting of these lines and redirect the file as input to DEBUG. The *<Enter>* line represents an extra press of the Enter key. (Caution: The *Notes* in the program are references and are not to be typed.)

```
A
MOV AX,3FF
INC AX
MOV ES,AX
ES:
CMP WORD PTR[3],45          (Note 1)
JNE 103
ES:
CMP BYTE PTR[0],4D          (Note 2)
JNE 103
INC AX
MOV DS,AX
MOV DX,0
MOV AL,58                   (Note 3)
MOV AH,25
INT 21
RET
<Enter>
RCX
23
N VECTOENV.COM
W
Q
```

Note 1: The preceding method assumes that the length of the environment is *exactly* 1,104 bytes, as set by the SHELL statement in CONFIG.SYS. The program locates the environment by looking for a memory block of that length. I chose 1,104 because it is a length that no other memory block is likely to have.

If you want a different length, the number must be a multiple of 16; divide the number by 16 and then convert to hex to get the value (45, in this case) that you must use in this CMP instruction.

Note 2: This CMP instruction looks for the M that marks the beginning of each memory block.

Note 3: The hex value 58 (88 decimal) is the number of the interrupt vector that I use to point to my environment. If you have problems with that vector (for example, if it is being used by another program), find another vector to use as your environment pointer and put its number (in hex) in this MOV instruction. In that case, you must also use that number instead of 58 in every program that uses the vector to find the environment.

The following is ENVCHARS.COM, a program which places into the environment characters that cannot be entered manually. (Caution: The *Notes* in the program are references and are not to be typed.)

```
A
JMP 172
NOP
DB  'COMMA=',2C,0
DB    'SEMI=',3B,0
DB     'EQU=',3D,0
DB      'CR=',0D,0
DB      'LF=',0A,0
DB     'BSP=',08,0
DB     'TAB=',09,0
DB     'PCT=',25,0
DB     'QUO=',22,0
DB    'FROM=',3C,0
DB      'TO=',3E,0
DB    'PIPE=',7C,0
DB     'SPC=',20,0
DB     'SUB=',FF,0
DB     'EOF=',1A,0
DB     'ESC=',1B,0
DB     'BRK=',03,0
DB     'DEL=',7F,0
DB  0
MOV AL,58                              (Note: the vector number)
MOV AH,35
INT 21
INC BX
ES:
CMP WORD PTR [BX-1],0
JNZ 178
MOV DI,BX
MOV SI,103
MOV CX,6F                             (Note: 6F is the total length of
REP                                    the strings in hex.)
MOVSB
RET
<Enter>
```

```
RCX
8B
N ENVCHARS.COM
W
Q
```

ENVCHARS.COM will not work unless VECTOENV has been run first. Place both programs in your AUTOEXEC.BAT file. Be sure that the programs are in the correct sequence: VECTOENV first, then ENVCHARS.

Note that ENVCHARS.COM does not find or remove any variables already present in the environment that have the same names. If a variable by one of these names exists, ENVCHARS creates another variable by the same name. The first duplicate variable, however, is used. For example, if your environment has a variable named COMMA that contains the string **comma**, and you then execute the two programs, you will have two environmental variables with the same names.

> **COMMA=comma**
>
> **COMMA=,**

If you have a batch file that indirectly uses COMMA, such as **ECHO %COMMA%**, the result will be the word comma. Check your environment and delete any names that conflict.

9.36 Trick: Have a batch file prompt you for a value to SET in the environment.

The following is an interactive, environment-setting program called GET.COM that you can use in batch files. You specify, as a command-line parameter after the word GET, the name of an environmental variable that you want to set; the program prints a message asking you to enter the value to be assigned to that variable.

Suppose that a batch file contains the command **GET FILENAME**. When that command is reached, you will see the following message on-screen:

> Enter value of FILENAME:

The program waits for your response. Typing **PREPARE.BAT** puts FILENAME=PREPARE.BAT into the environment and removes any previous value of FILENAME.

To create GET.COM, start DEBUG and then type the following commands, or create an ASCII file containing all these commands and redirect the file as input to DEBUG. If you create an ASCII file called GET.INP, type

DEBUG < GET.INP. (Caution: The *Notes* in the program are references and are not to be typed.)

```
A
JMP     0195
DB      'Enter value of '
DB      '                    '     (Note 1)
DW      0
DW      0
DW      0
DB      64
DB      0
DB      '                    '     (Note 2)
DB      '                  '
DB      '                  '
DB      '                  '
MOV     SI,80
MOV     AL,[SI]
CBW
MOV     [012B],AX
INC     SI
INC     SI
LEA     DI,[0112]
DEC     AX
MOV     CX,AX
REPZ
MOVSB
MOV     [0129],DI
MOV     BYTE PTR [DI],3A
INC     DI
INC     DI
MOV     BYTE PTR [DI],24
LEA     DX,[0103]
MOV     AH,09
INT     21
MOV     DI,[0129]
MOV     BYTE PTR [DI],3D
LEA     DX,[012F]
MOV     AH,0A
INT     21
```

```
LEA     BX,[0130]
MOV     AL,[BX]
CBW
MOV     [012D],AX
MOV     AL,58
MOV     AH,35
INT     21
DEC     BX
INC     BX
ES:
CMP     WORD PTR [BX],+00
JZ      021A
LEA     SI,[0112]
MOV     DI,BX
MOV     CX,[012B]
REPZ
CMPSB
JNZ     01DD
MOV     CX,0080
MOV     AL,00
REPNZ
SCASB
XCHG    BX,DI
DEC     BX
MOV     SI,BX
DEC     BX
INC     BX
ES:
CMP     WORD PTR [BX],+00
JNZ     01FF
MOV     CX,BX
SUB     CX,SI
JCXZ    021D
MOV     AX,ES
MOV     DS,AX
INC     SI
REPZ
MOVSB
MOV     AX,CS
```

```
          MOV      DS,AX
          DEC      DI
          MOV      BX,DI
          INC      BX
          MOV      DI,BX
          LEA      SI,[0112]
          MOV      CX,[012B]
          REPZ
          MOVSB
          LEA      SI,[0131]
          MOV      CX,[012D]
          REPZ
          MOVSB
          ES:
          MOV      WORD PTR [DI],0000
          RET
          <Enter>                              (Note 3)
          RCX
          137
          N GET.COM
          W
          Q
```

Note 1: DB has 23 spaces between the single quotation marks, thus providing for a maximum length of 20 characters in the name of the variable.

Note 2: These 4 lines each have 25 spaces, allowing up to 100 characters in the value assigned to the variable.

Note 3: Do not type <Enter>. Press Enter instead to leave this line blank.

Before you use GET.COM, you must run VECTOENV.COM, presented in Trick 9.35.

9.37 Trick: Maintain a counter in the environment so that a batch file can count passes through a loop.

The following program, INCR.COM, increments a counter kept in the environment. The routine is simple; it assumes a two-digit decimal counter in the form COUNTER=nn. nn can be any value from 00 to 99, but must always be exactly in two-digit format.

If the variable COUNTER is not present in the environment, the program does nothing. If the variable is present, the program adds 1 to the value, leaving it in the environment where it is. You are responsible for initializing COUNTER (with a SET command) before you enter the loop, testing its value (with an IF command), and exiting when it reaches your chosen limit. (Caution: The *Notes* in the program are references and are not to be typed.)

```
A
JMP 10B
NOP
DB 'COUNTER='
MOV AL,58                    (Note: the vector number)
MOV AH,35
INT 21
MOV SI,103
MOV DI,BX
MOV CX,8
REPE
CMPSB
JE 126
INC BX
ES:
CMP WORD PTR [BX-1],0
NE 111
RET
ADD BX,8
ES:
MOV AX,[BX]
ADD AH,1                     * Note:
CMP AH,3A                    * These
JL 138                       * five lines
MOV AH,30                    * can be
ADD AL,1                     * modified.
ES:
MOV [BX],AX
RET
<Enter>
RCX
3C
N INCR.COM
W
Q
```

To decrement the COUNTER, change the five lines marked (*) in the preceding program to read:

```
SUB AH,1
CMP AH,2F
JG  138
MOV AH,39
SUB AL,1
```

Change **N INCR.COM** to **N DECR.COM**; you now have two-way counter control.

Suppose that you have a batch file that utilizes more than the 9 parameters. SHIFT gives you access to parameter 10, 11, and so forth. However, you may need to use some of the first parameters later. You can save all the parameters in the environment using the following batch file:

```
SET COUNTER=01
:LOOP
SET PARM%COUNTER%=%1
INCR
SHIFT
IF NOT (%1)==() GOTO LOOP
SET COUNTER=
```

Notice that COUNTER is set to 1. The first parameter is SET to PARM%COUNTER%, or in this case, **PARM01**. The INCR program is run, changing COUNTER to 02.

10

Backing Up and Restoring Your Hard Disk

My first personal hard disk failure was in 1979. After two months of using my disk, the drive failed. The last good backup copy I had was several weeks old. After more than a week's work, I managed to restore most of the files. Some files were lost permanently.

That lesson left a lasting impression. I am pleased to say that since 1979 I have had only two other hard disk failures, during which I lost only a few files—a good track record considering the number of operations I perform.

Although hard disks are becoming increasingly more reliable, they are not everlasting. You should not get lured into a false sense of security. All hard disks have failures; the only uncertainty is when.

One failure, however, is still common: user error. Some typical user errors include overwriting good files with out-of-date files, erasing files in the wrong directory, and reformatting the wrong hard disk. User error, a more frequent culprit than any other type of hardware failure, is insidious (you typically don't discover your mistake until later) and its results can be as devastating as losing the entire hard disk. Backup—the subject of this chapter—is therefore extremely important.

This chapter introduces some general guidelines on backing up and presents some strategies in planning how different types of backups can meet your backup needs. The chapter also discusses steps to take before and after backing up your hard disk, including remedial steps if something should go wrong. Suggestions are offered for using some third-party backup software and tape backup units, which can speed the backup process and make the process more convenient. Specific suggestions for using the DOS-provided tools of BACKUP, RESTORE, COPY, and XCOPY also are presented in this chapter.

A Philosophy on Backing Up

Most people make backups far too infrequently. Granted, on most occasions, backups go unused. Unfortunately, when you do need to restore files, it's too late to back up.

You should view making backups as a form of insurance. You don't buy insurance to cover the times when things go right, but rather for the times when things go wrong. Few people are self-insured (have no insurance) because the results are catastrophic. If one key file is corrupted or missing, the results can be catastrophic to your business or to you personally. Will the self-insurance of your hard disk cover the catastrophe?

Although the importance of making backups frequently cannot be overemphasized, this chapter also considers the time and work to both back up and restore files and emphasizes making the backup process short and efficient. You typically will back up files 10 times more frequently than you restore them. For this reason, this chapter sometimes advises sacrificing convenience when restoring files for convenience when backing up.

How often you back up is related to change: how many files changed and how much effort changed them. You need to back up changed files, the only ones that are at risk. To this purpose, I offer three practical guidelines for when to back up—the next three tips.

10.1   **Tip: Make backups when the amount of work to re-create files is greater than the time and material to back up and restore files.**

Make backups when the time to re-create the lost data exceeds the resources spent in backing up and restoring. These resources include your time and the cost of the backup media. If you can easily reconstruct the lost data, you don't need to make backups. If the lost data is difficult or impossible to reconstruct, make backups. You should make backups not only when you create or change data, but also when you make significant changes to your directory structures. If you don't want to repeat the work, make backups of the changes.

Take a few seconds to imagine two different disasters. Suppose that your entire disk fails or that a single subdirectory is erased. Given your current state of backup media, how long would you need to re-create the data on your disks? Think about the number of diskettes you would need to handle, programs you would need to reinstall, and data files you would need to reconstruct. If the amount of time to perform these tasks would exceed a couple hours, make backups. If several critical files cannot be reconstructed, back them up. If subdirectories are at risk, back them up soon.

10.2   Tip: Make backups when files are at risk.

If your computer shows signs of instability, make backups. If you are editing the sectors within the FAT or a directory, make backups. If you are running any program (such as a defragmenter) that might destroy megabytes of data if a disruption occurs, make backups. Anytime inadvertent operations (such as running a low-level format, FDISK, or FORMAT when you have more than one physical hard disk drive) could damage many files, don't consider the idea—just make backups.

I have heard too many horror stories from friends and associates who ran into trouble when they were doing low- or high-level formatting or repartitioning. They backed up only the drive that was to be affected. Moreover, too many megabytes have gone West because someone punched the wrong letter or number, ignored the confirmation message (after all, the users knew that they were about to format a disk drive), and unleashed a data terminator on the wrong disk drive. Don't run any low-level formatter or FDISK without backing up all hard disk drives. Strongly consider backing up all drives before running FORMAT (even though inadvertently reformatting a disk with a volume label is difficult).

10.3   Tip: Don't waste your time making too many backups.

Making too many backups is not practical. You waste too much time; and handling backup media is clumsy. You must have current backups of your files, but you need not make backups of files that have not changed since your last backup or files you can replace easily. To make backups painless and productive, take a few minutes to assess your backup needs. Overdoing the backup procedure is as wasteful as underperforming the task.

Making a Backup Plan

Implementing the previous guidelines is not difficult. Remember that backup is a game of deltas (or changes). You must capture the complete state of the hard disk, and then capture the deltas (the new and changed files). The only tricks to the process are how to capture the disk, how to capture the later changes, and when each should be captured.

A good backup plan requires a modest amount of planning. You examine your files and the disk subdirectory structure. You judge how often files change and the difficulty in replacing damaged or lost files. These facts determine the files to back up, the type of backup, and how often to back up.

A good example of backup planning is found in large data processing installations—sites with hundred or thousands of megabytes of on-line, disk-based information. The next tip discusses the need to use multiple sets of backups as well as shows the origin of the many concepts presented in this chapter.

10.4   Tip: Use at least two generations of master backups and two generations of incremental backups.

Consider the procedure used by large data processing shops. Each week or month, the shops make a master backup of all files. Most shops maintain four sets of master tapes or cartridges and usually send the backup sets off-site for storage. Some sites maintain also the first master backup of the month for one year.

Each day, the shops make a set of incremental backups of the changed files. Each day has a different set of tapes or cartridges. Monday's backup media is used on only Mondays, Tuesday's media on Tuesdays, and so on for the remainder of the week.

The primary reason for using multiple sets of backup media is undetected corruption. Although physical damage is readily apparent, and some logical damage is quickly noticed (if the equivalent to the file allocation table is scrambled), some content scrambling is not immediately noticeable. Damage to a file's contents is not detected until you use the file. The stories about erroneous multimillion-dollar checks can often be attributed to scrambled files rather than simply to computer miscalculations.

When the damage is found, the site returns to the previous backup. If this file is damaged, the site keeps returning to earlier versions until an undamaged version is found. The previous version is mended until the proper health is restored to the file.

Using a multitude of backups also makes re-creating a damaged or destroyed file easier for most systems that use transaction logging. Either the damaged file is rolled back and rerolled forward to undo the damage, or an undamaged version is rolled forward. Because transaction logs are huge (a record is made for every transaction against the database), the files periodically must be copied to removable media and started again from the beginning.

Catastrophic disasters are another reason for using multiple backup media. Most master tapes or cartridges are usually kept off-site. If vandalism, fire, or another catastrophe hits the site and destroys the system and backup media, most of the information is intact. When no loss of information is allowed (with systems that run 23 1/2 hours a day), every backup is duplicated and sent off-site.

Multiple backup sets also can protect you if a particular backup is bad. If the backup media is flawed or the backup is "hosed" (incorrect or logically damaged), the most work lost is one cycle's worth. When incremental backups are daily, the most work lost is one day.

Keep in mind also that the life span of your backup media is limited. With diskettes and tapes, the finite life span is based on the number of reads and writes to the media. The life span for cartridges (which are removable Winchester packs and are rated as any hard disk) is based on hours of use. By using multiple sets, the wear is distributed among the various diskettes, tapes, or cartridges; and the life span of the media is lengthened.

If a site backs up files based on an archive attribute rather than a file date, multiple backup sets can offer much needed protection. Premature recycling of the backup media causes loss of backup files (and the potential need for the responsible supervisors to spruce their resumes).

Most of these techniques apply to your miniature data processing site— your computer. If your information is not absolutely critical, you need not back up so often, nor use so many backup sets. However, at least two master backup sets and at least two incremental sets are crucial. If a corrupted file remains undetected, you need that previous backup. If one set is flawed, the other set contains the files. You may lose some information, but you don't lose more than one cycle's worth.

I still have some master and selective backups from several years ago. The backup copies became archives, and I discarded the original files from my hard disk. I am amazed that I have used those old backups a few dozen times for restoring then-useless files. Keeping an occasional master backup is helpful.

10.5   Tip: Use a combination of master and incremental backups.

Consider this basic strategy: Back up the entire disk periodically and then back up either selective files or files in selected areas more frequently. The right combination makes the backup and restore processes manageable.

Master backups capture the entire disk, usually on a directory- by-directory, file-by-file basis. Because master backups take the most time, you don't run them as frequently. *Incremental backups*, which capture only portions of the disk, take less time. You capture the entire disk every week, month, or couple of months; and then capture more frequently the files that have been added or changed since the last master backup.

In your backup planning, you can use two types of incremental backup procedures. A *full incremental backup* processes all files that have changed. A *selective incremental backup* processes only some of the files that have changed. Selective incremental backups typically capture critical files spread among several subdirectories or in a set of subdirectories. Both types of incremental backups are useful. Later tips discuss when a full or selective backup is appropriate.

Creating a Backup Plan from the Bottom Up

Use a bottom-up approach to planning your backup needs. Bottom-up planning means that you focus first on your files, focus second on the subdirectory trees holding those files, and finally focus on the way you will back up the disk.

This bottom-up planning uses the logic that the frequency of the master backup (the topmost layer) depends on the frequency and length of the incremental backups (the second layer). The incremental backups depend on your backup program (the third layer), and your subdirectory layout and your files (the bottom layers).

Base the frequency of the incremental backup on need and convenience. The need varies by the frequency with which files change (including new files), the importance of the files (the difficulty to re-create the files and their changes), and how many files in a subdirectory are affected. The convenience is determined by the size of the backup and the ease of using the backup procedure. When the incremental backups take almost as long as a master backup, consider performing a master backup instead.

To establish a backup plan, follow these steps:

Step 1: *Determine what files are changed or added on a subdirectory basis.*

Step 2: *Assess how easily you can re-create the files.*

Step 3: *Combine this information to form an incremental backup plan. Decide on one of three methods: full incremental backup, selective incremental backup, or a variation of selective incremental backup.*

Step 4: *Decide on a timetable for the plan: a fixed, flexible, or hybrid schedule.*

Each of these steps is detailed in the tips that follow.

10.6   Tip: Determine what files are changed or added in each subdirectory tree.

Keep the quantity (number and size of files) and frequency of change in mind. Knowing both your directory structure and your programs (specifically, the files your programs use) will give you a pronounced advantage.

You can use the command **ATTRIB *.* /S** to look at all files that have the archive attribute turned on. Every file marked with an A in the list is a new or changed file. Note where the files are located and how many files in each subdirectory are affected.

10.7   Tip: Assess how easily you can re-create the files or changes to the files.

For this task, separate program files from data files. You always can re-create program files from their original diskettes (although the time involved can be burdensome). Most program files do not change, although configuration files can and do change. Count configuration files and programs that have been manually patched with additional instructions as data files. (Remember: If you lose those patches, you cannot reconstruct the new program.) Assess what data files can be reconstructed, partially reconstructed, or not reconstructed at all.

10.8   Tip: Combine the information determined by the preceding two tips to form an incremental backup plan.

You can use one of three types of incremental backups: full, selective, or a variation of selective. A full incremental backup covers all changed files and added files in every incremental backup. Program-wise, a full incremental backup is the easiest to perform. All backup software provides this capability. Unfortunately, as the length of time between master backups grows (and more files are added or changed), this type of incremental backup takes the most time to perform. Conversely, this type of backup lets you restore files in the least amount of time.

A selective incremental backup might stage the incremental backup by subdirectory group. For this plan, you process individual subdirectories— the subdirectory trees holding the eligible files. This type of backup requires more ongoing planning and care than a full incremental backup. The reward is that an incremental backup takes less time.

The keys to the selective incremental backup plan are the backup software and subdirectory layout. If the backup software can easily include or exclude subdirectories by name, the plan can be implemented and is practical. With one run of the backup software, you can cover the major directories. Conversely, DOS's BACKUP program is less than ideal for this work. With BACKUP, you must run the backup software on each different subdirectory tree, making the process both clumsy and more lengthy.

A variation of the selective incremental backup plan stages the backup by the difficulty of replacement. With every incremental backup, you catch the impossible-to-replicate or most vulnerable files. With every other backup, you cover these files plus files that are moderately difficult to re-create. Every third backup catches all changed and added files, including the files that are easy to re-create. Programmatically, this plan requires the most setup work and may be difficult or impractical to execute. Again, the features of your backup software are the key. If your software accommodates selection or exclusion by file name and subdirectory, you can effect this plan.

Deciding When To Back Up

10.9   Tip: Decide on a timetable for backing up.

Decide whether you should use a fixed or flexible schedule for backing up. Usually, a practical hybrid produces the best results.

With a fixed schedule, you perform a master backup on a certain day of the calendar—such as the first workday of the month or every sixth Friday. (A set day of the month is easiest to remember.) You perform incremental backups on their own schedule—such as every day, couple of days, week, or couple of weeks. The incremental backups are based on how critical your files are (how difficult they are to re-create) and on convenience. You perform either full incremental backups (grabbing all added or changed files) or selective backups (grabbing particular added or changed files).

The flexible schedule is based on two subjective criteria: one for the master backup and one for incremental backups. You perform the master backup when the incremental backup simply grows too large or too clumsy for easy management. And you run the incremental backups whenever needed.

Establishing the guidelines for need is easiest when data files are organized by program or project. You mentally keep track of the amount of work performed by a program or on a project. When the amount of work passes a threshold point, too much work would be needed to reconstruct the files. You perform an incremental backup of the subdirectories that hold the files. Because this backup is selective, it should take little time and should be run every time you pass that certain point. When you use these flexible guidelines, consider performing too many backups rather than too few.

Regardless of the timetable you choose for backups, remember to back up frequently and as soon as possible any critical files that have been changed or added to. You should back up moderately critical files frequently; back up noncritical files when convenient. The idea is to make the incremental backups quick and yet cover all needed files.

For either plan (fixed or flexible), violate the schedule based on the at-risk guideline given in a previous tip. Anytime you might perform a dangerous operation, first make sure that all files are backed up. (If the files are intact, this may be a good time to make an early master backup.) Vary or change the schedule also when an incremental backup will skip an irreplaceable file. If needed, back up this file or these files separately. (Using COPY and XCOPY for this purpose is ideal.)

Forgetfulness or laziness endangers your plan. You must be disciplined and adjust your schedule to changing needs. If you forget to back up, if you forget files that become critical, or if you don't back up as frequently as needed, any disaster will pen a sorrowful epitaph for the lost data.

Remember the old management saying, "Plan your work and work your plan." Also recall the corollary, "Throw the plan out when it doesn't work." Be flexible, but stay disciplined.

Using the Archive Attribute for Incremental Backups

10.10 Trap: Be careful when you base incremental backups on the archive attribute.

You can back up new and changed files on the basis of the archive attribute, which DOS turns on when a file is created or modified. All backup software supports using the attribute for backup. For example, the /M switch tells BACKUP to process any file that has the archive attribute set. Using the archive attribute alone for backup, however, can lead to one trap—missing files that should be backed up. Rotating backup sets while using the archive attribute can cause another trap—destroying the latest revision of a backup file.

Keep in mind that the archive attribute can be set or cleared manually using a program such as ATTRIB. XCOPY /M also clears the flag. If you manually clear the archive attribute on files before you back up, those files will not be backed up using BACKUP /M. New files and the most recent revisions of files are at risk.

If you copy files using XCOPY /M, for instance, the copied media, not the BACKUP-processed media, contains the files. BACKUP /M does not catch the files because XCOPY /M turns off the archive attribute. When you need to restore all files, you must remember to use the normal BACKUP media and also check the XCOPY diskettes. One of the two contains the most current version of the files. If you have a poor memory, you may need to use the trial-and-error method of restoration. Restore the BACKUP version first, check the backup file's date and time against the XCOPY version, and then decide whether the XCOPY file is more recent.

The other trap is losing revisions when you reuse the backup media. Normally, BACKUP destroys the old files (either on the backup diskettes or in the \BACKUP directory when the target is the hard disk) before writing the new files. If you give the /A switch, BACKUP preserves the established files and *adds* the new files to the end of the old files.

You can lose files when any of the following situations occur: the files change between master backups; the files do not change consistently with the /M backup cycle; or the backup diskettes are reused without the /A switch.

Suppose, for example, that you use two incremental backup sets with the /M switch, but not the /A switch. On Monday and Wednesday of one week, an arbitrary file changes. Both Monday's and Wednesday's backup catch the file. The Monday revision is lost on Wednesday when you reuse the first set of backup diskettes. Because Wednesday's backup set contains the file, this loss does not present a problem. When you reuse Wednesday's set, however, you lose the most recent version. If the file must be restored before the file changes again, you lose several generations because only the master backup now holds the file.

You should use BACKUP /M only when establishing a new incremental backup set—the first time you use the set after a master backup. After the set is established, add the /A switch each time you reuse the set; otherwise, the most recent revisions held by this set will be lost. Using the archive attribute for backup is valid, but you must be cautious.

10.11 Trap: Don't rotate incremental backup sets based on the archive attribute among each other.

If you use multiple incremental backup sets, don't rotate sets among each other. In other words, don't use one incremental set with /M, use another set with /M, use the first set again with /M /A, and then the second set with /M /A. You will be unable to find the correct versions of the files.

Any given file changes arbitrarily, and either or both sets may contain the backup file. The question becomes which set has the most current backup. When restoring one set, the most current version of the file for that set emerges. When restoring two sets, each set can hold versions of the file for different days. The proper set to restore last is almost random.

Suppose, for example, that you rotate two incremental backup sets each week. The file changes during the first three weeks, but not the fourth week. The first backup set gets the file on weeks one and three. The second set gets the file on week two.

You are naturally inclined to restore the backup sets in forward order, from the oldest set to the most recent. In this case, the wrong version of the file would be restored. After restoring the file from the first set, you have the right file. The mistake would be in restoring the file from the second set; this action would replace the more recent copy with a previous version.

For this reason, do not rotate incremental sets among each other. If you use more than one incremental backup set, use a set for a period of time and then use another set. Do not return to the earlier set until after you perform a new master backup. You may then recycle the set safely.

Using a Date and Time Stamp for Incremental Backups

10.12   Tip: Use the date and time stamp for full or selective incremental backups.

Instead of using the flip-flop archive attribute, you can back up using the date and time stamp that DOS maintains for each file. This type of backup offers similar functionality to using the archive attribute for selecting files. You can back up added and changed files on the disk (for a full incremental backup) or files within selective subdirectories (for a selective incremental backup). The benefit to using the date as the basis for backup rather than the archive attribute is that the restore process is simplified.

To perform a full incremental backup, you sweep the entire disk using the date facility of your backup software (for example, the /D switch for BACKUP). If you finished your day by running the master backup (no files changed after you ran the backup), use the form

> **BACKUP C:\ A: /D:*date* /L**

(The /L switch is discussed later in this chapter.) The *date* should be the day after you made the master backup. The /D switch backs up files added or changed on or later than the given date. Because you want to skip files added or changed on the day of the master backup (because those files already reside on the master set), you add one day.

If you added or changed files on the same day you made the backup, add the /T switch. In keeping with the preceding example, use the form **BACKUP C:\ A: /D:*date* /T:*time* /L**. The *date* in this case should be the date of the master backup, not the day after. The *time* for the /T switch should be the time of the backup. Like when you use the /D switch, BACKUP processes files with a file time later than the given *time*.

For BACKUP (and most backup software), the form of *date* and *time* should be identical to what you use for the DATE and TIME commands, respectively. Keep in mind that changing the COUNTRY directive in CONFIG.SYS changes what BACKUP recognizes as valid dates and times.

Remember also that the clock is a 24-hour clock. For example, enter 13:00 for 1:00 p.m.

The beauty in this scheme is the simplicity in which the files are restored. You must use only two sets of backup media—the last master and last full incremental set. To restore all files, you restore the last master backup, and then you restore the incremental set.

Note some problems that exist with this scheme. First, the incremental backup takes longer as more files are changed or added. In addition, when you reuse a set, the most current revisions of accidentally deleted files are lost. (This does not occur when you use the /M /A combination.) You can minimize this second problem by using several incremental backup sets (and finding the problem before you reuse the set) or by using the /A switch.

You also have the problem of losing a good revision of a file that has been partially corrupted and discovering the error later. You can avoid the loss by using the /A switch (which I find impractical because it uses too many backup diskettes) or by using more backup sets. Using more backup sets lengthens the time between reusing backup sets, meaning that more time is available to discover a problem file before the backup set is destroyed. Although using more backup sets increases the probability of preserving the good revision, the method remains fallible.

You can make the ongoing full incremental backup process faster. For the first full incremental backup, use the required date, or date and time, of the last master backup. For subsequent incremental backups, use the date, or date and time, of the last full incremental backup instead of the last master backup. In this scheme, you process only the files that are changed or added since the last incremental backup, not all files that were changed or added since the last master backup. Because you process fewer files, the backup process takes less time.

You can strengthen this technique by using separate backup media for each run and not reusing the media between master backups. Each set of media contains all the files that have been added or changed since the previous backup. Because you reuse the media only after another set (the master backup) has the last revision of the file, no revision will be inadvertently lost. If following this advice takes too many diskettes, you can reuse the incremental backup sets with the /A switch and recycle the media as described in the preceding tip: use /A the second time you use the set between master backups.

Considering Backup Alternatives

Although this chapter uses the DOS BACKUP and RESTORE programs in a number of examples, you should consider other solutions for your backup needs. For example, two other DOS-provided utilities, COPY and XCOPY, can serve a useful role in your backup routine. DOS-provided utilities, however, do not meet every person's needs. If your backup plan calls for the frequent backup of different subdirectory trees or the capability to exclude certain files or subdirectories within a tree, neither BACKUP nor XCOPY offers an easy solution.

If you are looking for faster backup performance or greater versatility, you should consider using third-party backup software, which offers functions and features not in BACKUP or XCOPY. If you have large disk partitions (in particular, hard disks exceeding 60M), diskette-based backups quickly can become overwhelming; you should consider the speed and efficiency of tape backups. Even if you continue with the DOS-provided programs for backup, you also can benefit from disk cachers. All three items are discussed in the next sections.

Using COPY and XCOPY for Selective Backups

10.13   Trick: Use COPY and XCOPY for selective backups.

Don't ignore COPY and XCOPY for selective backups. Often, you quickly can handle the files in a key directory or subdirectory chain with these utilities. When you are working on one or two projects at a time and the files are in one or two subdirectories, COPY or XCOPY works well.

The key is convenience. If the files fit conveniently on a single diskette or two, COPY or XCOPY can be an efficient backup aid. If you want to back up all files in one subdirectory, COPY works well. If you need to back up files in one subdirectory tree, XCOPY works well. In both cases, you can use one command to copy all needed files.

The advantages to this scheme are quick execution and less backup media space for the files. COPY and XCOPY run quickly. When reusing the backup media, COPY and XCOPY save space by replacing outdated versions of the file on the backup media (if the versions have the same file name).

Note that this technique has some disadvantages. While COPY and XCOPY can save space, the previous versions of the file are lost (unless you rotate the backup media for this task and lose some of the space advantage). In addition, when you must back up files in more than one subdirectory, COPY may be clumsy or inadequate. Because COPY does not sweep directories, you must run the command several times. Also, COPY cannot handle files from a single subdirectory that spans more than one diskette; you cannot easily go back and copy the remaining files.

XCOPY can handle files in multiple subdirectories in the same part of the subdirectory tree. If the files are in different subdirectory trees, however, XCOPY may be clumsy or inadequate. XCOPY can handle files that fill more than one diskette, but you must use the archive attribute (/M or /A switch, with or without the date switch, /D) to copy the remaining files.

When you need to back up a file larger than the backup media, COPY and XCOPY are useless. In this case, you must use backup software that splits the file across the media. (All backup software has this capability.) The other contention is name clash (when two files from different subdirectories have the same name). Don't place these files in the same destination directory. The last file to be copied wins, and you can't afford the loss.

In spite of these cautions, you can use COPY and XCOPY effectively for selective backups. COPY and XCOPY fit into my backup scheme when I am working within a key directory (or two) that holds several difficult-to-replace files. If the files fit on one or two diskettes (and no file is larger than a single floppy), I simply back up the entire key subdirectory or use the /D switch with the date of the last master backup. (If I will span more than one diskette, I use the ATTRIB trick and set the archive attribute on for the second run of XCOPY.) The process is fast, efficient, and safe—my key criteria for a good backup.

Using Third-Party Backup Software

10.14 Tip: Explore third-party backup software if you need more speed or diverse functions.

Several third-party hardware and software combinations contain features that make BACKUP look somewhat pale. While BACKUP has set the minimum standards, the third parties excel in both speed and diversity.

Some third-party software solutions can change your current floppy disk drives into speed demons. Software such as Intelligent Backup, CoreBack,

DS BACKUP™, and Fifth Generation's FASTBACK and FASTBACK PLUS®
can back up in 1/10 to 1/20 (pre-V3.3) or 1/2 to 1/10 (V3.3 and later) the
time of the BACKUP command. You don't have to change your hardware;
the software simply exploits the hardware to make the backup faster.

Speed gives you an excellent advantage. You lose the excuse that the
backup takes too much time. When a full 20M backup takes only 10 to 20
minutes rather than 1 hour, you are inclined to make the backup more
often. When incremental backups take a few minutes rather than 10 to 20
minutes, you make incremental backups as often as needed.

But speed is not the only advantage. Most programs offer the same
selection criteria as BACKUP, meaning that they can back up files by
archive attribute, date and time stamp, or both. In addition to this basic
level of capability, many backup programs offer other features.

One feature, for instance, allows you to include or exclude a set of
subdirectories or subdirectory trees in a selective backup. When you can
apply the same inclusion/exclusion facility to individual files, you have
another beneficial feature. You also can use the archive and data criteria
with either feature. This method allows selective backups that process the
needed subdirectories and files, skip the unneeded files, and run
painlessly.

Most programs use menus, command files, or both to activate the various
features. I prefer having both. You can use the menus to establish the
backups; you can use the command files, which the program reads for its
directions, to automate the backup procedure. When you run master
backups weekly and incremental backups daily, for example, you can
establish DAILY and WEEKLY command files.

Some software programs pack even more features. Although I use with
bias FASTBACK and FASTBACK PLUS for my examples, most programs
have similar options.

If you have two identical floppy disk drives, FASTBACK and FASTBACK
PLUS will use both drives for the backup. These programs speed the
backup process by spending less time waiting for you to change diskettes.
(Pay attention when using this feature. Because the program processes
1.2M diskettes in about 1 minute, the machine may wait needlessly for a
distracted user.)

Data compression can reduce the number of backup diskettes. Because
less data is sent to the floppy disk drive (usually the slowest link in the

backup chain), the backup may be faster. FASTBACK PLUS offers three data compression options: compress on-the-fly during idle CPU time, plain compress, and don't compress. The plain compress option reduces the number of diskettes used, but the backup process takes longer.

Several backup programs can preview the backup set and give an estimate of the backup size. Usually, the estimates are close. When data compression is in effect, however, the estimates are high. I use fewer diskettes than the program estimates—a problem with which I can easily cope.

Formatted diskettes are not required. If the diskette is not formatted, the program formats it quickly. Be cautious with programs, such as FASTBACK, that format diskettes their own way. When you use the diskette in other DOS operations, DOS returns a `General failure` error. If you do not know that the diskette was processed by FASTBACK, you might suspect the diskette is blank and format it. (Attaching a label, as mentioned earlier, can prevent this mistake.)

If you want to implement a comprehensive plan for backing up, explore the third-party solutions. I abandoned DOS's BACKUP several years ago after encountering FASTBACK. Today, my backup program of choice is FASTBACK PLUS. Because I admit bias for this software, I suggest that you explore the various contenders.

Using a Tape Drive

10.15 Tip: Consider a tape drive for large hard disks.

When scores of megabytes are involved in the backup process, consider a tape drive. I think the magic number for considering the switch is 40M. When the number of backup diskettes grows past 30 (27 1.44M diskettes are needed for a 40M drive), inserting, handling, and storing the diskettes is clumsy. A contemporary tape drive can store up to 60M on a single removable tape.

An obvious advantage is that one tape can hold most or all of the hard disk. Other advantages include more convenient storage and handling of the backup media, faster backup processing (you don't have to wait to change floppy diskettes), and an unattended backup process (the single greatest advantage). When the backup takes 10 to 20 minutes or more, the most convenient time to run the backup is at lunch or at night when you don't use the computer. You can start the backup and then let it run unattended.

Most tape drives come with their own backup software. You can use some of the backup software mentioned in the preceding tip with tape drives also.

Tape drive software may offer two backup modes: a sector-by-sector *image* mode and the standard *file-by-file* mode used by all other backup software. (If the program offers only one mode, it is the file-by-file backup.) You customarily should use the file-by-file mode.

Restoring a single file or subdirectory from an image mode backup is time-consuming. To restore a single file or subdirectory from an image mode backup, you must back up the current state of the drive, restore the entire drive from the backup, copy off the needed files, restore the drive to its current state, and then copy the needed files.

The image mode, nonetheless, has occasional uses. In certain cases, for example, you may want to back up a damaged hard disk in image mode; this method can make some logical repairs easier after the hardware is repaired. Sometimes image backup is faster than file-by-file backup. When the disk is collapsing, any backup works; you may not have time for a full file-by-file backup. Also, when you are about to run an all-or-nothing procedure (formatter or disk partitioner) that will affect the entire disk, image backup is appropriate. In case of damage, the entire disk will probably be unusable; therefore, restoring the entire disk would be appropriate.

One unique use for image mode backup is to make the testing fair when you want to determine the effectiveness of various disk cachers and defragmenter software packages. Because the test times vary if any changes are made to the layout of the disk, the state of the disk is preserved using an image backup. The tests on the respective disk cachers and defragmenters are performed, and then the disk is restored to its original state to test another program. (This is about the only time you want the disk to return to its original fragmented state.)

Tape drives have declined in price significantly in the past four years: average prices fall in the $400 to $700 range. Most tape drives fit into a full-height disk drive bay, and many fit into a half-height drive bay. The tape drives are offered as factory-installed options for many high-performance 286- and 386-based systems. If you have a large hard disk, consider the advantages of a tape drive. The usefulness and convenience in handling the backup media can far outweigh the cost.

Using Disk Cachers

10.16   Trick: Use disk cachers to speed backup and restore operations.

Cachers can speed the backup and restore processes considerably. By keeping the FAT and directories in memory, the backup or restore time can be reduced by one-fifth or more. (DOS BUFFERS usually speed backing up more than restoring.) Also, all known disk cachers are safe to use with BACKUP and RESTORE.

Note one caution about using a cacher during the backup or restore process: using on-the-fly verification during the process is useless. The programs usually verify the information written in the cacher rather than on the disk. For this reason, you can solve the lack of verification by using a separate verification pass, turning off the cacher for the target drive (if either is possible), or backing up more frequently.

Preparing for Backup

A plan without action is worthless. After creating your backup plan, you must execute the backups. Before actually running the backup software, however, you should complete a number of steps. The steps should be followed when you run any backup software or hardware-software combination, not only DOS's BACKUP or XCOPY programs. Some steps make the backup process as fast as possible; other steps ensure that the backup produced is correct.

You can execute the following suggested steps in almost any order:

Step 1:   *Have on hand enough media (or prepared media) to handle the backup need.*

Step 2:   *Move or remove any files that do not need to be backed up.*

Step 3:   *Uninstall any copy-protected software, if necessary.*

Step 4:   *Make sure that a correctly configured DOS is in use.*

Step 5:   *Make sure that no programs will conflict with the backup.*

Step 6:   *Make sure that the disk to back up is intact.*

Step 7:   *Activate any verify function, if necessary.*

The tips in this section describe each step and explain its importance.

Estimating the Needed Backup Media

10.17   Tip: Use CHKDSK and some simple calculations to estimate the number of backup media needed.

How many diskettes or tapes will you need to back up your fixed disk? Two more questions answer this one: What are you backing up? What is the capacity of the backup media you are using?

Undoubtedly, the files from a 20M hard disk will fit on a 20M backup tape, as almost any hard disk would fit onto any large tape. If the backup media holds less than the originating disk, however, you need to perform a couple of quick calculations. If you use diskettes, the calculations can be slightly complex.

If your hard disk is full or nearly full, follow these steps:

Step 1:   *Convert the capacity of your backup media into the same units of measurement (K or M) as your hard disk.*

Step 2:   *Divide the capacity of your hard disk by the capacity of your backup media.*

Step 3:   *Round up any fractional result.*

Step 4:   *If you are unsure, add one more diskette.*

For example, 10M of hard disk capacity divided by .360M of floppy diskette capacity equals 28 diskettes (27.777 rounded up). Or 20M of hard disk capacity divided by 1.2M of floppy diskette capacity equals 17 diskettes (16.777 rounded up). Or 40M of hard disk capacity divided by 1.44M of floppy diskette capacity equals 28 diskettes (27.777 rounded up). If you are unsure or are using DOS pre-V3.3, add a diskette.

If your hard disk is not full, the calculations are just slightly more complex:

Step 1:   *Run CHKDSK on your hard disk. (Another reason for running CHKDSK is discussed later in this chapter.)*

Step 2:   *Truncate the number of bytes in your user files to the nearest .1M (100K).*

Step 3:   *If the number of bytes in hidden files exceeds .1M, round to the nearest .1M and add the result to the user files figure.*

Step 4:   *Divide the user bytes in M (or the sum of user and hidden bytes) by the capacity of the backup media.*

Step 5:   *Round up any fractional results.*

Step 6: *If you are not confident or are using DOS pre-V3.3, add one to the resulting figure.*

You round all numbers to the nearest 100K because 100K represents from 6 percent (1.44M diskettes) to 27 percent (360K diskettes) of disk space. This figure comes close enough for an estimate.

Actually, the figure errs on the high side, and you rarely need the extra diskette. Remember that CHKDSK lies: it reports allocated space, not space actually used by files. An average of 12 to 20 percent of disk space is wasted by file slack—the unused space that is allocated but not used by a file. Because BACKUP now combines all files into one larger file, the slack is almost eliminated, and the estimated number of needed diskettes may actually drop by one or more.

If you are performing an incremental backup, use a super-DIR command to determine the amount of space used by the files. Use the same file name with the super-DIR command as the name you will give to the backup program. Round to the nearest 100K and divide by the backup media capacity. (Notice that I exclude DIR. DIR does not sum the space taken by the files, only the free space for the entire disk.)

Formatting Backup Diskettes

10.18 Tip: Before running BACKUP, collect and format enough backup diskettes.

For BACKUP pre-V3.3, the diskettes you use for backup files *must* be formatted before you run BACKUP. If you run out of formatted diskettes, you must exit BACKUP, format the diskettes, and start the entire backup over again. (If you used the trick of setting the archive attribute on, you can avoid restarting BACKUP from scratch. This trick is discussed later in this chapter.)

The problem of running out of formatted diskettes was resolved for V3.3 and solved for V4. (The problem of running out of usable diskettes, however, was not solved.) To make the backup process more efficient, format the needed diskettes before you run BACKUP V3.3 and later. Although BACKUP can run FORMAT, having BACKUP execute FORMAT makes the backup processing longer. Also, the interruption can disrupt your concentration. If you fail to give the /F switch to FORMAT V3.3, you are in the DOS pre-V3.3 boat (you will need to restart BACKUP).

10.19 Tip: If you don't think that you have enough formatted diskettes, use the /F switch with BACKUP V3.3 only.

To use the format feature for BACKUP V3.3, you must use the /F switch. /F directs the program to execute FORMAT automatically if it finds an unformatted diskette in the target disk drive. Therefore, give the /F switch as a safety play if you are not completely sure that the backup will fit on the formatted diskettes.

If you do run out of formatted diskettes and BACKUP runs FORMAT, try to estimate how many diskettes you still need and format them at one time. You can format more than one diskette before you return to BACKUP. Instead of wasting time running FORMAT for each diskette individually, format all diskettes at once.

10.20 Tip: When formatting backup diskettes, don't lower the capacity of the diskette.

When you format the diskettes manually, don't lower the capacity of diskettes. You want the maximum storage capacity from your floppies. Don't put DOS on the diskettes; don't use /4 for high-capacity diskettes; and don't format 720K diskettes for use in a 1.44M drive. You can, however, use the /V switch with FORMAT V3.3 to create a volume label if you like. (FORMAT V4 automatically requests a volume label; use one if you want.) A volume label takes a directory entry but does not take up any other space on the diskette. BACKUP ignores volume labels.

10.21 Tip: Attach labels to your backup diskettes.

You should always keep a group of backup diskettes together. However, if the diskettes are shuffled and you need to restore files, the task of reordering the diskettes is easier if you've attached labels to them. Also, some backup programs, such as FASTBACK, do not produce a DOS-readable diskette. If a backup disk is not labeled, you might accidentally format it and lose backup files.

When preparing the diskettes for BACKUP, write on the label of each diskette an identifying batch number or letter (such as A, B, or C), the source drive (if you have more than one), and the number of the diskette. Start with 1 and number each diskette sequentially. Later in this chapter, I'll give a tip for reordering "mystery" diskettes.

Deleting Unneeded Files

10.22   Trick: Delete or remove unneeded files before backing up.

Why back up unneeded files? Because unnecessary files needlessly slow the backup and restore processes and use more media than required. Delete any files you do not need—for instance, word processing backup files. You can delete needless backup files from the hard disk because you will have a second copy of the files on the backup media. The only reason to keep the past generation of the file is in case the current generation has a problem—for example, you made the wrong change to a file. In this case, correct the file and kill the backup.

However, if you have any doubt about a file, keep it! It is safer to process excess baggage than to lose a file. Delete only files you are absolutely sure you no longer need.

If you have files you want to keep but no longer use, move the files off the hard disk onto a diskette or other media. Run XCOPY or backup software to back up an entire program and then remove the program from the disk. This procedure does not speed the entire process or use less media, but makes the restore process easier because you will not restore unneeded files. If you later need these files, you simply copy or restore them to the hard disk; you don't have to wade through the entire backup set.

Uninstalling Copy-Protected Software

10.23   Tip: Uninstall copy-protected software that uses hidden files.

Although copy protection is almost a thing of the past, some programs still use this form of protection. Programs that use a key diskette (which must be inserted in the disk drive before the program starts) do not present a problem. But programs that install on the hard disk a hidden file that is position-dependent do. Although you can back up this type of file, you cannot restore it dependably. If the file does not return to the exact same clusters on the disk (and it usually won't), the backup is wasted. Even worse is the fact that one of the two or three hard disk installations you can make from the diskettes will be wasted.

Before backing up, you must reverse the steps that installed the software. Usually, the software provides an uninstall program. Before you run the backup software, follow the directions and uninstall the program (which bumps the install counter up by one, allowing you to install the program again). Back up in the normal manner and then reinstall the program.

You must uninstall only during high-risk situations (low-level or high-level formatting or running FDISK), when there is a high probability the hard disk will be destroyed. Otherwise, you can run the backup software without uninstalling the copy-protected software. The backup copy just won't work on that software.

Using a Correctly Configured DOS

10.24 Trap: Don't use an unconfigured version of DOS if you need the BUFFERS command.

This trap applies mainly to those using DOS pre-V3.3. Those early versions of DOS start with too few buffers. The BUFFERS directive of CONFIG.SYS has a dramatic effect when you use versions of BACKUP and RESTORE before V3.3. If you boot from a floppy diskette (for example, after you reformat the hard disk-based boot drive), make sure that the start-up diskette has the appropriate BUFFERS directive.

Years ago, I made the mistake of booting from a copy of the original PC DOS V3.1 master diskette when I was restoring my hard disk. This diskette, an exact copy of the master, did not have a CONFIG.SYS file. With 20 disk buffers, the old BACKUP and RESTORE process took 1 1/2 hours on a 20M disk. (The new versions of BACKUP and RESTORE take half this time.) By using the 3 native buffers that the older DOS used, the process took 3 hours! If you use a BUFFERS directive in your CONFIG.SYS, make sure that the DOS you are running during the backup and restore process uses this directive with the appropriate number of buffers specified.

Being Cautious with Conflicting Software

10.25 Trap: Be cautious when using any TSRs while backing up.

Unfortunately, some terminate-and-stay-resident (TSR) programs can interfere with the backup process. Any TSR program that grasps the DOS disk interrupts can cause a backup program not to work totally, or worse, not to work correctly. The problem can be insidious because you may not get an indication that the backup is incorrect until you need to restore the files.

Most known TSRs are safe to use with backup and restore programs. If a TSR should not be run with backup and restore software, that fact is acknowledged in the program's documentation. Conversely, most non-DOS backup and restore programs warn in their documentation that some TSRs should not be running while using the program.

If you are unsure of a new TSR, do not trust the backup disks completely until you check and verify all files that have been backed up. Usually, only a couple of small backup runs are needed to test the effects of the TSR on the backup procedure.

10.26   Trap: Avoid backing up a drive that has JOIN, SUBST, or ASSIGN in effect.

All three commands—JOIN, SUBST, and ASSIGN—manipulate the logical structure of DOS. In the case of ASSIGN or SUBST, you may back up the wrong drive. Using an ASSIGNed or SUBSTed drive as the source backs up the drive or subdirectory given in the ASSIGN or SUBST command, not the physical drive named in the BACKUP command. For instance, backing up an ASSIGNed drive backs up the assigned-to disk and backing up a SUBSTed drive backs up the underlying subdirectory, not the named drive. You can back up the assigned-to or substituted-from drive safely, but do not use an ASSIGNed or SUBSTed drive as the destination for the backup.

If you back up a drive that has been JOINed, you back up a temporary logical directory structure. You also back up more files than physically exist on the disk partition (which may be more files than you intend). The problem is formed in the backup, but realized in the restoration. If the directory structure during the restore operation is not identical to the structure that existed while backing up, expect problems. The restoration program creates and copies files to the new subdirectories. You end up putting more files on the partition than existed before. When your disk space runs out, you have a clue that you've made a mistake during the backup.

If you always operate with the identical JOIN in effect, you can back up and restore safely. (Some programs, however, have an allergic reaction to JOIN; don't trust the first few backups fully until you know that this procedure is safe.) Because DOS does not display the summed size of the joined disks, you may encounter a problem when you try to judge the size of the backup.

Ensuring the Integrity of the Disk Drive

10.27 Trap: Backup software cannot cope with logical or physical damage.

Backup software presumes that the disk is error free; the software cannot cope fully with disk damage—logical or physical. If it stumbles on an error, the software may abort its run or produce an incomplete backup (skip files and continue). In either case, all files are not backed up.

Early detection and prevention of a problem is less work than curing the problem after the fact. To prevent this stumbling, you must detect and repair any damage to the disk before you run the backup software.

10.28 Tip: To detect logical damage, run CHKDSK before you run any backup software.

Logical damage usually allows the most insidious errors because it does not give clear physical clues (error messages) as does most physical damage. The logical damage of cross-linked files is not noticed during normal operations until one of the files is used. Suddenly, the program using the file either spits nonsense or crashes. A peer into the file shows nonsense. Invalid clusters are usually easy to detect. The program using the file goes into a tailspin and crashes.

When your backup software encounters logical damage, the software does one of two things: perpetuates the logical damage by backing up the damaged files, or crashes. The cause of the crash may come with a loud complaint (an error message) or with a whimper (an obscure error message or no message at all). Either way, your backup is incomplete or incorrect.

To detect any logical disk damage, always run CHKDSK (without the /F switch) before you back up the disk. This step alerts you to the magnitude of the problem so that you can take the remedial actions needed before further problems occur. If the damage is minor, repair it before you proceed with the backup. (For more information, see the section on handling backup problems.) If the damage is major, use the other tricks in this chapter to back up as many files are possible, attempt to repair the damage, and then back up the remaining files.

Verifying Your Backups

10.29   Tip: Use DOS's VERIFY flag to verify backups.

While not backing up a disk is a poor operating policy, making an incorrect backup is almost as bad as no backup. If the backup does not have all the needed files or is otherwise unusable, files are in jeopardy. Your backup is of little use if the only backup copy of a file is unusable. Backups must be right.

BACKUP does not have a verify switch, but follows the status of the DOS VERIFY flag. If you want to verify the backup files, give the VERIFY ON command before you run BACKUP. Remember that the backup time will almost double when you use VERIFY ON. If the backups must be right, however, the extra time spent will be worthwhile.

If you do not customarily operate with VERIFY on (and I don't), turn VERIFY OFF after you run the backup. Other than the case of making backups, VERIFY is useful only to ensure that marginal hardware is functioning properly. Keep in mind also that disk cachers invalidate the VERIFY function.

10.30   Tip: If you are about to destroy your hard disk files, always verify your backup set or make two backup copies.

If you plan to destroy the hard disk version of your files, you want first to make sure that your only remaining copies don't have any mistakes. If you are going to destroy original disk files, *always* verify the backup set or make two backup copies of the disk. The first backup offers insurance against finding an error in the backup later; the second set offers almost absolute insurance against having an unrecoverable error in both sets. Although making two backup copies is more expensive in time and backup media than verifying your backup set, making an additional backup is more reliable.

Backing Up in Special Circumstances

10.31   Trap: Back up multiple partitions on hard disks separately.

Remember that DOS treats each disk partition as a separate disk drive. When the physical disk fails, partitions are lost. This fact is obvious after a moment's thinking. Keep in mind that backup software backs up only one drive at a time, and you must run the backup software on each drive.

I've rarely seen this mistake with beginners (who do not remember there is only one underlying disk drive). And I've rarely seen this mistake when the drive has several equal-sized partitions. The mistake comes when you use large and small partitions, such as 32M and 8M on a 40M drive. The small drive occasionally gets some useful files and suffers from a lack of attention for backup. When the entire drive fails, most files are backed up, but the structure and files of the "little guy" are lost.

Don't forget to back up the "little guy" every once in a while. When the entire drive fails, you won't be caught short.

10.32 Trap: Be cautious when using a hard disk as the backup device.

You might consider, for several good reasons, using a second physical hard disk as the recipient of the backup files. The backup and restore processes are much faster on a hard disk than on floppy diskettes. Because the backup media is not changed, the entire backup process can proceed with no or little intervention. The backup files are organized neatly into two files in one directory, and you don't have diskettes to lose or shuffle. Because the chance of the hardware failing on two physically different hard disks is minute, the procedure is safe.

On the other hand, if the backup hard disk fills, the problem is difficult to resolve. You must delete files to complete the backup. You may need to delete the BACKUP and CONTROL files in the \BACKUP subdirectory or delete other unnecessary files.

While two disk drives seldom fail simultaneously (although a power problem, such as a power line transient or lightning, or fire can catch both drives), both probably are tied to the same disk controller or interface card. (This is not the case when one disk drive is a disk drive on a card.) If the disk controller or interface fails, you cannot use the computer until you fix or replace the disk card.

With removable media, you can move the files to another system much easier than pulling out a hard disk (or even a hard card). If you have multiple systems, you can be up and running while the other system is being fixed. Storing all backup files on a second hard disk, therefore, is normally ill-advised.

10.33   Tip: RESTORE in DOS V3.2 and earlier cannot handle files from BACKUP in DOS V3.3 and later, but RESTORE in DOS V3.3 and later can handle any backup files.

The backup programs in DOS V3.3 and later changed from those in earlier versions. BACKUP and RESTORE in DOS pre-V3.3 place individual files on the backup diskettes with a 128-byte header. The header contains the administrative information, the original subdirectory for the file, the date and time, and a marker if the file is a partial file split across backup diskettes. Each backup diskette is topped by a file named BACKUPID.@@@, which gives the date and time of the backup and the backup disk number.

DOS V3.3 and later combines the backup files into one large "data" file called BACKUP.XXX. The BACKUPID.@@@ file is replaced by a CONTROL.XXX file. (The XXX is the number of the diskette in the backup sequence.) CONTROL.XXX holds the location information on each file that was contained previously in the backup file header.

Because of this change, BACKUP in DOS V3.3 and later works two to four times faster than in previous versions. RESTORE in DOS V3.3 and later also has a modest improvement in speed.

Another improvement in RESTORE in DOS V3.3·and later is that it is backward-compatible and can handle backup diskettes from any version of BACKUP. RESTORE detects the older BACKUP file format and adjusts itself accordingly. This detection makes moving between DOS pre-V3.3 and DOS V3.3 or V4 easier.

Unfortunately, the reverse is not true. RESTORE in DOS pre-V3.3 is not compatible with the new methods used in BACKUP DOS V3.3. The problem comes when you need to return to a system that uses a version of DOS prior to V3.3 and when the backup disks were produced by BACKUP in DOS V3.3 or later. This can occur, for example, when you need a previous version of DOS because of some allergic reaction with the new DOS, your programs, and the computer; or when you are transporting files *en masse* to another system. The latter case occurs most frequently.

You have these choices: use some other program for backup (FASTBACK, Intelligent Backup, or others; or XCOPY if no file spans more than one directory); patch RESTORE in DOS V3.2 or earlier to use in DOS V3.3 or later; or patch BACKUP in DOS V3.3 or later to use with DOS pre-V3.3. My personal preference is the first choice: use another type of backup program.

Backing Up with BACKUP

DOS's BACKUP command can handle most of your backup needs. The command, improved significantly for DOS V3.3, works much faster than before. The BACKUP command can handle backing up based on the archive attribute, date, and time; split files larger than the backup media; and manage all files within a subdirectory tree. The syntax for BACKUP appears in table 10.1. This section discusses some tips, tricks, and traps for using BACKUP most effectively. Some of the information here, however, is applicable to all backup software.

Table 10.1
BACKUP Syntax

Syntax

    *dc:pathc***BACKUP ds:***path\\filename.ext* **dd:**

      /S /M /A /D:mm-dd-yy /T:hh:mm:ss /F /L:logfile

ds: is the mandatory name of the drive holding the files to be backed up.

path is the starting directory for the backup.

filename.ext is the name of the file(s) to back up. Wild cards are allowed, and *.* is used for an omitted file name.

dd: is the mandatory name of the drive, hard disk or floppy, which will receive the backup files. When a hard disk is the destination, the files are stored in the \\BACKUP subdirectory.

Switches

/S	Backs up all *subdirectories* (sweeps), starting with the specified or current directory on the source disk and working downward
/M	Backs up all files *modified* (archive attribute on)
/A	*Adds* the backup file(s) to an existing set
/D:date	Backs up any files that were changed or created on or after the specified *date*, whose form is identical to the DATE command. (The DATE form must match the form specified in the COUNTRY directive.)
/T:time	Backs up any files that were changed or created on or after the specified *time*, whose form is identical to the TIME command and is also locale-specific
/F	*Formats* the destination diskettes if necessary. This switch is used in DOS V3.3 only.

/L:logfile   Creates a *log* file. The log file has the date and time and a line-by-line listing of the files in the backup with their backup diskette number.

                The log file name is in the form of *d:path\filename.ext*. If the full name of the log file is omitted, the log is placed in \BACKUP.LOG on the source disk.

10.34 Tip: Always give the starting directory in the source file name.

A classic backup mistake for those not fully acquainted with the directory structure of the disk is defaulting to the wrong current directory and not backing up the entire disk. You think that you backed up the entire disk, but actually only a section of the disk is saved.

I made this mistake several times when I started using DOS V2. From within a subdirectory, I ran the command **BACKUP C:*.* A: /S**. I watched as BACKUP copied the current directory and its subdirectories. Because some subdirectories were copied, I thought that the entire disk was copied.

I noticed the folly several weeks later when I gave the same command from the root directory of the disk, and BACKUP took three times longer to run. After checking the backup diskettes to ensure that BACKUP hadn't malfunctioned, I breathed a sigh of relief to have discovered the error before I needed the backup diskettes.

Unless you are sure that you want to back up only the current directory (and its subsequent subdirectories, if you give the /S switch), always specify the starting subdirectory in the source file name. As a double check, watch the first few file names that BACKUP posts on-screen. If the file names are not what you expect, stop BACKUP, examine the problem, and try again. Don't get caught short.

Making a Master Backup

10.35 Tip: To make a master backup, use BACKUP d:*.* A: /S /L /F for DOS V3.3; omit the /F for DOS V4.

To back up the entire disk, use the preceding command or the shortened form **BACKUP d:\ A: /S** (BACKUP inserts *.* for the missing file name). With DOS V3.3 and later, the source drive name is required. Giving the destination name is a good practice because the current disk drive is seldom the disk to receive the backup files.

Using the /F with DOS V3.3 is a highly recommended safety play. In case you run out of formatted diskettes, you can format more on-the-fly and continue the backup. This switch is unnecessary for DOS V4 because that version runs FORMAT automatically when needed and does not recognize the switch.

Use /L to produce a log file, just in case you need to track the processed files later. Give a path and file name, and remember that name for use with incremental backups.

Your first backup should be a master backup of the entire disk. After a period of time, you will want to make a new master backup. Don't forget to use another set of media for the new master backup. By rotating master backup media, you always can salvage a file in case of an error in the backup media or return to a previous version of a file, if needed.

Logging Backups

10.36 **Tip: Use the BACKUP /L switch to track the contents of the backup set.**

Because the directory of a BACKUP disk does not reveal the backup files, you have only two choices in decrypting the contents of the backup file. You either can dump the contents of the CONTROL.XXX file or use the /L switch when you make the backup. The best approach is to use the /L switch whenever you back up.

The /L switch produces a text file that logs the backup. The first line of the log contains the date and time of the backup. The remaining lines list the path and name for each file, preceded by the backup disk number. You can reuse log files. If a previous log file exists, BACKUP appends the next set of information to the previous log.

If you use the /L switch and omit the complete file name, the program places the log file in the root directory of the source disk and uses the name BACKUP.LOG. If you do give a name for the log file, you must enter a colon between the **L** in the switch and the file name (such as **/L:C:\BIN\BACKUP.LOG**). Be sure that you put the log file on the source, not the destination, if you are using diskettes.

The rules about current names for the /L switch are slightly different. If you omit the disk drive or path name, the program uses the source disk drive and current directory, respectively. If you give either or both, give a file name also. DOS makes no presumption about the file name and uses the final name in a path, resulting in an error.

You can produce a log file to check what files BACKUP processed and to confirm that the files you wanted were backed up. When you need to restore one or several selective files, you can search the log, find the needed diskette, and hand this diskette to RESTORE. You don't need to process each diskette to find the correct file.

Note: RESTORE does not use the log file. That file is for your use. Because no other directly usable traces exist to help you find the backup file you need on your backup media, you should use the /L switch whenever you back up.

10.37   Tip: Place the log file in a subdirectory. Use the same file for logging the master and associated incremental backups.

This tip maintains the philosophy of keeping the root directory uncluttered. Either create a separate subdirectory to hold the log file(s), or place the log file(s) in an existing subdirectory. For example, you can keep the file(s) in the \DOS subdirectory or in a directory called \BCKUPLOG.

When you are backing up, give the path and file name (the preferred way, if appending to an existing log), or move the file to the selected subdirectory later. You should use separate file names to make finding the required information easier. For example, you can use **/L:C:\BCKUPLOG\CDRIVE.LOG** for the log of drive C: and **DDRIVE.LOG** for the log of drive D:. Using the backup date, such as **/L:C:\DOS\JAN88.LOG**, helps identify the particular backup run or set of runs.

Logging all associated backups in one file is helpful for identifying quickly which incremental backup has the most current copy of a file. Use one backup log file for a master backup and use the same name with the incremental backup sets. When you need to restore a file, start from the end of the file and search backward for the first occurrence of the file name. The first (actually the last) record will be the set that holds the latest revision of the copy.

Making Incremental Backups

10.38   Tip: To make a new incremental backup based on the archive attribute, use BACKUP /M. To append to an established incremental backup, use BACKUP /M /A.

To start a new incremental backup set based on the archive attribute, use **BACKUP /M**. The program processes the files whose archive attribute is on (usually the files added or changed since the master backup). For example, to perform a complete, new incremental backup by the archive attribute on drive C:, use the form **BACKUP C:\ A: /M /S /L**.

When you reuse the same set for the next incremental backup, you need to add the /A switch to tell BACKUP to *append*. Forgetting the /A switch destroys the old backup files on the media and may cause you to lose revisions of the files. To add new revisions, use the form **BACKUP C:\ A: /M /S /A /L**. (The switches can be in any order.)

10.39   Trap: Put the last backup diskette of the set in the drive before you use BACKUP /A, or you may lose files.

When you give the /A switch, DOS expects the previously used backup diskette to be in the floppy disk drive you specify. BACKUP does not wait. BACKUP prompts you to insert a new diskette if the drive does not contain a diskette, if the diskette is not a backup diskette, or if the backup diskette is not the last diskette in the set. The trap is that BACKUP obliterates any files (by formatting the diskettes or erasing the files) on the next and subsequent diskettes, and you lose backup files. Prevent this problem by placing the last diskette of the set in the disk drive before running BACKUP with the /A switch.

10.40   Tip: If BACKUP cannot process an in-use file, rerun the command using the same diskettes and the /M /A switch.

Occasionally, BACKUP notes that a file is being used by another program or another computer (if you are on a network). That file is locked from use. If this happens, rerun BACKUP as many times as necessary, using the same backup media (in fact, leave the last backup diskette in the drive) and the same switches. If you are using only the /M or /D switch (with or without the /T switch), however, add the /A switch. That switch adds the file to the backup without disrupting the other files.

10.41   Trick: Use the log or any backup diskette from the set to give the correct date and time for /D and /T.

If you don't run your master backup on a specific date of the month (such as the first) or you just can't remember what day you ran BACKUP, use the log file from the backup run. If the log is not available, run a directory of the last diskette from the master backup set. The date and time of the CONTROL.XXX or BACKUP.XXX file gives the exact date and the general time. Use this date and time for the /D and /T switches.

Because the backup takes more than a few minutes, the times on the various diskettes in the set vary. You can, however, safely use the time from any diskette in the set. The time matters only if another activity occurred during the backup (and usually none does). Because DoubleDOS and DESQview allow concurrent activities, users of these programs should be wary when using this trick.

If you perform a second subsequent incremental backup, use the same basic trick. Find the date and time from any diskette in the last incremental set. If you used the /A switch on the set, use the last diskette. Only the diskettes that have additional files record the final dates and times for their CONTROL.XXX or BACKUP.XXX files. Fortunately, using an earlier date and time backs up more files than needed, not less. The backup takes more time, but the files are not in jeopardy.

10.42   Trap: Never use a time switch without a date switch.

You can use a date switch without a time switch, but not the converse. Using a time switch without a date switch is usually folly. You would process all files that have been added or modified after the given time of day, but on any day. If you give the time switch **/T:12:00**, for example, you back up any file that was added or changed on or after noon, including almost all DOS V4 files. (Most have a file time of noon and a file date of 6-17-88.) Backing up these files gives you a backup set with too many files. If you notice the mistake, abort the backup, start over, and give the appropriate command.

This trap also applies to RESTORE's time switches, /L and /E. Using either switch without an appropriate date switch restores files accurately based on the time, but randomly on the date.

Labeling and Storing Your Backups

10.43   Tip: After you make your backups, label the container holding the backup media.

On the first diskette in the box and on the outside of the box, I like to attach Post-it™ notes. These notes tell the source disk, the date and time of the backup, the type of backup (full, partial, or name of the related group of files), the diskette group (if you have multiple boxes of diskettes), and the type of backup program used. When I back up again, I peel off the old notes and replace them with new ones. I use this same procedure with tapes, putting one note on the tape and updating the note on the tape container.

At a glance, the outer note gives me all the information I need. (The inner note is in case the outer note comes loose.) I know which backup set to restore or recycle. Because I use four different backup programs (XCOPY, BACKUP, FASTBACK, and FASTBACK PLUS), I also know which restore program to use. Although I now mainly use FASTBACK PLUS, my older archive backup copies use the older programs; therefore, I need to know which restore program to use.

10.44   Tip: If information is critical, consider off-site storage for your backup media.

You need not rent a safe-deposit box or have a fireproof safe to use this technique. Simply keep a copy of your backup media for your work machine at home, or a set for your home machine at work. Although you may need to wait a day or a weekend to get the media, it will be accessible. In case of disaster, you will be amply rewarded. Don't think disaster cannot happen. Although the chance is not great, the results are devastating.

On one frosty January morning, years ago, I noted two police cars sitting across the parking lot as I pulled into my parking spot directly in front of the brick strip center where I worked. As I gathered some printouts from the car, one police officer approached me and asked my purpose for being there. I replied that I was going to work. Pointing to my building, he hinted that my work would be interrupted that day.

Fire had broken out in the middle of the night, and one half of the strip center was in rubbles. The remaining half was smoke filled. A fire wall in the middle of the center stopped the fire from spreading to our location, two store sites away. Our site was untouched by the fire itself. The smoke and soot, however, permeated everything, including diskettes within folders in locked file cabinets.

We spent the next two weeks cleaning and reconditioning equipment. Fortunately, the Winchester disks on the machines survived. If the Winchesters had died, the reconstruction would have taken several more weeks. If the fire had gutted the entire center, reconstruction would have taken several months.

Interestingly, several sections of the building were wired with alarms. Most alarms dial a number and are not continuously in touch with the alarm company. The fire knocked out the power and phone lines to the entire building quickly. Our alarm was backed by batteries, but the fire got the phone lines before the system sounded. Because the fire may have started with the wiring, even smoke detectors connected to the alarm system (including the type backed by batteries) may have failed to send out the distress signal.

The reason to store backups off-site should be apparent. Disaster probably will never happen. But when it strikes, the punch is a knockout.

Handling Backup Problems

If you encounter problems before or during the backup process, you should suspect your backups. Your backups are likely either to be incorrect or not to contain all the needed files. The tips in this section include some suggestions for solving backup problems, such as first detecting logical and physical damage, and a tip on forcing backup programs to skip damaged files. This section also gives a graphic example of what can happen if disk damage is not detected in time.

10.45 Tip: Evaluate whether to repair physical damage before or after backing up.

As with logical damage, the backup program can stumble when it encounters physical damage, such as a bad sector. The program may crash or allow you to sidestep the errant file. As with logical damage, the backup set will be incomplete.

If you detect physical damage before you back up, you should decide whether to repair the physical damage before or after the backup. If the damage is isolated to one or a few files and the repair is easy and swift, repair the damage and proceed with the backup. However, if the remedial software is complex, puts other files at risk, or more than a few files are affected, you should back up all files you can, repair the problem, and then back up the remaining files. The same procedure should be used if the state of the disk is too fragile to postpone backup.

If you discover the error while backing up, you normally can force the backup program to sidestep this file (using a Retry or Ignore response) and back up the remaining files. I strongly recommend using this brute force to finish the backup. If the state of the disk is fragile, the quickest backup is required so that the fewest number of files remain at risk. You always can remedy the problem and back up again, if the disk lasts long enough.

If you are exceptionally careful, you can use RECOVER to make a minor repair. RECOVER is not harmful when you use it on one file. If you are not exceptionally careful, however, RECOVER can cause problems. When you use RECOVER on an entire disk, the recovery is usually more painful than simply losing the disk.

10.46   Trick: Before backing up a disk (whether or not you detect a problem), turn on the archive attribute for all files.

Sometimes you can detect, but cannot cure, logical or physical damage before you run the backup software. If running the remedial software places other files at risk or the state of the disk is so fragile that you cannot postpone the backup, you should back up anyway. Two things can happen when you run the backup: the backup software can skip the problem files (manually or automatically), or the software can crash on the problem files. In either case, some files will not be backed up. Therefore, you need to take some extraordinary steps to get all the files.

The trick involves forcing the archive attribute for the files which will be backed up. You set manually the archive attribute on for the files before running the backup software. As the backup software processes the files, the archive attribute is turned off. If the backup software stumbles, the software can be rerun looking for those files whose archive attribute is still on. Hence, the backup software does the difficult search for files not yet backed up. This trick can be used on any disk (even a disk with no known problems), but excels in solving problems when a known problem exists with a disk to be backed up.

To employ this trick, use **ATTRIB *.* +A** (or other change-mode software) on the files you will back up. Use the same full file name with ATTRIB that you will give to the backup software. Also, use the /S switch with ATTRIB if you will be backing up more than one subdirectory. After ATTRIB completes its work, run the backup software. If, for any reason, the backup run is incomplete, use BACKUP /M /A (or the appropriate options for your backup software) to catch the remaining files, and then place the files on the same backup media.

This trick has a further benefit. Assuming that the backup software stopped because of a problem (usually a bad sector error rather than a logical problem), turn off the archive attribute manually for the problem file(s) before rerunning the backup software. If you use this procedure, you can safely back up the remaining files on the disk, skipping the errant file. After the remaining files are backed up safely, you can take the required remedial steps without jeopardizing additional files. After the problem is solved, back up the salvaged files separately.

10.47 Trap: If you encounter a problem during backup, suspect the backup copies. Even verifying the backup files does not mean that all files are backed up.

When writing this book, I tested various disk software on two different COMPAQ Deskpro 286® systems. One was at Que Corporation; another was at a friend's workplace. Because COMPAQs run at various speeds, the machines were ideal for testing the effects of processor speed on disk performance. The reason for using my friend's 286 system was that his Deskpro was fitted with a third-party XT-style disk controller, ideal for demonstrating the effects of data path width on the disk speed.

While running Kolad's HTEST®, I noticed that the interleave of my friend's two 20M hard disks on the system was wrong. The manufacturer's recommended interleave was 3 (which his disks were using); the best interleave would be 5. His current data transfer was half of what was possible. Also, his disk was badly fragmented; to get the best possible performance, I would need to run a defragmenter or simply back up, format, and restore the disk.

With permission, I operated on the computer. To judge relative times, I handled each disk differently. I used the "long" procedure on one disk: back up the disk, physically reformat the disk, repartition the disk, logically format the disk, and then restore the files. I used the "short" procedure on the second disk: back up the drive, run a nondestructive interleave setting such as Kolad's HOPTIMUM or Gibson's SpinRite, and then run a defragmenter (in this case, FASTTRAX) on the disk. (Regardless of the interleaver or defragmenter used, the disk files always first should be backed up. Any error can be calamitous.)

To speed both processes, I first deleted all temporary and backup files from the disk (again, with explicit permission). This freed several hundred K of disk space.

I used FASTBACK for the backup process. While operating on drive C:, FASTBACK froze. When I noticed the problem, I stopped FASTBACK and ran CHKDSK. CHKDSK reported that one file had invalid clusters, meaning that its FAT chain was damaged. I deleted the file, reran CHKDSK, and then restarted FASTBACK to pick up the remaining files in this subdirectory and subsequent subdirectories.

I eyeballed C:'s directories to make sure that all files had been covered. I then ran FASTBACK's verify mode (located in the FRESTORE program). After assuring myself that the backup files were correct (which was vital because I encountered a problem during the backup), I used the on-board routine in the disk controller to low-level reformat the disk. After the low-level format was completed, I FDISKed, FORMATted, and restored all backup files to the disk. This entire process took more than three hours. (The "shorter" process took about two hours.)

My friend returned the next week and was impressed with the improved performance. What was also impressive was the new amount of free disk space on drive C:—several additional megabytes.

Why were several additional megabytes free? Was the free space simply the result of deleting backup files or the result of a mistake? By deleting the errant file, did I destroy additional files? Did FASTBACK incorrectly verify the files and allow partial files to be restored? Or did FASTBACK not restore all the files?

The post-mortem revealed the mistake. If you guessed that FASTBACK did not restore all files, you made the correct call, although you may not have guessed the right reason.

I checked with a coworker; the errant file was a test file and was deleted safely. Because no additional errors were reported when CHKDSK was run a second time, I knew that no other files were affected. Because verify was successful, I knew that the backed up files were intact.

The problem was that the verify function had given a false sense of security. FASTBACK performed as well as could be expected. No backup software can handle a corrupted FAT. Although all the backup files verified successfully, not all files had been backed up. One week later, we discovered that two complete sets of subdirectories were missing from C:. When I started FASTBACK again, I had missed the two subdirectories. When the disk was reformatted, those files were destroyed.

Luck or a deity smiled on my folly. I had a copy of one missing set of files, and my friend had a copy of the second set of missing files. Only a small amount of revisions were lost.

The preceding tips, tricks, and traps present ways to prevent these mistakes. The first and most obvious solution is that I should have run CHKDSK before I started the backup. Doing so would have disclosed the logical problems before the backup software ran into a problem. By correcting the problem before the backup, the entire disk (except for that errant file) would have been backed up successfully.

Second, I could have backed up files based on the archive attribute during the second backup run. FASTBACK (as well as BACKUP and most other backup software) clears the archive attribute when the file is backed up. By using the archive attribute on the second run, FASTBACK would have hunted and found the files I missed.

A lack of paranoia prevented this solution. Had I issued the command **ATTRIB +A C:*.* /S** before running the backup software, I could have used this solution. I did not expect any complications, however, because my friend did not alert me about any problems. (Suggestion: Be more paranoid when you use someone else's system.) Because I did not know the layout of the disk, I could not guarantee that the files not yet backed up would have had their archive attribute on. Backing up based on the archive attribute was dismissed.

(By the way, using ATTRIB after the first run also would have been ineffective. If I did not notice the additional subdirectories during the second backup run, how would I have known to set the attributes of the missing subdirectories using ATTRIB?)

Third, I could have made two complete backup runs for each disk. Given the sequence of events, this technique would have worked. After discovering the problem file during the first run, I could have used the second run to catch all the files. (This solution was dismissed for a lack of diskettes, laziness, and overconfidence. I did not see enough diskettes on hand for two complete runs of FASTBACK per disk; I did not bother asking a coworker if more were handy; and I thought that the backup was successful.)

Fourth, I could have started again from the beginning to back up the entire C: drive. I also dismissed this method because of overconfidence and laziness. The files did verify successfully; I thought that I had been clever in getting the remaining files; and I did not want to take the time to redo the entire backup.

My conclusion from this investigation: Files were lost unnecessarily because of my failure to correct outstanding errors before running BACKUP and my failure to start the backup from scratch when the error was encountered. This is a mistake I will make only *once*.

Remember: Backup software cannot cope with disk damage. If the software encounters a problem during the backup, be suspicious of the backup files. Verifying the backup files is not enough. Those files may be unreliable or incomplete. If you are not positive that all the files have been backed up, either redo the entire backup or perform a second backup.

Restoring Files

You use RESTORE, the counterpart of BACKUP, to restore files backed up by BACKUP. Table 10.2 shows the syntax for the command. RESTORE is the only program that copies backup files back to the disk.

Table 10.2
RESTORE Syntax

Syntax

   *dc:pathc***RESTORE ds:** *dd:pathd\\filenamed.extd*

   /S /P /M /N /B:date /A:date /L:time /E:time

ds: is the mandatory name of the disk drive holding the backup information.

dd: is the name of the drive to which files are restored.

pathd is the starting path to the directory that will receive the restored files.

filenamed.extd is the name of the file(s) to be restored. Wild cards are permitted, and DOS assumes *.* if the path *and* file name are omitted.

Switches

/S	Restores files to the specified or current directory and all subsequent *subdirectories*
/P	*Prompts* whether a file should be restored if it is marked as read-only or has been changed since the last backup (archive attribute on)
/M	Restores all files *modified* (archive attribute on) or deleted (missing from the destination) since the backup set was made
/N	Restores all files that *no longer* exist on the destination
/B:*date*	Restores all files created or modified on or *before* the *date. date* is based on the file's directory date and is identical in form to the DATE command (whose DATE form matches the form specified in the COUNTRY directive).
/A:*date*	Restores all files created or modified *after* the *date*
/L:*time*	Restores all files modified at or *later* than the specified *time. time* is based on the file's directory time and is identical in form to the TIME command (also locale-specific).
/E:*time*	Restores all files modified at or *before* the specified *time*

RESTORE, a versatile program, was improved for DOS V3.3 to allow you to select the files you want to restore. The tips in this section highlight some situations that the newer features of RESTORE resolve. Because many other restoration programs offer the same features as RESTORE, the advice in this section applies to those programs as well.

10.48 Tip: Always keep handy a configured DOS diskette that contains your restoration program.

This tip uses simple logic. If your hard disk is destroyed, your hard disk copy of the restoration software is lost also. If you don't have a copy of the restoration software on a floppy diskette, your backup diskettes are useless.

Because almost all restoration programs are distributed on diskette, the original diskette contains the software. However, if the original diskette is not handy (it is at home or at the office, and you are at the other location), you are delayed in restoring the backup files.

Keep on hand a start-up diskette that holds the DOS files, such as FDISK and FORMAT, and the restoration software. If you must repartition or reformat the hard disk, the single diskette holds the software you need. As mentioned in Chapter 15 on troubleshooting, this diskette also can hold any disk-sector editor or other troubleshooting software you might use. This "disaster repair" diskette gets the call when the hard disk begins to fail.

10.49   Trap: You must RESTORE files to their original subdirectories.

RESTORE embeds into the CONTROL.XXX file the original subdirectory that contains the file. When restoring files, RESTORE uses the given or default path name to search for eligible files. RESTORE then restores each file to the same subdirectory that originally held the file.

Unlike COPY or XCOPY, which use the destination name to designate the eventual location of the files, RESTORE uses the destination name as a selection criteria. You therefore can use RESTORE to move files between systems, but not to move files to different subdirectories. Using a different destination name with RESTORE causes the program to restore the wrong files or not to restore any files at all.

10.50   Tip: To restore an entire disk from several backup sets, use the master backup and then restore incremental sets from the earliest to the most recent.

If you are restoring the disk from a master backup set and incremental backup sets, you must restore files forward in time. The master backup is the starting base of files, and the incremental sets hold the more recent versions. Unless you need to retrieve a less recent file, you must roll the disk forward by using the incremental backup sets in the order they were made. With this technique, the least recent copies are restored first and then overwritten by more recent copies. When the final incremental backup set is restored, the most recent backup copies of your files are restored.

10.51   Tip: To retrieve a select file or group of files, check your backup log for the appropriate diskette.

When you need to restore a single file or selective group of files, the last backup set usually contains the file. If the file does not change frequently, however, a previous backup set may contain the file.

If you are unsure which set has the most recent version of the file, use the backup log produced by the /L switch. Simply search for the file or subdirectory name using a text editor or word processor. (If the log covers more than one backup set, look for the last occurrence of the name.)

Once the right entry is found, write down the diskette number or numbers and move backward to find the line that contains the backup date and time. When you locate the line, use the date and time to find the right backup set.

10.52   Trap: Unless you know which diskette in the set holds the version of the file you want, start with the first backup diskette.

RESTORE does allow you to restore backup diskettes out of order. If you are restoring files selectively and know which diskette holds the file, you can start with the right diskette and work toward the end of the set.

You cannot, however, randomly reorder the diskettes in two cases. The first case is when a file is split across two diskettes. RESTORE is insistent about getting the diskettes in the correct order. You should never restore only part of a file anyway. If necessary, restore the entire file and then grab the section you need.

The other case is when you don't know which diskette holds the backup file. In this case, start with the first diskette and work toward the end. When all the files that should be processed are restored, you can stop RESTORE safely.

10.53   Trick: Use RESTORE and some logical deductions to reorder backup diskettes.

Attempting to identify the backup diskettes electronically under DOS pre-V3.3 is difficult. BACKUP in those versions of DOS does not leave many readily identifiable clues. From a directory of any backup diskette, you usually can guess the source drive of the files. The directory also can give clues as to when the backup was made or to what group the diskette belongs. (The directory date of the BACKUPID.@@@ file is the clue.)

If you haven't attached labels to your diskettes, guessing the order of the diskettes within the set requires more detective work. Once on a friend's system, I resorted to feeding diskettes to RESTORE, having RESTORE tell me this was the wrong diskette, and then trying another diskette. (The second time this happened with a different friend, I debugged the layout of the BACKUPID.@@@ and found the diskette number. The number is a two-byte hexadecimal word starting at byte number two, the third byte.)

Fortunately, DOS V3.3 and later leaves two clues. First, the name of the CONTROL.XXX and BACKUP.XXX files give the number of the diskette. And, second, either file gives the backup date.

10.54   Trick: If you don't know which backup set to use when restoring one or more files, use the procedure you use for restoring an entire disk.

If you cannot find which backup set has the right file, restore in forward order. Try to restore the files from the master backup and then restore from each incremental backup set from oldest to most recent. The forward restore order usually guarantees that the most current version is the surviving version.

10.55   Trick: If you know the approximate file date of the backup file, you can shorten the restoration process by using the RESTORE /A switch.

If multiple versions of a file exist on the backup media, you eventually get the most current version of the file, but you waste time in restoring versions that were later overwritten and you further fragment the restored disk. If you know the approximate date of the backup file (not the date of backup, but the date of the file), you can shorten the restoration process by using the RESTORE date switches.

The */A:date* switch restores files that have a directory date *on* or *after* the specified date. If you know that the file was modified on or after an approximate date, you can use that date to exclude earlier versions. If several copies of the file were stored on the backup set, RESTORE skips the copies with the earlier dates. If the backup set has several copies of the file with the same date, you also can use the **/L:time** switch to skip over earlier revisions. (Because knowing the exact time is more difficult, give the /L switch only if you happen to remember the approximate time.)

10.56   Trap: If you recycle multiple incremental backup sets using the /M /A switches, be selective when you restore files.

Keep in mind one inherent trap when you use more than one incremental backup set with the BACKUP /M and /A switches and flip-flop between sets. Because a file changes at an arbitrary date, more than one backup set may have the file, and any of the backup sets may have the most recent version of the file.

If you are not sure which set has the most recent version, you play a game of Russian roulette with your restore procedure. Any order of restoring the file from the backup diskettes may be wrong. If you make this mistake, you can unload the gun by selecting the version of the file to be restored. The trick is using RESTORE's /A and /L switches and a little work.

To restore the right version of the file, pick any incremental backup set (usually the most recently used set, but any set will work) and try to restore the file. Don't use the /A or /L switch yet. If the file is not on this set, try the next set.

After you have restored a file from the backup set, note the date and time of the file. Restore the file from the next backup set using the RESTORE /L and /A switches with the file's date and time. RESTORE skips any out-of-date versions and restores only a more current version. If a more current version is restored and more backup sets remain, use the RESTORE command again and give the newer date and time with the /L /A switches. Keep repeating the process until you use all backup sets and have the correct file.

You usually can omit the time switch. If you back up a file more than once a day or rotate sets within the same day, however, you must give the /A switch.

10.57   Trick: To restore only deleted files, use RESTORE /N.

RESTORE /N, which is similar to REPLACE /A, is the easiest way to restore deleted files. REPLACE A/ adds new files to a disk if files by the same name do not exist in the destination subdirectory. RESTORE /N restores backup files to the destination if the same file name does not exist on the destination. If you need to restore only deleted files to the disk, use RESTORE /N. The program skips backup files that match the names of the files in the destination.

10.58   Trick: To restore both deleted files and files that have become corrupted, use RESTORE /M /P.

RESTORE /M processes two types of files. First, the command processes files that no longer exist in the destination directories; this function is identical to the /N switch. In addition, the /M switch processes files that have the archive attribute set.

The switch is almost counterintuitive. While restoring deleted files makes sense, restoring outdated files generally does not. The /M switch is the "logical bomb" switch. When something explodes in the subdirectory and deletes or inadvertently modifies files, you need to return to the backup file.

If you can use one full file name to capture the only file or set of files that need to be restored, you may not need the /M switch. One wild-card file name, however, may not restore all the files you need. On the other hand, one file name might also restore too many files.

Rather than running RESTORE several times, you can use the /M switch to catch just the deleted and modified files you want to restore. RESTORE /M will restore any file whose archive attribute is on. To prevent RESTORE from overwriting a current version of another file (which should not be replaced), either use the ATTRIB command to turn off that file's archive attribute or use the /P switch.

The /P switch does not limit the selected files. All files that match the destination name and chosen switches are eligible for restoration. The /P prompts you so that you can choose which files should be replaced.

RESTORE /M /P allows you to replace the missing files quickly and to confirm individually the replacement of any changed files. The /P switch is easier to use than ATTRIB. For safety, always use the /P switch with the /M switch when you use any wild-card file name with RESTORE.

10.59   Trap: Renamed or moved files are restored if you use the /N or /M switch.

If you use the /N or /M switch, RESTORE performs a directory-by-directory, file-name-by-file-name comparison. Unfortunately, RESTORE /N or /M can be fooled. If you rename a file or move a file to a different subdirectory, RESTORE /N or /M restores the backup file to its old name and into its previous directory. On the other hand, when you use the /N switch, if a dissimilar file with the same name is created, renamed, or moved into the directory, RESTORE will not restore the correct file.

This process presents two harmless side effects. If you have moved or renamed the file, you restore an outdated version. In that case, simply remove it from the hard disk. If a file exists with the same name and prevents restoration of a file you need, either rename, move, or delete the conflicting file. Then run RESTORE again.

Generally, only one or two files are in conflict. Therefore, you can use an exact file name to restore each of those files. If you must use a wild-card name with RESTORE and you used the /M switch during the first restoration, use the /N switch the second time. Only the files not existing on the disk will be restored (which is what you want), and the chance of inadvertently restoring a wrong copy of a file is eliminated.

10.60 Trap: Don't use APPEND with RESTORE /N or /M.

APPEND can trick any program into finding files in the APPENDed subdirectories. Unfortunately, APPEND can also fool RESTORE. For example, if a different file by the same name as a deleted file exists in the APPENDed subdirectory, RESTORE /N or /M assumes that the file exists and does not restore the deleted file. If APPEND finds that one of the matching files from the APPENDed subdirectory has been modified, RESTORE /M restores the wrong file, and the newer version is lost.

Don't run APPEND before you use RESTORE /N or /M. If APPEND is active, deactivate the command with **APPEND ;**. Failing to heed this warning will result in a file being skipped (correctable) or the wrong file being replaced (usually too late to correct).

10.61 Trick: To restore a previous version of a file on a backup set, use RESTORE /B /E.

The /B and /E switches are RESTORE's "too late" switches. Suppose, for example, that you have made changes to a file, backed up the file, and now need an earlier version of that file. Or perhaps you've backed up and then you discover a corrupted file; the most recent backup copy also may be corrupted. Whenever you want to return to an earlier revision of a file, you can use RESTORE's /B and /E switches.

The **/B:*date*** switch restores files whose dates are on or *before* the specified date. The **/E:*time*** switch restores files whose file times are the same or *earlier* than the given time. By giving the file date minus one day or the date and time minus one minute, you can restore the earlier version from the same backup diskette set. If this version is not the one you want, repeat the RESTORE command and use this retrieved version's date minus one or the date and time minus one. Keep repeating the process until you get the correct version.

This approach presents only one problem: RESTORE will restore earlier versions of the file, which were subsequently overwritten by later versions. If you have a good idea of the date (and time) of the version you want, you can use the /A and /B switches (and the /L and /E switches) to narrow the criteria to a few minutes, a day, or a couple of days.

Neither the /B nor /E switch is required when the backup set contains only one earlier version. If different backup sets have different versions, just run RESTORE on each backup set until you have the right version. However, if you are not sure whether a backup set has the current file (which would have the same date and time), use the /B and /E switches with RESTORE and give an earlier file date, or the same date but an earlier time.

10.62   Tip: If you are restoring an earlier version of a file, preserve the current file by renaming or moving it before you use RESTORE.

Remember that RESTORE will write the previous version of a file over the current version. If you want to preserve any or all of the current file, you must rename the file or move it into another subdirectory. (Another alternative is to copy and rename the file, and then let RESTORE overwrite the current file.) This tip will protect the current contents of the file so that it will not be lost.

10.63   Trap: Be cautious when restoring read-only files with the /P switch.

Read-only files do not customarily change and do not require restoration. You might have to restore a read-only file, however, when the current file is marked read-only, because BACKUP does not record the read-only marking. If you do need to restore a read-only file, you must use the /P switch. Using this switch is the only way that RESTORE will process a read-only file. As mentioned earlier, RESTORE confirms the replacement when you give the /P switch.

RESTORE will not overwrite a file marked read-only unless the /P switch is given. If you are restoring backup files to the hard disk, seriously question whether a file currently marked as read-only should be overwritten.

By definition, a read-only file cannot be altered normally. Also, the file causing the question is on the destination disk (not marked read-only on the backup disks). Because read-only files do not change, the files normally don't need to be restored. The current copy on the disk should be correct.

Starting with DOS V3.3, neither BACKUP nor RESTORE processes the two hidden system files. The IBMBIO.COM and IBMDOS.COM (or IO.SYS and MSDOS.SYS) files are not backed up or restored. If you need to restore either file, use the SYS command.

In one particular case, however, a read-only file should be restored. If a file was incorrectly altered before the read-only attribute was turned on manually, you should turn off the attribute on the hard disk-based file, restore the correct copy, and then turn the read-only attribute back on.

Practicing with Your Backup Software

10.64 **Trick: Practice using your backup and restore software before you need to restore files.**

Most people approach the first few backup operations and almost all restore operations with nervous apprehension. You're not sure whether you have given the command correctly or whether the missing file will be restored properly. You can inspire confidence in yourself, your procedures, and your backup setup by doing a small amount of practice.

Try backing up either the entire disk or a selective subdirectory or two. Then attempt immediately to restore some files from your backup media. Because the disk files and the backup files are identical, no files are at risk. Experiment with the commands, learn how the switches work, feel free to make mistakes, and gain the needed knowledge and confidence.

When you actually need your backup set for the first time, you will have enough anxiety and problems. You don't want the thrill of discovering your restoration software to add to the general anxiety. Practice and make sure that your hardware, software, and experience is correct before you have the need.

Part III

Customizing Your System

Includes

Using a CONFIG.SYS File

Using Device Drivers

Customizing the Video Screen and Keyboard

11

Using a CONFIG.SYS File

DOS's configuration file, CONFIG.SYS, gives you unprecedented flexibility to alter functions and add devices to your system. This chapter and the following one offers advice on some, but not all, CONFIG.SYS directives. Because some directives fit more appropriately with the underlying subject that the directive affects, they are covered in other chapters of this book. For example, BUFFERS is discussed in Chapter 3, SHELL in Chapter 9, and switches with the ANSI.SYS device driver in Chapter 13.

This chapter starts with advice on modifying your CONFIG.SYS file (manually or with installers provided by many application programs). Various CONFIG.SYS directives are discussed next, including advice on REM, STACKS, FCBS, FILES, and LASTDRIVE. The DOS V4 INSTALL directive is covered, and some methods to assist in using several different CONFIG.SYS and AUTOEXEC.BAT files on the same computer is presented. The next chapter covers two remaining directives, DEVICE and DRIVPARM, and discusses peculiarities in using some floppy disk drives.

Modifying Your CONFIG.SYS File

CONFIG.SYS is an ASCII text file read by the computer upon DOS start-up. Most computers have an established CONFIG.SYS, however some may not. This section covers some tips about modifying and establishing a new CONFIG.SYS, including those circumstances when a program or batch file may automate the process.

11.1 Tip: You must place the CONFIG.SYS in the root directory of the start-up disk.

The CONFIG.SYS file must be in the root directory of your boot disk. DOS does not search anywhere else for the file. If you normally boot from a

325

hard disk and the system boots from a floppy diskette instead, the system uses the CONFIG.SYS on the floppy diskette (if one exists). If the system can't find the file (the file is under a different name or in a different directory), DOS uses the default values for all settings.

11.2   Tip: When you make changes to CONFIG.SYS, start DOS again to activate the changes.

Any changes you make to a CONFIG.SYS file are activated only at the next DOS start-up. DOS does not read the file at any other time. If you make changes to the CONFIG.SYS file, you must start DOS again to activate the changes.

11.3   Tip: Check the documentation of new hardware and software for the necessary CONFIG.SYS directives.

Most hardware and software packages indicate in their documentation what directives must be added to CONFIG.SYS and what commands should be added to AUTOEXEC.BAT. If the provided installation program does not make changes, use a text editor to add or edit manually the required lines.

If you need to change the CONFIG.SYS file, save the previous file under a different name and make only one set of changes at a time. If you make a mistake, finding the changes are easier.

11.4   Tip: Use the highest needed value for any CONFIG.SYS directive.

CONFIG.SYS is an exercise in maximums. You must set directive values for the most extreme case. If one program states that it needs **FILES = 10** and another states that it needs **FILES = 20**, use **FILES = 20**. Unless you want to swap CONFIG.SYS files and reboot, the CONFIG.SYS you use must handle the most extreme case.

11.5   Trick: Copy your CONFIG.SYS before you run any program installer.

In this age of sophisticated program installers, most installers allow you to specify the correct destination directories and install the appropriate statements in your CONFIG.SYS and AUTOEXEC.BAT files. (Note: A program installer is an extensive batch file or program that copies the needed files from the distribution diskettes and configures the software.) The program installers with Microsoft application products are the best examples of both extensive and well-behaved installers. Some installers, however, are ineffective or troublesome. The extent of the problems they present varies. I dislike any installer that doesn't act exactly as I do.

Some installers do the proper checking, confirm with you that the changes are needed, and then rewrite the entire CONFIG.SYS (and possibly the AUTOEXEC.BAT file), incorporating the changes. These installers convert all lines to all upper- or lowercase letters. I use uppercase letters for the directives and lowercase for the remainder of the line so that I can spot and separate the directive keyword from the arguments. One minor "nit" with these installers is that I dislike editing the file to restore my capitalization.

Another small problem is that some installers do not examine CONFIG.SYS, and they add redundant lines. Many application programs, for example, require a **FILES = 20** directive; the installer appends the line to the CONFIG.SYS file—even if the line already exists. (When values for a directive conflict, DOS uses the last directive encountered. Although DOS's start-up is not effected, the additional line is unneeded and potentially confusing when later editing the file.

Some installers pose more serious problems. These installers examine the file, see a different value, remove the old line, and add a new directive. This procedure is acceptable if the installer confirms the replacement when the value is more than required, not less. In Chapter 3 on disk performance, I suggest that fewer BUFFERS are better with a disk cacher. I also use a larger than typical FILES statement because some of my TSRs keep files open. I've had installers remove my **FILES = 30** directive and substitute a **FILES = 20** statement. I've also had installers demand that my meager 7 buffers be replaced with 15 or 30.

The worst type of installers assume that you have no CONFIG.SYS, create one automatically, and destroy the existing file. I've had this problem with a variety of installers from major software publishing houses—the worst from a major database/graphics house.

The automatic addition or replacement of existing CONFIG.SYS lines is not always welcome. The insistence that certain values are best is also unwelcomed. The destruction of existing CONFIG.SYS files is inexcusable. When that happens, I begin to doubt the usefulness of the entire package that accompanies such an installer. Fortunately, most publishers have changed their installers, but a few problem installers still exist.

For safety, copy your CONFIG.SYS (and AUTOEXEC.BAT) file before you run any installation program or batch file. If the installer modifies your CONFIG.SYS file unfavorably, you can create the proper file from the copy and the additions provided by the installation program. If you have the option, write the changes to a different file. Then incorporate the changes

into a new copy, merging your previous CONFIG.SYS file with the new
directives. This procedure makes problems that occur when you first use
the package easier to resolve. (For more suggestions, check the tips on the
REM directive that appear later in this chapter.)

Be suspicious of any program that provides a batch file for installation.
Check the batch file carefully. If you see anything that affects CONFIG.SYS
(or AUTOEXEC.BAT), know what the installer will do before you run it.

Using CONFIG.SYS Directives

DOS V3.3 includes 10 directives for CONFIG.SYS; DOS V4 provides 13
(see table 11.1). Many have default values or actions that DOS uses if it
does not find the CONFIG.SYS file on start-up or if you do not give the
directive in the file. You should take time to get familiar with the default
values and effects of each CONFIG.SYS directive.

Know the effects of the various directives. The directives alter the
performance, capabilities, and reactions of DOS. For some users, the
default values or actions are sufficient. In many cases, however, the
default values or actions are not sufficient. The result of using the defaults
(or using insufficient values) can be obscure or indirect. Often, a directive
is needed as a response to what appears to be an unrelated problem.

For users of DOS V3.3 and later, the default value or action for FILES and
SHELL, followed by DEVICE, cause the most problems. (Before DOS V3.3,
omitting BUFFERS caused a large performance crunch.) For example, if a
SHELL directive is not used, DOS loads the command interpreter from the
root directory of the start-up disk and establishes an environment size of
168 bytes (128 bytes for DOS pre-V3.3). If you need to increase the size of
the environment in response to an **Out of environment space** message,
you need a SHELL directive.

If no DEVICE directives are given, DOS uses only the device drivers in the
IO.SYS file. If a hardware item requires a device driver, you cannot use the
item without loading the device driver via a DEVICE directive.

An obscure error is when DOS runs out of file handles. The running
program may give the error message **File not found** or **Cannot open file**.
The file exists and is ready for use; the program, however, exceeded
DOS's capability to track so many open files at once. If you do not know
the effects of the directives (in this case, FILES), you may not realize the
cause of the problem.

Table 11.1
CONFIG.SYS Directives

Directive	Use	Default
BREAK ON|OFF	Controls the check for Ctrl-Break	OFF
BUFFERS = number	Sets the number of disk buffers	3, 5, 10, or 15 (usually 15)
COUNTRY = ccode, codepage, file	Sets the locale for country-specific information	001, 439 (no country file)
DEVICE = file	Loads a device driver	No device driver loaded
DRIVPARM = switches	Sets the disk drive characteristics	No change in drive characteristics
FCBS = maxopen, neverclose	Sets the number of DOS V1 file control blocks	4, 0
FILES = files	Sets the number of usable file handles	8
* INSTALL = file	Installs a terminate-and-stay-resident program (TSR)	No TSR loaded
LASTDRIVE = drive	Sets the last logical disk drive	E, or last physical disk if more than 5
* REM	Allows a remark	Not applicable
SHELL = file	Loads the command interpreter	\COMMAND.COM \COMMAND.COM /P /E:168 (V3.3 and later)
STACKS number, size	Controls the number and size of program stacks	9, 128
* SWITCHES switches	Sets the mode of the Enhanced Keyboard	No switch

*New to DOS V4

11.6 Tip: All directives except DEVICE and INSTALL are order-independent.

All CONFIG.SYS directives are independent of each other and can appear in any order. When creating, adding to, or editing a CONFIG.SYS file, you may order the directives any way you want.

The only exceptions are the DEVICE and INSTALL directives, which can appear anywhere in the file. However, DEVICE directives and INSTALL directives may need to appear in a certain order.

Instead of burdening the user to place CONFIG.SYS directives in a specific order, DOS contains the sophistication to fully "shake and bake" the CONFIG.SYS file. DOS reads the configuration file several times as it prioritizes the different directives into categories: configuration directives (BREAK, BUFFERS, FCBS, FILES, LASTDRIVE, and STACKS), DEVICE directives, and the SHELL directive. All directives within a category are processed as a group before the next group is processed.

With the DOS V4 additions of the INSTALL directive and expanded memory use, the internal prioritizing by DOS becomes more important. The order for DOS V4 is configuration directives (except BUFFERS when the /X switch is used), DEVICE (and BUFFERS /X), INSTALL, and SHELL.

The major reason for the change is DOS's use of expanded memory. The expanded memory manager must be in place before DOS can use expanded memory for its buffers (a BUFFERS /X directive) or use FASTOPEN /X (because FASTOPEN can be loaded via an INSTALL directive). Under DOS V4, DOS defers processing a BUFFERS /X directive until all DEVICE directives are handled, and then executes INSTALL directives. Rather than forcing the user to have the appropriate line to load the expanded memory manager before a BUFFERS /X or FASTOPEN /X directive, DOS manages the CONFIG.SYS file intelligently.

For convenience, you may want to place all non-DEVICE, non-INSTALL directives at the top of the file, all DEVICE directives in the middle of the file, and all INSTALL directives at the end of the file. This organization makes the file easier to read and maintain (particularly when the CONFIG.SYS file spans more than one-half screenful of directives).

11.7 Tip: Only the BREAK and REM directives do not affect the size of DOS.

Remember that almost every directive takes some space from the 640K DOS RAM area. If DOS memory is tight, you should know the size impact of each directive on DOS memory. Each increment above the default value increases DOS's size for BUFFERS, FCBS, FILES, LASTDRIVE, and STACKS. Each decrement below the default value, except LASTDRIVE, decreases DOS's size. For COUNTRY, DEVICE, INSTALL, or SHELL, the increase depends on the specifics of the directive (the size of the installed device driver or program).

Using Remarks

11.8   Trick: Use REM to add comments or remove lines temporarily from your CONFIG.SYS.

In DOS V4, you can use REM to place a nondisplayed comment in your CONFIG.SYS file. You can insert comments that remind you of the function of each section or line in the file—particularly when certain lines are order-dependent.

The primary use of REM is to "comment out" directives in order to change the action of the CONFIG.SYS file. Rather than deleting lines or copying and editing the original CONFIG.SYS file, you can use REM to make DOS skip processing the line. When you need DOS to act on the line, simply remove REM.

With DOS pre-V4, you also can use this trick, but the trick is inelegant. Place REM (or any other nondirective word) at the start of the line. The usual error message, `unrecognized command in CONFIG.SYS`, appears on-screen. Although this message makes the technique visually unappealing, DOS does not process the line and you simply ignore the message.

Controlling the Stack

11.9   Tip: To handle the Internal Stack Failure error, use STACKS = 12, 256.

Starting with DOS V3.2, DOS changed its internal stack services. The infamous `Internal Stack Failure` error results from those odd occasions when the new scheme (more appropriate for today's computer use) is sent into a hopeless chase of its own tail. If this problem occurs, add a **STACKS = 12, 256** line to your CONFIG.SYS.

To explain the use of this command (and when to vary from this tip), you should understand the stack and the changes that occurred between DOS V3.1 and V3.2. The stack is a repository in RAM, used for temporarily storing values and memory addresses. The CPU cannot hold all temporary information; it needs a high-speed, temporary storage site. While executing any program (including an operating system), all CPUs require this RAM for internal housework.

The system treats the area as a pile; therefore, the name *stack* is appropriate for this RAM area. The system pushes information from the CPU onto the top of the stack; the information later pops from the top of the stack back into the CPU. (The actual mechanics vary among processor families. Some work the RAM-based stack in ascending order, some in descending order.)

Before DOS V3.2, DOS used one single stack. The stack was small, and when it overflowed (too many pushes and not enough pops), the system acted in a somewhat random, but always undesirable fashion. The best result was an immediate crash (lock up). The worst case was a random traipse through memory and a walk over disk-based information (destroying data on the disk); then the system crashed. The one constant effect was that all information being processed at the time of the crash was lost. The other effects were arbitrary. Because DOS did not defend itself from this error, it could not notify you of the damage nor display any error message, making the event even more confusing for the user.

The more frequent causes of stack overflows were errant programs, RAM failures, and too many hardware interrupts (generated by devices demanding attention). Errant programs and most RAM failures were consistent in their behavior. Errant programs crashed (when you followed the same operations), and RAM errors were caught by the infamous parity error hardware. Hardware interrupt failures are reproducible, but seem arbitrary. Re-creating the exact circumstances of the error can be difficult.

Computers can service devices in two different ways: polling (checking to see whether something needs to be handled) or interrupts (the electronic equivalent to a tap on the shoulder). The PC family mainly uses the interrupt method. When the device requires attention, the peripheral generates a unique interrupt for the CPU. For example, interrupts are generated when you press a key, the communication port receives a character, or the hard disk completes a writing operation.

When the interrupt occurs, DOS drops whatever it is doing and reads a specific location in memory. This location contains the address of the specific interrupt handler (software instructions) to be executed for this type of interrupt. DOS executes the interrupt handler, appeases the device, and returns to its previous task.

The problem is that the CPU can be interrupted while handling an interrupt. Until the subsequent interrupt is completed, the information from the nested (previously executed but still unfinished) interrupt handler is left on the stack. If too many interrupts occur, DOS literally blows (overflows) its stack.

The most frequent cause of stack overflows was the Enhanced 101-key Keyboard on PC XT 286s. The ROM-based interrupt handler for the keyboard took slightly longer to process keystrokes. If the user pressed too many keys too quickly, DOS blew its stack. The same was true for pressing too many keys during other interrupt events, such as using communications programs.

DOS V3.2 and later is more robust. As the computer uses more peripheral equipment (scanners, disk drives, and the like), more hardware interrupts are possible. To address the problem, DOS maintains smaller, multiple, reusable stacks in a "stack pool."

DOS itself uses one stack frame (the DOS documentation's name for a single stack). As interrupts are generated, DOS gets and assigns to each interrupt an additional stack frame from the pool. As each interrupt is satisfied (the CPU completes the interrupt handler), the stack frame is returned to the pool, ready for reuse.

One benefit to this scheme is that DOS can track internally the use of each stack. If a stack will overflow or if more interrupts occur than DOS has available stack frames, DOS detects the error. Instead of destroying information (other than the work in progress) and crashing whimperlessly, DOS sounds the alarm **Internal Stack Failure** and crashes.

The second and greater benefit is that you can set the number and size of the stacks. If you get the stack failure message (or want to prevent a stack overflow), you need to change the system to generate fewer interrupts (impractical) or use the STACKS directive to cover the worst stack-use case. Use the following syntax to set STACKS:

    STACKS = number, size

number is the stack frames (8 to 64 are allowed), and **size** is the number of bytes for each stack frame (32 to 512 bytes are allowed, in increments of 16 bytes).

If you have a good grasp of your system, you can judge the worst case and issue the appropriate directive. Because I have neither the patience to find the best value nor the desire to get the stack failure message, I've adopted 12 stack frames with 256 bytes per frame—a scheme that usually works.

11.10   Tip: If you need to alter the stacks, increase the number of stacks and then increase the size of the stacks.

Most stack failures occur because of too many interrupts rather than too little stack space. If you do get the stack failure message, start the computer again, fix the damage that may have occurred, and then increase the number of stacks by one or a couple. If you do not have a STACKS statement, add one that gives at least 10 stacks of 128 bytes (DOS starts with 9 stacks of 128 bytes), and then start the computer again.

Try to reproduce the failure, knowing that if you're successful, the system will crash. (Don't work on useful data!) If the system crashes, increase the number of stacks again. If you get past 12 stacks, start increasing the size of the stacks to 256. This procedure solves almost all problems. (If the problem persists, increase the number of stacks to 20, 512. If the problem still exists, something else is wrong with the computer.)

Adjusting DOS for FCBS and FILES

11.11   Tip: Although most programs do not use FCBs, many old and some new programs still do.

DOS and programs use two methods to communicate which files should be opened and where and when to move within those files. One method (FCBs) is a DOS V1 holdover; the other method (file handles) are used by almost every program today. The difference in communications methods can be important to you if you use SHARE or if you use DOS V4. If you have a program that uses the holdover method, this tip applies to you.

The origin of the file control block (FCB) is in the old Digital Research CP/M® (a popular operating system for 8080- and Z80-based computers). DOS V1 used this method exclusively. The FCB is established by the running program and contains the name of the file and part of the file to use. DOS, on appropriate function call, opens, reads, writes, or closes a file based on the FCB.

The second method of file handles is used by DOS V2 and later. When opening a file, programs give DOS a file name; DOS returns to the program a 16-bit number (the *file handle*). In turn, programs indicate to

DOS which file to use via the file handle (the returned number) rather than the clumsy FCB. Most importantly, the file handle method allows large files (up to 4 billion bytes), path names, and file-locking functions—all of which are not possible with FCBs.

Today, FCBs are almost forgotten. Most contemporary programs do not use FCBs (however a few new programs and many older programs still do). Two clues that a program uses FCBs are that the program works with DOS V1 or is ignorant about subdirectories. To accommodate these programs, all versions of DOS, including V4, maintain compatibility. These relics from a bygone era continue to work with DOS.

(The reason some "contemporary" programs use FCBs is that DOS did not provide direct services to programs to manipulate volume labels and subdirectories. DOS V3 provided subdirectory renaming; DOS V4 provides volume label functions. However, an FCB is still needed to read or write a subdirectory as a file.)

11.12   Trap: If your programs use FCBs and you use SHARE or DOS V4, you may need the FCBS directive.

The problem with a program's use of FCBs is in two areas: when file-locking facilities might be needed or when large disk partitions (greater than 32M partitions) are used. Both cases requires the use of SHARE.EXE. If you use SHARE with any DOS version, particularly DOS V4, programs that worked previously may suddenly not find files or be halted by DOS. The reason is that SHARE.EXE governs the number of FCBs used.

DOS internally and transparently translates the FCB type of operation to a file handle type of operation. The program does not know of DOS's translation, and the program and DOS work correctly. Also, if SHARE is not used, an unlimited number of FCBs can be used.

DOS cannot perform file-locking functions with FCBs. Nor does DOS protect from being destroyed files that are too large to be addressed through the use of an FCB. The first case applies to those using DOS V3.1 or later on a network or with several programs simultaneously. The second case applies to those using disk partitions larger than 32M, possible with DOS V4. In these cases, SHARE.EXE adds to DOS the functions needed to protect files from errant FCBs operations.

The ground rules for FCBs change when using SHARE.EXE. When SHARE is loaded and unless DOS is explicitly instructed otherwise, only enough areas are available to translate 4 FCB-based files to file handles for DOS V3, 16 for DOS V4.

Some programs abandon FCBs, assuming that DOS has an unlimited number of FCBs or that the FCBs will be closed automatically by DOS when the program ends (which is not always true). Because programs have this sloppy habit that would needlessly waste FCBs, DOS recycles FCBs on a least recently used basis. When a new FCB area is needed and none is available, DOS disregards the oldest FCB area and reuses this space. This action allows the reuse of abandoned FCBs.

Unfortunately, if a program uses too many FCBs, an in-use FCB can be recycled. Because DOS cannot communicate with a running program about which FCB should be recycled or which FCB has been recycled, a program may suddenly be incapable of reading or writing to a file. The specific reaction to this circumstance (from quiet acquiescence to error message) depends on the program.

To eliminate this problem, use the FCBS directive. The syntax for the directive is as follows:

FCBS = maxopen, neverclose

maxopen, the maximum number of FCBs for use at a time, defaults to 4. Each FCB specified takes 32 bytes. **neverclose** is the number of FCBs DOS will not recycle automatically if the program attempts to use more than **maxopen** FCBs. The default is 0.

If **neverclose** is less than **maxopen**, DOS recyles the least recently used FCBs above the number specified by **neverclose**. In other words, no FCBS directives allow DOS V3 to use only 4 FCBs, and all 4 can be recycled behind a program's back. (However, SHARE V4 resets the defaults to 16 FCBs with 8 recyclable FCBs.) Specifying **FCBS = 4, 2** means that 4 FCBs are usable simultaneously, but the first two FCBs used will not be recycled; the later two FCBs can be recycled. If **maxopen** and **neverclose** are equal (such as **FCBS 4, 4**), no automatic recycling occurs.

If a program attempts to read or write a file with an FCB that DOS recycled or to address a part of the file that cannot be reached using an FCB, DOS gives a read or write error to the program. The reaction to this error depends on the program.

If a program attempts to open another file and no FCB is available (you have stopped DOS from recycling FCBs), DOS gives an `FCB unavailable` message and DOS does not open the file. The result of these errors are seldom desirable and depend on the program. In most cases, you will have a chance to respond to the message. Unlike with other critical errors, the only offered responses are `Fail` and `Abort`.

If a program that uses FCBs acts erratically or you get an error message that appears out of place from DOS, the program, or both, FCB recycling is the probable cause. For DOS V3.3 and earlier, immediately add or change your FCBS directive to something such as 8,8 or larger and restart DOS.

If you use DOS V4 with SHARE and you omit the FCBS directive, SHARE adjusts FCBS to 16,8. If you use an FCBS directive and get an error, either remove the FCBS directive or increase the given values.

11.13 Tip: Although most applications demand the FILES = 10 directive, some multiple file-use applications demand FILES = 20.

The 37-byte file handle is the contemporary way that programs access files. With more powerful programs comes the ability to use more files at a time. Some text editors can edit scores of files in many windows. Some database applications can use 8 to 16 files at once. With today's demanding programs, more simultaneous file handles are needed.

If your program cannot find a file that does exist, you most likely need to increase the number of file handles. The syntax is identical for DOS V2 and later, but the limit changes:

> **FILES = number**

number is the number of file handles that may be used simultaneously. For DOS V2, the limit was 99; V3 and later limit the number to 255. Usually, a value of 10 to 15 corrects most file handle problems.

11.14 Trap: When you give the FILES directive, remember that DOS uses five file handles automatically.

DOS, which uses file handles for communicating with devices, takes five handles "off the top" of the FILES directive. DOS uses one handle each for the five standard devices: standard input (the keyboard, CON), standard output (the video display, CON), standard error (also CON), standard auxiliary (the communications port, AUX), and standard printer (PRN).

DOS defaults to eight handles, leaving three handles for your programs to use. Because many programs use more than three files simultaneously (not just for data files, but also program overlays), you may need to use the FILES directive.

However, when counting the maximum possible number of files that may be open at once, don't forget the 5 handles that DOS uses. If you will have 10 files open at once, the correct value for FILES is 15, not 10.

11.15   Tip: If you run on a network or use multitasking software, increase the number of FILES.

FILES is a system-wide parameter, not a per-process number. DOS restricts a process to a maximum of 20 files. Because handles come from FILES (the system-wide number), no program bumps into the per-process limit (20) until you set FILES past that limit (FILES = 21, for example).

The problem comes when you are on a network or use any multitasking software, such as DOS's PRINT. In those cases, the programs you use need handles from the system-wide number. A lack of file handles, not memory conflicts, can cause a program that functions fine when PRINT is not loaded to complain about not being able to open files when PRINT is activated. If you use a network or multitasking software, consider adding five to your current number of FILES; five is a sufficient number for most uses.

Establishing More Drive Names with LASTDRIVE

11.16   Tip: If you use SUBST, use LASTDRIVE to establish at least three additional disk drive letters.

You probably need to include the LASTDRIVE directive in your CONFIG.SYS file if you use the SUBST command. The directive allows you to establish additional dummy disk drive letters for use with SUBST or other logical chicanery commands.

Usually, the highest letter DOS allows is E or the last logical or physical drive (installed through a CONFIG.SYS device driver), whichever is alphabetically greater. For example, a PS/2 with a 20M drive has physical drives A: and C: (drive B: is used, in this case, as a synonym for drive A:). DOS can use drives D: and E: for SUBST (or for any other programs that perform this type of logical structure alterations). Additional installed device drivers reduce the available letters. Using VDISK consumes the letter D. If you run another driver, such as DRIVER.SYS, the letter E is exhausted, leaving no drive letters for SUBST.

A computer can start without free letters. For example, a PS/2 Model 70 that has a 121M disk drive subdivided into three partitions uses drives A: through E: to start. Fortunately, DOS parcels additional letters to device drivers so that VDISK, DRIVER.SYS, and other devices are not trapped.

To prevent problems, find your current highest drive letter and increment it by three letters. Most users do not need more than three SUBST disk drives; therefore, the "last letter plus three" is a comfortable letter to give LASTDRIVE. For the first example (additional device drivers), the directive would be **LASTDRIVE = H**. For the latter example (starting without free letters and using VDISK and DRIVER.SYS), the directive would be **LASTDRIVE = J**. If you use more SUBST disk drives, set the letter higher for the LASTDRIVE directive.

Note: The last letter you can use with LASTDRIVE is Z. Also, you do not give the colon after the drive letter in the command—one of the few times the traditional colon is not used. For each drive above E:, the size of DOS is increased. For DOS V3, the increase is just over 60 bytes per additional drive. For DOS V4, the increase is just over 80 bytes.

11.17 Trap: If you add more block devices, adjust LASTDRIVE accordingly.

Don't forget that as you add block device drivers which use disk drive letters, the free letters designated by LASTDRIVE get consumed. When you edit the CONFIG.SYS file to add a new device driver, don't forget to change LASTDRIVE also.

11.18 Tip: If you use a CD-ROM, make sure that you include a LASTDRIVE = Z statement.

The Microsoft CD-ROM extension allows DOS to use the 550M storage capacity of CD-ROMs. The extensions come in two forms: one form is a device driver customized by the CD-ROM provider, and the other is a TSR program usually called MSDEX.EXE. The device driver contains the low-level routines to read the drive; the extensions install the modifications to DOS in order to use the "big" drive.

Because the CD-ROM holds so much information, most programs use several logical drive names to access the information on the drive. To ensure that enough unused logical drive names are available, set **LASTDRIVE = Z** in your CONFIG.SYS. (Most CD-ROM installation programs do this for you.)

Using INSTALL

11.19 Tip: You can run any program with DOS V4's INSTALL directive.

One addition to DOS V4's repertoire of CONFIG.SYS directives is INSTALL; this directive uses the following syntax:

> **INSTALL** = *d:path***filename.ext** *parameters*

d:path\\ is the optional drive and path name to the program. **filename.ext** is the root and extension for the program file. *parameters* are any optional parameters you give to the program. DOS runs the named program with its parameters, as if you gave the program from the command line or within a batch file. However, the program runs before DOS loads the command interpreter and executes the AUTOEXEC.BAT file.

To establish an INSTALL directive, imagine the line you would use to run the program from the DOS prompt. Simply add the drive, path name, and file extension (.COM or .EXE only; batch files are not allowed). Suppose, for example, that you typically run the following command:

> **SHARE /F:4096 /L:30**

You can use the following INSTALL directive:

> **INSTALL = C:\\DOS\\SHARE.EXE /F:4096 /L:30**

The drive name is required if the drive that holds the file is not the start-up drive; the path name is required if the file is not in the root directory. Because PATH always runs after INSTALL directives, you cannot depend on DOS to use PATH to find the file. Also, DOS makes no assumptions about file extensions; therefore, always use the extension.

You can run any program with an INSTALL directive. Running programs that are not terminate-and-stay-resident (TSR) draws a complaint from DOS, but the program still runs.

11.20 Trap: INSTALL directives can be order-dependent.

Because all other CONFIG.SYS processing is completed as groups, the INSTALL directives are not order-sensitive to other directives. Depending on what programs INSTALL loads, however, the directives can be order-dependent among themselves. If an INSTALLed program depends on other programs being run first, the directive is order-sensitive. Otherwise, the order of the INSTALL directives or their position within the CONFIG.SYS does not matter. For example, none of the suggested INSTALLable programs in the DOS V4 manuals (SHARE, KEYB, NLSFUNC, and FASTOPEN) are dependent on each other and can appear anywhere in the file and in any order.

11.21 Trick: Use INSTALL to run a TSR.

Why run a program via INSTALL in CONFIG.SYS rather than from an AUTOEXEC.BAT file? Consider the following four reasons.

First, because CONFIG.SYS files change less frequently than AUTOEXEC.BAT files, you can load the always-run TSRs with INSTALL.

Second, because INSTALL hits the system before any AUTOEXEC.BAT file program (including the request for DATE and TIME), any national language support program can change the display or keyboard to the appropriate code page before you must respond to any prompt or inquiry. This procedure makes the system easier to use. (Note that device drivers, which always are loaded before INSTALLed programs, don't get this benefit.) This second reason for using INSTALL is not alone too compelling, because you alternatively could place the statements for running programs at the beginning of your AUTOEXEC.BAT.

The third reason is that vital system programs (such as SHARE.EXE), nondevice driver RAM disk programs (ones you run at the DOS command line), and network programs, always run before any other programs that require this support. By placing the INSTALL line in CONFIG.SYS, the installed program always gets installed first. However, you can duplicate this action by moving these lines to the top of the AUTOEXEC.BAT file.

The fourth reason is the clincher—something that cannot be done by placing the lines in the AUTOEXEC.BAT. You can stop a batch file by pressing Ctrl-Break; you can stop a CONFIG.SYS file only by pressing Ctrl-Alt-Del. Unless you halt the start-up of DOS, you cannot stop a program from loading with INSTALL.

The applications for this feature are not plentiful, but reasonable. The weak point in any security software (or in making sure that the entire AUTOEXEC.BAT file runs) is that Ctrl-Break will halt the batch file. INSTALL hardens the start-up procedure. Because CONFIG.SYS does not recognize Ctrl-Break, the INSTALLed program runs as long as this CONFIG.SYS is used.

(Yes, the new weak spot is that the machine will still start from the floppy disk drive. Removing the floppy disk drive is one drastic approach. The other approach, possible with machines such as those from Zenith, allows you to specify which drive series or exactly which drive will be used on start-up. Specifying the hard disk as the only start-up drive will discourage most nondedicated crackers.)

If you want a TSR to run even if you press Ctrl-Break, use the INSTALL directive. Remember that you can use non-TSR programs (though DOS complains with a warning message). Non-TSR programs, however, are more appropriate in your AUTOEXEC.BAT file.

Creating the Boot-o-matic

How can you use 2 megabytes of device drivers and TSRs that compete for 640K of DOS memory? And how can you use 2 or more different versions of an operating system on the same computer? The trick is in using the boot-o-matic approach to DOS—booting with different CONFIG.SYS and AUTOEXEC.BAT files.

11.22   Trick: If you need several different CONFIG.SYS and AUTOEXEC.BAT combinations, use different start-up diskettes or use an automated method to restart DOS.

You can use several start-up diskettes, a series of batch files that copy the proper configuration and batch files to the root directory, or a program that handles the copy-and-reboot procedure. All three approaches work well.

If you want to use two different versions of the operating system (or two different operating systems, such as DOS and OS/2, or DOS and UNIX), you need to use the diskette approach. Construct start-up diskettes for both systems, even if the hard disk normally starts with one of the two. Depending on whether a diskette (or which diskette) is in the floppy disk drive, you can use either operating system.

This approach had a unique use during the writing of this book. One test machine, a PS/2 Model 60, could run four different operating systems: DOS V3.3, DOS V4.00, DOS V4.01, and OS/2. To test the behavior of different commands on different programs, I inserted the appropriate diskette and restarted the machine. This method was an invaluable time-saver although it has less than practical applications for most users.

To use different CONFIG.SYS and AUTOEXEC.BAT files with the same DOS version, you can use the diskette approach. First, construct and label a diskette for each CONFIG.SYS and AUTOEXEC.BAT combination. When you need to use the program, insert the correct diskette and restart DOS. Keep the CONFIG.SYS and AUTOEXEC.BAT files you use most often on the hard drive. That way, you slow the start-up of DOS only when you need a different setup.

The boot-o-matic diskette is the reason I use full file names in the CONFIG.SYS file. I simply copy the CONFIG.SYS file from my hard disk to a start-up floppy diskette. The file works without alteration, and I don't need to copy any additional files. Because every file name includes the drive and path name, DOS finds the command interpreter, device driver(s), and INSTALLed program(s) on the hard disk. I need to change the CONFIG.SYS file only to include or exclude the appropriate drivers or program for this start-up diskette. Again, I always use full file names.

Another trick is to keep the same basic AUTOEXEC.BAT file on the hard disk and have the diskette version of AUTOEXEC.BAT run the hard disk version. I sometimes use a diskette version of AUTOEXEC.BAT that has the following three lines:

@ECHO OFF

C:

AUTOEXEC

You can find some variations on this theme in Chapter 9 on advanced batch file techniques.

Using batch files or a program to swap CONFIG.SYS and AUTOEXEC.BAT files is another alternative. Make a series of configuration and autoexecuting batch files. For each set, make a batch file that copies to the root directory the files with the names CONFIG.SYS and AUTOEXEC.BAT. The final line in each batch file runs a program that restarts DOS, such as WARMBOOT.COM (a Ctrl-Alt-Del in software). This program is available through user groups and time-share services. Place the swapping batch files in a PATHed subdirectory, and place the CONFIG.SYS and AUTOEXEC.BAT files in their own subdirectory.

The program approach is even easier. I have used a public domain program called REBOOT.COM that I got from CompuServe, and I like the results. I establish separate CONFIG.SYS and AUTOEXEC.BAT sets and place them in a subdirectory called \CONFIGS. Each pair has a symbolic root name, such as CDROM, WINDOWS, NORMAL, or STD. The CONFIG.SYS does not use an extension, but the AUTOEXEC.BAT file uses the .BAT extension. Typing **REBOOT name** causes REBOOT to copy the appropriate configuration file to the root directory under the name CONFIG.SYS. If a .BAT file exists, it is copied to AUTOEXEC.BAT. All I have to do is enter one command, and REBOOT performs a warm boot and my machine comes up with the new setup.

For example, I have a different set of files for normal use (NORM), Microsoft Windows (WINDOWS), my Amdek CD-ROM player (CDROM), a memory-resident debugger called Periscope II (DEBUG), Ventura Publisher® (VENTURA), and a stripped-down CONFIG.SYS (LEAN). Each of the diskettes, my swapping batch files, and my swapped files have one of these names on the label.

None of these approaches are maintenance free. If you change a commonly used device driver or a command, you may need to edit several CONFIG.SYS or AUTOEXEC.BAT files rather than one or two. In spite of the maintenance problems, inserting a diskette and pressing Ctrl-Alt-Del is easier than going through multiple cycles of editing, saving, restarting DOS, using the program; and then editing, saving, and starting DOS again. Having one command to change both files and restart the system is more practical and efficient.

Years ago, I disdained any hard disk that could not be used to start DOS. I considered using a boot diskette as ineloquent. Now trying to cram too many device drivers and too many TSRs onto my system at one time has made me come full circle. I now recommend the use of diskettes to start DOS as one solution to this problem.

12

Using Device Drivers

Device driver software extends the functionality of DOS over various devices. The DEVICE directive instructs DOS to load and execute the device driver. This chapter discusses the DEVICE directive, placement of device drivers on your system, and several device drivers provided with DOS. The chapter also discusses the expanded memory managers and the PC DOS device drivers that provide expanded memory: XMA2EMS.SYS and XMAEM.SYS.

Using floppy disk drives is the subject of the latter part of the chapter. Once installed, DOS occasionally needs help in recognizing the disk drive. The chapter's last section examines and contrasts the final CONFIG.SYS directive, DRIVPARM; its device driver counterpart, DRIVER.SYS; and problems with formatting diskettes.

Placing DEVICE Directives

A device driver is a piece of software that gives DOS control over the device. The device driver is the low-level software responsible for communicating commands and user data from DOS to the device and relaying device information and user data from the device to DOS.

The IO.SYS file of DOS provides the device drivers for the common or built-in devices of the computer. To control new or different devices, however, DOS needs additional device drivers. Because most device drivers are loaded at DOS start-up, the appropriate place for informing DOS of additional device drivers is the DEVICE directive of CONFIG.SYS.

12.1   Tip: DEVICE directives may be order-dependent.

Although you can place CONFIG.SYS directives in any order, DEVICE directives may be order-dependent—not on other directives, but among themselves. In some cases, DOS and your software do not care about the order; in other cases, however, the order can affect how you use the computer. In several cases, the device driver or system will not work if the directives are out of order.

When executing the DEVICE directives group, DOS executes each directive in the order encountered. DOS executes the first DEVICE directive in the file (loads and installs the device driver), executes the second DEVICE directive, and so on until all the DEVICE directives are executed. If a specified device driver needs to be loaded before another, the affected DEVICE directives are order sensitive.

Most character-oriented device drivers do not depend on a certain order. Device drivers that concern printers, the communications port, or a mouse (bus, serial, or mouse port) usually are independent of each other and other device drivers. If a single device driver supplements or replaces a character device—the system console (CON), the serial ports (AUX or COMx), the clock (CLK), or the printer (PRN or LPTx)—the order of the device drivers generally does not matter.

On the other hand, device drivers are order sensitive when the same device is involved. For example, any console driver that works with ANSI.SYS is usually order-dependent. The EGA.SYS driver provided with Microsoft Windows 2.x must be loaded after ANSI.SYS. If you reverse the order, you lose the features of EGA.SYS.

Another example is when you install an external drive in a PC XT or AT. This combination uses one additional adapter and two device drivers. The first device driver, which IBM calls EXDSKBIO.DRV, lets the computer recognize the hardware adapter. The second device driver, DRIVER.SYS, tells DOS how to set up the disk drive. EXDSKBIO.DRV must be loaded before DRIVER.SYS; otherwise, the drive is unusable.

Device drivers that use extended memory (regardless of the purpose) may be order-dependent. Remember that IBM VDISK allocates extended memory from the bottom up; Microsoft's scheme for RAMDRIVE (RAM disk) and SMARTDRV (disk cacher) allocates from the top down. HIMEM.SYS, the extended memory manager, requires the first 64K of extended memory. Although ill-advised, you can use HIMEM.SYS with VDISK.SYS by loading HIMEM.SYS before VDISK.SYS. HIMEM.SYS hides the first 64K of extended memory from VDISK.SYS. When it loads, VDISK.SYS settles on top of HIMEM.SYS, and the two coexist.

Conflicts in extended memory can cause strange ordering with older versions of disk cachers. In some cases, a disk cacher must be loaded before the RAM disk software; otherwise, the cacher will not recognize "footprints" of VDISK or RAMDRIVE and subsequently destroy the RAM disk's data. In other cases, a disk cacher must be loaded after VDISK or RAMDRIVE; otherwise, the RAM disk will destroy the cacher instead.

Other memory conflicts concern expanded memory managers. The manager must be loaded before other device drivers can use the memory. If you want to use an expanded memory RAM disk or disk cacher, the DEVICE directive for the expanded memory board must appear before the directive that loads the RAM disk or disk cacher.

For IBM PC DOS V4 and 386-based computers, the IBM 386 extended memory control program, XMAEM.SYS, must be loaded before the expanded memory manager, XMA2EMS.SYS, is loaded. Otherwise, XMA2EMS does not recognize that the 386 can use extended memory as expanded memory.

All block device drivers depend on a certain order. This dependence does not cause conflicts, but does present a problem in drive letter "shifts." DOS assigns the floppy disk drives the names A: and B:. The first hard disk (or disk partition) is drive C:. Subsequent hard disks or partitions are set with ascending letters. Because the drivers for these devices are built into DOS and are usually available (you don't often remove physical disk drives from your system), these drives are not transient, and the assigned drive names are constant.

The problem lies in transient disk drives, such as RAM disks, logically remapped drives, tape drives, and CD-ROM players. The drive letters are not fixed, and they can shift. DOS assigns the letters to each device as DOS encounters and loads the appropriate device driver. If you change the order of the DEVICE line, you change the disk drive letters.

Suppose, for example, that you use VDISK.SYS and DRIVER.SYS and that your system has two hard disk partitions, making the current in-use drive names A: though D:. If VDISK comes first in the CONFIG.SYS file, VDISK gets the next available drive letter—E:. The logical drive indicated by DRIVER.SYS receives F:. Reverse the order: the logical drive is E:, and the RAM disk is drive F:. If your batch files or programs expect the RAM disk to be drive E:, you encounter problems.

12.2 Tip: When you add device drivers, check the documentation for dependencies or conflicts.

When you add DEVICE directives to your CONFIG.SYS, examine the documentation for the package. Some unrelated peripheral or software will no longer work with certain drivers. Look in the documentation for references to both order dependencies and conflicts. (Better yet, know these dependencies before you buy the package and reduce the surprise element.)

The documentation for the package normally states any known dependencies (another driver must appear before or after this driver) or conflicts (don't use this driver with some other driver). The installation program or batch file, if either is provided, also may give clues. Always check the READ.ME file (the popular name for the disk-based file addendum accompanying most packages) for last-minute discoveries.

In most cases, when the documentation states that its device driver must be first or last, its DEVICE line must appear before all other DEVICE directives (first) or after all other DEVICE directives (last). You usually can place all non-DEVICE directives before or after the DEVICE directives and can intersperse the other directives between the DEVICE statements.

12.3 Trick: Group your device drivers by type. Put new DEVICE directives after established directives for the same type.

Group the DRIVE directives by device type. Put the console-related DEVICE statements together; put the disk drive-related directives together; and put the memory-related device drivers together. This procedure is not required, but helps when you later add a new device.

When you add the DEVICE directive, the surrounding group provides a reminder to question any dependencies or conflicts. Also, by keeping interdependent device drivers together, you have a lesser chance of forgetting the dependency and later reversing the DEVICE lines when you edit your CONFIG.SYS.

In addition, by keeping block device drivers together and adding a new device driver to the end of the group, you preserve the operating order of disk drive letter assignments and reduce program and batch file maintenance. The new block device gets a new letter not used by another drive; therefore, you need not worry about changing programs or batch files that use a specific disk drive name. You still need to worry about batch files with SUBST commands that use the now-assigned letter.

If your batch files and programs depend on drive E: to be the RAM disk, for example, add the DEVICE line for a new block device after the RAM disk directive. The RAM disk remains as drive E:, and you do not need to edit the batch file or reinstall programs. However, any batch file or program that depends on a SUBST of drive F: (or whatever letter the new device uses) must be changed.

Consider two exceptions to the guideline set forth in this trick. First, when dissimilar drivers have dependencies, keep the order-dependent drivers together. Second, when you want the new block device to get a specific drive letter ahead of a current device, violate the suggestion in this trick.

12.4 Tip: On a hard disk, place all DOS device drivers in the DOS directory; place all other device drivers in one subdirectory.

To reserve the root directory for only vital start-up files and subdirectories, you can and should place device drivers in subdirectories. To keep all DOS files in one subdirectory, place the DOS-provided device drivers (ANSI.SYS, DRIVER.SYS, and so on) in your DOS subdirectory.

Keep all other device drivers, however, in a separate subdirectory. A good meaningful name for this subdirectory is DRIVERS. The easiest location for this subdirectory is either \DRIVERS, a subdirectory of the root, or a location that is a subdirectory of your main utility directory, such as \BIN\DRIVERS or \UTIL\DRIVERS.

The reason for this placement is threefold. First, maintenance is easier with this scheme. You easily can replace all old DOS device drivers with new DOS device drivers when you upgrade DOS.

Second, you know where to copy or move the device driver (into \DRIVERS, \BIN\DRIVERS, or \UTIL\DRIVERS) when you install a program. Keeping the device drivers in a separate directory also reminds you that you may not need all device drivers provided with a program. When you install a program, you often copy the entire contents of the installation diskette to a subdirectory. When you copy or move the device driver files, you are reminded to copy or move only the needed files and delete the ones not applicable to your setup.

Third, editing the DEVICE directives is easier. You have only two path locations to specify: \DOS and \DRIVERS (or the appropriate names for your subdirectory setup). DOS-provided drivers reside in \DOS; all others reside in \DRIVERS. The scheme is easy to use and remember.

12.5   Tip: On a floppy disk-based system, place all device drivers in a single directory.

To keep the root directory as uncluttered as possible, move all device drivers into a subdirectory, such as \DRIVER. On high-capacity diskettes, move the device drivers to a subdirectory in order to keep the directory listing short. Because DOS uses these files only when booting, they do not need to be on the PATH (the only reason to keep the files in the root directory).

12.6   Tip: Always use a full file name in the DEVICE directive.

Use a full file name in the DEVICE directive. For example, don't load ANSI.SYS with the name **\DOS\ANSI.SYS**. Instead, use **C:\DOS\ANSI.SYS** for a hard disk or **A:\ANSI.SYS** for a floppy diskette.

Because the files are not in the root directory, you must give the path name so that DOS can find the files—an obvious reason. The reason to give a drive name is less obvious. By using drive and path names, you can copy the hard disk's CONFIG.SYS file to a startable floppy diskette and use that diskette without changes.

Configuring Expanded Memory

Expanded memory managers have the most diverse syntax I've seen. Accordingly, each expanded memory manager uses unique arguments for its DEVICE directive. I cannot possibly attempt to give examples for all expanded memory managers.

To cope with the confusion of installing the expanded memory manager, know the hardware-related terms for expanded memory. These terms, presented in table 12.1, are used directly or indirectly in arguments for the EMS device driver.

12.7   Trap: Use only the EMS driver written for your EMS memory board.

Although all EMS boards provide the same basic functions, almost every one works differently. The specific software instructions differ from board to board. Although rare exceptions exist, you cannot use an EMS manager for a board from one manufacturer with a board from another manufacturer.

An EMS memory board has two principal elements: the RAM and the bank-switching circuitry to shuffle the physical memory in and out of view of the CPU. The bank-switching circuitry uses I/O ports.

Table 12.1
Glossary of Expanded Memory Terms

Term	Definition
Page	A 16K piece of expanded memory
Page, physical	(1) A page of physical RAM on the EMS board
	(2) The location in conventional memory in which a specific EMS logical page is mapped (addressed)
Page, logical	The number assigned by the EMS manager to a particular physical 16K page on the EMS board
Handle	A process identification number given to a program and used to group logical pages
Page frame	The starting location in conventional memory (less than 1M memory) where a 16K page of expanded memory is addressed; a synonym for definition 2 of physical page. The frame can designate one page or all contiguous pages.
Ports	The input and output terminals of the computer, used to control the EMS hardware

A CPU has three ways to communicate with the parts outside of the CPU. One way is using memory addresses—the way that information is brought in and stored between CPU registers and RAM and ROM. The second method is hardware interrupt lines; when "pulled" (activated), these cause the CPU to jump and execute an established routine. The third way is I/O ports. Most ports are connected to some type of device. For example, the CPU talks with the communication adapter (or issues commands) and reads the active status of the video display through ports.

Ports, which are eight-bit wide locations that can be written or read, act like memory. However, some ports are used for one-way communications. The CPU can write a read-only port, but reading a write-only port produces random nonsense. The specific I/O of a port depends on the connected device.

Most EMS boards use the same range of ports, starting at either 258 hex or 268 hex. Although the EMS boards may use the same range of ports, the specific use of each port differs between the boards. For this reason, you cannot mix and match expanded memory managers. The EMS manager must be written specifically for the expanded memory board. If you use PC DOS V4, for example, you cannot use the XMA2EMS driver unless you use IBM memory boards.

The contradiction is that if you use a 386 processor, you can use the
XMAEM.SYS and XMA2EMS.SYS combination. Because the 386 can treat all
memory (including extended memory) as expanded memory, no special
expanded memory board is required. XMAEM makes any extended
memory look like expanded memory, making XMA2EMS usable. The use
of XMAEM.SYS is discussed in a later section of this chapter.

12.8   Tip: Specify EMS page frame values in hexadecimal.

All address values for the EMS manager are in hexadecimal. Hexadecimal,
which is base 16, works well for expressing binary values with groups of 4
bits. Two hexadecimal digits represent the range of 0 to 255 (0 to FF in
hex). Four digits represent 0 to 65,535 (0 to FFFF in hex, which is 64K).

As a quick reference for creating DEVICE directives to load the EMS
manager, 16K is 400 hex, and 64K is 1000 hex. Four contiguous 16K pages
would be addressed at 000, 0400, 800, and C00. (The trickiness is the letter
C, 12 in decimal notation.) If you want to specify 4 individual page frames
starting at segment D000 (the 832K point, which normally is an empty
space of 64K), the addresses would be D000, D400, D800, and DC00.

You may notice a difference between the 4-digit numbers used by EMS
managers and the 5- to 6-digit numbers that a device uses in an absolute
range of addresses. An EMS manager uses segment addresses, which are
16-byte paragraphs. To translate an absolute address into a segment
address, simply lop off the last digit from the absolute address. For
example, the absolute address for the EGA BIOS is C0000; the starting
segment address is C000.

12.9   Trap: The page frames for EMS memory must be empty.

The EMS memory scheme establishes peekholes (16K memory sections) in
conventional memory through which the EMS hardware and software
exposes and hides pages. No other piece of the computer can use these
peekholes. If two pieces of hardware attempt to use the overlapping
locations, then one, the other, or both items work incorrectly, and the
system acts erratically.

When EMS memory and another memory board or hardware adapter
conflict, items in EMS memory can be corrupted, and the hardware
adapter can act strangely. The worst cases occur when a disk cacher is in
expanded memory or a disk or network adapter conflicts with EMS
memory. In these cases, disk files, including files not used in a session, are
corrupted.

Although you can use any nonconflicting space, including the space between 64K and 640K on machines not equipped with 640K of RAM, this is a dubious choice. Most EMS boards allow you to *backfill*—use some memory on the expansion board to fill in the missing RAM beneath 640K. Backfilling allows all programs, rather than just those that use EMS memory, to benefit from the memory on the expansion boards. I suggest using the backfilling option instead of shortchanging all programs.

12.10 Trick: When you install the EMS manager or add new expansion boards, know what memory addresses the adapters use.

When you first install the EMS manager, knowing what memory addresses an adapter that RAM or ROM uses is helpful. Table 12.2 lists some locations used by common adapters. Avoid using these locations for the EMS manager.

If an adapter in your system does not appear, examine the documentation or use the trial-and-error method (try the EMS hardware at various locations, and if something goes wrong, try another address for the page frames). The documentation is preferred to trial-and-error; a problem in memory address conflicts may not be apparent for hours or even weeks.

The safest common locations to use for EMS page frames are D000 (if you are not using a networking board) and C000 (if you are not using an EGA card). Try these locations first and then start using other locations or pitching boards if both fail.

Don't forget that problems can occur when you change your setup (add a new expansion board or replace a board). Any board with ROM can conflict with an established setup. Therefore, almost any expansion board (other than those that exclusively provide additional RAM) can conflict. Most standard serial, parallel, game port, or combination boards (with or without memory) do not conflict.

Conflicting boards include specialty floppy disk adapters, any hard disk adapters, all video adapters, all network cards, and some I/O boards, usually those that provide unusual interfaces such as IEEE-488 (GPIB) interfaces or data acquisition functions. When you add one of these boards, keep in mind that you may need to revise the arguments for the EMS manager.

Table 12.2
Locations Used by Common Adapters

Summary of Memory Usage

Address	Used by
00000 – 9FFFF	System RAM
A0000 – BFFFF	Display adapter space (see the following)
C0000 – DFFFF	Adapter ROM/RAM space (see the following)
E0000 – EFFFF	System ROM expansion
F0000 – FFFFF	System ROM (including ROM BASIC)
100000 – FDFFFF	Extended memory (286/386-based systems)
FE0000 – FEFFFF	Reserved (286/386-based systems)
FF0000 – FFFFFF	Advanced BIOS ROM space (286/386-based systems)

Display Adapter RAM Use

Address	Used by
B0000 – B1000	MDA (Monochrome Display Adapter)
B8000 – BCFFF	CGA (Color/Graphics Adapter)
B0000 – B7FFF	EGA (Enhanced Color Graphics adapter) with monochrome monitor
B8000 – BFFFF	EGA with non-EGA color monitor
A0000 – BFFFF	128K–256K EGA, all EGA+ adapters
A0000 – BFFFF	VGA (Video Graphics Array)

Adapter Memory Area

Address	Used by
C0000 – C3FFF	EGA BIOS
C4000 – C5FFF	No common use
C6000 – C6FFF	PGA (Professional Graphics Display) BIOS
C8000 – CBFFF	Hard disk BIOS
CC000 – CFFFF	No common use
D0000 – D7FFF	Network card BIOS

Using PC DOS V4 and Expanded Memory

PC DOS V4 pioneers the use of expanded memory by DOS. The following sections discuss the use of expanded memory and PC DOS V4. Note that the advice in this section does not apply to DOS V3.3 or earlier nor to MS-

DOS V4. MS-DOS V4 automatically uses any expanded memory manager for BUFFERS /X or FASTOPEN /X.

Using XMA2EMS.SYS

12.11   Tip: To use expanded memory with PC DOS V4 and IBM expanded memory boards, use XMA2EMS.SYS.

Use the XMA2EMS.SYS device driver so that you can use IBM memory boards that offer expanded memory with PC DOS V4. The name is an acronym for extended memory area (XMA) to EMS memory. Using the syntax shown in table 12.3, add a DEVICE directive to your CONFIG.SYS file to activate the page-switching functions of the IBM memory boards.

Table 12.3
Syntax for XMA2EMS.SYS

DEVICE = *d:path*\XMA2EMS.SYS FRAME = address0 Px = addressx
  P254 = address1 P255 = address2 /X:size

d:\path	The drive and path to XMA2EMS.SYS
FRAME = address0	The starting address for a 64K section of memory that is used as the page frame for four contiguous pages. FRAME cannot be used with Px = addressx.
Px = addressx	The page frame for an individual 16K page. The x is 1 through 4. Px cannot be used with FRAME = address0.
P254 = address1	The page frame for logical page 254, the page used for BUFFERS /X. If unspecified, one of the four page frames are used.
P255 = address2	The page frame for logical page 255, the page used for FASTOPEN /X. If unspecified, one of the four page frames is used.
address	The segment address for a page frame, in the range of A000 through E000. All page frame addresses given to FRAME, Px, P254, and P255 must represent an unoccupied space (no conflicting system ROM or adapter RAM or ROM) of 16K.

Generally, you can load the driver by including the following line:

DEVICE = C:\DOS\XMA2EMS FRAME = D000

This command installs XMA2EMS at the absolute address D0000, an expansion location unused in most systems. That location, however, conflicts with network adapters. If you receive an error message, see the tips on resolving conflicts later in this chapter.

FRAME = D000 sets up 4, contiguous, 16K EMS page frames at addresses D000, D400, D800, and DC00. This method is simpler than specifying individual pages (Px). The following arguments are the same as using **FRAME = D000**:

> **P0 = D000 P1 = D400 P2 = D800 P3 = DC00**

You may need to use the Px arguments if 64K of conventional memory space is not free. Setting individual pages is discussed in the troubleshooting tips later in this chapter.

12.12 Tip: Use the /X switch to reserve some extended memory for other uses.

Normally, XMA2EMS uses all available expansion memory (the dual mode extended/expanded memory on the IBM expansion adapters) as expanded memory. This precludes all programs from using any of this expansion memory as extended memory.

Most disk cachers, for example, run slightly faster on a PS/2 that uses extended memory rather than expanded memory for the cache. You can tell XMA2EMS to use only some of the available memory with the /X switch and use extended memory for the cache.

The syntax for the /X switch is **/X:size**, where **size** is the number of 16K pages of memory that should be treated as expanded memory. The minimum size is 4 (four 16K pages or 64K). The maximum size is the amount of expansion memory (in K) divided by 16.

The /X switch sometimes calls for some reverse thinking—calculating how much extended memory to use rather than how much expanded memory to use. To calculate how much extended memory to reserve, take the amount of memory to be used as extended memory, subtract that figure from the amount of expansion memory, and then divide the result by 16K.

For example, a disk cacher uses 1/2M (512K) of a 2M memory expansion for extended memory. The amount of expansion memory is 2048K (2M). To reserve 512K, subtract 512K from 2048K; then divide the result (1536K) by 16. The result equals 96 pages; therefore, you use the switch **/X:96**.

If you use a 286 computer that has 1M on the system board, you must consider one additional factor. The RAM is organized as 640K of real memory plus 384K of extended memory. Therefore, you can use the system board's 384K to reserve less expanded memory.

For example, for a PS/2 Model 60 with 2M of expansion memory, you specify **/X:120** so that you can use 512K with the extended memory cache. The system board provides 384K, meaning that only 128K from the 2M expansion must be reserved. Therefore, the calculation is as follows:

(2048K – 128K) / 16K = 120 pages

When you reserve expansion memory, remember that an "extra" 384K is available.

12.13   Tip: To use expanded memory for PC DOS V4's BUFFERS, use the P254 argument. To use expanded memory for PC DOS V4's FASTOPEN, use the P255 argument.

This tip, presented hesitantly, is for PC DOS V4 users only. Do not use this tip if you use DOS V3.3 or MS-DOS V4. DOS V3.3 does not support using expanded memory for BUFFERS or FASTOPEN, and MS-DOS V4 does not require the P254 or P255 arguments. Many problems exist in using PC DOS V4's scheme for using expanded memory. The BUFFERS and FASTOPEN sections of Chapter 3, "Improving Disk Performance," detail this problem.

If you want to use expanded memory to hold PC DOS V4's BUFFERS, you must add the **P254 = address** argument. If you want to use expanded memory for PC DOS V4's FASTOPEN command, you must add the **P255 = address** argument. Because each of these arguments creates a separate page frame, you must have another 16K of empty memory space for either function, or 32K of empty memory space for both functions. This space cannot overlap nor be the same as the memory areas specified in a FRAME or Px argument.

Two normally empty locations are C000 and C400. You can add the following arguments to the XMA2EMS line:

P254 = C000 P255 = C400

This command sets page 254 (BUFFERS /X) at C000 and page 255 (FASTOPEN /X) at C400. You can interchange the arguments and addresses (use C400 for P254 and C000 for P255). You also can use different 16K locations as long as those locations are not being used. If any conflicts occur, the device driver will not install. The trap that follows explains the consequences.

12.14 Trap: For PC DOS V4.00, keep a startable DOS diskette on hand before you add or change the XMA2EMS.SYS directive and use BUFFERS /X.

PC DOS V4.00 is gracious about using the wrong arguments or syntax with XMA2EMS. If conflicts occur, XMA2EMS.SYS hints at the problem. PC DOS V4.00 gives an error message (which lists the number of the errant line in the CONFIG.SYS file) and continues its start-up.

Unfortunately, PC DOS V4.00 won't start if XMA2EMS.SYS does not load or if you omit the P255 argument and use the BUFFERS /X directive. If the buffers cannot be placed in expanded memory, the system halts. You need to start DOS from a diskette (if you are trying to start from the hard disk) or from another diskette (if you were starting from a diskette).

For this reason, always keep a configured, start-up diskette on hand when you change the arguments in the XMA2EMS.SYS DEVICE directive under DOS V4.00. Any mistakes will freeze you out of the system unless another bootable diskette is handy. (When this first happened to me, I had to use a DOS V3.3 diskette to start the system and correct the mistake. This procedure would have been impossible had I used greater than 32M partitions.)

This problem concerns PC DOS V4.00, not later versions. Under PC DOS V4.01, BUFFERS /X does not install if XMA2EMS.SYS does not load or if the P255 argument is omitted. DOS continues the start-up, which allows you to edit the CONFIG.SYS file and reboot.

12.15 Trick: If you use HIMEM.SYS and XMA2EMS.SYS, load HIMEM.SYS before XMA2EMS.SYS.

This trick applies to those using a 286-based IBM computer with dual-mode memory. Remember that XMA2EMS.SYS converts this memory into expanded memory. Unfortunately, HIMEM.SYS cannot run unless the first 64K of extended memory is not used. To use both device drivers, load HIMEM.SYS before XMA2EMS.SYS. HIMEM captures the first 64K of expanded memory, and XMA2EMS.SYS works correctly.

Depending on the machine, using XMA2EMS.SYS before HIMEM.SYS may or may not work. If the system board has split memory (640K real and 384 extended), the combination works. If only expansion memory is available, the reverse order does not work, and HIMEM.SYS will not install.

Troubleshooting XMA2EMS.SYS

12.16   Trick: To check for conflicting memory addresses, use XMA2EMS.SYS without arguments.

One of the benefits of using XMA2EMS is that the device driver displays informative error messages. If you have a 386 system or the appropriate IBM memory expansion board, you can use XMA2EMS's messages to find possible free spots for the page frames.

To spot possible page frames, load the device driver without any arguments. XMA2EMS loads, sees that a page frame is not specified (no FRAME or Px arguments), and then checks the memory addresses between A0000 and E0000. Simply ignore the `No page frame specified` message and look for the following two messages:

> `Possible 16KB page available at address xxxx`
> `Possible 64KB frame available at address xxxx`

Because the computer pauses, you can write down the address and press any key to continue. First, look for an available frame (the second message) and use that address. Give the xxxx in the message for a **FRAME =** argument. If you also want to use P254 or P255 for BUFFERS /X and FASTOPEN /X, respectively, look for two more open spaces in the first error message. Use one of the available addresses for P254 and a different one for P255 (if both are given). Remember that P254 and P255 must have different addresses and cannot overlap an address given to FRAME.

When you have determined the correct addresses, edit the CONFIG.SYS file and add the appropriate arguments to the XMA2EMS directive. After you save the file, restart the system. If you don't get any error messages, you've installed XMA2EMS correctly.

If you haven't installed XMA2EMS correctly, you get another error message:

`Specified page address conflicts with installed adapter at address xxxx`

In this case, you've used a bad address or an address that conflicts with an adapter. Check to be sure that you've given the correct addresses and start DOS again. However, if XMA2EMS does not display the preceding message, you do not have 4 contiguous 16K pages free for use by EMS memory (see the information in the next trick).

XMA2EMS is not infallible; it checks only the segment addresses from C000 to E000. If you are not using an EGA or VGA or have less than 640K installed, you may have enough empty space for a 64K page frame, but XMA2EMS.SYS will not report this fact. If no other 64K page frames are displayed, and you know that this space is empty, use the address with the FRAME or Px arguments.

12.17 Trick: If you have one or more 16K pages free or if you don't have more than 64K free for use with P254 and P255, use the Px arguments.

If you do not have a full 64K available (cannot use a FRAME argument) or if you want to use BUFFERS /X or FASTOPEN /X when only 64K or less free memory space is available, you can still use XMA2EMS. The trick is in specifying the page frames individually using the Px arguments.

If you have only 1 to 4 contiguous 16K pages free, you must use Px. In ascending order, specify P0, P1, P2, and P3, using a different address. To find the address, look at the **Possible 16KB page available** message. If only 1 page is available, use only P0. If XMA2EMS shows 3 pages, use P0, P1, and P2. If 4 pages are available, use P0 through P3.

You face a tough choice if fewer than 6 pages are available and you want to use BUFFERS /X and FASTOPEN /X (or if fewer than 5 pages are available, and you want to use either BUFFERS /X or FASTOPEN /X). To use either or both, you must reduce the Px arguments. You sacrifice some of your program's performance with expanded memory in order to gain the use of these features by DOS. I recommend against this sacrifice. If you have fewer than 6 free pages, don't use BUFFERS /X and FASTOPEN /X.

12.18 Trap: If four contiguous pages are not available, some LIM V3.2 programs do not work.

One of the differences between LIM V4.0 and LIM V3.2 is that the page frames do not need to be contiguous. Only a few programs written for LIM V3.2 assumed that four contiguous pages were always available. Software written for LIM V4 recognizes this difference and avoids the trap of too few pages or noncontiguous page frames. However, a few programs (none by major publishing houses) make this assumption.

If you need to specify page frames individually that are not contiguous or if four pages are not available, your LIM V3.2 software may not work. You have only three choices: remove the conflicting hardware, don't use the software, or run the software on a different computer.

This problem, not an indictment of IBM's device driver, is that too many boards are competing for limited address space. The same conflict occurs if you use any EMS board in the system. The EMS V3.2 board would conflict with the offending hardware, leaving the machine without the capability to use EMS memory. The software will not function with a LIM V4.0 board (which would use noncontiguous page frames). Under these conditions, the third alternative (run the software on a different computer) may be the best choice.

Using XMAEMS.SYS

12.19 Tip: To use expanded memory on any 386 system, use XMAEM.SYS before XMA2EMS.SYS.

Because a 386 can treat all extended memory as expanded memory, you can use any 386-based system and any 386 memory board with DOS V4 device drivers. Simply use the XMAEM.SYS device driver (extended memory area emulator).

XMAEM.SYS is a LIM activator for 386 systems. XMAEM.SYS activates the page-switching hardware on the 386 CPU that permits the use of extended memory as expanded memory.

The following shows the syntax for the device driver:

DEVICE = *d:path*/XMAEM.SYS *size*

size is the optional amount of memory in K to be used as expanded memory and is a multiple of 16K. The minimum value for *size* is 64; the maximum is all available extended memory (the default if you omit *size*).

Notice that the size for XMAEM.SYS is not identical to XMA2EMS /X's size switch. XMAEM size is in K, not 16K pages. If you use the technique for calculating the amount of expansion memory to use as extended memory, don't divide the result by 16. If you do, you will reserve too much space for extended memory.

When you use the XMAEM/XMA2EMS combination, XMAEM size takes precedence. If you use size in both, XMA2EMS's /X:size switch is ignored. Also, remember that the directive to load XMAEM.SYS must appear before the directive for XMA2EMS.SYS. If you reverse the order, XMA2EMS.SYS fails to load, and expanded memory is not available. If you use BUFFERS /X under PC DOS V4.00, the system halts.

Remember that XMAEM.SYS and XMA2EMS.SYS work on any 386-based computer. You are not restricted to using IBM hardware, only PC DOS V4. Also, remember that XMA2EMS.SYS must load properly; you must resolve any conflicts before you can use expanded memory successfully.

Also note that the XMAEM/XMA2EMS combination does not offer the functions, speed, or other LIM activators. If you are interested in other 386-control programs, refer to Chapter 1 on the CPU and memory.

Configuring DOS with DRIVPARM and DRIVER.SYS

The CONFIG.SYS directive DRIVPARM and the DOS-provided device driver DRIVER.SYS have many similarities. Both are activated with CONFIG.SYS, and both work primarily with floppy disk drives. The switches and default values for both, shown in table 12.4, are identical.

Table 12.4
DRIVPARM and DRIVER.SYS Syntax and Switches

Syntax

  DRIVPARM = /D:ddd /T:ttt /S:ss /H:hh /F:f /C

  DEVICE = d:path\DRIVER.SYS /D:ddd /T:ttt /S:ss /H:hh /F:f /C

Switches

Switch	Description
/D:ddd	Physical *drive* number; 0–127 for floppy disk drives, 128–255 for hard disks; 0-based for floppy disks, 128-based for hard disks; mandatory switch, no default value
/T:ttt	*Tracks* per side; 1–999 (80 tracks)
/S:ss	Number of *sectors* per track; 1–99 (9 sectors)
/H:hh	Number of *heads* per disk; 1–99 (2 sides)
/C	Disk *changeline* hardware supported (no change line support if switch is omitted)
/F:f	Device type or *form factor* (2). The values for form factor include the following:

Value	Type
0	160–360K disk drives
1	1.2M disk drive
2	720K disk drive
7	1.44M and all other disk drives

Although both DRIVPARM and DRIVER.SYS establish the physical characteristics for the disk drive, only DRIVER.SYS establishes logical characteristics (another logical disk drive). The next few tips explain this difference.

12.20   Trap: Do not give incorrect information to DRIVPARM or DRIVER.SYS.

When you use DRIVPARM or DRIVER.SYS, do not understate or overstate the number of heads, tracks, sectors, form factor, or changeline support. The drive acts erratically or does not format properly. Using the wrong drive number parameter (/D:ddd) or omitting this parameter has undesirable results. The worst case is the possible destruction of the FAT or root directory; this destruction occurs when you indicate that the drive has changeline support when the BIOS or drive does not.

Note one exception to this trap: the case when DOS cannot format a diskette with a lower capacity than the disk drive. One workaround is telling "white lies" to DRIVPARM, as explained later in this chapter.

Using DRIVPARM with Floppy Disk Drives

12.21   Tip: To format a diskette on a "foreign" floppy disk drive with DOS V3 and later (except for PC DOS V4), use DRIVPARM /D:d.

You use the DRIVPARM directive to establish the physical formatting characteristics of any floppy disk drive. You primarily use DRIVPARM with the loosely fitting term "foreign" floppy disk drives—usually microfloppy disk drives. Foreign is defined as "not originally supported"; this term does not mean that the disk drive is manufactured in another country.

The entire Personal Computer family was designed to use minifloppy disk drives. The ROM BIOS of the system contains the number of heads, tracks, sectors, motor start time, and other information for the supplied floppy disk drive. Many clone makers followed IBM's lead in embedding this information in ROM.

When a new disk drive type was added, the ROM BIOS may need to be changed to support the new drive and the IO.SYS file must be changed. ROM BIOS changes are easily implemented for new machines (such as the PC AT, XT/286, and PS/2), but older machines may be struck from getting a new ROM BIOS that supports the new drive. The IO.SYS file always changes, and each version of PC DOS except V3.1 supported a new or changed floppy drive type.

In the last few years, microfloppy disk drives have gained significant use. In many cases, owners have replaced a 360K or 1.2M disk with a 720K or 1.44M disk drive. The new drive works properly when reading or writing diskettes. DOS, starting with V3.2, reads the disk parameter block from the diskette and knows the proper characteristics (heads, tracks, sectors) for the drive. This change was made so that DOS would be more flexible (and because the media identification byte would someday be incapable of defining all drive types).

The problem occurs when formatting a diskette in the foreign disk drive. In most cases, DOS, on reading the ROM BIOS, assumes that the original disk drive is still installed. Although you can install the disk drive type (also known as a form factor) in the CMOS memory of many AT-like systems, many versions of DOS do not use this information. Therefore, you can use the drive for all operations except formatting new diskettes.

To solve this problem, Microsoft added the DRIVPARM directive. DRIVPARM modifies the drive parameter block, which contains the information used by formatting functions within DOS. (FORMAT no longer contains the actual formatting routine. Starting with DOS V3.2, the formatting routines became internal system functions.)

You should use DRIVPARM on replacement or add-on disk drives that connect to the original diskette adapter but are not identical to the replaced disk drive. Usually, the foreign disk drives are 720K or 1.44M microfloppies. After you set the parameter, you can use the disk drive for formatting.

Suppose, for example, that you replace the second disk drive on an AT-like system with a 720K disk drive. You use the following full syntax for the directive in CONFIG.SYS:

DRIVPARM = /D:1 /F:2 /T:80 /S:9 /H:2 /C

From left to right, the switches tell DOS that the affected drive is the second physical floppy disk unit; has a 720K form factor, 80 tracks, 9 sectors per track, and 2 recording heads; and supports the drive changeline.

The confusion for DRIVPARM (and DRIVER.SYS) is the numbering base and the changeline. The numbering scheme for disk drives is 0-based for floppy disk drives and 128-based for hard disks. The second physical floppy disk drive is 1, not 2. The second hard disk is 129, not 128. Remember that all disk parameters except sectors are 0-based. (Sectors start their numbering with 1.)

The changeline support is the floppy disk drive's "door opened" signal. The disk drive pulls the hardware line when you open the disk drive door (or push the ejector button on a microfloppy). When DOS (or any disk caching software) notices this signal, the software presumes that you have changed the diskette and either invalidates all buffered information for the drive or demands that the diskette be returned to the drive in order to complete writing information. Notice that the changeline does not mean the diskette has been changed, just probably changed. Also, note that floppy disk drives for the original PC, XT, and its clones do not have this support.

The preceding command is excessively wordy. Because DRIVPARM and DRIVER.SYS use certain default values, you instead can use the following shorter directive:

DRIVPARM = /D:1 /C

You can use the following brief syntax to add a 1.44M disk drive for drive B:

DRIVPARM = /D:1 /F:7 /S:18 /C

One major difference and some subtle differences exist between DRIVPARM and DRIVER.SYS. Later tips in this chapter discuss these differences. Also note that some implementations of MS-DOS do not respect DRIVPARM. Actually, the problem occurs because of a conflict with the ROM BIOS and DOS's IO.SYS device drivers. Some suggestions are made in later tips for handling these problems.

12.22 Trick: To use DRIVPARM with PC DOS V3.x and MS-DOS V3.3, use DRIVPARM ^A^A^A /D:ddd.

A change in the primary developers for DOS caused an interesting quirk in the development of DOS: DRIVPARM was "broken" (the directive was not recognized) in MS-DOS V3.30. Before V3.2, Microsoft was the primary developer, and IBM was the principal secondary developer. Starting with V3.2, the roles reversed.

PC DOS does not support DRIVPARM (IBM prefers DRIVER.SYS). IBM takes the Microsoft code and "disconnects" DRIVPARM by changing the CONFIG.SYS directive parser (the code responsible for deciphering directives). Microsoft does support DRIVPARM and reconnects the directive. During the development of DOS V3.3, IBM disconnected DRIVPARM, and Microsoft forgot to reconnect it. Therefore, both versions contained the code for using DRIVPARM, but neither PC DOS V3.30 nor MS-DOS V3.30 recognized the directive.

The solution is to trick the CONFIG.SYS parser by using a triple Ctrl-A sequence rather than an equal sign. The triple Ctrl-A was thrown away by the parser, and DOS used DRIVPARM. Therefore, you can use DRIVPARM with all versions of DOS (PC or MS-) except PC DOS V4. If you use PC DOS V3.x or MS-DOS V3.30 to set drive B: as a 720K disk drive, include the following line in your CONFIG.SYS:

DRIVPARM ^A^A^A /D:1 /C

The ^A is a Ctrl-A sequence, not a caret followed by an A. When you type this sequence, you get a "smiling face" character. Remember that the triple Ctrl-A is the substitute for the equal sign; don't use an equal sign in the directive.

Remember: This trick is not required for any version of MS-DOS other than V3.30 (an updated version of MS-DOS, V3.30A, reconnected DRIVPARM) and cannot be used with PC DOS V4. IBM broke DRIVPARM forcefully. Also, some versions of MS-DOS have problems in using DRIVPARM correctly. If you need to establish the parameters for a foreign disk drive under PC DOS V4 or have other problems, use DRIVER.SYS or find a special formatting program. Both of these methods are covered in separate tips.

12.23 Trap: With MS-DOS, you may need a special program to format a diskette with a lower capacity than the disk drive or to format a standard-capacity diskette.

Unfortunately, DRIVPARM does not control the "autoshift" of formatting. To format a 360K diskette in a 1.2M drive or a 720K diskette in a 1.44M drive, DOS must use a different disk parameter block for the reduced number of both tracks and sectors for 360K diskettes or of only sectors for 720K diskettes. Setting DRIVPARM does not control this routine. The DOS FORMAT program uses internal system functions to tell the IO.SYS to make this change. To complete the change, the IO.SYS ultimately calls the routines in the ROM BIOS.

Because of differences in ROM BIOS and DOS implementations by computer manufacturers, all but a few older versions of DOS implementations can format a 360K diskette in a 1.2M disk drive, and not all versions of DOS can format a 720K diskette in a 1.44M disk drive. Some implementations of DOS also do not recognize DRIVPARM. FORMAT aborts or produces a 1.2M microfloppy diskette on the 1.44M drive.

This inability to format correctly is almost astonishing—after all, the disk drive under the same implementations of DOS can read and write the diskettes. The problem is usually in the manufacturer's customization (or lack thereof) of FORMAT; a properly written format program should establish the correct parameters for formatting. PC DOS does not have the shift problem; only some versions of MS-DOS do. The problem occurs when you format the diskette, not when you use an already formatted diskette.

You can use one of four workarounds. The first workaround is to use a different formatting program. Several programs in user-group libraries and on bulletin boards or time-share services (such as CompuServe Information Service and The Source[SM]) set the drive parameters and format the diskette correctly. Exact file names vary, but FMT720 and FMT144 are popular. Because the parameter setup is important only when formatting a diskette, this solution is both practical and efficient. If DOS does not recognize DRIVPARM (as in PC DOS V4) or mishandles DRIVPARM, this workaround is the only solution.

The second workaround is a program that sets the drive parameter block correctly and works for unrecognized or mishandled DRIVPARMs. You can find one such program, called DRVPARM, in some user-group libraries and on time-sharing services. The switches for DRVPARM are the same as those for DRIVPARM and DRIVER.SYS. The only problem is that a diskette with the correct parameters must be in the disk drive when DRVPARM runs. This requirement is not practical if you want to change the parameters on drive A: on start-up. (Because a diskette is in the drive, DOS tries to start DOS from the floppy diskette.) DRVPARM is also not practical when you don't have a diskette formatted to the correct capacities.

The third workaround is to have two CONFIG.SYS files—one for the 1.44M setup and one for the 720K setup. Start DOS using the appropriate CONFIG.SYS file. Although this approach is somewhat clumsy, it works. The fourth approach is to use DRIVER.SYS to establish the correct parameters with a new logical disk drive.

12.24   Trap: You need to change some 1.44M disk drives to format exceptional diskettes.

Before you install a 1.44M disk drive, note that all 1.44M disk drives are not alike. If you look at a 1.44M microfloppy diskette (hold the diskette face up with the shutter toward you), you notice two holes in the diskette—one in each of the upper corners. The right hole is the write-protect hole; the left hole is the high-capacity indicator. Many 1.44M disk drives use this latter hole to sense whether a 720K or 1.44M diskette is in the drive. IBM does not use the capacity-sensor in the disk drive; therefore, IBM disk drives and PC DOS ignore the hole.

Some third-party disk drives, however, do use the sensor, although generic MS-DOS does not. These disk drives will not format a 1.44M diskette at 720K, nor format a 720K diskette at the 1.44M capacity. The stumbling block is the disk drive, not DOS. Usually, changing a jumper on the interface board within the floppy disk drive disables the sensor; however, some drives do not offer this option. To solve this problem, you need to check the documentation for the disk drive.

Using DRIVER.SYS with Floppy Disk Drives

12.25 Trick: To establish another logical disk drive or to compensate when DRIVPARM alone does not work, use DRIVER.SYS.

DRIVER.SYS is the DOS-provided alternative to DRIVPARM. You can use DRIVER.SYS to copy files between similar-sized diskettes when you have two physically dissimilar disk drives. You can use DRIVER.SYS in place of DRIVPARM when DRIVPARM does not work—when FORMAT does not work or when external floppy disk drives are used on some systems.

The syntax for the DRIVER.SYS device driver is shown in table 12.4; the switches are identical to those for DRIVPARM. DRIVER.SYS performs the same function as DRIVPARM but with one important addition. Each copy of DRIVER.SYS produces a new logical disk drive from the same physical disk drive.

Recall that DOS always has two logical floppy disk drives, even if only one physical drive is installed. When one drive is installed, the name drive A: or B: references the same disk drive. Therefore, you can copy files between diskettes by using a command such as **COPY A:MYFILE B:**. DOS knows that the same physical disk drive is in-use and prompts you to place the proper diskettes in the drive.

If you have two dissimilar physical floppy disk drives (such as a 1.2M and a 1.44M disk drive), copying files directly between two 1.2M (or 360K) diskettes or between two 1.44M (or 720K) diskettes is impossible. Because two drives are physically present, A: and B: reference two different drives. The same command copies files between a 1.2M diskette and a 1.44M diskette.

You can use DRIVER.SYS to establish additional logical floppy disk drives from each physical disk drive. Therefore, you can copy files between the media that fits each disk drive. To use the new drive letters, you must change only the COPY command.

External floppy disk drives on some systems may need DRIVER.SYS. When the drive is connected by an additional expansion board or when two internal diskette drives are already in-use, DRIVER.SYS is usually required. For example, using an external disk drive on an AT-like machine requires an additional adapter and another device driver (IBM calls this driver EXDSKBIO.DRV). The device driver lets the computer use the disk drive, but doesn't inform DOS of the specific parameters for the drive. In this case, you must use DRIVER.SYS to inform DOS.

Note: Not all computers that use external disk drives require DRIVER.SYS. You don't need DRIVER.SYS, for example, when you add an external disk drive to a PS/2 that has a single internal drive. The PS/2's ROM BIOS and PC DOS's BIOS recognize the different drive types and can handle a single external drive added to a single floppy system.

To establish another logical disk drive from the same physical disk drive, use **DEVICE = DRIVER.SYS** once for each additional logical drive. For example, to establish another logical drive for a 1.44M disk drive B:, use the following command (assuming that DRIVER.SYS is located in C:\DOS):

    DEVICE = C:\DOS\DRIVER.SYS = /D:1 /F:7 /S:18 /C

DOS assigns the next available disk drive letter to the logical device. On a two hard disk partition machine, this line assigns the name E: to the drive. Therefore, to copy MYFILE between 1.44M (or 720K) diskettes, you use the command **COPY B:MYFILE E:**.

Unlike other device drivers, DRIVER.SYS can be loaded any number of times. You can create as many new logical disk drives as you want. Be sure, however, that the correct physical drive number is specified in each invocation of DRIVER.SYS. The physical drive number has no relationship to the logical drive letter that DOS assigns. Confusing this fact and using an incorrect drive number is the leading mistake made with DRIVER.SYS.

If you use a version of DOS that does not autoshift when formatting with DRIVER.SYS, you might be able to use additional copies of DRIVER.SYS and some tricks to solve the problem. For example, you can use the following lines:

    DEVICE = C:\DOS\DRIVER.SYS = /D:1 /F:7 /S:18 /C
    DEVICE = C:\DOS\DRIVER.SYS = /D:1 /F:7 /S:9 /C

The first line establishes the first additional logical disk drive with the correct parameters for a 1.44M disk drive. The second line establishes an additional logical drive with the "short" parameters to format a 720K disk drive. This technique works with some computer and DOS combinations.

Notice that the form factor for both invocations is 7. With most versions of DOS, the form factor must be correct to enable the drive to format with the required recording head write current. However, you might experiment with a form factor of 2 in the second line.

You can use DRIVER.SYS when DRIVPARM won't work (because of a faulty DOS-ROM BIOS combination or some external disk drives) and when you need to copy on like-sized diskettes (minifloppy or microfloppy) when the machine has dissimilar drives. For a different and faster method of copying between floppy diskettes, see the section on copying files in Chapter 7.

12.26   Trap: The drive names that DOS assigns to DRIVER.SYS logical drives are not intuitive.

The major difference between DRIVPARM and DRIVER.SYS is that DRIVPARM changes the drive in-place (the DOS drive name stays the same), and DRIVER.SYS creates a new logical disk drive. DRIVER.SYS displays on-screen the letter assigned to the logical disk drive. Failing to remember this letter, however, has side effects.

The first effect is a several letter offset between the original disk drive letter and the new logical drive letter. DOS assigns new logical drive letters after the last hard disk partition is settled on start-up. The order assignment happens in the following manner: skip A and B (regardless of the number of physical floppy disk drives), assign each hard disk partition the next ascending drive letter, and then assign others (block device drivers loaded with DEVICE directives) on a first-come, first-served basis. When this occurs, the regular name for the floppy disk drive is two to four letters different from its new logical drive name, and you frequently may use the wrong drive letter.

Copying files between the physical drive and new logical drive is an uncommon operation that is both infrequent and not intuitive. In your mind, you may visualize a floppy disk drive with a name of A or B, but you don't automatically spot a disk drive with the new name of E, F, or G. Suddenly, you cannot provide the correct name, and you stumble and give the wrong drive name.

The same problem occurs when you need to format a diskette with the changed parameters. Suppose, for example, that you use DRIVER.SYS because the second disk drive, a 1.44M microfloppy drive, will not format properly. The new logical drive name is drive E:. When you format a 1.44M diskette, you must use **FORMAT E:** rather than a command such as **FORMAT B: /F:1440K**.

This trap is common because diskette formatting is an infrequent operation, and the process is not intuitive. You easily can give the original drive letter rather than the correct logical letter. When you make that mistake, FORMAT churns out the wrong type of diskette or issues an error message.

12.27 Trick: Place DRIVER.SYS directives after block device drivers, particularly RAM disks.

The "first-come, first-served" rule means that other DEVICE directives for block device drivers (such as VDISK or RAMDRIVE) either affect or are affected by DRIVER.SYS. If these lines appear before DRIVER.SYS, DRIVER.SYS gets higher letters. If these lines appear after DRIVER.SYS, the other devices get higher letters.

This aspect causes problems only when you add or change CONFIG.SYS. The drive letter assignments are both predictable and stable. When you change the directive, however, you may need to alter batch files, programs, SET commands, or LASTDRIVE directives to accommodate the new logical disk drives.

If your batch files, programs, or SET commands depend on a specific letter for a RAM disk or other block device driver, place DRIVER.SYS directives after these DEVICE directives. Only the new logical floppy disk name changes, not the established names. Therefore, you don't have to change batch files and programs that depend on the established drive letters.

My setup, particularly for my RAM disk, is ingrained in my mind. Because I use the DRIVER.SYS drives infrequently (only for formatting and copying) and I use the RAM disk frequently, I prefer to have the RAM disk receive the next drive name after the hard disk.

When you add DRIVER.SYS, however, you still must change any batch file, program, or command that uses SUBST commands with the now-occupied drive letters. You need to alter LASTDRIVE to restore the same number of empty logical drive letters. Doing this maintenance work is easier than changing the order of all DEVICE-loaded drives.

12.28 Tip: If either DRIVPARM and DRIVER.SYS can work, favor DRIVPARM.

I prefer DRIVPARM to DRIVER.SYS because DRIVPARM does not change the order of my disk drives (eliminating the need to alter my established batch files, SET commands, and programs, or learn a new disk drive letter). A second reason is that I have more free conventional memory for my programs' use. DRIVER.SYS occupies about 240 bytes of memory. Although this is a small amount, I want all the free memory I can get. My advice is that although DRIVER.SYS can work, use DRIVPARM. If DRIVPARM doesn't work, then consider DRIVER.SYS among your other options.

13

Customizing the Video Screen and Keyboard

You can use a variety of techniques to customize your video display and keyboard. The ANSI.SYS device driver provided with DOS, the DOS editing functions, and several DOS commands provide ways to configure your screen and keyboard settings to your needs.

In this chapter, you learn to enter ANSI control sequences directly from the keyboard; set the color and mode of the video display, use the environment to keep track of the current mode and colors so that they can be restored later; and make ANSI recognize a character other than the escape character as the lead-in for a control sequence. You also learn how to configure the cursor shape, set the typematic rate of the keyboard, and create special characters and boxes.

Using The ANSI.SYS Device Driver

The American National Standards Institute (ANSI) has defined several standards that provide software portability for hardware interfaces. ANSI standard compatibility is also available with the ANSI.SYS device driver provided with DOS systems.

ANSI.SYS provides three capabilities that work on all MS-DOS-based computers: setting screen modes and colors, positioning the cursor, and reassigning the meaning of any keystroke sequence.

To use ANSI.SYS, you must have the **DEVICE=ANSI.SYS** line in your CONFIG.SYS file.

You send to ANSI special character strings that it recognizes as instructions. These strings begin with a standard lead-in: the escape character (27 decimal, 1b hex) followed by the left bracket [(#91). ANSI.SYS commands are often called *escape sequences*. The ANSI.SYS functions and escape sequences are listed in Appendix C.

Each sequence ends with a letter, which indicates the instruction and terminates the sequence; the instruction's parameters, if any, fall between the [and the letter. For example, **Esc[2J** is the clear screen instruction. If [2J is printed by DOS and ANSI.SYS has been loaded, the screen is cleared.

Whatever is displayed on-screen goes through ANSI and is checked for those characters. If ANSI encounters a #27 followed by a #91 in a stream of characters going to the screen, those two characters—and the rest of the instruction that follows them—are pulled out of the stream and intercepted by ANSI.

DOS, however, sees the escape character as the cancel-line editing sequence. Because you can't type the escape character directly, you need some program trickery to get an escape character to the screen. The trickery is covered in various tips, tricks, and traps in this section.

Using ANSI.SYS Escape Sequences

13.1   Tip: When you use a numeric code in an escape sequence, use the character form of the decimal-based number.

Numeric codes in ANSI sequences have three functions:

- For cursor positions, the numbers represent the coordinates or number of columns or lines to move.
- For erasing the display or screen settings, the numbers represent the mode (such as the **2** in **Esc[2J**, which designates the command to clear the entire screen).
- For reassigning keyboard keys, the number represents the ASCII character or the extended code for a key.

When used outside of double quotation marks, the numbers must be in decimal-character, rather than binary form. For example, the erase-screen sequence is **Esc[2J**. The **2** in the sequence is the character 2, not ASCII value 2 (as in **CHR$(2)**). To set white characters on a blue background, the sequence is **Esc[37;44m**. You type the **33** and **44** as actual characters, not **CHR$(33)** and **CHR$(44)**.

13.2   Tip: Separate multiple numeric codes or strings with a semicolon.

To use multiple numbers or strings for keyboard reassignments, separate each number or string with a semicolon. This prevents the color-setting sequence **Esc[33;44m**, for example, from reading as 3, 34, and 4, a combination that can produce arbitrary results.

13.3   Trap: Don't use a semicolon just before the command letter in the sequence.

The final letter in an ANSI sequence is the command letter. ANSI does not see this letter if a leading semicolon is used. For the example in Tip 13.2, **Esc[33;44;m** is incorrect.

13.4   Trap: Keep the command letter outside the quoted string.

Just as if a semicolon were used before the command letter, ANSI does not recognize the command letter if it is inside the quoted string. For example, you cannot reassign the F10 special function key with the sequence **Esc[0;68;"DIRp"**. The **p** must be outside of the double-quoted string.

13.5   Trap: Use the correct case for the ANSI command letter.

ANSI is case-sensitive; the use of upper- and lowercase letters is significant for the ANSI command letter. For example, you cannot use a lowercase *j* for the erase-screen sequence or an uppercase *M* for the set-screen attributes.

13.6   Tip: If you omit a numeric parameter, the assumed value is 0 or 1.

Depending on the sequences used, ANSI makes assumptions about missing values. For screen attributes, the assumed value is 0. For cursor positioning, the assumed value is 1. For example, giving the cursor-positioning sequence **Esc[f** (which omits the row and column coordinates) is the same as giving **Esc[1;1f**. In some situations, the default value works correctly; in others, the default value may not work.

Using ASCII Codes with ANSI.SYS Sequences

13.7   Tip: You can use binary ASCII codes within double-quoted strings.

The codes for the ANSI.SYS program are interpreted (translated) into the ASCII character scheme. The ASCII codes are listed in Appendix B.

When ANSI encounters a double-quoted string, ANSI uses the ASCII codes for each character. This means that a numeric code **71** is the same as the string **"G"** in an escape sequence. You can switch freely between the use of typeable characters within double quotation marks and numeric codes outside of double quotation marks. The technique eliminates the use of the semicolon between every character.

For example, to reassign the F10 special function key to type DIR, you use the following sequence:

Esc[0;68;"DIR"p

You can substitute the letter **D**, whose ASCII value is 68. The sequence then becomes the following:

Esc[0;"DDIR"p

The **D** is placed within the double quotation marks, and the 68 (and following semicolon) is dropped.

Do not, however, place the numeric codes within strings. ANSI assumes that you want the number as a number, not the ASCII character represented by the number. For example, the following sequence is incorrect:

Esc[0;"68DIR"p

Customizing the Video Display

This section discusses the DOS functions and commands that enable you to configure the video display to your specifications. You learn techniques to send sequences to ANSI with EDLIN and other DOS commands, to set the color and the display of lines on-screen, and set the shape of the cursor.

Distinguishing between ANSI.SYS and the VT-100 Control Codes

13.8   Trap: ANSI.SYS is not a full implementation of VT-100 control codes.

The VT-100 is a Digital Electronics Corporation (DEC®) terminal. Features of this terminal are manipulated (set) with control codes. The VT-100 terminal is frequently emulated by software programs so that computers can communicate with other computers that expect a VT-100 on the other end.

Don't expect ANSI.SYS to replace a DEC VT-100 terminal, which implements all ANSI control codes. The DOS version of ANSI.SYS lacks three commonly used functions of the VT-100 terminal codes:

Esc[OJ or (Esc[J)	Erases from current cursor position to the end-of-screen
Esc[1J	Erases from current cursor position to the beginning-of-screen
Esc[1K	Erases from current cursor position to the beginning-of-line

For these reasons, you still need a VT-100 emulation program or full ANSI.SYS file (such as FANSI.SYS or NANSI.SYS, available through shareware or CompuServe).

The most problematic is the command for erase-to-end-of-screen (**Esc[0J**). The recognized shorthand is **Esc[J**. Unfortunately, ANSI.SYS interprets this as erase-screen, which does not have the desired effect.

Using BASIC with ANSI.SYS Sequences

13.9   Trap: You cannot use ANSI sequences in interpretive BASIC.

The Microsoft Interpretive BASIC versions (BASIC®, BASICA, and GW–BASIC®) shield the BASIC user from the operating system. An interpreter, such as Interpretive BASIC, takes each command (instruction) as it reads it and executes it, thus intercepting many of the DOS and computer interrupts. The same sheltering environment shields the ANSI device driver from any sequences you print. You cannot, therefore, use interpretive BASIC to print directly any ANSI sequences.

The caution does not apply to compiled BASIC versions, such as Microsoft's QuickBASIC® or Borland's Turbo BASIC®. You use both languages to create programs that print sequences to ANSI. (A compiler, such as QuickBASIC, takes in all commands in a program and translates the commands to a machine language program. This program must then be loaded or linked in order to be executed.) Also, the limitation does not apply to programs written in most other programming languages, including Pascal, C, Fortran, or Cobol.

13.10   Tip: You can use interpretive BASIC and the TYPE command to print ANSI sequences.

Although interpretive BASIC cannot print escape sequences directly to ANSI, you can use BASIC to create a TYPEable text file. The following program, in the general format of a BASIC program, creates a text file called SAMPLE.ANS.

```
10 OPEN "SAMPLE.ANS" FOR OUTPUT AS 1
20 PRINT #1, CHR$(27);"[";  rest_of_ansi_string
100 CLOSE #1
```

CHR$(27) creates the ASCII escape character. *rest_of_ansi_string* is the set of additional escape sequences for the command. You change this information to the ANSI sequence you want. After the program runs, you use the DOS TYPE command to send the contents to the display.

To use a newsprint display (black characters on a white screen), you enter the following for line 20:

20 PRINT #1, CHR$(27);"[30;47m"

To program the F10 special function key to type DIR <Enter>, you enter the following for line 20:

20 PRINT # 1, CHR$(27);"[0;68;";CHR$(34);"DIR";CHR$(34);";13p"

The construction of the line looks strange: it is longer than usual; the two **CHR$ (34)** sequences surround the double-quoted text; and semicolons are placed within the string. The result is the following sequence:

Esc[0;68;"DIR";13p

0;68 designates the F10 special function key. **CHR$(34)** produces a double quotation mark and surrounds the word **DIR**. To give ANSI a textual string, the string must be enclosed in double quotation marks. You cannot print a double quotation mark directly from BASIC. **13** at the end of the string inserts a carriage return (as if the Enter key were pressed) into the F10 key. When you press F10, DIR <Enter> is typed.

To use the program, make the appropriate change(s), save the new version of the program under a different name (if you want to use the changed version again), run the program, and then enter the following command:

TYPE SAMPLE.ANS

You can also run this program in immediate mode. In *immediate mode,* you put the lines into BASIC and have them interpreted immediately without first loading them. Simply call up BASIC, enter the lines without the line numbers (make sure that the appropriate ANSI string is entered in the second line), and then exit BASIC. You produce the text file without "running" a program.

Using EDLIN and TYPE To Print ANSI Sequences

13.11   Tip: You can use EDLIN and the TYPE command to print ANSI sequences.

Usually, when you press the escape character, DOS interprets the keystroke as "cancel the line." You can use use certain text editors, however, to enter the escape character. Even the DOS-provided, aging, line editor EDLIN allows an indirect way of entering an escape.

The trick to this tip is the use of the escape character **Ctrl-V** (**^V**), which EDLIN treats specially. The *escape character* tells the program to interpret the next character or characters in a special way. A Ctrl-V, for example, tells EDLIN to make the next character in the sequence a control character.

To enter a **Ctrl-A** in an EDLIN line, for example, you use the sequence **^VA** (the ^ indicates a Control character). You press the Ctrl key and hold it while you press V, and then you press A. To enter a Ctrl-C, use **^VC**. To enter an escape character, use **^V[**.

Following is the general form of an EDLIN line for an ANSI command:

   ^V[[*rest_of_string*

rest_of_string is the remainder of the escape sequence for an ANSI command. You must use the double left brackets **[[**. The first **[** is used with the Ctrl-V to create the escape character. The second **[** is part of the normal lead-in sequence for ANSI terminal commands.

To program the F10 special function key to type DIR <Enter>, you enter the following line:

   ^V[[0;68;"DIR";13p

To create the line for newsprint display (black characters on a white screen), you enter the following line:

   ^V[[30;47m

To create a file named NEWPRINT.ANS, use the following steps:

   Step 1. *Type* **EDLIN NEWPRINT.ANS**

     EDLIN loads, states New file, and then displays an asterisk (*). The asterisk is the EDLIN prompt.

Step 2. *Type* **i** *(the EDLIN command to insert lines), and then press Enter.*

A 1:* appears.

Step 3. *Type* **^V[[30;47m** *and press Enter.*

A 2:* appears.

Step 4. *Press the F6 special function key, which displays as a ^Z, and then press Enter.*

Step 5. *Type* **e** *and press Enter to end the session.*

Step 6. *At the DOS prompt, enter* **TYPE NEWPRINT.ANS**, *then* **CLS**.

The screen turns to black-on-white.

You can create any text file with EDLIN to perform any ANSI.SYS function. After you save the file, type the file name at the DOS prompt. If you change background colors, type **CLS** to clear the display and change the entire screen to the background color.

Using the PROMPT Command with ANSI.SYS

The PROMPT command lets you change the drab **A>** prompt to almost any string you desire. Issue the PROMPT command followed by the appropriate string, and your system prompt changes instantly. You use the metacharacters listed in table 13.1 to customize your prompt. All metacharacters are preceded by a $.

The most common prompt is now established by DOS V4's SELECT command, which puts the PROMPT command into the AUTOEXEC.BAT file. The command **PROMPT pg** displays the current drive and path followed by the greater than sign, as in C:\>. This prompt, which instantly shows the current directory, is especially useful when maneuvering through a large subdirectory tree.

You also can use $p in other prompts. Here is another example of a prompt:

PROMPT pdt_Check's in the mail: $

This command displays on a single line the drive and path, the date, the time, and the message Check's in the mail:. The final space followed by the **$** is important if you want a space to appear after the prompt. I use a space to distinguish easily the system prompt from what I type.

Table 13.1
PROMPT Metacharacters

Character	Use
$	$ (dollar sign)
_ (underscore)	Carriage return, line feed sequence
b	| (vertical bar)
d	Current date
e	Escape character (ASCII 1b hex, 27 decimal)
g	> (greater than symbol)
h	Backspace character (ASCII 8, Ctrl-H)
l	< (less than symbol)
n	Current drive letter
q	= (equal sign)
p	Current drive and directory
t	Current time
v	DOS version number
Any other	Ignored

My personal favorite is the prompt that demands a sense of humility from my computers:

PROMPT p_Yes, Chris? $

This command displays the path on one line and **Yes, Chris?** on the next.

13.12   Trick: Use PROMPT to send Escape sequences to ANSI.SYS.

To send the escape sequence to ANSI.SYS, use PROMPT with the $e metacharacter for the leading escape character. The advantage to using PROMPT is that the prompt string is readable and editable and does not require two files (the BASIC program and the text file). Also, the command can be used and reused readily within a batch file or from the keyboard. (You can use the command **SET** > *filename* to edit the prompt string.)

Following are several examples of prompt sequences and their results:

PROMPT $e[1;38;46m	Sets the screen to bold white characters on a cyan background
PROMPT $e[0;68;"DIR";13p	Sets the F10 key to type **DIR** and an \<Enter>
PROMPT $e[1;30;47m	Sets the screen to black characters on a white background

Now consider the following complex prompt:

PROMPT $e[s$e[1;341m$e[f$e[K$p $d te[1;36;40m$e[u$g $

This prompt displays the current drive, current directory, and current date on the top line of the screen in bold blue on red. Then the prompt returns to the current line, leaves the rest of the screen light cyan on blue, and displays the prompt >.

13.13   Tip: Use the CLS or ANSI erase-screen command after you have set the screen attributes.

Although the new screens take effect after the ANSI escape string is received, the new foreground/background attributes affect only the newly printed information. If you have just set the background colors, only the system prompt appears to be affected. To change the entire screen to the selected background color, either use the erase-screen ANSI command (**Esc[2J**) or issue the CLS command to change the background color.

13.14   Trap: ECHO must be ON if you use PROMPT within a batch file or the prompt does not print.

This mistake often appears with the AUTOEXEC.BAT file, as in the following example:

```
@ECHO OFF
<more batch file>
PROMPT $e[0;36m
CLS
<rest of batch file>
```

With the preceding AUTOEXEC.BAT file, the CLS within the batch file does not appear to work because ECHO OFF suppresses the printing of the prompt string until the batch file ends. The CLS within the batch file does work, but does not set the background color because the new system prompt has not printed.

To prevent this problem, use the following sequence, which ensures that ECHO is on just prior to issuing the CLS command:

```
@ECHO OFF
<more batch file>
PROMPT $e[0;36m
@ECHO ON
CLS
@ECHO OFF
<rest of batch file>
```

When CLS runs, the display from the batch file is turned on by the ECHO
ON statement; the system prompt then displays. ANSI.SYS gets the
message and sets the screen attributes; CLS clears the screen, and the
background color changes successfully.

You can use ANSI cursor-addressing functions to have PROMPT print
information at a specific row and column of the screen. A potentially
confusing side effect, however, is that the rest of the screen does not
appear to scroll correctly, if at all.

The problem is that the next DOS prompt appears one line after the
specific information written by PROMPT. Try this example, which places
the path (**$e[H$g**) on the top line and the date and time
(**$e[H25;1$d$e[H25;40$t**) on the bottom line:

PROMPT $e[H$e[25;1Hd$e[25;40H$t$e[H$g $

Notice that the cursor ends up on the second line. If the cursor was
previously in the middle of the screen, the display appears not to have
scrolled. Because most users expect the new cursor or prompt to follow
previously displayed lines, the new cursor position is unexpected.

Another example is the following prompt:

PROMPT $e[H$g$e[25;1H$d$e[25;40H$t $

The top lines scroll off the screen before you can read the path. Unlike the
preceding command, the order of writing is reversed. The top line is
written before the bottom line. When the cursor appears on the next line,
the entire display scrolls up by one line; the top line is lost.

The trick is preserving the current cursor position by using **Esc[u**. ANSI is
instructed to remember the current position of the cursor. You then move
to the line you want by entering either **Esc[#;#H** or **Esc[#;#f**. After
printing the information, issue an **Esc[s**. The cursor returns to the saved
position.

For example, to place the path on the top line, date and time on the
bottom line, and return to the same line and issue a >, use the following
PROMPT:

PROMPT $e[s$e[H$e[25;1H$d$e[25;40H$t$e[u$g $

The display scrolls correctly and appears more natural.

Setting the Cursor Shape

13.15   Trick: You can change the size of the cursor.

The cursor consists of from one to eight horizontal lines, numbered from line 0 at the top to line 7 at the bottom. By default, DOS uses a 6–7 cursor. Lines 6 and 7—the two lowest lines—form the default cursor.

Other cursor configurations include the following:

7–7	A single line (a thin cursor—the default cursor in BASIC)
0–7	The full block shape
0–1	The two top lines
3–4	The two middle lines

You can create a variety of cursor shapes, including a "wrap-around" or "double" cursor. With 6–1, you get lines 6, 7, 0, and 1—a double cursor.

You enter the following program, CURSOR.COM, in DEBUG to set the full block cursor:

```
MOV AH,1
MOV CH,0
MOV CL,7
INT 10
RET
```

The 0 and 7 in the second and third lines are the first and last line numbers for a block cursor; you can replace them with your choice of first and last lines. The length of this program is 9; you enter that number in CX (the count register). Run CURSOR.COM, usually from a batch file, each time you change the mode. The cursor stays the way you set it until the mode changes.

13.16   Trick: Set the cursor shape to your specifications.

This variation of CURSOR.COM sets the cursor so that you can type a sequence to set the cursor to your specifications at any time. The command **CURSOR 0–7**, for example, sets the cursor to cover lines 0 through 7—that is, a full block.

```
DEBUG
A
MOV CH,[82]
AND CH,7
```

```
MOV CL,[84]
AND CL,7
MOV AH,1
INT 10
RET
RCX
14
N CURSOR.COM
W
Q
```

Be sure to leave exactly one space between the R and the first parameter, and exactly one between the first and second parameters.

Using ANSI's Set/Reset Mode and the DOS MODE Command

13.17 Trap: If you give the Set (Esc[=h) or Reset Mode (Esc[=l) sequence without a parameter, the screen reverts to a 40 x 25 display.

For the screen attribute commands, no parameter means that a 0 is used. With Set Mode or Reset Mode, the screen reverts to the 40 x 25 black-and-white display. Because most users do not want the 40 x 25 mode, either give the Set/Reset Mode with the correct parameter or use **MODE CO80** or **MODE MONO** to reset the screen to the correct mode. The parameters for Set/Reset Mode are listed in Appendix C.

13.18 Tip: Set Mode and Reset Mode work identically, except for parameter 7.

The Set Mode and Reset Mode commands are identical, except for parameter 7. You can use Set Mode or Reset Mode to change video modes, from 40 x 25 monochrome to the newer 640 x 480 color mode.

Parameter 7, which controls how lines longer than the screen are handled, works differently in Set Mode than in Reset Mode. In Set Mode 7 (**Esc[=7h** or **Esc[?7h**), long lines are continued on the following line (a carriage return and line feed are inserted). In Reset Mode 7 (**Esc[=7l** or **Esc[?7l**), the additional characters overprint each other at the last column. DOS starts with wraparound on (as if Set Mode 7 is given). Unless you do not want to see the last part of a long line, avoid Reset Mode 7.

13.19   Trap: With DOS V4.0, if Set/Reset Mode parameters 14 through 19 are in effect, you cannot use the MODE CON LINES= command.

With DOS V4.0, you can set/reset the screen to several additional modes. The new modes include 640 x 200, 350, or 480 monochrome or color modes; or the 320 x 200 VGA mode. Unfortunately, when any of these modes are in effect, the **MODE CON LINES=** command does not work. You must restore the ANSI screen to the normal mode by using **Esc[=2h** or **Esc[=3l** or the **MODE CO80** or **MONO** command. After the screen is reset to its standard mode, you can use the **MODE CON LINES=** command.

13.20   Trick: For DOS V4.0, you can use 43-line or 50-line EGA/VGA modes with ANSI.SYS and MODE.

With DOS V4.0, you can use an Enhanced Graphics Adapter (EGA) or Video Graphics Array (VGA) in 43- or 50-line modes. The trick is to use the /L switch of ANSI.SYS and issue the **MODE CON LINES=** commands.

First, add the /L switch to the line that loads ANSI.SYS in your CONFIG.SYS file, as in the following line:

> **DEVICE = C:\DOS40\ANSI.SYS /L**

Then reboot your system and use the MODE command. Following is the syntax for MODE:

> **MODE CON LINES = ll COLS = cc**

The number of lines (**ll**) is 25, 43, or 50. For an EGA, use 25 or 43. For EGA+ cards (such as the Vega Deluxe™) or VGAs, you can use 25, 43, or 50.

To change the number of columns, you can use the **COLS=cc** portion. **cc**, the number of columns, is either 40 or 80. If you omit LINES or COLS, the number of lines or columns does not change. Also, **LINES = 43** or **LINES = 50** with **COLS = 40** looks strange.

Remember that using the extended number of lines does not work on all displays, nor does it work correctly with all programs. For example, both BRIEF (a text editor) and WordStar 5 use only 25 lines unless specially installed to use 43 or 50 lines. Running these programs in 43-line or 50-line mode means that the lower half of the screen is unused. Also, some programs may take exception to running in this video mode. Use **MODE CON LINES=25** before you run these programs and issue the desired **MODE CON LINES=** command when you finish.

13.21   Trick: Use MODE CO80 or MODE MONO to reset the cursor type and clear the screen.

Some programs leave the cursor and screen in a "state of disgrace." Also, you may abort some programs prematurely. Fortunately, running **MODE CO80** (for any graphics adapter, including monochrome monitors on a EGA or VGA) or **MODE MONO** (for monochrome adapters) clears the screen and usually restores the cursor to its previous color and state. Be aware that this trick does not work with all programs.

Setting the Colors

13.22   Tip: Keep track of the ANSI color codes.

ANSI uses the following color codes:

Code	Color	Code	Color
0	Black	4	Blue
1	Red	5	Magenta
2	Green	6	Cyan
3	Yellow	7	White

Setting and adjusting the screen colors and background intensity of the video display is an important convenience. To form the code used in a color-setting escape sequence, start with the digit 3 (for foreground color) and follow it with a color code from the preceding list. For example, the code 36 represents a cyan foreground.

Use the digit 4 to represent the background color. For example, the code 41 represents a red background. (See Appendix C for a complete list of ANSI terminal codes.)

The color-setting instruction to ANSI is the letter *m*, which must be in lowercase. The string, therefore, begins with the escape character and [and ends with *m*. In between are one or more numerical values—the parameters of the instruction—separated by semicolons. The following examples illustrate these sequences:

Esc[32m   Sets the foreground to green
Esc[44m   Sets the background to blue
Esc[33;46m Sets the foreground and background simultaneously, to yellow and cyan, respectively

Note that the semicolon is the only acceptable delimiter between parameters in an escape sequence.

You must use three parameters to specify the colors completely. Two parameters indicate the foreground and background colors; the other parameter denotes the intensity. To produce a high-intensity (bright) foreground color, use a parameter of 1 for high intensity and 0 for regular. The next two examples illustrate the sequences that control intensity:

Esc[0;34;43m   Sets regular blue on yellow

Esc[1;32;44m   Sets bright green on blue

Keep the parameters together rather than issue one by itself. Changing the foreground color doesn't in itself turn the intensity on or off. You must use the 0 parameter to turn off the intensity. The 0, however, also clears the colors to their default values—white on black. Therefore, unless you want the default, you must always follow the 0 with the other two parameters. To ensure the correct results, always include all three parameters and make sure that the 0 or 1 is always first, as in the two preceding examples.

13.23   Tip: Set the mode whenever you set or restore the colors.

You may need to set your screen colors again when you exit a program. Periodically, you may need to reset the screen mode (the screen width of 40 or 80 columns) as well. For convenience, you can create a batch file that sets your screen colors and mode.

Following are the ANSI codes that set screen mode. (A complete table of ANSI codes is found in Appendix C.)

Code	Screen Mode
1. Esc[=0h	40 columns, black-and-white
2. Esc[=1h	40 columns, color
3. Esc[=2h	80 columns, black-and-white
4. Esc[=3h	80 columns, color

Use codes 2 and 4 if you use a color monitor. Use codes 1 and 3 if you use a single-color monitor (green on black, amber on black, and so forth).

13.24   Trick: Use a batch file to set the mode and colors.

You can type the commands to set your screen colors, or you can use a batch file to do the same. You can also add a help screen that helps you remember the color numbers. The following batch file, SETCOL.BAT, includes a help screen.

```
ECHO OFF
IF %2. == . goto help
```

```
IF %1. == . goto help
IF %3. == . ECHO %Esc%[3%1;4%2m
IF NOT %3. == . ECHO %Esc%[%3;3%1;4%2m
CLS
GOTO end
:help
ECHO The proper format is
ECHO       SETCOL forevalue backvalue [intensity]
ECHO .
ECHO .    Where [intensity] is optional
ECHO .    -------- COLORS --------    - INTENSITY -
ECHO .    0-Black   4-Blue        0-Normal
ECHO .    1-Red     5-Magenta     1-Bold
ECHO .    2-Green   6-Cyan
ECHO .    3-Yellow  7-White
ECHO .
:end
```

When you type **SETCOL** with one or no parameters, the help screen is displayed, showing the proper syntax as well as the color and intensity values. If you give two parameters, the screen colors are set, but the attribute is not changed. If you include all three parameters, the screen colors are set with the appropriate intensity.

SETCOL.BAT uses the escape character from the environment. If you do not have the escape character in your environment, change

    ECHO %Esc%[3%1;4%2m

to

    PROMPT $e[3%1;4%2m$p

Also change

    ECHO %Esc%[%3;3%1;4%2m

to

    PROMPT $e[%3;3%1;4%2m$p

See Chapter 9, "Using Advanced Batch File Techniques," for more information on placing characters in the environment.

13.25 **Tip: Clear the screen with the same command used to set the colors, rather than with a separate CLS command.**

When you set the colors, it helps to have the entire screen change to the new background color immediately. You can add a **[2J** sequence, the escape sequence for clearing the screen. You can also add a CLS command; but you then need another line, and two lines take twice as long to execute. With SETCOL.BAT (see Trick 13.24), remove the CLS command and change the lines

```
IF %3. == . ECHO %Esc%[3%1;4%2m
IF NOT %3. == . ECHO %Esc%[%3;3%1;4%2m
```

to

```
IF %3. == . ECHO %Esc%[3%1;4%2m%Esc%[2J
IF NOT %3. == . ECHO %Esc%[%3;3%1;4%2m%Esc%[2J
```

Customizing the Keyboard

ANSI.SYS and other DOS functions enable you to customize the keyboard for convenience and better productivity. This section's tips, tricks, and traps deal with making the keyboard work for you.

Using the DOS Editing Keys

13.26 **Tip: Know the DOS editing keys.**

Several function keys can be used at the DOS command line and within some DOS programs, such as EDLIN and DEBUG. You can use the keys to edit the current line, or recall, edit, and enter a previous command line. The DOS editing keys are shown in table 13.2.

Other than the Backspace and Enter keys, the two editing keys used the most are F5, which places the current line into the template, and F3, which recalls the template. To edit the current line, press F5. You may use the remaining keys to alter the template before pressing Enter.

The F3 key recalls, in its entirety, the last line that was typed. To repeat the last command, press F3 and then Enter.

Be aware that if you have reassigned the six special function keys, you lose their editing functions. Reassigning keys with ANSI.SYS is discussed in another section.

Table 13.2
DOS Editing Keys

Key	Use
F1 or →	Copies the next character from the template to the current command line
F2	Copies all characters from the previous command line—up to but not including the character typed from the template—to the current command line
F3	Copies all remaining characters from the template to the current command line
F4	Deletes all characters from the template up to, but not including, the next key you type (opposite of F2)
F5	Places the current command line into the template and starts the current command line over
F6	Produces an end-of-file marker (^Z) when you copy from the console to a disk file
Ins	Enables you to insert characters on the command line without overwriting the template
Del	Deletes a character from the template
Backspace or ←	Deletes the previous character from the command line
Esc	Cancels the current command line

Using Keyboard Enhancers

13.27 Tip: Use a keyboard enhancer to make typing easier.

Keyboard enhancer programs make typing easier. There are two types of keyboard enhancers: command-line enhancers and keyboard macro programs.

Command-line enhancers store previous command lines. You can scroll through the list, reenter a previous command line, or edit and enter a command line. An example of a command-line enhancer is Scroll/Recall, which keeps the last 20 or more command lines and enables easy entry and editing of any previous command line.

Two slightly more powerful command-line enhancers are CED (Command EDitor) or PCED (Professional Command EDitor) from Software Cove. CED and PCED recall and edit command lines and enable you to build a group of keywords (called synonyms) that are dynamically substituted and passed to DOS. In essence, one command can be expanded to several phrases or lines. For example, the word WP can be defined as the separate commands **CD C:\WP : WP**. When you type **WP** and press Enter, DOS changes to the subdirectory **C:\WP** and executes **WP** (WordPerfect®).

Using keyboard macro programs, you can designate a one keystroke sequence to type a frequently entered command, phrase, or even several lines. You can use keyboard macro programs at the command line or within programs. These macro programs are indispensable with programs such as word processors or accounting packages when frequent, repetitive keyboard sequences are typed.

Keyboard macro programs have many advantages. The programs can "learn" a keyboard macro as you type it, making the process of creating macros easier. The programs have an editor that dynamically changes the key assignments while in a program. Many programs enable you to store the keyboard definitions in a disk file that can be stored, edited, and recalled at any time. ANSI.SYS has none of these features.

Examples of keyboard macro programs are Borland's SuperKey® and RoseSoft's ProKey™. Both can be used at the DOS command line or within a program.

When working with DOS (not your applications programs), you spend about one-quarter of the time typing information. Both types of keyboard enhancers offer potential timesavings and greater convenience.

Using ANSI.SYS for Keyboard Reassignment

13.28   Trick: Make your own key reassignments by using the Esc[p sequence.

You can use ANSI.SYS's reassign-key command, the poor man's keyboard macro facility, to make almost any key combination type almost any sequence of characters. You can redefine your keyboard by assigning a string of characters to one or two keystrokes. If you type a certain sequence frequently, you can assign the command (string of characters) to a certain key. For example, suppose that you often execute the following command:

DIR C:\DATA\123\BUSNESS

You can use ANSI.SYS to assign this command to function key F10, or perhaps Shift-F10. When you press the assigned key, the string is displayed on-screen as follows:

DIR C:\DATA\123\BUSNESS

Reassigning keys, an easy process, is similar to setting screen colors. As with setting screen colors, ANSI.SYS must be installed in CONFIG.SYS as a device.

The general form of the reassign-key command is

Esc[*sequence*

sequence can be any combination of decimal ASCII numeric codes or double-quoted strings, separated by a semicolon.

The key to be reassigned is based on the first or first and second codes. If the code is neither 0 nor 224 decimal (E0 hex), the first code is the key to reassign. This means that if the sequence does not start with **Esc[0**, **Esc[224**, **Esc["<>**, or **Esc["**α (<> is a NULL; alpha is the ASCII character 224 decimal, E0 hex), and a normal keyboard key is the target for reassignment. A list of all the keys, their ANSI assign codes, and ANSI's reassign-key sequences is found in Appendix C.

If the first code is 0 or 224, ANSI assumes that an extended key or Enhanced Keyboard extended key will be used. The second code designates the specific key. The remainder of the command up to the closing **p** is the new text for the key to type.

13.29 Trap: Do not reassign the extended code keys that are used by DOS.

DOS uses only the following extended code keys:

Code	Key(s)
59–65	F1–F7
75	Left arrow
77	Right arrow
82	Insert
83	Delete
114	Ctrl-PrtSc

When you press Ctrl-PrtSc, DOS echoes all screen activity to the printer. The other keys are used as DOS editing keys. If you redefine any of these keys, you lose their regular functions. If you have no use for the regular functions, you can redefine these keys; but remember that there are plenty of other extended codes you can use.

13.30   Trick: To redefine your keys, create a file that contains ANSI.SYS commands.

If you redefine several keys, you can create a file that redefines your keys without using a batch file or PROMPT. This can be done easily with EDLIN. The following file, KEYSON.TXT, redefines keys:

^V[[0;66;"DIR";13p

^V[[0;67;"TYPE "p

^V[[0;68;"COPY "p

^V[[0;93;"DISKCOPY A: B:";13p

KEYSON.TXT creates an EDLIN file with the following keys redefined:

Key	Definition
F8	DIR
F9	TYPE
F10	COPY
Shift-F10	DISKCOPY A: B:

Notice that the **^V[** in EDLIN causes an escape character to be saved in the file. The keys are defined when you type the command **TYPE KEYSON.TXT**.

13.31   Trick: To put an Enter, space, or double quotation mark within a key, use the character's number code.

ANSI does not recognize three characters within a string: the carriage return or Enter key, a space, or a double quotation mark. To place any of these within a key, you must use the numeric code that corresponds to the key:

Key	Numeric Code
Enter	13
Space	32
Double quotation mark	34

To place the string **ECHO "THIS IS A STRING"<ENTER>** into the F10 key, you use the following sequence:

Esc[0;68"ECHO";32;34;"THIS";32;"IS";32;"A";32;"STRING";34;13p

13.32   Trick: Use DEBUG and CTTY to turn ANSI V3 keyboard reassignment functions off and on without restarting the computer.

Some programs do not work correctly when you reassign keys. For example, some programs use the F1 key for help or the F10 key to exit the program. If you reassign the meaning of these keys and the program sees the change, you lose the use of the keys.

This trick, a bit of brilliance on the part of Ward Christensen, the author of the XMODEM Communication Protocol, involves changing a name inside the ANSI.SYS driver and using the change-console command, CTTY. For this trick, you will need to use DEBUG and make a slight modification to your CONFIG.SYS file.

Caution: Do not use this trick with PC DOS V4.

You change the CON (short for CONsole device) within ANSI.SYS to ANS. Use the following steps:

> *Step 1.* *Copy the ANSI.SYS file to ANSI2.SYS.*
>
> *Step 2.* *Invoke DEBUG by using the dialog shown in figure 13.1. Type the responses in bold. If you make a mistake, press Enter, then* **Q**, *and press Enter again. This quits DEBUG and you can start over.*

```
debug ansi2.sys
-s cs:0 fff 'CON'
xxxx:yyyy
-e yyyy
xxxx:yyyy 43.41<space> 4F.4e<space> 4E.53<Enter>
-w
Writing zzzz bytes
-q
```

Fig. 13.1. DEBUG dialog.

The trick is in the third and fourth lines of the dialog. The **S** command in line 2 searches memory for a string. DEBUG responds with an address (the segment represented by the **xxxx** and offset represented by the **yyyy**). The segment and offset are separated by a colon as shown in line 3. If more than one address appears (as in 282E:100A and 282E:702A), use the first address. For line 4, the number you enter after the **e** is the number after the colon from line 3.

The dialog shown in figure 13.2 occurred when I modified my ANSI2.SYS file for MS-DOS V3.3. Remember that the numbers **xxxx**, **yyyy**, and **zzzz** (which show the number of bytes in the file) in lines 3, 4, 5, and 7 may vary among DOS versions and implementations.

```
C:\DOS33> debug ansi2.sys
-s cs:0 fff 'CON'
4894:010A
-e 010a
4894:010A 43.41  4F.4e  4E.53
-w
Writing 066F bytes
-q
C:\DOS33>
```

Figure 13.2. DEBUG dialog modified for DOS V3.3.

After you have changed and saved your ANSI2.SYS file, change the **DEVICE = ANSI.SYS** directive in your CONFIG.SYS file to **DEVICE = ANSI2.SYS**. Restart your system and you're ready for quick-changing ANSI.SYS functions.

To activate ANSI functions and use the keyboard redefinitions, type **CTTY ANS**. To disable ANSI functions, type **CTTY CON**; your programs will use the normal function keys.

Remember to include CTTY ANS in your AUTOEXEC.BAT file to activate ANSI. If you often need to turn off ANSI for specific programs, use the batch file start-up and give the **CTTY CON** command before starting the program; give **CTTY ANS** as part of the cleanup.

This trick is useful when you use a program such as TAPCIS (a program that handles CompuServe communications). TAPCIS uses the special function keys and objects if you have programmed F10 to type DIR C:. I use the batch file shown in figure 13.3 to move to the TAPCIS directory, disable ANSI, start TAPCIS, and then clean up. The two CTTY commands that surround **TAPCIS** first disable and then reenable the ANSI functions.

```
C:
CD \TAPCIS
CTTY CON
TAPCIS %1 %2 %3 %4
CTTY ANS
```

Fig. 13.3. TAPCIS.BAT.

13.33   Tip: You may want to unassign certain keys prior to entering a program.

The file KEYSON.TXT (see Tip 13.30) reassigns the function keys F8, F9, F10, and Shift-F10. To unassign those keys, use EDLIN to create the following file—KEYOFF.TXT.

```
^V[[0;66;0;66p
^V[[0;67;0;67p
^V[[0;68;0;68p
^V[[0;93;0;93p
```

Notice that the assignment for the key is made back to the key. The key assignment is 0;66, the value of the key itself, rather than **"DIR"**. This procedure works for all keys.

Creating Special Characters and Boxes

You can use several techniques to create special characters and boxes on-screen. This capability is often helpful when you are creating a self-help menu system or on-screen messages. This section's tips, tricks, and traps deal with the construction of graphics characters.

Using Graphics Characters for Messages and Help Screens

13.34   Trick: Make your on-screen messages more attractive with graphics characters.

You can use the IBM graphics characters for the displayed messages in your batch files. Because these characters are built into the display adapter or array of the computer, they may be displayed on any screen. With these characters, you can highlight and add flair to important messages.

The line characters for boxes and screen characters (with ASCII values) are shown in figure 13.4. Figure 13.5 organizes the ASCII values for the box characters by type. Figure 13.6 shows the on-screen result.

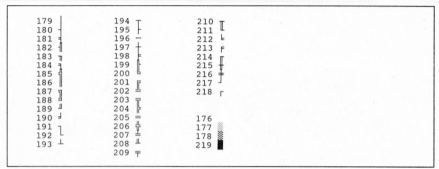

Fig. 13.4. Line characters for boxes and screen characters (with ASCII values).

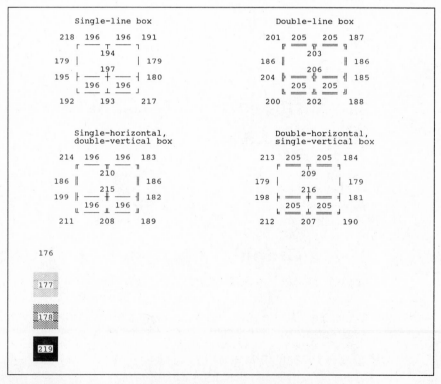

Fig. 13.5. ASCII values for the box characters organized by type.

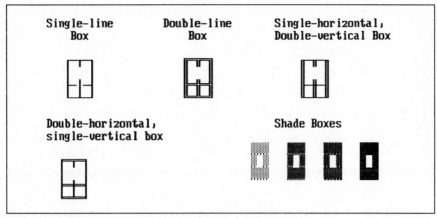

Fig. 13.6. Display of box characters organized in figure 13.5.

The keystroke sequence for entering the characters in your text editor varies slightly among editors. However, the Alt-keypad-number sequence works with almost all text editors.

To type a graphics character, hold down the Alt key, type on the numeric keypad the one- to three-digit ASCII code for the character, and then release the Alt key. The character appears. For example, to type the character for the double-line, upper-right corner of a box, hold down the Alt key and type **187** on the numeric keypad. When you release the Alt key, the character appears. Note that Num Lock does not need to be turned on; however, you can use only the keys on the numeric keypad (not the upper row of the QWERTY portion of the keyboard).

Typing the characters can be laborious; you must press and release the Alt key for each character. A trick is to type one or two characters and then use the text editor's block copy facility to replicate the characters. Some programs, such as SideKick Plus, can copy and paste the characters from an internal ASCII table function into a document.

Another trick is to use a keyboard macro program (discussed in the "Using Keyboard Enhancers" section) or the ANSI.SYS keyboard reassignment (also discussed in this chapter) to type the characters with certain keystroke combinations. Assign to a macro the graphics characters, not the original sequences that generate those characters. Although keyboard macro programs can type characters, most cannot approximate pressing Alt and typing 187 (or some other ASCII code for a different character).

For example, to assign the double-line, upper-right box character to the F10 function key, use the sequence

Esc[0;68;"<Alt-187>"p

Type the first quotation mark, hold down the Alt key, type **187** on the numeric keypad, release the Alt key, and then type the second quotation mark.

In a program, use the correct ASCII value for the character. For instance, use the following line in BASIC to create the ANSI sequence:

PRINT #1, CHR$(27);"[0;68;";CHR$(34);CHR$(187);CHR$(34);"p"

I do not favor the ANSI-sequence approach because you must assign many key sequences to cover the box characters. Also, the ANSI sequence cannot be changed in the middle of a program. I do favor assigning keys with a keyboard macro package. Most programs can load and save different keyboard definitions. Almost all have a pop-up facility to load, save, or clear the definitions quickly while within a program.

I have four different keyboard macro files for building boxes. These files use the box formed by the QWE, ASD, and ZXC keys on the keyboard (see fig. 13.7). Alt-Q, Alt-W, and Alt-E display the upper-left, upper-T, and upper-right box characters. Alt-A, Alt-S, and Alt-D display the left center-T, middle-T, and right center-T characters. Alt-Z, Alt-X, and Alt-C display the lower part of the box. For the vertical and horizontal line characters, I use Alt-L and Alt-M, respectively. (Tall and thin, short and wide is the visual clue.)

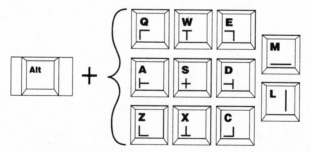

Fig. 13.7. Macro assignments for building boxes.

Be careful that your keyboard macro assignments do not conflict with your text editor. You may need to change the assignments for building boxes to

Ctrl-key or Shift-Alt-key combinations if your text editor already uses the Alt-key combinations.

I strongly suggest that you use a visual text editor or word processing program to arrange the line characters. You must often add spaces to make the box of characters enclose the message properly. This task is easier when you can move quickly from line to line. COPY CON is inadequate and EDLIN is barely adequate for this task.

Be careful when you use certain word processors. With some, you can create, but not edit, the document. For example, WordStar Releases 3 and 4 strip the most significant bit of characters when reading documents from the disk, even if you are editing in nondocument mode. You can create the batch file with WordStar; when you recall the document, however, WordStar strips the high-order bit from the graphics characters. The batch file lines are transformed into unattractive nonsense. (If this happens, abandon the document—don't resave it.) You will need a different text editor or word processor to edit the file. (Fortunately, WordStar 5 handles these files correctly.)

An example of a "pretty" printed file is WSRAM1.BAT (see fig. 13.8), which is another version of WSRAM.BAT presented in Chapter 3, "Improving Disk Performance." The corner characters are Alt-201 (upper left), Alt-187 (upper right), Alt-200 (lower left), and Alt-188 (lower right). The vertical line characters are Alt-186, and the horizontal characters are Alt-205.

```
@ECHO OFF
REM
REM Batch file to copy a file from the current disk, run WordStar,
REM and copy the file back to the current disk.

REM
REM Test for a file name.
REM
IF %1. == . goto help

REM
REM If you don't have an environmental variable named temp,
REM change the set temp= to the drive name of your RAM disk.
REM
:gettemp
IF %temp%. == . set temp=c:\

REM
REM If the named file doesn't exist, run WordStar with file name.
REM
```

```
IF exist %1 goto copyit
CALL ws %temp%%1
GOTO copyback

REM
REM If the file exists, copy it. If the copy exists, the operation was
REM successful. Run WordStar.
REM
:copyit
COPY %1 %temp% >nul
IF not exist %temp%%1 goto error
CALL ws %temp%%1

REM
REM Copy the file back.
REM
:copyback
COPY %temp%%1
GOTO end

:help
REM Print help screen.
ECHO
ECHO    ┌─────────────────────────────────────────────────────┐
ECHO    │ WSRAM - Use WordStar with RAM disk file.             │
ECHO    │                                                     │
ECHO    │ Usage: WSRAM filename                                │
ECHO    │                                                     │
ECHO    │        where filename is the name of the file to edit│
ECHO    │                                                     │
ECHO    │ Note: Filename must be in the current directory!    │
ECHO    └─────────────────────────────────────────────────────┘
GOTO end:

REM
REM Couldn't copy the file to the RAM disk. Report the problem.
REM
:error
ECHO
ECHO    ┌─────────────────────────────────────────────────────┐
ECHO    │ Error!                                              │
ECHO    │                                                     │
ECHO    │ I could not copy the file to %TEMP%!                │
ECHO    │ Check the RAM disk and try again.                   │
ECHO    │ Returning to DOS!                                   │
ECHO    └─────────────────────────────────────────────────────┘

:end
```

Fig. 13.8. An example of a "pretty" batch file.

Using Keyboard Stuffers To Type Special Characters

13.35 Trick: To "type" special characters from a running batch file, use a keyboard stuffer.

A fine line exists between keyboard macro programs and keyboard stuffers; each have a different purpose. The keyboard macro package "expands" a typed keystroke sequence into a series of characters. You type a key or keystroke sequence, and the macro program enters a series of keystrokes. The keyboard stuffer "transforms" a series of pseudo-commands into a sequence of characters. You give a command line argument or file name, and the keyboard stuffer simulates typing the keystroke sequences.

To illustrate the difference between these two programs, try to invoke, use, and end the keyboard macro program from a batch file. Let the batch file do all the work; after you start the batch file, don't type another character. This example fails with keyboard macro programs such as SuperKey. This type of program cannot type the Ctrl-/ sequence to make itself pop up from a batch file. On the other hand, a keyboard stuffer can read commands (as arguments in the batch file or from a separate file) and stuff the Ctrl-/ sequence into the keyboard buffer, which a terminate-and-stay-resident (TSR) program or DOS then reads as keystrokes. With a keyboard stuffer, you can type any special sequence, including Ctrl-Print Screen and Ctrl-Alt-Del.

Two programs that perform keyboard stuffing are STACKKEY by CTRLALT Associates (Barry Simon and Rick Wilson) and Fakekey. Both are useful for automating the typing of keystrokes that you need to activate TSRs or DOS features that a keyboard macro program cannot approximate. Because you can invoke keyboard stuffers within batch files, you can use conditional and control commands, such as IF and GOTO, to react to conditions. Most keyboard macros cannot handle this function. Keyboard stuffers are therefore worth investigating.

Setting the Typematic Rate of the Keyboard

The *typematic rate* is the rate at which a key is typed repeatedly when it is held down. Although most users like the typematic feature, typematic keyboards can be annoying. If the user "leans" on the keyboard (accidentally leaves the key pressed too long) or some item lands on the keyboard, the character is typed repeatedly.

13.36 Trick: Use DOS V4's MODE CON command to set the typematic rate of the keyboard.

With DOS V4, you can use the MODE CON command to set the typematic rate. Following is the syntax:

*d:PATH***MODE CON RATE = r DELAY = d**

RATE = r is the repeat rate for the keyboard. The rate ranges from 1 to 32. Table 13.3 shows the repeat rate for **r**. The normal typematic rate for computers is 20 (10 repetitions per second). The various values of **r** provide for a rate between 2 and 30 repetitions per second.

Table 13.3
Typematic Rate for MODE V4

r Rate	Typematic Rate	r Rate	Typematic Rate
1	2.0	17	8.0
2	2.1	18	8.6
3	2.3	19	9.2
4	2.5	20	10.0
5	2.7	21	10.9
6	3.0	22	12.0
7	3.3	23	13.3
8	3.7	24	15.0
9	4.0	25	16.0
10	4.3	26	17.1
11	4.6	27	18.5
12	5.0	28	20.0
13	5.5	29	21.8
14	6.0	30	24.0
15	6.7	31	26.7
16	7.5	32	30.0

DELAY = d is the amount of time the keyboard should wait before starting automatic typing. The delay ranges from 1 to 4 and represents the time of 1 second to 1/4 of a second (the time is 1/**d**). The usual computer delay time is 1/2 second.

Use caution when decreasing the delay or increasing the repeat rate. Your fingers will need to adjust to the new rate. If you keep a finger on a key too long, you will see dozens of autotyped characters dash across the display if the rate is too high or the delay rate is too low. You can always adjust your typing style (if your reflexes are good) or simply use **MODE CON** again to adjust the rate.

PART IV

Troubleshooting
Your System

Includes

Troubleshooting Logical Damage

Troubleshooting Physical Damage

14

Troubleshooting Logical Damage

I have several friends who are pilots. They tell me that 10 percent of their training teaches them how to fly 90 percent of the time. The remaining 90 percent of training covers the other 9 percent (take-offs and landings) and the 1 percent when things go wrong. Welcome to troubleshooting, where the tips, tricks, and traps cover those 1 percent occasions when things go wrong.

There are two principal types of damage: logical and physical. For example, a file is damaged if the contents are not intact or if the disk that holds the file develops a bad spot. If the contents are incorrect (including a simple transposition of one bit, missing information, or mangled information), the file is considered to be *logically damaged*. If a bad spot develops that prevents a part of the file from being read or written to, the file is considered to be *physically damaged*.

Logical damage is content-related; physical damage is media- or disk-related. Logical damage means that the contents of a file or a key DOS housekeeping area is corrupted. Physical damage means that something affects the physical use of the area or entire drive. The "read-versus-use" test demonstrates the difference between logical or physical damage. If a hardware error occurs while the disk reads the information (from an empty disk drive to a bad sector to an unresponsive disk drive), the problem is physical. If no hardware error occurs while the disk reads the information, but the information is unusable or garbled, the problem is logical damage.

This chapter covers the subject of logical damage to your system, including its causes and the remedies. Discussed are the consequences of stopping your program or computer abruptly, and tips on the times you *should* stop the computer quickly. The chapter includes an extensive discussion of CHKDSK, the DOS-provided program that can repair many forms of logical damage, and techniques that can be used with a disk-sector editor to repair some forms of logical damage. The chapter also introduces the set of steps to take when programs or disks act erratically.

Logical and physical damage are closely related. Obviously, physical damage (a bad sector) causes logical damage, because the affected sectors cannot be read. Some symptoms and remedies of logical damage are found in the next chapter, which covers the second half of the troubleshooting procedure—physical damage.

Ungraceful and Premature Terminations

A program or system can terminate in one of three ways: gracefully, prematurely, or ungracefully. A *graceful termination* occurs when the program or system completes its activity in an orderly fashion. A *premature termination* occurs when DOS performs the proper cleanup, but the program does not complete its activity. An *ungraceful termination* occurs when the program or system terminates awkwardly. Premature and ungraceful terminations can happen in the following cases: you press Ctrl-C or Ctrl-Break, you choose the **Abort** option during a critical error, the system locks up, an errant program runs amok, you restart DOS prematurely, or you lose power.

Most programs defend themselves from leaving the system in a state of disgrace. However, deliberately forcing the program to end prematurely (such as pressing **A** for **A**bort during a critical DOS error or halting the system) and certain program malfunctions can leave the system in a less-than-ideal condition. The effects of a premature termination range from lost data to several corrupted files. The effects of an ungraceful termination range from an unstable DOS to physical or logical damage to a single file, group of files, or the entire disk.

To understand the consequences of undesirable terminations, understand the opposite—the steps in the process of a graceful termination. The consequences of failing any or all steps become apparent.

A program terminates gracefully when it closes all files, removes any temporary files created by the program, frees allocated memory, and restores the original values if the program altered the hardware-software interrupt vector table. The first process is important; the second process is a courtesy; and the third and fourth processes are important if DOS is not restarted. The effects of each aspect are covered in the following tips; later tips cover the remedies.

The Consequences

14.1 Trap: If open files are not closed, you can lose information, and the disk can be logically damaged.

When DOS closes a file, DOS writes any pending information to the file, updates the directory entry (the date/time stamp and file size), updates the file allocation table, and frees the file handle (the subject of the FILES directive). The first three steps are important for file and disk integrity; the latter step is important only when the system is not restarted.

DOS closes automatically any files left open by programs that terminate while using DOS services. Most programs also close files explicitly on exit as good practice. Remember that DOS never closes explicitly file operations based on FCBs (the subject of the FCBS directive).

In fact, many programs close files explicitly several times while they run to ensure that the information is safe. Some programs have switched to the newer, faster method (called *commit file*) that was introduced with DOS V3.3. That method writes the information and updates the directory and FAT, but leaves the file open. The process is faster because it avoids the time-consuming task of reopening the file. For files that are read but not written, however, the closing files process is abbreviated simply to freeing the file handle. Remember this key fact: *When there is no writing, there is no danger.*

DOS and the program must cooperate when closing files. Program writers realize the difference between the program closing the file and DOS closing the file. The difference is not subtle.

When the program closes a file properly, the program directs DOS to write all information that the program holds in its buffers (internal working areas). When DOS closes the file, all information given to DOS is written, and DOS updates the directory entry and FAT housekeeping areas. The major difference concerns the program's internal buffers. If only DOS closes the file, the program can have information trapped in its buffers. DOS is unaware of the additional information that should be written.

Failing to complete the entire file-closing process successfully is the leading cause of corrupted files and logically damaged disks. The nature and timing of this "logical lightning strike" dictate the exact damage. When a file is closed, DOS updates the FAT, writes the data, and updates the subdirectory entry. DOS's buffering can change the exact order.

If the program is stopped before it commits or closes the file, you lose information; the subdirectory entry may or may not be correct; and the FAT is not updated correctly. If you stop DOS during the file-closing processes, information may or may not be recorded; the subdirectory entry may or may not be correct; and the FAT may or may not reflect the correct chain for the file. When the three (the stored file, the subdirectory entry, and the FAT) do not agree, they are logically inconsistent, and the disk is logically damaged. Subsequent tips discuss how to recover from most logical damage.

14.2   Trap: If a program stops suddenly, RAM can be trapped.

An internal state of disgrace can occur when a program does not free allocated memory. The computer uses two types of allocated memory: memory allocated automatically by DOS (and freed automatically) and all other memory (which the program must free). If the program leaves before freeing this memory, this RAM is not usable by other programs. The only remedy is to restart DOS.

When starting a program, DOS allocates conventional RAM to the program. The amount depends on the program type: .COM files get 64K, and .EXE files get whatever the .EXE file's preamble (established when the linker creates the .EXE file) requests. When the program ends, DOS frees the program's memory.

All other memory used by the program is allocated (requested) dynamically by the program and must be deallocated (freed) by the program. Because DOS does not have the intelligence to free automatically any other memory when the program ends, any EMS and XMA memory, or any additional conventional memory used by the program, must be freed explicitly by the program. If the program aborts before freeing this type of memory, the memory is trapped.

Most programs are conscientious about freeing memory if the program causes the halt, and most programs are careful to handle being aborted (the program traps the cause, cleans up, and then exits). The program cannot, however, handle all causes for program halts (both within the program and outside the program), and memory still can be trapped.

14.3   Trap: Stray interrupt vectors cause erratic operations.

A mashed interrupt table inevitably leads to erratic operations. (An *interrupt table* is a list of memory addresses established by the ROM BIOS and DOS.) On receiving a hardware or software interrupt, the CPU reads the appropriate value from the table and executes the instructions at the specified memory address. (The entries within the table are called *vectors*.)

DOS (via COMMAND.COM) changes some of the interrupt vectors to point to the executing program. When the program terminates through normal DOS services, the interrupts are restored. Many programs, however, establish their own routines to handle certain interrupts, such as Ctrl-Break or an open floppy disk drive door. These routines, called *interrupt handlers*, are used instead of the system-established routines to trap the interrupt.

When a program installs its own interrupt handler, the program saves the original value of the interrupt vector and then changes the vector to point to its own interrupt handler rather than to DOS's. When the CPU gets the interrupt, the CPU jumps to the program's interrupt handler, not to DOS's.

Some programs—most notably TSRs—selectively trap an interrupt. Many TSRs monitor a special indicator, such as a certain keystroke sequence (Ctrl-Alt, for example). The unobtrusive and well-behaved TSR, on installation, reads the interrupt vector, installs the vector in itself, and then changes the original interrupt vector to itself.

The procedure of read, install within, and then change is required in order for interrupts to be *chained*. Chaining means that more than one program uses the information from the interrupt. If the keystroke or other indicator is not for the TSR, the TSR passes the keystroke or indicator to the next software program in the chain. If no TSR uses the indicator, it finally passes to DOS. This procedure allows numerous TSRs to grab and process the same interrupt.

Unfortunately, when the program or TSR ends, so does the new interrupt handler. A program or TSR that leaves the interrupt vector pointing to "empty space" is a poor programming practice. Restoring interrupt vectors is critical; otherwise, the computer executes random data when the affected interrupt is generated. This occurrence is seldom desirable.

Programs, on graceful exit, always change the affected vectors back to their originally held addresses. The situations that cause a program to end before it frees its allocated memory can cause the interrupt vectors to be left pointing into empty space.

TSRs, on graceful exit, restore the previous value of the interrupt vector. Removing TSRs out of order, however, also can leave interrupt vectors pointing into space and can trap memory. Tips, tricks, and traps that describe the problems and remedies are offered later in this chapter.

14.4   Tip: If DOS and your programs don't remove temporary files, you should.

Removing temporary files is a good, not a critical, practice. When the program terminates gracefully, DOS automatically removes the files created by DOS V3.2 and later versions' temporary-file services. If the program did not use this temporary-file facility, the program must kill the file.

A good practice is to remove manually temporary files that were inadvertently left by programs. In some cases, the temporary file has a fixed name. When you rerun the program, the file is destroyed. In other cases, you simply use the ERASE command to remove the file. Use the advice given in Chapter 7 on files to help identify the temporary file (a $xx file or a file with hexadecimal digits).

14.5   Trick: Know if and when the program writes to the disk.

If you must abort a program or restart DOS prematurely, knowing your program helps. You don't need to disassemble programs, but you should know the answers to the following questions: Does the program write information to the disk? If so, what information and what files are written? When during the processing is information written?

These facts are important for making intelligent guesses about potential disk damage. If a failure occurs with programs that only read information, no damage occurs. (You can lose work, but that is another subject.) If a failure occurs during the writing process, you incur a risk.

By knowing which files the program uses and especially which files the program writes to, you know which files to suspect. By knowing what information is written at what time, you can guess whether the stop occurred before or after information was written. You then can guess whether the stop left the file intact. And if the file is not intact, you can know the extent of the damage.

If a program ends abruptly, you lose unsaved work. You can guess the extent of the loss and damage almost by program type. For programs that work sequentially on "complete" files at a time (word processors, spreadsheets, DOS filters, and so on), the extent of the damage is usually the loss of the current revision. Previously saved files should be intact.

Random-access database programs, including accounting programs, can have missing pieces. If the file is simply missing the just-entered work, you can reenter the missing transactions. Database work, however, is seldom so simple. The file may be corrupted (the missing data causes the program to choke, or garbage has been written into the file). Also, databases normally work with several related files at a time. The damage in one file can affect the use of other files. If you know whether the information has been fully or partially written and if you know which file can affect other files, you can guess what may be missing.

For either type of program, files not closed by the program may have inconsistencies between the directory entry and the FAT. Also, if you lose power during a write, you can add the potential of physical damage to the file, directory, or FAT.

The Causes

14.6   Trick: Know the cause of an ungraceful termination.

The critical question is: "Were the program and DOS able to clean up their act?"

Premature termination usually means that you lost in-progress data, but the program wrote all other information. The file may be incomplete, but the file system is intact—the directory entry and FAT are correct. In other words, the program cooperated with DOS to perform an orderly termination, but the program had more work to do. Although this type of termination sometimes happens because of errors, premature terminations usually happen when you abort the program.

Ungraceful terminations also can damage the file system and unrelated files. When outside causes (in DOS or the system) force a program to end, the termination may be less than orderly. As before, you lose not-yet-written information. DOS may or may not be able to clean up. The key is the cause of the termination—the subject of the following tips.

14.7   Tip: Three different events can terminate your program.

Three classes of events can kill a running program: CPU exceptions, Ctrl-C and Ctrl-Break, and critical errors. Each terminator has a different effect, but all three have the same result.

CPU exceptions usually, but not always, are caused by errant programs or errant data. The most frequent examples of CPU exceptions, listed in their order of frequency, are divide-by-zero, divide overflow, numeric coprocessor errors, and unrecognized instruction errors. Unless the CPU or math coprocessor is faulty (a rare circumstance), errant programs are the usual cause. The program should always check the data before trying an operation that triggers the exception. Unexpected, nonsensical data (from the user or from a disk-based file) catches a program off guard.

A CPU exception error causes an ungraceful termination. DOS slaps the program out of memory immediately. The program and DOS perform no cleanup work. The penalty is loss of in-progress work as well as loss of open disk files. (The directory entry and FAT may be inconsistent, and in this case, the disk is logically damaged.)

Ctrl-Break and Ctrl-C (the subjects of a later tip) cause either a premature or an ungraceful termination. In either case, DOS stops a program when it recognizes Ctrl-C or Ctrl-Break, but DOS restores its own changed vectors. If the program modified other interrupt vectors or allocated memory, the termination was ungraceful. (You must restart DOS manually.)

For Ctrl-C and Ctrl-Break, DOS also closes all open files. In that case, DOS updates correctly the directory entry and FAT. If the program has given to DOS all the information to write, the information is written (making the stop a premature termination). If the program has information in its own internal buffers, the information is lost. The penalty for this ungraceful termination is missing information and possibly corrupted files.

Critical errors are device-based errors. The causes range from disk drive doors left open, to bad sectors, to off-line printers. COMMAND.COM displays the error and the **Abort, Retry, Ignore, Fail** message. (The exact wording of the message varies depending on the version of DOS and the specific device involved.) If you answer **R**etry, DOS tries the errant device operation again. If you answer **I**gnore or **F**ail, DOS gives control back to the program. (What happens next depends on how well the program is prepared for the problem.)

When you answer **A**bort to an error, particularly a disk error, you have an ungraceful termination. The program drops dead, and DOS skips all cleanup work. The consequences of a wrong answer are obvious.

14.8 Trap: Four different events or errors can terminate the operating system and program.

Four events kill an operating system along with the program. When a program is killed, DOS handles the problem with or without some guidance from you. Because certain events also kill DOS before it can perform any cleanup work, events that kill a system are worse than program terminators. The killers, listed in order of the severity of potential damage, include premature DOS restart, memory parity errors, power failures, and errant programs.

These killers get all in-progress information and stop DOS before it can close files and update the file system. Usually, the effects are similar to those of an ungraceful program termination. You may, however, encounter higher-risk, higher-damage situations if DOS is writing to the disk or to the directory.

The highest risk to the file system occurs when DOS is writing to the disk. If DOS starts but cannot complete the actual disk write, you encounter numerous problems. The file is damaged; the directory and FAT are inconsistent or scrambled (severe logical damage); and the disk's physical format may be damaged.

If you catch (kill or stop) DOS when writing to the file, the file is corrupted. If you catch DOS when writing to the directory, all files whose entries are in this sector are in trouble. (Although the file's data is intact, the directory sector is corrupted and you may not be able to find the affected files.) If you catch DOS when it is writing the FAT, the FAT sector is corrupted. A corrupted FAT sector means that all files which have information that this sector points to may be orphaned or cross-linked.

When you press Ctrl-Alt-Del or the hardware reset button when you don't mean to reset the computer, you *restart DOS prematurely.* If you do this in the middle of a program that is writing information, you end up with orphaned clusters, damaged directory entries, and corrupted files. Timing, in this case, is everything. Don't press Ctrl-Alt-Del or press the hardware reset button until you are convinced that it is needed. Then avoid hitting the panic button until the program is no longer writing information.

You cannot catch DOS in the middle of a single-write operation with Ctrl-Alt-Del or Ctrl-Break. The BIOS detects both keystrokes and generates an interrupt. When DOS performs the actual disk write (or disk read) routines, however, it does not acknowledge the interrupt. The interrupt is detected as soon as DOS is finished with the actual write or read. Ctrl-Alt-Del can cause file corruption and disk inconsistencies but cannot cause physical damage. Pressing the hardware reset button may or may not be delayed. The effect of a premature hardware reset can cause more serious problems, including physical damage.

Memory parity errors can happen at any time. Memory parity errors occur when the computer detects that what it wrote into a memory location is not what is now there. The error occurs only when the computer gets information from memory, not when it is storing information.

The chance that a parity error will occur during the most critical time (writing information to the disk) is small. Besides, if you call DOS to write to the disk, you don't want errant instructions within DOS (the effect of executing a parity-errored location). The parity checking stops DOS from butchering the disk. Most other times, however, the error comes from the data to be written or any area otherwise used by the program. These occasions can leave clusters orphaned and information dangling.

The consequences of *losing power* and pressing Ctrl-Alt-Del are not identical. For Ctrl-Alt-Del, DOS completes the immediate disk operation before servicing the reset sequence. For a power down, the system is completely defenseless. Losing power during a disk write causes more problems than just lost information and an inconsistent or scrambled file system.

When power is withdrawn from the computer and disk drives, the in-progress information written is garbage, including the error-checking-and-correcting information (ECC) and the track-sector identification. The result is damage to the physical format—a bad sector. Depending on the sector miswritten, one file, one subdirectory sector, or one FAT sector is shot. You cannot predict a power failure, but you can control hitting the power switch. Hitting the power switch during a disk write is a fatal mistake.

Errant programs can be a locked program (running in an infinite loop), a runaway program (stepping on different areas of memory), or a buggy program. Most errant programs are ungraceful system terminators. Not only do you lose in-progress data, but the errant program can (emphasis on *can*, not *will*) direct DOS into bizarre operations, such as scribbling all over the disk. This process can leave many different files corrupted (including subdirectories) and can corrupt the FAT. This event is infrequent, but the effects are both negative and arbitrary. Stopping an errant program is usually more important than the ill effects of stopping DOS.

You can prevent some damage, but you cannot prevent all causes of the damage. For this reason, always have backups. If you are a skilled user, you also can take additional steps (such as FAT and partition information saving) to reduce the effects of a disaster.

Stopping the System

The system terminates gracefully when you turn off the system or restart DOS as long as some prior conditions are met: all foreground programs are terminated gracefully, all background programs are stable, all disk buffers are flushed, and the disk heads on stepper motor drives are parked. If you turn off the system or restart DOS at other times, you risk problems.

In some circumstances, however, you may not be able to avoid stopping the system abruptly. For example, you may not have a choice if the program goes astray or the system locks up, or the choice may be made for you in the case of a power failure. Specific damage and remedies are found in this chapter.

Knowing When To Stop the System

14.9 **Tip: Avoid terminating the system (turning off or restarting DOS) when the system is not quiet.**

You always can turn off your computer or restart DOS if your system is quiescent, as indicated by the following three conditions:

- The system is at the DOS command line (indicating that no foreground programs are active).
- The disk drive has completed any writing activity (firmly acknowledged by the drive in-use indicator being unlit).
- No background programs are running.

If all three conditions are met, you can stop the system safely because the computer is idle.

Given the information in the previous sections, the reason for having the foreground program terminated gracefully is obvious. Background programs (programs not displayed on-screen) can cause problems, however. Having all background programs stabilized means that the program (such as a print spooler) has finished its work; all information that should be preserved is written to the disk (some TSRs can hold information, but must be told explicitly to write the information to disk); and all files are closed. You do not need to terminate each TSR individually; you can just restart the system if all required information is written to the disk.

Having all disk buffers flushed means that DOS has written the information to the disk and updated the directory entry and FAT. Because DOS flushes the appropriate disk buffers immediately after a file is closed, the file and FAT are updated as soon as the drive accepts the information.

Some disk cachers may defer the writing of information (see Chapter 3, "Improving Disk Performance"). The graceful shutdown waits until the cache is flushed manually or the delayed-write deadline expires (a period of 1 to 10 seconds). Some cachers even trap the Ctrl-Alt-Del sequence. Note that electrons travel faster than any disk flush; cachers are therefore defenseless against power loss.

For those using stepper-motor disk drives, remember to park the disk heads before turning off the system. Parking heads is the bit of preventative maintenance discussed in Chapter 2, "Knowing and Protecting Your Disk Drives." The caution applies only to stepper-motor hard disk drives, which do not park their disk heads automatically.

14.10   Tip: If you are using a background program, don't trust seeing the system prompt.

When you run background programs (normal programs used with multitasking software or TSRs), the DOS prompt does not indicate an idle system. The computer is processing in the background; work is occurring out of view. Seeing the DOS prompt means only that the foreground program is completed. Your background programs are still at work.

Before you halt the system, make sure that all background processing is completed. Check that each program has completed its work and is idle. Either page through each of the various programs (by switching the display) or use a program process checker (such as the one provided with DESQview).

All TSRs must be quiescent, and you must write to disk any changed information held in memory. Programs such as Ready!™, the outliner from Living Videotext, and SideKick® and SideKick Plus, which have notepads or notepad and outliner features, permit you to change the files in memory and write the file manually later. If you pop out of the program without saving the revisions, you must pop back in and save the changes; otherwise, you lose them. For these programs, make sure that you have saved any needed information before you turn off the computer or restart DOS.

14.11 Trap: If the in-use light goes on when it shouldn't, be ready to stop the program.

When the in-use light on the drive goes on, DOS has selected the drive for reading or writing. If the light goes on when no program should be reading or writing to the disk, you may have an errant program. Be ready to kill the program once you have an indication that the program may be clobbering files.

14.12 Trap: Audible disk activity is a better indicator of an in-use program than a disk drive light.

Don't always trust the disk drive in-use light, particularly on floppy disk drives. The light is an indicator, not the Bible. The light may remain on when the disk access is complete, stay on because of an errant software instruction, or go off because of a delay in writing to the disk.

On floppy disk drives, the light is turned on when the drive is selected and turned off when the drive is deselected. Given the motor start time, the time between light on and actual activity is one-half to one second. Some drives keep the light on until the motor stops—another half-second to one second after the activity is completed. Also, if only one type of indicator is used, you cannot distinguish between reading and writing operations. (I like the Omtek disk drives used in some COMPAQ computers; the light is green during reads, red during writes, and amber at all other times.)

The general phrase was, "While the light is on, leave the diskette in the drive." Here's the new phrase: "If the program is writing, listen for the disk heads and motor to stop; then wait for the light." In other words, pulling out the diskette during a read operation is not good, but it is not damaging to the disk. On write operations to the diskette, wait until the coast is clear.

The in-use light on a hard disk is a better indicator because the hard disk drive is always spinning. Hard disk and floppy disk drive lights, however, are poor indicators when the drive light stays on or when there are long pauses between writes. If the light is stuck, an errant program can stomp on the software vector used to light the disk. Because the light is on only during the time that surrounds the actual read or write, the light may go out with programs that do considerable processing between write operations.

If you have a stuck light and don't know whether to halt the program, listen to the disk drive. If you don't hear any activity for 20 seconds or more, halt the program. If the light goes off and you don't know whether the program is stuck, note the amount of information that the program is processing and wait between 30 seconds and 5 minutes (for larger input data). Always respect the please wait message a program gives. Also, if the program shows any sign of life, such as changing on-screen prompts, wait until the prompts stop changing before you start the countdown.

Stopping with Ctrl-Break or Ctrl-C

14.13 Trap: Ctrl-C is not always recognized; Ctrl-Break is more frequently, but not always, recognized.

Two completely different routines detect Ctrl-C and Ctrl-Break. Ctrl-C is recognized by DOS routines; Ctrl-Break is recognized by ROM BIOS keyboard routines. The result is that one may be recognized when the other is not, and the effect of the two may not be identical.

Whenever you press a key, the ROM BIOS's keyboard handler generates a hardware interrupt. The handling of most keystrokes is deferred until DOS is ready. However, certain keystrokes—such as Ctrl-Alt-Del, the Sys Req key, and Ctrl-Break—request immediate handling. When the keyboard routine detects Ctrl-Break, the routine executes interrupt INT 1B.

On the other hand, the keyboard routine does not perform any special processing of Ctrl-C. The keystroke is left in the keyboard buffer for DOS. If DOS sees Ctrl-C as the first character of an input line (which happens when Ctrl-C is the only character in the keyboard buffer), DOS treats Ctrl-C specially and executes DOS software INT 23. At all other times, Ctrl-C is treated like any other character.

The difference is not subtle. Ctrl-C is position sensitive; Ctrl-Break is not. Ctrl-C is detected on only one condition—when it is the first character in the keyboard buffer. If, on reading a line of input, Ctrl-C is not the first character in a line, DOS ignores the keystroke.

For example, you might use Ctrl-S and Ctrl-Q combinations to pause and free the screen. One of these characters typed out of sequence ends up being ahead of Ctrl-C. Until DOS consumes the other characters, it ignores Ctrl-C. If you type a normal character ahead of Ctrl-C, Ctrl-C is consumed but not processed.

Ctrl-Break is not position sensitive. You press Ctrl-Break, and it gets DOS's attention, eventually. The attention the keystroke receives depends on the BREAK setting.

Note one other difference between Ctrl-C and Ctrl-Break. Remember that separate routines initially recognize both—DOS's INT 23 and the ROM BIOS's INT 1B. Most versions of DOS grab the 1B interrupt, clear the keyboard buffer, change the character into a Ctrl-C, and let DOS execute its interrupt 23. This translating of INT 1B into INT 23 may be destroyed by an errant program on an ungraceful termination. In other words, Ctrl-Break rarely bypasses the normal DOS cleanup. A bypassing of the cleanup routines happens only on unstable systems, on which DOS should be rebooted anyway.

Programs that trap Ctrl-C routines catch Ctrl-Break because the Ctrl-Break interrupt eventually executes the Ctrl-C routines. If, however, your DOS version does not point the Ctrl-Break routine at the Ctrl-C routine (and programs do not trap Ctrl-Break explicitly), Ctrl-Break can break a program when Ctrl-C would not.

In another case, neither Ctrl-C nor Ctrl-Break are recognized immediately as a stop-program sequence. Programs can use two different DOS input/output function calls. One set of routines recognizes either as a command to halt; the other treats both as normal characters. If the program uses the latter input routines, neither keystroke is normally recognized.

14.14 Trap: Turn off BREAK, unless you need to stop a disk-intensive task.

The timing of DOS's acknowledgment of Ctrl-Break and Ctrl-C depends on the setting of the BREAK directive and command. (You can set BREAK in CONFIG.SYS or as an internal DOS command.) Because you normally do not want to interrupt a program that is performing disk or other types of nonconsole I/O, BREAK is usually left off. If, however, the program requests little input or produces little output, you may need to set BREAK ON.

DOS always checks for a Ctrl-Break or Ctrl-C sequence when performing a character I/O function call (with the exception of certain DOS console I/O function calls that treat Ctrl-C as a normal character and ignore Ctrl-Break). The following character I/O calls always are checked:

- Console input (keyboard) and output (display)
- Communications adapter input/output
- Printer input/output

If your program uses a healthy number of these calls, you can break out whenever one of these DOS functions are used. If your program performs few of these calls, you may need to set BREAK ON to stop a program.

Basically, when the program does not perform console, communications, or printer functions, DOS ignores Ctrl-C and Ctrl-Break if BREAK is OFF. If the program is computative or disk intensive, you cannot stop the program using Ctrl-C or Ctrl-Break. If you need to stop this type of program, set BREAK ON. When the program calls on DOS, DOS detects and processes the abort sequence before processing the function call.

You can't stop a program until it calls on DOS. Because no in-progress functions, particularly disk writes, are affected by an arbitrary Ctrl-C or Ctrl-Break, you must wait for DOS to digest the abort sequence. This does not mean that data is affected. Also, notice that for a disk write in progress, the entire process of writing the data and updating the FAT is completed. Updating the directory entry for the affected file is incomplete, but DOS cures this by closing the file. FCB-based files are not closed automatically, and these files may be left with orphaned clusters.

You rarely want to interrupt a program prematurely, particularly a program that is writing to the disk. For this reason, turn off BREAK. Set BREAK ON manually before you run a program you may need to interrupt. Then run the program and turn BREAK OFF. You can implement this technique with a batch file.

Beware of ill-behaved programs that call the ROM BIOS directly and programs that trap Ctrl-C or use certain DOS console I/O. Certain programs bypass DOS and use the ROM BIOS for screen writing, console input, or certain disk functions. In those cases, Ctrl-C or Ctrl-Break never stops the activity. Also, several DOS direct-console I/O function calls treat Ctrl-C as a normal character. In those cases, neither Ctrl-C nor Ctrl-Break works. Setting BREAK ON, however, does halt the program when any other DOS function is used. If the program has an interrupt handler to trap INT 23, neither Ctrl-C nor Ctrl-Break stops a program at all.

Using the Panic Buttons

14.15 Trick: Use the panic buttons in this order: program's delay sequence, program's cancel procedure sequence, program's abort procedure, Ctrl-C or Ctrl-Break, Ctrl-Alt-Del, hardware reset switch, power switch.

If you need to stop an errant or inadvertently run program, follow the steps outlined in this trick to halt a procedure within a program, the program, or the computer itself, in that order. You should make every attempt to end gracefully. When a graceful termination is impossible, you must abort the program prematurely. If that doesn't work, you must abort DOS.

First, if a program offers and can detect its own help or other pause sequence, use that procedure as a panic button. Pause the program while you assess the problem. You might thereby gain the time to take appropriate corrective actions or to cancel a command.

Second, use the cancel procedure to halt the specific program operation. Use this procedure first whenever you are convinced that you've used the wrong option in the program. Because you already know the problem, you simply need to cancel the procedure.

Third, use the program to shut itself down. If the program offers a quick exit sequence, use it. Some in-progress information may be lost or incomplete, but the shutdown is usually orderly. The recorded information within the file and file system will be intact.

If none of the preceding suggestions are offered or recognized by the program, you may need to use the next three options to halt the program.

Fourth, use Ctrl-C or Ctrl-Break to abort the program. During console, communications, or printer I/O, DOS halts the program. To halt the program during other DOS calls, you must have BREAK ON.

The exact time of the Ctrl-C or Ctrl-Break check varies and might make a difference. Input routines check for Ctrl-C or Ctrl-Break when they get the character. Output routines check for Ctrl-C or Ctrl-Break just before they exit and the output reaches the device. DOS also checks for Ctrl-C or Ctrl-Break when entering the remaining function calls if BREAK is ON. The resulting "mess," if any, from using Ctrl-C or Ctrl-Break varies because of this difference.

Fifth, press Ctrl-Alt-Del to stop a program. Use this procedure if you need to stop an errant program. Other than for stopping an errant program or a completely erroneous operation, do not use this procedure before all pending disk activity is completed.

The sixth panic buttons are the hardware reset switch and the master panic button—the power switch. You should use these panic buttons if you need to kill the system and Ctrl-Alt-Del does not work. (The program has written over the keyboard handler and probably destroyed most other entries in the interrupt vector table.) Restarting DOS not only makes sense, but is imperative. (Remember that the keyboard handler can be trapped by programs and that Ctrl-Alt-Del can be disabled. Do not assume that because Ctrl-Alt-Del doesn't work that the program is errant.)

If you need to restart the system, generally you should opt to use the provided hardware switch rather than the power switch. The reset switch forces a warm boot of DOS and skips the power-on self-test. The power switch goes through the entire start-up sequence, which takes more time. A hardware malfunction, however, may require the use of the power switch.

Again, unless the program is errant or the operation is inadvertent, never use the reset switch or especially the power switch while writing to the disk. Pressing the power switch during a disk write is an invitation to physical damage.

Repairing the Damage

After a premature or ungraceful termination, one of the first steps in ensuring the integrity of the file system is to check for logical damage to the file system. Logical damage is insidious because it can propagate and flourish, causing damage to additional files. Also, repairing logical damage becomes more difficult as time passes. The reason for the damage remains unknown and can strike again. For these reasons, giving attention to damaged files is a secondary consideration. You must first be sure that the logical structure of the disk is intact.

CHKDSK

14.16 Trick: If the program or system prematurely or ungracefully ends, immediately run CHKDSK.

CHKDSK is the best program to use as the starting point for determining logical damage. Although the apparent purpose of CHKDSK is to display memory and disk usage, CHKDSK does far more. CHKDSK analyzes the file system of the disk, examining the FAT, comparing each subdirectory entry size against the FAT, and checking the integrity of each allocation chain in the FAT. CHKDSK also can repair many forms of logical damage.

After you abort a program that writes to the disk, run CHKDSK. After you halt the system (or the system dies) while you are running a program that writes to the disk, always run CHKDSK after you restart DOS. Notice an important warning emphasized in Trap 14.24: Do *not* run CHKDSK with the /F switch initially. If CHKDSK reports no errors, you can turn your attention to checking the in-progress files that the program uses.

If CHKDSK reports any errors, ignore the warning message about the missing /F switch. Any corrective action taken by CHKDSK is not permanent. You want to gauge the type of error before you take permanent corrective action. If you did not give the /V switch before, repeat CHKDSK with /V switch. You also may want to redirect the output to the printer (**CHKDSK >PRN**). Use later tips to take corrective action.

14.17 Trap: Do not run CHKDSK on a disk with a JOIN, SUBST, or ASSIGN in effect or on a networked disk.

CHKDSK processes only real disk drives on the system. CHKDSK does not run on a logical disk generated by the SUBST command or a disk that was rerouted with the ASSIGN command. CHKDSK also does not analyze a network disk drive. To prevent the results of the program from being arbitrary and damaging, CHKDSK notes the pseudo-disk and displays an error message.

CHKDSK analyzes a drive that is the object of a JOIN, but not the guest portion (the disk drive joined to the host drive). CHKDSK skips the guest and issues the following warning:

Tree past this point not processed.

Before you run CHKDSK, break any ASSIGN commands. Do not use CHKDSK on the SUBST pseudo-drive; run CHKDSK on the physical drive that holds the substituted subdirectory. Generally, break JOIN to analyze the host disk drive. Always break JOIN to analyze the guest disk drive.

14.18 Trap: Be cautious when using any form of redirection and piping with CHKDSK.

When you run CHKDSK to analyze potential logical damage, never redirect the output of CHKDSK to the same disk you are analyzing or use the same disk for piping (as in the command **CHKDSK | MORE**). Depending on the type of logical damage, the temporary files or directed output file may compound the damage.

Be cautious when you analyze the current disk drive. Without a disk drive name, the resulting output file goes to the current disk drive, which can cause further damage. If you analyze the current drive, give a different disk drive name (floppy disk or hard disk partition) when you redirect CHKDSK, or use any drive but the analyzed drive to catch the redirected output. If you use CHKDSK in a pipe, make another disk the current disk drive before you run CHKDSK; otherwise, DOS uses the current disk drive for temporary files and can mangle the disk further.

This warning does not apply to redirecting the output to a printer—this type of redirection does not affect the disk. The warning also does not apply when you redirect output to a disk that has a clean bill of logical health or when you use another disk drive for the piping of CHKDSK. Because there is no logical damage to the disk, there is no damage to compound. If, however, you are at all unsure, redirect the output to a different disk or switch current disk drives.

14.19 Tip: If you get a critical error from DOS while running CHKDSK, avoid answering Ignore.

If you get a critical error from DOS when you run CHKDSK (the Abort, Retry, Fail, Ignore, message), avoid answering **I**gnore. CHKDSK incorrectly diagnoses the disk, and the error or warning messages from CHKDSK can be meaningless. If you use the /F switch, answer **I**gnore as an absolute last resort—use **I**gnore only when you've taken all other corrective actions. If you answer **I**gnore, the corrective action taken by CHKDSK can be incorrect and inflict further damage.

If you get a critical disk error, use **R**etry (several times if needed) and then use either **F**ail (preferred) or **A**bort (if you must kill CHKDSK because of a bad sector or drive failure). Use **I**gnore as the last resort.

14.20 Tip: CHKDSK can get "lost" with damaged or nondamaged disks.

In two instances, CHKDSK can get confused and abort. The instances have similar causes and do not necessarily mean that the disk is damaged. Two messages indicate that CHKDSK is confused:

> Cannot CHDIR to root
>
> CHDIR .. failed trying alternate method

Failures are usually caused by corrupted interrupt tables or insufficient RAM. You can trace both failures to a program that leaves DOS in a state of disgrace or an errant terminate-and-stay-resident program. Another potential cause is a temporary hardware malfunction in the disk controller or interface. A bad copy of CHKDSK has been loaded.

Reboot DOS and run CHKDSK again. This procedure clears the state of disgrace and almost all temporary hardware malfunctions. If CHKDSK works correctly, you solved the problem.

If, however, the message reappears before you run a program (including certain disk-oriented device drivers, AUTOEXECed programs, and TSRs), try the following technique: strip down CONFIG.SYS and AUTOEXEC.BAT to the bare minimum, reboot DOS, and try again. If you again receive an error message, it is likely that either CHKDSK is corrupted (try another copy of CHKDSK), or the disk is badly damaged. If the fresh copy of CHKDSK reproduces the error, the disk is damaged.

Repair any damage you can, back up all the files you can (or just the files you need), and either restore a previously stored FAT (using a FAT saver program) or reformat the disk (floppy or hard). Or simply retire the diskette.

14.21 Trick: If CHKDSK locks up, rerun CHKDSK to aid in fixing the problem.

CHKDSK locks up in only one case—if it enters a loop in which one link in the file's chain in the FAT points back to an earlier link. Remember that CHKDSK traces the chain of entries in the FAT for each file. During the trace, CHKDSK can encounter an errant entry that points to a previous FAT entry for the file. CHKDSK enters an endless loop, moving forward to trace a chain, encountering the incorrect entry, jumping back to the previous part of the file's chain, and looping again. The chase continues forever.

When CHKDSK displays no messages and performs no apparent activity for about 30 seconds, or the drive runs forever, you know that CHKDSK locked up. The FAT sections that are part of the chase eventually become memory-resident in DOS's disk buffers. When this happens, the drive light goes out until you restart the computer. If the buffers cannot hold the FAT sections, you will probably hear a repeating rhythmic series of head movements.

You must halt CHKDSK: Hit the panic buttons. Either use Ctrl-Break or restart DOS (Ctrl-Alt-Del, reset switch, or power switch). After you halt CHKDSK, you have two sets of choices: back up or repair the FAT. In both choices, you must try to diagnose the specific file that has the bad FAT chain.

No matter what you do, the backup software will stumble when it encounters the looping chain, and the backup will be incomplete. In most cases, however, you should try backing up the disk.

The major backup problems include detecting the looping FAT chain and getting a corrupted copy of other files. Detecting the errant entry is easier (although repair may not be). The trick is running **CHKDSK >PRN** and then running **CHKDSK /V**. CHKDSK will probably give another error message before it dies. Use **CHKDSK >PRN** to print a copy of the errant files. After CHKDSK dies, halt the program, restart DOS, and then run **CHKDSK /V**.

The /V is *verbose* mode: CHKDSK displays the name of each file it analyzes and comprehensive information about the encountered problems. You can use this information to determine what actions to take if you encounter an error. More importantly, when CHKDSK dies, the last named file on the display is the file with the looping chain. Write down the path and file name and then halt CHKDSK.

Use the redirected output from the first run of CHKDSK to skip problem files. Make a master backup and skip any errant file (particularly the looping file). The archive attribute trick mentioned in Chapter 10, "Backing Up and Restoring Your Hard Disk," may be the easiest method. Then make a selective backup that contains only the errant files, but do not back up the looping file. Remember that the entire backup is suspect and should not be trusted. Other logical damage may exist.

Your other alternative is to repair the FAT. You have three choices: manual repair, automated repair, and automatic replacement. All three choices have margins of error—the errant file may not emerge intact, or other files may be condemned to electronic death.

Manual repair involves finding the errant file. Then you must trace the chain until the errant entry is found, correct the errant entry, and write the corrected FAT sector to the disk. The next tip and the information in Appendix A cover manual recovery, which I have accomplished on a 60M hard disk in less than 5 minutes.

As the automated choice, use a FAT saver/restorer, such as HTEST/ HFORMAT's GETSEC/PUTSEC, Norton's FATSAVE, or MACE's SAVE-RESTORE. The FAT saver is covered in Chapter 15, "Troubleshooting Physical Damage."

For the last choice, replacement of the FAT, use FORMAT. This procedure signs the death warrant for the remaining information on the disk. If you have a good disk-sector editor and some knowledge of the disk, this method requires the most concentration. This method can be the quickest or the most futile, but it can correct the problem with few side effects.

14.22   Trick: Use a disk-sector editor to cure a looping FAT chain.

You can fix a looping FAT chain manually with a good disk-sector editor. The amount of disk fragmentation determines the recovery speed. If the disk is largely defragmented (defragmented or formatted recently, or has a large amount of free space), you can perform a quick repair of the file. If the file is badly fragmented, the task takes longer.

For a disk-sector editor, I like Norton's NU (although other programs have similar qualities). NU shows the information from the FAT in decimal form, making the search process easier.

You must trace the chain of the looping file, the last file shown by CHKDSK /V. First, find the starting cluster number and then trace each cluster until you spot the looped entry. The task is quick on disks with 16-bit FATs (disk partitions larger than 16M) and more difficult on 12-bit FATs.

Use the information presented in Appendix A for finding the starting cluster number for the errant file. Although determining the exact location within the FAT is somewhat laborious, the process is not difficult. After you find the first cluster, use the cluster's contents as the new starting sector number and repeat the process. Continue the process until you find the errant entry, or you find that the chain is properly terminated.

The end-of-file indicators are values from FF8 to FFF (floppy diskettes to less than 16M disk partitions) or FFF8 through FFFF (16-bit FATs). If you find that the chain is properly terminated, something else is wrong. You may have made an error when following the chain. Repeat the process again.

I use one shortcut in the FAT chase. On a fairly defragmented disk, the entry chain will be both contiguous (one number after another) and ascending. When you follow the chain, start at the first entry and scan down the list for continuously ascending numbers. If you spot a number that is out-of-order, raise the question flag. You will probably need to jump forward in the file to continue the chase.

Pull a panic trigger when you see a FAT entry that has a descending value. The only way a FAT chain loops is when one cluster entry points to the previous part of the chain. Note the current location of the FAT (either as the corresponding cluster number or the sector and byte in the FAT that holds the value) and the value held by the pointed-to cluster.

If you find the errant entry, write down the original value. Then repair the entry by using the disk-sector editor. Substitute an end-of-chain indicator for the entry (FFFF for 16-bit FATs, FFF for 12-bit FATs). This action deliberately orphans the remaining part of the file, but makes the disk usable again. Store the changed sector, restart the system, and then run CHKDSK /V again. If CHKDSK runs, you have repaired the disk successfully.

You probably will see two new additional messages, one about an invalid file size and a second about one or a few new orphaned clusters. These messages are correct. If the first run of CHKDSK did not produce orphaned clusters, the new orphans belong to the errant file. Use the advice in the next section on orphaned clusters to reconstruct the file.

Orphaned Clusters

14.23 Tip: Lost clusters occur when DOS cannot close a written-to file or damaged directory.

If you get the following message, you have orphaned clusters:

```
xxxx lost clusters found in yyy chains
Convert lost chains to files (Y/N)?
```

Orphaned clusters have two causes. The most probable cause is that the program or DOS was stopped before DOS finished committing or closing the file. This error, which occurs only when extending a previous file or when creating a new file, means that CHKDSK has found some clusters without an owner (a file) on the disk.

When a file is extended or created, DOS marks the clusters used for the write as in-use, forging the link in the file's FAT chain. DOS then writes the information. DOS, on committing or closing the file, updates the file's directory entry. Orphaned clusters (lost clusters) occur because the process is interrupted. The FAT chain is incomplete; the file's directory entry is inconsistent; and data may or may not exist on the disk.

The second cause, a physically or logically damaged directory, is infrequent, but grave. Either a sector that holds directory information has been incorrectly written (logically damaged, usually by an errant program) or has gone bad (physically damaged). If you see any messages about incorrect directory entries, do not run CHKDSK /F immediately. See the section on inconsistent and damaged directories for details on handling this problem.

If no messages concerning directories appear, mend the file system by running CHKDSK /F and then taking appropriate action.

14.24 Trap: CHKDSK /F processes orphaned clusters, even if you respond No to the message "Convert lost chains to files (Y/N)?"

CHKDSK changed between DOS V2 and DOS V3. This important difference is one reason you should run CHKDSK without the /F switch to detect a file-system problem.

When CHKDSK detects orphaned clusters, it asks the *lost chain conversion* question:

> `Convert lost chains to files (Y/N)?`

The gathering of orphaned clusters is by chain. A *chain* is a set of clusters linked together in the FAT. The clusters in the chain are usually contiguous, but not always. The chain may be adjacent to the file that should hold this information (from which DOS was prevented from properly linking), or the chain and file may be noncontiguous.

CHKDSK's response to your answer to the conversion question differs depending on whether or not you have given the /F switch. If you have not given the /F switch, CHKDSK reports the amount of disk space that could be freed regardless of your answer to the conversion question. If you answer Y, CHKDSK reports the number of files that would be created.

If you give the /F switch and answer Y to the conversion question, CHKDSK bundles each chain and places them in a file called **FILExxxx.CHK**, where the four **x**'s are the number of the file. CHKDSK places the file in the root directory of the disk.

If you give the /F switch and answer N to the conversion question, CHKDSK simply marks the orphaned clusters as free. You lose almost all hope of finding what information was lost. In DOS V2, answering N meant that you could use CHKDSK /F again and recover the orphaned clusters later. In DOS V3, you get one shot with CHKDSK /F. Miss that shot (answer N instead of Y), and the information hits the computer equivalent of the black hole.

14.25 Trick: Unless you are positive that you don't need the orphaned clusters, always answer Y to the lost chain conversion question.

Usually, an ungraceful termination causes all written-to but not yet closed or committed files to leave orphaned clusters. When clusters are orphaned, the information may not exist in the correct file, but you can recover and add the information manually to the file. In most cases, you should convert orphaned clusters to files.

You may not know what information was lost from what file—a second reason for answering Y. By looking at the information within the lost clusters, you might be able to determine which file was affected and whether the information is usable. Remember that DOS cannot ascertain which file owns this chain. The file's contents may be your only clue. For this reason, you usually should convert the orphaned clusters to files. This is also the reason to run CHKDSK after an ungraceful shutdown; the only files affected should be the files being processed by the terminated program. The orphans should belong to these files only.

You should destroy orphans without reservation on only two occasions. First, you can destroy orphans when you are working with a program that produces a single file to hold the results. Because the information is incomplete, you must again run the program that produces this results file. The current results file is incomplete: you can discard it. (If, however, the partial results are usable in any way, do not destroy the orphans.)

Second, you can destroy orphans if you know that the affected files are temporary files which can be used only by the program. If the file is in a compact or indecipherable form (usually binary information in a database) or is used only to hold in-progress work that is later written into a final format (such as temporary .ARC files that must be fully processed to be usable), you may not want to attempt to reconstruct the file manually. If the orphans are unusable, destroy them.

In all other cases, convert the orphaned clusters to files. You can reconstruct the file manually if needed. In some cases when new files are created, the entire chain is the intact new file; the file simply did not have its directory entry adjusted. You can always delete the converted files later if the information is worthless.

Once DOS frees orphaned clusters, you play the needle-in-the-haystack game to reconstruct the file. Later in this chapter, I'll discuss some detective techniques for using this information to reconstruct files.

Cross-Linked Files

14.26   Trick: To correct cross-linked files, copy the files to another disk, delete the cross-linked files, and then restore the files.

Cross-linked files are a severe form of logical damage. CHKDSK displays the following message (one message per cross-linked file):

> *<filename>*
>
> is cross-linked on cluster xxxx

Two or more files think that they own the same clusters of the disk. Remember that each entry in the FAT points to the next cluster for the file. When two or more different chains in the FAT point to the same cluster, the files are cross-linked. The damage occurs when DOS is halted while writing to the disk or when an errant program writes incorrect information to the FAT directly. For cross-linked files, there may be a winner (the file's

FAT chain is correct) and several losers (incorrect entries and lost portions of a file), or just several losers.

This cross-linked message usually trails the lost clusters message. The lost clusters and cross-linked message occur when the first FAT (but not necessarily the second FAT) has cross-linked files. (The file allocation table is so critical that DOS keeps two copies, one after the other.) This is another reason that you should not run CHKDSK /F immediately. You actually want to repair the disk before you attempt to recover orphaned clusters. The last step in repairing the disk usually cures the orphaned clusters.

CHKDSK cannot correct a cross-linked file. You must perform the corrective steps manually and in the proper order:

- You must copy (and not move) all cross-linked files to another disk—another partition or a floppy diskette.
- After you copy all the files, delete the cross-linked files.

You must perform these two steps in the proper order (and do not move the files). If you delete one of the cross-linked files before you copy all the others, the FAT is cleared. If you delete an incorrect file before you copy the correct file, the correct file is truncated.

After you copy the files, examine each one. If the file is intact, copy it back to the original disk after CHKDSK gives the disk a clean bill of health. If the file is not intact, you can use this partial file as an aid in reconstructing the file, or simply restore the file from your backup media.

If you detect the logical damage immediately after the failure, with the proper tools and some knowledge, you may re-create the files. If the first and second FATs are not identical, one FAT (usually the second FAT) may be correct and hold the correct chain for all the cross-linked files.

Copy the cross-linked files to another disk, but do not delete the files. Using a disk-sector editor, such as Norton's NU program, find the starting cluster number in the FAT from the file's directory entry. Examining both the first and second FAT, trace the file's chain. If the chains are different, use the sector editor to copy the file, sector-by-sector, to another disk under a similar (but not identical) file name. After you copy all the files, examine the contents of the recovered files and attempt to repair the files.

Also, if you defragment your disk regularly, you might look at the starting cluster number from the file's directory entry and copy manually, into another file on a different disk, enough contiguous clusters to equal the file's length. You might be missing a cluster or two, but the recovered file may be a better starting point to attempt to repair the file.

Once you complete the repair, delete the originally cross-linked files. Remember that once you delete the original files, recovering them is difficult to impossible. After you delete the cross-linked files, rerun CHKDSK without the /F switch to see whether the repair is complete.

Invalid Clusters and Allocation Errors

14.27 **Tip: Attempt to copy or copy and repair a file with an invalid cluster before you run CHKDSK /F.**

An invalid entry for the FAT is a cluster number that points to a nonexistent cluster on the disk. The entry is either 1 (an invalid number because DOS starts with entry 2) or a number higher than the number of clusters for the disk. This damage usually occurs from an errant write to the directory entry or the FAT, which happens with a premature system shutdown or an errant program.

CHKDSK produces two different messages for an invalid cluster. The following message is displayed when a FAT entry contains the invalid cluster number:

<*filename*>

`has invalid cluster, file truncated`

The following message is displayed when the subdirectory entry contains the invalid cluster number:

<*filename*>

`First cluster number is invalid,`

`entry truncated`

In the first case, the file chain in the FAT is corrupted at the point of the invalid cluster. All entries from the invalid cluster on are probably nonsense. All entries before the invalid cluster are probably correct. For the second case, the starting cluster number in the file's directory entry is nonsense. DOS does not know where the file's chain is in the FAT.

In either case, CHKDSK /F truncates the file at the invalid cluster number. For invalid entries in the FAT, the file is truncated at the FAT entry that contains the invalid cluster number. The latter part of the file, the section beyond the invalid cluster, is lost. For the invalid cluster number within the directory entry, the file size and invalid cluster number are set to zero, and the entire file is lost.

The reason to run CHKDSK without /F is obvious. You have a chance to make some manual repairs before CHKDSK snips at the file. When you run CHKDSK /F, DOS corrects the error but leaves the file with missing information. Run CHKDSK /F if your backup copy of the file is intact. Because the invalid cluster is usually caused by an error that occurred when writing the subdirectory or FAT, the chances are strong that the error occurred when updating the file. The last backup is probably out-of-date. You may want to try recovering the file.

14.28 Trick: Use a disk-sector editor to repair an invalid cluster in the FAT.

When a file has an invalid entry within the FAT, you can try a partial repair and a full repair. The partial repair works by just using CHKDSK /F. The full repair requires a bit of luck, a strong knowledge of DOS and the FAT, and a good disk-sector editor, such as Norton's NU.

Start the full repair by turning BREAK ON and by copying the file to another disk. DOS may display an error message about completing the copy, or the disk may whirl forever. Before you start the copy, turn BREAK ON. If the system goes into a tailspin, halt CHKDSK with Ctrl-Break.

Be aware that the just-made copy is probably corrupt at the point of the invalid entry. Examine the copy anyway. If the copied file is complete and intact (which means that the original file is intact), simply run CHKDSK /F to truncate the stray clusters from the original file.

After you copy the file, you can attempt a manual repair of the FAT without using CHKDSK. This trick works if the file is not fragmented. Also, attempt this repair only if you have a current backup of all other files (in other words, back up now).

Back up the hard disk or DISKCOPY the diskette in case you make a mistake. Using a disk-sector editor, find the starting cluster number in the FAT and trace the chain in the FAT until you see the incorrect cluster number in the chain. (Use the information in Appendix A for help in determining a valid and invalid number.) Write down the sector and byte number for the errant entry (based on the disk sector, such as offset 312 in sector 12) and the current errant value.

The trick is to change the errant entry to point to the next cluster of the disk. If the file is not fragmented, the next cluster number should be the next cluster. After you change the entry, copy the file to another disk and check the file. If the copy of the file is correct, the original file is correct. Run CHKDSK again to ensure that everything is correct (no cross-linked clusters). If CHKDSK reports a new cross-link involving this file (or any other new error), use the disk-sector editor to restore the original errant value to the errant entry. The manual repair was incorrect, and this technique will not work.

Remember: Always make a fresh backup before you bypass the normal DOS process and edit a FAT or subdirectory directly. If you make a mistake and cannot reverse the error manually, you may need to format the disk and restore from backups.

14.29 Trick: If CHKDSK reports orphaned clusters and an invalid cluster within the FAT, use the lost clusters to restore the file.

If CHKDSK reports orphaned clusters and an invalid cluster within the FAT entry, the orphaned clusters probably belong to the file whose FAT chain is broken. You must first recover the orphaned clusters, examine the new file to see whether the recovered clusters are part of the truncated file, and then join the pieces.

Run CHKDSK /F to truncate the file; answer Y to convert the lost chains into files. Then examine each new **FILExxxx.CHK**. If you know that the new file is a piece of the old file, ascertain the order of each piece. Normally, the truncated file is the first piece. After you have all pieces to the file, join them in the correct order to produce another file on a different disk.

You can use the COPY command with the /B switch (binary copy) to join the pieces. For example, if the order of the pieces is MYFILE.TXT, FILE0001.CHK, and FILE0000.CHK, you use the following command:

COPY MYFILE.TXT+FILE0001.CHK+FILE0000.CHK A:MYFILE.XTX /B

After you piece the file together and are sure that it is completely correct, delete the original file, copy the pieced-together file (with the correct name) back to the disk, and delete the appropriate **FILExxxx.CHK** files. When you create these new and questionably intact files, keep the root name and fudge a new extension that resembles the original extension so that you know what temporary file is the surrogate for which damaged file.

14.30 Trick: If a file's directory entry has an invalid starting cluster, use CHKDSK /F and the orphans to reconstruct the file.

If a file has an invalid starting cluster, DOS has lost track of the entire FAT chain(s) for the file. The chains, however, probably still exist on the disk.

Any orphaned clusters may be the missing file. Use CHKDSK /F to truncate the file and gather the orphaned clusters into files by answering Y to the conversion question. If only one chain is recovered, examine the **FILExxxx.CHK**. If the file is correct, delete the errant directory entry and copy the file back into the correct directory using the original file's name.

If you have several chains, piece the file together by following the advice in the preceding tip. Once you join the pieces correctly, copy the good file over the errant file (remember to correct all other damage before you perform the copy).

14.31 Trick: Use CHKDSK /F to fix a file with an allocation error.

The following message indicates an allocation error:

> *<filename>*
> Allocation error for file, size adjusted

This message indicates an inconsistency between the file size in the directory entry and the number of clusters allocated to the file in the FAT. This problem occurs when extending a file. DOS allocated the clusters for the addition; the addition probably was written successfully; but DOS was terminated before updating the file's size in its directory entry.

Generally, this error is harmless—in almost all cases, the information was written to the disk. The problem is that the file size in the directory entry is too small or too large. CHKDSK /F adjusts the directory entry, not the information stored in the file. CHKDSK's resolution is to count the number of clusters in the chain, multiply this number by the cluster size (bytes per cluster), and update the directory entry with the size.

The adjustment can have side effects if the data was not written to the disk. If information is missing, your program may object. If the file is adjusted upward, some extraneous information may exist at the end of the file. Some programs (for example, word processing) may object to or display the extended information. You may need to edit the file to remove the garbage.

Ensure that CHKDSK is reporting an error for a file, not a directory. If CHKDSK gives this message for a directory, the problem may be severe. Read the section on inconsistent and damaged subdirectories before you proceed with CHKDSK /F.

Non-DOS Disks

14.32   Trick: The non-DOS disk message may indicate a damaged FAT, not a non-DOS disk.

The following CHKDSK message indicates that the disk under analysis may or may not be a DOS disk:

> Probable non-DOS disk
> Continue (Y/N)?

Because CHKDSK can mangle a disk, CHKDSK checks that a non-DOS disk is never analyzed inadvertently. Although this step is not so important on unformatted diskettes (because there is no useful information to mangle), this check is important for disks formatted by a different operating system or program, such as XENIX or FASTBACK.

Generally, the test is correct. The test is so simple, however, that a slightly mangled FAT can produce an error. CHKDSK simply reads the second sector of the disk and checks the first two entries in the FAT (the first three or four bytes) that hold the media ID byte. If the entries do not start with an appropriate media ID byte, followed by two or three bytes of FF hex, CHKDSK declares the disk a potential non-DOS disk.

If you encounter this message and did not give the /F switch, answer Y to continue processing. If you see nonsensical file names or subdirectory names with a slew of errors, CHKDSK is right. The disk is either unformatted or has been formatted under a different operating system or program.

If you don't get the error messages, you probably have a slightly mangled FAT. Something has mistakenly rewritten the first two entries in the FAT. The mistake is easy to correct if you have a disk-sector editor. Simply read the first sector of the FATs (you should do both at once, although simply writing the first FAT eventually corrects the second FAT). Replace the errant media ID byte with the correct value and write the sector back to the disk.

The cause of the mangled FAT should be of concern. If you get this error periodically, you have an errant program or hardware. For example, some programs are disruptive when you run out of disk space. Beware of disk cachers or DOS's BUFFERS and, especially, the memory that holds the cache. Run CHKDSK /V frequently to track the cause of the problem.

When the problem crops up, suspect any program you ran between the times CHKDSK *did not* report and *did* report the problem. Also, suspect that other damage may occur to the FAT.

Inconsistent and Damaged Directories

14.33 **Tip: If CHKDSK reports a problem with a directory, examine all other messages before you take action.**

When CHKDSK analyzes the logical structure of the disk, it analyzes each entry in each directory. If CHKDSK encounters a problem in the logical or physical structure of the directory system, CHKDSK sounds an alarm.

Unfortunately, CHKDSK may spew out several different types of error messages when only one problem is detected. For example, if a subdirectory entry is misread, CHKDSK complains about an invalid subdirectory entry and a bad directory link.

When you get any directory-based error, examine all errors before you use CHKDSK /F or take any other action. Sometimes the combination of error messages gives the correct clue so that you can determine the specific problem that caused the CHKDSK messages.

14.34 **Tip: If CHKDSK reports that the . or .. has a bad attribute, size, or link, use CHKDSK /F to repair the entry.**

Each subdirectory has two fixed entries: the . (named the dot, designating the parent directory) and the .. (named the double-dot, designating the current directory). A stray program write or ungraceful shutdown can cause these two special directory entries to have a problem with their file attributes, file size, or FAT linkage.

The only DOS file attribute that should normally be on for a subdirectory is the directory attribute (although the hidden or system attribute can be set). The size of a subdirectory should be 0. The bad link means that the starting cluster number is incorrect.

CHKDSK /F can repair the first two problems easily and usually can repair the bad link problem. In the first two cases, CHKDSK /F simply clears all attributes (except for the subdirectory attribute) and zeros the file size. In the case of the bad link, CHKDSK /F restores the correct starting cluster from the parent directory. If the parent directory is undamaged, the process is effective and safe.

CHKDSK /F cannot repair the . or .. entry if the pertinent entries in the parent directory are damaged. This event comes with portents—CHKDSK should produce a warning or error message about the subdirectory's parent directory. If other messages appear, do not run CHKDSK /F without first determining the complete extent of potential damage to the subdirectory system.

14.35   Tip: If CHKDSK reports an invalid current directory, the disk may be damaged.

During its analysis of the the disk, CHKDSK can report a potentially grave directory error:

    Invalid current directory

This message may be accompanied by other warning messages about orphaned clusters. CHKDSK received a disk error from DOS when it attempted to read the directory. The message may appear if you use the **I**gnore or **F**ail response to a critical DOS disk error.

The invalid current directory message means that a sector which holds the directory information may be physically damaged. If the sector is physically damaged and is unreadable, up to 16 directory entries are affected. The damage may, however, extend to more than 16 files. If one of the affected directory entries is a subdirectory, all files in the subdirectory and its subsequent subdirectories may be affected.

This message is usually accompanied by one of the two following messages:

    Processing cannot continue

    Unrecoverable error in directory
    Convert directory to file (Y/N)?

If you get the first message, the disk directory structure may be so badly damaged that CHKDSK is confused, or CHKDSK may simply be confused for other reasons. If you get the second message, answer N. In either case, restart DOS and rerun CHKDSK.

If the message appears again, this directory is damaged. Attempt to back up as many files from this subdirectory tree as you can. If needed, rerun CHKDSK /F and then answer Y to convert the subdirectory to a file. If the damage is physical (a bad sector), you can use RECOVER on the file to hide the bad sectors (see the section on RECOVER in Chapter 15 for more information).

Unfortunately, converting a directory to a file also means that all files in this and subsequent subdirectories are lost and will appear as orphaned clusters. If the disk is not badly fragmented, the various **FILExxxx.CHK** files in the root directory are the files and subdirectories from this directory. (Because you use the /F switch to fix the directory, you must answer Y to convert the lost chains to files; otherwise, you lose the information.)

After the orphans are processed, use the tips in the section on invalid clusters and allocation errors to rebuild files or to restore files from your backup. Afterward delete any unwanted **FILExxxx.CHK** files.

14.36 Tip: If CHKDSK mentions that a subdirectory is invalid, CHKDSK has probably confused a file for a directory, or the subdirectory is damaged.

If CHKDSK detects a problem with a subdirectory entry, it responds with the name of the errant subdirectory entry followed by this message:

`Invalid subdirectory entry`

This message has three potential causes. The first cause is that some stray write has turned off the subdirectory attribute for the subdirectory's **.** or **..** entries. A second cause is that the directory is severely damaged. The third cause is that CHKDSK interprets a file as a directory. Interpreting a file as a directory can occur if a stray write to the subdirectory turns on the subdirectory attribute for the file's directory entry.

If the damage is slight (such as a wrong attribute setting within the subdirectory), no other error messages are produced. Running CHKDSK /F fixes the problem without any other intervention.

CHKDSK may respond, however, with further messages about an invalid current directory, a bad link, or the inability to recover a **.** or **..** entry. This message indicates that either a file has been interpreted as a subdirectory, or the subdirectory is severely damaged. In either case, CHKDSK asks the following question:

`Convert directory to file (Y/N)?`

Generally, answer N to this question. Then restart DOS and rerun CHKDSK. If the message appears again, answer Y to the question if, and only if, you know that the file is a file—not a subdirectory. Remember that you must use the /F switch with CHKDSK, or the correction is not written to the disk.

If the file is a subdirectory, attempt to copy all files from this subdirectory (which may be futile), and then follow the directions in the preceding tip on handling a damaged current directory.

Alternatives to CHKDSK

14.37   Tip: Use a program like Norton's Disk Doctor as an alternative to CHKDSK.

A recent entry into the logical-physical diagnosis and repair program is the Norton Disk Doctor (NDD.EXE), included with the Norton Advanced Utilities V4.5 and later versions. If you find CHKDSK cryptic or confusing, NDD is a valuable aid.

NDD is a menu-driven replacement for CHKDSK, which reads and diagnoses many forms of logical damage to a disk. NDD can diagnose and repair most forms of logical damage. Unlike CHKDSK, NDD can diagnose problems with any boot or partition record and cure discrepancies between the two FAT copies.

In addition, NDD can test for physical damage. NDD can test a disk for bad sectors and can reformat a floppy diskette that has bad sectors (using the same approach as SpinRite).

Because the Norton Advanced Utilities is menu-driven, the program is easier to use and understand than CHKDSK. You do not need the /F switch. When a repair is needed, the program asks whether you want to proceed with the repairs. You can diagnose and repair the disk in one run without suffering the effects of inadvertently losing orphaned clusters. A further benefit is that NDD can recover from DOS's RECOVER program (RECOVER is discussed in Chapter 15.) If you can't decide between the Norton Advanced Utilities and the Norton Utilities, NDD justifies completely the purchase price difference between the Utilities and the Advanced Utilities.

15

Troubleshooting Physical Damage

This chapter describes problems that result from physical damage to your system. Generally, physical damage is rooted in a physical problem, such as a bad disk sector. Included are tips for diagnosing the problem and taking corrective action. Disk diagnostic programs and methods of handling bad sectors are explored. The chapter discusses the causes of certain DOS critical errors, as well as methods of handling the errors. The DOS RECOVER program and the important third-party tool, the FAT saver, are examined in this chapter.

In many cases, physical damage has caused logical damage. To cure the logical damage, you must fix the physical damage first, and then effect the cures covered in Chapter 14, "Troubleshooting Logical Damage."

Diagnosing Drive Failures

One of the more difficult tasks facing DOS users is determining the cause and extent of a disk problem—from the drive not responding to an operation to a bad sector. Unfortunately, DOS provides only clues to a disk problem, not the specifics of the failure.

While DOS is starting up, certain messages can appear that indicate a problem. After DOS starts and fails to use a disk properly, it issues a critical error message in the following form:

> *type* **error reading** *device*
> *type* **error writing** *device*

DOS asks for correct action with these options:

    Abort, Retry, Ignore, Fail?

The DOS message states the specific problem found, but not the underlying cause. For example, an open floppy disk drive (no diskette inserted or a drive door left open) and a malfunctioning floppy disk drive can be the cause of the error message **Not ready**. To diagnose the problem, you must use the error message and the surrounding circumstances to determine the underlying cause of the problem.

You can diagnose four basic types of potential errors. The first and easiest to find are "pilot errors," which are caused by an inadvertent operation. The most frequent pilot errors include forgetting to insert a diskette into a disk drive or forgetting to close a disk drive door. A quick glance at the disk drive reveals the error.

The next three types—media faults, logical format problems, and drive-related hardware failures—are more difficult to identify and distinguish. Media faults are usually bad sectors. *Bad sectors* are faults in the physical format of the media. The other problems—logical format problems and drive-related hardware failures—can, however, give the same errors as bad sectors. Worse, physical problems (bad sectors or drive-hardware failures) that occur in key DOS disk areas (the boot records, FAT, or directory) can manifest themselves as logical format problems.

The next two sections cover the possible DOS error messages, the underlying causes, and some remedies. Later in this chapter, other remedies are discussed.

DOS Disk Start-Up Problems

15.1 **Tip: If you don't receive any message from DOS on start-up, either the floppy disk is not formatted properly, or the hard disk has a hardware failure.**

Remember that the sequence for loading DOS is different for floppy diskettes than for hard disks. With a floppy diskette, DOS loads and executes the first sector of the diskette. On all formatted DOS diskettes, the first sector contains the bootstrap loader; the loader is responsible for initiating the actual DOS start-up. If the diskette is not formatted, formatted by a different operating system, or formatted incorrectly, the computer loads and executes nonsense (whatever information happens to be recorded in the first sector).

With a hard disk, no error message is a grave sign of trouble. The start-up sequence almost guarantees that some message is displayed. If no message is given, either the master boot record of the disk is partially damaged, or the drive-related hardware has failed. Try booting from a floppy diskette and using the hard disk drive. Depending on the error messages you receive, you may be able to tell whether the drive hardware or the master boot record has failed. A hard disk diagnostic program can confirm a drive-hardware failure.

15.2 Tip: If a "Disk boot failure" message is displayed, either the start-up files were placed incorrectly on the disk, or the drive has a failure.

The message Disk boot failure is displayed when a diskette or disk partition has a copy of the two DOS start-up files in their correct directory position (the first two entries of the root directory), but the bootstrap routine could not load one or both files. The most likely cause for this message is incorrect (all versions of DOS) or fragmented (DOS pre-V3.2) start-up files. Because DOS post-V3.1 handles fragmented start-up files, the latter cause is important only to users of earlier versions of DOS.

If a second attempt to start the computer fails, start from a different diskette or from a floppy diskette (if you are attempting to start from the hard disk). Use SYS on the errant disk. If this procedure fails and DOS displays some sort of write error, the sectors that hold the start-up files are bad. Other disk-based errors indicate one other possibility—drive-hardware failure.

15.3 Tip: If you receive the message "Error loading operating system," the hard disk master boot sector is good, but the partition's boot sector is faulty.

The message Error loading operating system is produced only when you start from a hard disk. DOS loaded the master boot record but had problems loading the partition's boot record. The cause can be a drive-hardware fault or a stray write that altered the start-up partition's boot record.

Try starting DOS again from the hard disk. If this fix fails, start DOS from a floppy diskette. Use the SYS command on the start-up partition to reestablish the correct boot sector. If this procedure fails, the problem is hardware-related.

15.4 Tip: If DOS reports "Bad or missing Command Interpreter," either COMMAND.COM is missing, corrupt, or incorrect; or your SHELL directive is incorrect.

The Bad or missing Command Interpreter message indicates that the two DOS start-up files are loaded and running, but DOS could not find and load COMMAND.COM successfully. This occurs for a number of reasons. For hard disks, the most probable reason is an incorrectly phrased SHELL directive in CONFIG.SYS. For all disks, COMMAND.COM may have been been erased or corrupted, or the wrong version of COMMAND.COM is on the disk.

Start the computer from a different diskette (or use a diskette rather than the hard disk) and then check COMMAND.COM. If the file is missing, copy it to the disk. If the file is present, check the SHELL directive in your CONFIG.SYS.

If the file is present and all SHELL directives are correct, copy a known good copy of COMMAND.COM to the disk. If this procedure does not produce a startable disk, suspect drive-hardware problems. If COMMAND.COM disappears from the disk again or this message appears later, some program or batch file is erasing the file or copying an out-of-date version of COMMAND.COM over the correct version. Pursue this probability.

15.5   Tip: If DOS states "Configuration too large," memory may be a problem, or a recent change to your CONFIG.SYS file is errant.

The message Configuration too large indicates that there is insufficient memory to load and configure DOS with the various directives of CONFIG.SYS (BUFFERS, FCBS, STACKS, FILES, and DEVICE). If you have changed your CONFIG.SYS file, look at the changed directives (new device drivers loaded or alterations for internal directives). One or more of these settings is in error. Either reduce the setting (usually the BUFFERS setting), or remove unneeded device drivers.

If, however, you have started DOS successfully in the past with this CONFIG.SYS file, memory may be a problem. Restart DOS to clear any transient hardware problems. If the error reoccurs, the machine thinks that it has less memory than is actually installed. Usually, a memory failure is detected by the hardware of the computer, but exceptions are possible. Run the diagnostics for your computer and test your memory.

15.6   Tip: If you receive the message "Missing operating system," the boot record on the start-up DOS partition is probably incorrect.

The message Missing operating system appears only when you try to start DOS from the hard disk. The master boot record for the disk loaded but could not load the DOS partition's boot record. The three probable causes include incorrect DOS boot partition information (either you did not FORMAT the partition with the /S switch or did not use the SYS command), corrupt DOS boot partition information (a stray write or bad sector problem), or an incorrect master partition record.

You can solve most problems by starting the computer from a floppy diskette and using the SYS command on the DOS start-up partition. If SYS does not work, you must back up the disk and reformat.

Before you run SYS, run FDISK first to make sure that the partition information is correct. If the partition information is correct, use the SYS command. If the partition information is not correct, first see the section on repairing key housekeeping areas.

15.7   Tip: If DOS displays the "non-system disk or disk error" message, you are attempting to start DOS from a nonbootable disk.

The nonsystem disk message indicates that the start-up disk has a valid boot sector (the diskette or hard disk was formatted properly), but the two DOS start-up files are missing from the disk. Either you used FORMAT without the /S switch, or you did not use the SYS command.

If you are starting from a floppy diskette, use a start-up DOS diskette that you know works. If you are starting from the hard disk, check the first floppy disk drive. You may have left a nonstartable diskette in the drive. If you use a microfloppy drive, eject the diskette. If you use a minifloppy drive, open the drive door. Start DOS again.

DOS Disk Errors

15.8   Tip: If DOS complains of a "data," "read," or "write" error, the usual cause is a bad sector or drive failure.

A read or write error indicates that DOS had a problem reading information from or writing information to the disk. A data error is a catch-all error message that indicates that DOS could not read or write a disk sector correctly. The principal causes for the errors include improper diskette insertion, alignment problems, incorrect media type (floppy disk drives only), bad sectors, or a drive failure.

If you are using floppy diskettes, suspect the diskette before you suspect the drive. Be sure that you inserted the diskette correctly. Also, be sure that you use the correct diskette type for your drive. Using a 1.2M diskette in a 360K drive or a 1.44M diskette in a 720K drive can cause this problem.

If DOS fails to read (or write) a diskette formatted on a different computer, suspect an alignment problem. The message does not indicate that either your disk drive or the disk drive that produced the diskette is defective; it is more likely that one drive is on the low side of allowable alignment tolerance, and the second drive is on the high side of alignment tolerance. Having either drive aligned should remedy the problem.

If the problem is in a hard disk, suspect a bad sector rather than a drive failure. Because the media is not removable, the preceding problems are inapplicable.

The seriousness of the read, write, or data error depends on the location of the error on the disk. If the problem is a bad sector and the sector is already being used by a file, you lose some data. If you write to an unused portion of the disk, the current write will be faulty, but you may be able to save the information again. If the bad sector is in a key DOS housekeeping area, the situation is serious to grave. See the section on repairing physical damage for more information.

15.9   Tip: If DOS complains of a "Not ready" drive for a floppy disk drive, make sure that you have shut the door and inserted the diskette properly. For a hard disk, suspect a hardware failure or boot record failure.

DOS gives a **Not ready** message when the drive fails to signal DOS that it is ready. The diagnoses and remedies are different for floppy disks and hard disks.

For floppy disk drives, the error can occur if the drive hardware has failed (either the disk drive itself or the controller card), or the media is not ready. The most probable cause is that the media is not ready. Either the drive is empty, a diskette is not inserted properly, or a floppy drive door was left open. Make sure that you inserted the diskette properly or close the door. If this does not work and the error is repeated when you use a different diskette, the drive hardware is most likely at fault.

For hard disks, the **Not ready** error indicates that the disk drive is not recognized or is not responding. For new disk installations, some configuration information is incorrect, or the drive is not properly installed.

For working disks, three circumstances can cause the problem. The most frequent cause with AT-like and PS/2-like systems is a loss of the configuration information in the CMOS RAM. You usually get a start-up error message stating that the machine is not configured. Your computer does not know the type of disk drive being used. Using the setup program for your computer reestablishes the information. (If you lose your configuration more than twice in a month, try replacing the battery in the computer.)

The second most likely cause is a hardware fault in the controller or the disk drive itself. If DOS cannot perform any operation with the drive, suspect hardware failures. A hard disk diagnostic program can confirm this problem.

The third, but least likely, cause is a loss of the master boot record of the hard disk. DOS does not know where the disk partitions are located. Usually, a different message seen only during start-up (Invalid partition table) indicates this problem.

15.10 Tip: If DOS reports a "Sector not found" or "Seek" error, the problem is a bad sector or faulty drive hardware.

If you get a Sector not found error, DOS found the correct track for a sector, but could not find the sector. A Seek error indicates that DOS could not find the track for the sector.

The unfound sector is usually a physical flaw in the media in the physical housekeeping information, or the sector has been destroyed. If you have a copy-protected diskette, don't be suprised if you get the Sector not found message. If this problem occurs with a hard disk, suspect a drive-hardware failure rather than a bad sector.

The Seek error on floppy and hard disks is another indication of a drive-hardware failure. Because the physical housekeeping information for each sector identifies the track that holds the sector, only a fully damaged track could produce this error with a floppy disk drive (an improbable event). If the Seek error occurs with a different floppy diskette, the failure is with the drive hardware.

For hard disks, most Seek errors are drive failures, including read-write head failures and servo-platter problems. In most cases, the disk drive has failed. In some cases, the controller has failed. In either case, you need further diagnosis and repair.

15.11 Tip: If DOS displays a "General failure" error message for a floppy diskette, either the wrong diskette is in-use, or the diskette is not inserted properly.

The General failure message, another catch-all message from DOS, indicates that DOS cannot determine the type of diskette in the disk drive.

The usual causes include the wrong type of diskette in the disk drive (for example, a 1.44M formatted diskette in a 720K drive), an unformatted diskette, an improperly inserted diskette, or an open drive door. Check the disk drive and diskette.

15.12   Tip: If DOS displays a "General failure" or "Invalid drive specification" message for a hard disk partition that previously worked, either the drive hardware is faulty, or the partition information for the disk may have been destroyed.

If DOS displays a General failure or Invalid drive specification message for a working hard disk, you have a grave problem. The General failure message indicates that the disk drive is not currently recognized as being formatted. Because the drive was formatted, you probably have a failure in the disk drive hardware, most likely the controller board.

If DOS displays an Invalid drive specification message, DOS does not recognize the drive at all. This message indicates that the master boot record for the disk drive, which contains the partition information, has been destroyed. In this case, see the section on repairing key housekeeping areas and Chapter 4's section on partitions.

Remember that the Invalid drive specification message also can occur from an unstable DOS or a JOIN or SUBST command. Before you take action on an invalid master boot record, restart DOS to ensure that a DOS problem is not interfering with the access of the disk.

If you are using IBM PC DOS V4, note that PC DOS V4 checks the boot sector of each partition. If the OEM name in the boot sector does not read IBM followed by a space, PC DOS V4 does not recognize the partition. Using a disk-sector editor and the information in Appendix A, you can fix this problem.

15.13   Trick: Observe situations when the error is displayed, what the error concerns, and the actions of your disk drive for clues about the disk problem.

If the DOS error messages are not conclusive, other clues can tell you about disk problems. Four of the biggest clues in further identifying the causes of disk problems include the location of the trouble spot, the drive head movement, the in-use indicator, and the timing of the DOS error.

DOS always tries operations several times before it gives the first and subsequent critical error messages. Because the operations are tried several times, you can note some characteristic behaviors for the drive light and disk drive heads, as well as the time it takes DOS to respond with an error message. The error's location can also offer some clues.

When you get a disk error while DOS is running, use the **R**etry response, watch the in-use indicator, and listen to the disk drive. If the attempt is unsuccessful, try a different disk operation and watch the result. If you have two hard or floppy disks, try operations on a different drive. If you have two partitions on a hard disk, try operations on both partitions.

For any disk, if the in-use indicator does not light, the problem is probably in the disk drive controller rather than the drive itself. If the in-use light does not go off, suspect controller failure but also suspect that DOS itself may be unstable.

If you normally hear the disk drive heads move when the drive is in-use but do not hear the movement now, suspect the controller and the disk drive. (The more likely cause is the disk controller.) Conversely, if you hear a low grinding sound or a set of rapid movements, the problem is in the drive media.

DOS's quickness at returning from an error also can give a clue. On a floppy diskette, a retry from most errors (except a general failure) should take two to five seconds. On hard disks, the response should be one to three seconds. A quicker response indicates a problem with the controller card; a slower response usually indicates a problem with the disk drive itself or the controller (more likely the drive media, then drive electronics, then controller electronics).

The final clue is trying a different disk operation. If you can get a directory of the disk or read other files on the same diskette or disk partition, the problem is isolated to a part of the disk. The causes are either bad sectors or a drive failure related to only one disk drive head.

If you have a second, similar type of disk drive (either a second floppy disk drive or second hard disk drive), try an operation on the other disk drive. The disk drives need not be identical (you can have any two floppy disk drives or any two hard disk drives), but the other disk drive must use the same disk controller board. If this operation fails, the controller is at fault. If the operation works, the drive is at fault.

If you have multiple partitions on a hard disk, try operations using a different partition. If the operations on the partition work normally, the partition information may be bad, or a bad sector may have developed in a key DOS housekeeping area on the faulty partition. Because you are using one physical disk drive and controller, the problem is not in the controller or disk drive.

In any of these cases, run a disk diagnostic program, which can pinpoint drive problems, to determine the extent of the problem.

Disk Diagnostics

15.14   Tip: If your disk drive shows signs of instability, run a disk diagnostic program to determine the problem.

If your disk drive shows signs of instability, you should run a diagnostic program as quickly as possible. The diagnostic program can help pinpoint whether the drive hardware is bad or the media itself is at fault. Most computers come with an elementary set of diagnostic programs. The programs are a good start but are not exhaustive.

By running a typical diagnostic program on a floppy disk drive, you can determine whether the problem is with the disk drive or with the controller. The diagnostics usually cannot determine which half (the drive or the controller) is the problem. The diagnostic program will, however, indicate whether you should suspect the floppy drive subsystem.

Remember that you need some formatted diskettes that do not hold worthwhile information. The diagnostics will destroy all information on the disk; therefore, do not use diskettes that contain useful information.

For hard disks, diagnostic programs provided by the computer manufacturer normally do not write to the hard disk. You usually can use these programs safely without backing up the hard disk.

These diagnostic programs can neither diagnose errors that involve writing to the disk nor test the disk drive extensively. For this reason, a drive may pass the rudimentary test provided by the computer manufacturer but still be faulty. Because a diagnostic program does report major failures, however, you should run the program periodically.

15.15   Tip: If you need more extensive hard disk testing or features, or want to repair some hard disk problems manually, consider third-party disk test programs.

Run the disk diagnostics provided with the computer. If the program shows errors, you have a clue that the hardware is faulty. A problem might exist even if the diagnostics do not report a problem. If you still suspect the drive, you need a program that performs more extensive testing. Consider third-party disk test programs.

You can select from two classes of disk test programs. One class, which uses the DOS services, primarily checks for bad sectors. These programs include the Norton Utilities's DT (Disk Test) and the Mace Utilities's Diagnose. Each program reads the disk sector-by-sector several times and reports bad sectors. Both programs can aid in repairing the problem.

Because these programs do not destroy information on the disk, you can use them without first backing up. You cannot, however, use these programs if the drive is unresponsive or DOS does not recognize the disk partition. Also, a large number of bad sectors simply indicates that you have a major drive problem, but does not tell you the specifics of the problem.

The second class of disk test programs provides better disk drive testing. Some favorites include Gibson's SpinRite and Kolad's HTEST. Both programs perform a more comprehensive test of the disk drive head movement and tracking and perform a more thorough bad-sector analysis. Either program can help pinpoint whether the disk drive or the controller is faulty.

You can direct both programs to write to the disk drive, but this feature can destroy information already recorded. SpinRite attempts to perform these tests in a nondestructive manner. If an error occurs while SpinRite is writing information back to the disk, however, you can lose information. If you plan to use either program to write to the disk, back up all information from the entire disk, if possible, before you run the program.

Consider one reason to use HTEST rather than SpinRite. SpinRite requires that the master partition information and each partition's boot sector must be intact. HTEST bypasses DOS and operates on the disk directly; HTEST can therefore diagnose problems that SpinRite cannot.

When one or two new bad sectors are involved in one location, I usually use a Norton or Mace program to locate and hide the bad sectors. I am, however, immediately suspicious of the disk drive. At the first opportunity, I back up and use SpinRite or HTEST. If a key DOS area is involved (any boot sector, the FAT, or root directory), I may need to follow further steps. See the section on repairing key housekeeping areas for more information.

Repairing Physical Damage

Bad sectors, which cause DOS to stumble and information to be lost, are a sign of physical disk damage. Bad sectors can be caused by stray magnetic fields, stray disk writes, oxide binder breakdown, disk head crash, foreign objects, drive-related electronic or mechanical failures, and poor handling.

Bad sectors indicate one of two forms of physical damage: electronic scrambling of the disk housekeeping information or a physical fault in the media. In many cases, you can mend the first form of damage, scrambled physical housekeeping information. The second form of damage, flaws or damage to the magnetic media, is not curable. You can, however, circumvent the ill effects.

Another form of bad sectors is drive-related failures, either electronic (failure of a part on the drive or controller) or mechanical (failure of the spindle, motor, or head movement). Technically, drive failures are not a form of physical damage but can cause bad sectors. Drive failure requires service on the disk drive or controller; repairing this type of failure is beyond the scope of this discussion.

Finding the cause of the bad sectors is important; fixing the damage and salvaging damaged files is even more important.

Although the DOS FORMAT command can initially diagnose bad sectors, marginally bad sectors can eventually turn into true bad sectors, and other new bad sectors can develop. Several third-party tools, discussed later in this chapter, are available to diagnose marginal sectors.

If a new bad sector is detected and a file resides in this bad sector, DOS's RECOVER program can recover some of a file. In addition, you can use FORMAT or a low-level format program to fix physical damage. These programs and the procedures for handling bad sectors are discussed in this section.

Using RECOVER

15.16 **Tip: If a file is damaged by bad sectors, use RECOVER to knock out the bad sectors.**

The RECOVER command salvages a file with bad sectors. You should run the command, with the following syntax, on any file with bad sectors:

*dc:pathc***RECOVER** *d:path\\filename.ext*

When you run RECOVER on a file, RECOVER attempts to read as much information as possible from the file. The salvaged information is written to a new copy of the file. RECOVER then deletes the original file and marks detected bad sectors as in-use in the FAT. The marking prevents other files from being stored in the unusable areas.

You safely can use RECOVER on any file. RECOVER cannot, however, recover information trapped in the bad sector. The damage is irreversible. Also, I don't recommend using RECOVER on an entire disk. Both subjects are discussed in the next few tips.

15.17 Tip: You usually can salvage a RECOVERed text file and some types of data files, but you should discard any RECOVERed program files.

Although any file with a bad sector should be RECOVERed, you should use only certain salvaged files. The information in the bad sectors is lost. RECOVER is acceptable for salvaging text and some data files. If the damage is not severe, use a text editor or the original program to re-create the missing information. If the damage is in critical areas, your recovery efforts may be better spent using your most recent backup of the file to re-create a new file.

Do not use any program files you salvaged with RECOVER. Restore the program files from your backup copies or the original program diskette. The results of using a recovered program are unpredictable: the program may do no damage, or data and files may be destroyed.

15.18 Trap: Avoid running RECOVER on a disk.

You can run RECOVER on all files of a disk, but you should run RECOVER on a disk *only if* the root directory of the disk is bad. Use another remedy (short of reformatting the disk) rather than RECOVER. Run RECOVER on the disk as a last resort; you can spend more time recovering from RECOVER than you gain.

Use the following syntax to run RECOVER on a disk drive:

*dc:pathc***RECOVER** *d:*

RECOVER travels down the chain of links in the disk's file allocation table and re-creates files. The program re-creates the root directory and places each file in the root directory under the name FILExxxx.REC. In addition, the program converts all subdirectories to normal files and gives them the same name, FILExxxx.REC. All previous file and subdirectory names are destroyed.

RECOVER cannot recover more files than the root directory can hold, typically 512 files for a hard disk. To recover the remaining files, you must delete files and rerun RECOVER until you salvage all files.

RECOVER's recovery work is not trivial. All file and subdirectory names are replaced with the cryptic name FILExxxx.REC. You don the mantle of a detective to discover the true contents of each FILExxxx.REC file. Your only clues include the file's size (the original file date and time vanish with the file name) and the contents of the file. All other traces of identity vanish.

You can use the DOS TYPE command to display the ASCII equivalent of the file's contents. This method works for text files and some data files. You also need a disk-sector editor program that displays the file's contents as ASCII and hexadecimal digits, such as DEBUG or Norton's NU program. Experience and ardent work are your only guides.

Years ago, I ran RECOVER on a backup copy of a diskette. The process of identifying the files took about four hours. The diskette held less than its 360K rating. I cringe when imagining the effort to recover a higher-capacity floppy diskette. I shudder when I imagine the effort to recover any hard disk.

15.19 **Trick: If you must run RECOVER on a disk, first copy all good files from the disk, delete the copied files, remove any unneeded subdirectories, and then run RECOVER.**

Because RECOVER turns all files and subdirectories into FILExxxx.REC files, you can lessen the detective work by eliminating "suspects." By copying and then deleting all good files from the disk, you lessen the time it takes to find the files you want to salvage. The same advice applies to subdirectories. Once you copy the files in the subdirectory to another disk, remove the subdirectory. You will have one less file to investigate after you run RECOVER.

Curing Bad Sectors with Formatting

15.20 **Tip: You can remove most bad sectors only by formatting a floppy diskette or low-level formatting a hard disk.**

With RECOVER, you can recover files and mark out bad sectors in the FAT. This procedure prevents other files from using the flawed area. The damage still exists, however. The only way to remove the damage to the physical format of the disk is to reformat or stop using the disk.

For floppy diskettes, you can use FORMAT to reformat the diskette. FORMAT performs a physical format of the diskette and reestablishes the physical housekeeping information.

For a hard disk, you must redo the low-level format of the hard disk. FORMAT reestablishes the logical housekeeping information but does not re-create the physical housekeeping information. To fix damaged physical disk information, only a low-level format works.

You have three choices. As the first choice, you can back up the entire disk (if the disk is divided into partitions, you must back up all partitions on the disk), physically reformat the disk, use FDISK to reestablish the partition(s), FORMAT each partition, and then restore the files.

As the second choice, you can back up the disk and then use a "nondestructive" disk program, such as SpinRite. SpinRite reads the data from each track, physically reformats each track (which heals some bad sectors), and then restores the data to the track. Given a choice, the second approach is both easier and faster.

The third choice is to format physically only the affected track or tracks (you cannot physically format an area less than a track). If no useful data resides in the affected area (or you can move or easily restore the data), you can use some of the low-level format programs such as Kolad's HFORMAT to "spot" format the single track. (If bad sectors still exist after the track is formatted, you can hide any remaining bad sectors with a program such as Norton's DT or Mace's Diagnose.)

If you use this option, exercise extreme care that no other track is formatted; otherwise, you will lose information. (Backing up the entire disk first is strongly advised before spot formatting.)

For either floppy diskettes or hard disks, if the damage to the disk is physical (oxide breakdown or otherwise flawed media), the bad sectors cannot be removed. Also, electronic and mechanical drive failures cannot be cured. You must live with the reduced capacity of the disk or retire the media (either discard the diskette or send in the hard disk for repair).

If the key housekeeping area is affected, you need further action. The next section of this chapter discusses potential remedies.

Repairing Key Housekeeping Areas

There are three key DOS housekeeping areas for a diskette; four for a hard disk. The three areas for all disks include the boot record, the FAT, and the root directory. The fourth area—the master boot record—exists only on hard disks.

A most catastrophic failure is a bad sector that develops in any of these areas. If a faulty master boot record exists, DOS, on start-up, will not recognize the entire hard disk. If an errant boot record exists, the characteristics (track, sectors, root directory entries, and so on) of the diskette or hard disk drive partition are lost. An errant FAT means that the search for files turns into the proverbial needle-in-the-haystack chase. Each errant root directory sector loses the tracking information on 16 files or subdirectories.

The same effect of losing these key information areas is produced if you inadvertently change the partition information with FDISK, inadvertently use FORMAT on a hard disk partition, or a program performs a stray write.

You can minimize the ill effects of any of these catastrophes with some third-party programs and a small amount of diligence. The next section explains a vital tool.

Using FAT Savers

15.21 Tip: Buy and use a FAT saver.

FAT savers can be life-savers if damage occurs to the FAT or root directory of the disk. Both the Mace Utilities and Norton Advanced Utilities include such programs.

FAT savers consist of one program (such as Norton's FR.EXE) or two programs (RXBAK.EXE to save and UNFORMAT to restore). One program or part of the program stores a copy of the directory and file allocation table in the last part of the disk or on another disk. Because the file allocation table is saved, the name *FAT saver* often is used. Because you use the saved information most frequently to restore from an inadvertent format, the term *unformatter* is equally descriptive.

FORMAT does not destroy the data on the disk; FORMAT destroys the FAT and root directory. The second part of the FAT saver restores the directory and file allocation table of the formatted disk from the copy. If the copy of the root directory and file allocation table is fully up-to-date, you can recover all information on the disk.

You can, however, lose some information on the fixed disk if the stored copy of the directory and FAT is out-of-date. The stored copy quickly becomes a history of your fixed disk as you copy, delete, and add new files. The copy becomes inaccurate as the root directory and FAT change. When you restore the out-of-date copy, the files that have changed are lost.

Most unformat programs recommend that you run the FAT saver portion each time you start the computer. Place the command in your AUTOEXEC.BAT file or include the command in a shutdown batch file that you run at the end of the day. (A sample batch file, SHUTDOWN.BAT, is found in Chapter 2). The most information lost is one session's worth. I like the end-of-day approach better because most problems occur when you start the computer.

These programs are excellent but are best supplemented by a good set of backup diskettes. I use the FAT restorer program to recover most of my information and then use the backup diskettes to recover the remaining information. The best solution is to be careful when you format disks. Unfortunately, bad sectors that develop in key DOS housekeeping areas are unforeseen and usually unavoidable. The FAT saver can help undo the damage done by a bad sector.

15.22   Trick: Include the FAT saver program in your AUTOEXEC.BAT file or shutdown batch file.

You should run the FAT saver frequently so that you do not lose information. You can automate the process by including the FAT saver program in your AUTOEXEC.BAT file or shutdown batch file.

Running the FAT saver from your AUTOEXEC.BAT file ensures that the program saves automatically the key housekeeping areas each time you start your system. Placing the file in a shutdown batch file means that you manually save the FAT before you leave the computer.

Because you are most vulnerable to disk errors when you start the computer, run the FAT saver from the shutdown batch file. This method captures the image of your key housekeeping areas before you turn off the machine. The image is more current than running the FAT saver at the start of a session.

Remember that if you use the shutdown approach, you should run the FAT saver after any defragmenter but before a disk head parker. The disk head parker must always be last.

Diagnosing Bad Sectors in the FAT

15.23   Tip: If DOS reports an error reading either FAT1 or FAT2, back up the disk immediately and be prepared to reformat the disk.

The file allocation table, the area that actually tracks each cluster on the disk, is so critical that DOS keeps two copies, one after the other. If a physical problem develops with one copy, you can use the other FAT.

You have a physically damaged FAT when DOS reports the following error:

> File allocation table bad drive d

Or CHKDSK reports the following error:

> Disk error writing FAT n

n is either 1 or 2. If both FATs are named, the problem is grave.

When you detect a physically damaged FAT, end your current work quickly and immediately back up the disk. The disk is "dying." If the message comes from DOS, give the **R**etry response several times, if needed, and **A**bort if **R**etry does not work.

The only cure for a bad sector in a FAT is to reformat physically the tracks that hold the FAT. You will probably also need to reformat the disk logically. Because the action destroys the FAT and root directory, you must preserve the files on the disk immediately. If only one FAT is affected, back up or copy all your files now before you proceed. If both FATs are affected, back up or copy any files you can. If the problem is on a hard disk with multiple partitions, you should back up the other partitions also.

If the problem is a floppy diskette, reformat the diskette using FORMAT or discard the diskette. FORMAT cannot cure physically damaged media and tolerates no bad sectors in the key housekeeping areas. If the sectors cannot be cured by FORMAT, FORMAT reports that the diskette is unusable if you choose to reformat it. I prefer to pitch the diskette because the more frequent cause of floppy diskette bad sectors is physical media damage, not electronic damage.

If the problem occurs with a hard disk partition, you also can run a FAT saver, but do not overwrite the previously saved copy of the key housekeeping areas. If possible, write the copy to a diskette instead. You may need the old copy to restore the disk.

After you save all files from the hard disk, run the physical format program either on the entire disk or the tracks that hold the FAT. I prefer to reformat only the errant tracks using a program such as HFORMAT. The spot formatting takes less time.

After you format the disk, you can use DOS FORMAT /S or the FAT restorer to reestablish the housekeeping areas.

Appendixes

Includes

Facts About Disks and DOS

ASCII Codes

ANSI Terminal Codes

Facts about Disks and DOS

The internal disk housekeeping of any operating system is complex. Although DOS is no exception, you can understand the internal housekeeping with minor effort. This appendix discusses some background on the tips, tricks, and traps in this book and explains the interrelationships of hard disk partitions, File Allocation Tables, and directories.

DOS Start-Up Files

DOS has three start-up files. In this book, the first start-up file is called IO.SYS (the basic input/output system). The IO.SYS file provides the low-level control routines for handling the computer and attached devices. The IO.SYS file supplements the ROM BIOS of the computer. The second start-up file, called DOS.SYS in this book, provides the high-level routines your programs use to control the computer. The third file is the command interpreter, COMMAND.COM.

The actual names of the first and second start-up files vary among implementations of DOS. For PC DOS, IBM uses IBMBIO.COM for IO.SYS and IBMDOS.COM for DOS.SYS. MS-DOS, provided by Microsoft, uses IO.SYS and MSDOS.SYS.

Some implementations, including COMPAQ, adopt IBM's names and call their start-up files IBMBIO.COM and IBMDOS.COM; others change the name. For example, Toshiba's implementation of MS-DOS uses TBIO.SYS for IO.SYS but keeps MSDOS.SYS; Zenith uses IO.SYS and ZDOS.SYS (for DOS.SYS).

The exact names can be significant when you are updating to a new version of DOS. When placing the start-up files on the disk, the SYS command must erase the previous IO.SYS and DOS.SYS files. If the files have different names, SYS will not work. To avoid this problem, most manufacturers standardize, using either the Microsoft or IBM names.

If you upgrade from one implementation of DOS to another and the SYS command does not work, examine the root directory of the disk. The two start-up files are marked with the system, hidden, and read-only attributes. You may need to erase the two files manually in order for SYS to work. If this does not work, use a disk-sector editor to zero out (place 0's in all locations of) the directory entries for both start-up files.

Logical Housekeeping Areas

When you format disks with FORMAT, three logical housekeeping areas are established. The three areas are used to start DOS, define the characteristics of the disk, hold the initial list of files, and map the in-use disk space. The three areas include the following, in their order of appearance:

Boot sector	Contains the bootstrap loader and the media parameter block
File Allocation Table	Contains the list of clusters of the disk and the chain of clusters used by each file
Root directory	The starting directory of the disk

The following sections first examine the boot sector, then the directory, and finally the File Allocation Table. Note that this discussion applies to both floppy diskettes and hard disk partitions. The hard disk, partition tables, and master boot record are discussed later in this appendix.

Boot Sector

The boot sector contains two sets of information. The general layout of the boot sector is shown in table A.1. The first set of information is the bootstrap routine that the ROM BIOS loads into memory. The second set is the information that describes the diskette or hard disk partition.

The boot sector is the first sector of the disk or disk partition. The boot sector of a floppy diskette is on track 0, side 0, sector 1 (sector numbers start with 1, not 0). For a hard disk, the boot sector is the first sector of the primary partition. Because you can place different operating systems on the hard disk, the physical location of the "first" DOS sector can vary. Customarily, the DOS primary partition is first, and the boot sector is located on cylinder 0, head 1, sector 1.

Table A.1
Boot Sector Information

Offset (hex)	Length (bytes)	Description
00	3	Jump to bootstrap code address
03	8	OEM/Product Name
0B	2	Bytes per sector
0D	1	Sectors per cluster
0E	2	Number of reserved sectors (usually for the boot sector)
10	1	Number of FATs
11	2	Maximum number of root directory entries
13	2	Number of sectors in the media
15	1	Media Descriptor Byte
16	2	Number of sectors per FAT
18	2	Number of sectors per track
1A	2	Number of heads

For DOS pre-V4 and partitions less than or equal to 32M

Offset (hex)	Length (bytes)	Description
1C	2	Number of hidden sectors

For DOS V4 and partitions greater than 32M
or partitions that cross the 32M boundary

Offset (hex)	Length (bytes)	Description
1C	4	Number of hidden sectors
20	4	Total number of sectors in logical media (V4, greater than 32M disks)

For DOS V4

Offset (hex)	Length (bytes)	Description
24	1	Physical drive name (0 for floppy, 80 hex for hard disk)
25	1	Reserved
26	1	Extended boot signature partition (29 hex)
27	4	Volume serial number
2B	11	Volume label
36	8	Reserved (currently, FAT type)

For all DOS versions

Offset (hex)	Length (bytes)	Description
variable	variable	Bootstrap loader
01DB	11	Name of IO.SYS file
01E6	11	Name of DOS.SYS file
01F1	13	Reserved
01FE	2	Signature bytes (55AA)

Bootstrap Loader

The bootstrap loader (named from the expression "Pulling oneself up by the bootstraps") is a small program that either loads and starts DOS or tells the user that the disk is not bootable. The loader determines whether the disk is bootable by searching the first two entries in the root directory for the names of the start-up files (IO.SYS and DOS.SYS). The names are buried at the end of the bootstrap code.

If the loader does not find the files, the loader displays the nonsystem disk message (the exact wording varies among DOS versions) and waits for you to press a key. If the loader finds both names, it assumes that the disk is startable and calls on the ROM BIOS to bring the IO.SYS and DOS.SYS files into memory. Then the program transfers control to these files.

The bootstrap loader assumes that IO.SYS is on contiguous sectors on the disk. If IO.SYS is not contiguous, the bootstrap loader does not complete the loading, and the system locks up. The same lockup occurs if the DOS.SYS file is not stored on contiguous sectors with DOS pre-V3.2. (DOS V3.2 and later can handle a split DOS.SYS file.) If the system locks up while starting, you must use another diskette to start DOS.

Media Parameter Block

The second set of information in the boot sector is the description of the media. The media parameter block gives a comprehensive description of the physical and logical layout of the disk. The only information not included in the media description is the number of tracks or cylinders for the disk (DOS calculates this number). To determine the number of tracks or cylinders, DOS uses the following formula:

total number of sectors / (sectors per track x number of heads)

With DOS pre-V3.2, DOS used a key byte in the File Allocation Table to determine the type of disk. Because DOS was literally running out of combinations for this key byte to handle new types of disk drives, DOS began using the media parameter block, starting with DOS V3.2. With this block, DOS is more flexible in handling nonstandard types of floppy and hard disk drives; you can use more types of disk drives with DOS without requiring a special device driver. (You still may need to use device drivers with certain disk drives.)

The "death disk" mentioned in the section on diskettes in Chapter 4 comes from this change in DOS. Some format programs under MS-DOS pre-V3.2

did not write this block properly. The result was a diskette that caused DOS to act erratically or to lock up.

Root Directory and Subdirectories

Each disk has a starting or root directory. Because of the construction of DOS, the root directory is fixed in size. This size limits the number of files you can store in the root directory.

Each directory entry takes 32 bytes; each directory sector (root or subdirectory) can hold 16 files. Multiply the number of sectors for the root directory (found in the media description block) by 16 to determine the number of files the root directory can hold.

Because the root directory is limited, DOS introduced the concept of a hierarchical directory system in DOS V2. Under this system, which was borrowed from the UNIX operating system, a directory can hold another directory.

Consider the following important aspects about DOS's use of directory entries:

- The first character of the file name is used to test whether an entry is valid, deleted, or empty.
- The directory entry holds the file attributes.
- The directory entry holds the file size.
- The directory entry holds the starting point in the FAT for the file, not the complete list of disk areas used by the file.

Table A.2 covers the contents of a directory entry. These entries hold most DOS housekeeping information about the file.

Figure A.1 details the layout of some directory entries. The entry shows the two IBM PC DOS system files, a deleted file, and an empty directory entry.

Unlike other operating systems, the directory entry does not hold the list of disk sectors occupied by the file. The directory entry holds a pointer to the FAT. To know the location of a file, you must know how the FAT works.

DOS normally uses 00 to indicate a value of zero or empty value in a directory entry. However, DOS uses spaces to pad the root name or extension if the name is less than eight or three characters, respectively.

Table A.2
Directory Entry

Offset (hex)	Length	Purpose
00	8	Root name of file
08	3	Extension
0B	1	File attributes
0C	10	Reserved for DOS
16	2	File time in packed DOS form
18	2	File date in packed DOS form
1A	2	Starting cluster number
1C	4	File size

First Character of File Name

Character (hex)	Special Meaning
00	Unused directory entry
05	Replaced with E5
2E	Alias for current directory (.). If entry is 2E 2E (..), entry is alias for parent directory.
E5	Deleted directory entry
All others	First character of root name

File Attributes Stored in Directory

Value (hex)	Meaning
01	Read-only
02	Hidden
04	System
08	Volume label
10	Subdirectory
20	Archive (turned on whenever file is modified)
40	Reserved by DOS
80	Reserved by DOS

Subdirectories are similar to the root directory, but subdirectories are a type of file (a functional difference). You can extend subdirectories to hold as many files as you have available disk space. Structurally, the only difference between a subdirectory and root directory is the special . and .. entries; these entries exist only in subdirectories.

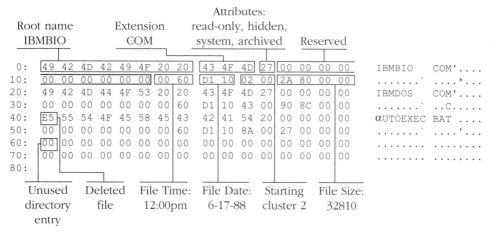

Fig. A.1. Directory entries.

The first two entries of all subdirectories are the **.** (shorthand for the subdirectory directory) and the **..** (shorthand for the parent directory). DOS places a subset of directory information into these two entries. Both entries have a file date and time (which reflects when you created, not modified, the subdirectory). The subdirectory attribute is set for both entries. The starting cluster number in the **.** actually points to itself, the starting cluster for the subdirectory. The **.** does not point back to the parent directory. All other values in the directory entries are zero.

File Allocation Table

The File Allocation Table (FAT) has two purposes. First, DOS uses the FAT to track the locations used by each file on the disk. Second, DOS uses the FAT to determine the amount of free disk space and what locations should be assigned to a file you create or extend.

Become acquainted with one term that relates to the FAT—a cluster. A *cluster* is a set of adjacent disk sectors. DOS does not allocate disk space on a sector-by-sector basis. (This method is inefficient when using large disk drives.) DOS allocates space on the basis of a cluster.

Clusters are the *allocation units* mentioned in DOS V4's CHKDSK messages. The number of sectors grouped into a cluster varies, depending on the type of media. Theoretically, a cluster can group from 1 to 256 sectors per cluster; practically, a cluster groups 1 to 16 sectors. Most floppy diskettes use 1 or 2 sectors per cluster (512 to 1K of space per cluster). Hard disk partitions under 18M or over 128M use 8 sectors per cluster (4K clusters). Hard disk partitions between 18M and 128M use 4 sectors per cluster (2K per cluster).

FAT Entries

To understand how the FAT works, visualize a chessboard. Each square on the board is numbered from 1 to 64. The object is to visit each square on the chessboard. To complicate matters, you cannot move from square 1 to square 64. Instead, each square holds a piece of paper, and the paper holds the number of another square. To visit the next square, you must follow the number on each piece of paper.

Suppose, for example, that you start at square 1 and read the piece of paper. The paper says number 2. You go to square 2, and the paper there says 3. The paper on square 3 says 10. You jump to square 10; the paper says 16. You jump to 16, and the paper says 18. You continue jumping from square to square until all 64 squares are visited.

Each square has a number based on its position on the chessboard, and each square contains the number of another square. To clear the chessboard, you must follow the chain established by the pieces of paper to jump from square to square.

The FAT is similar to the chessboard in several ways. Each square in the FAT is an entry for one specific cluster. Each cluster contains either a number or a special value. If the cluster contains a number, you jump to that cluster. You continue jumping until you reach a cluster that holds a special value. The special values for FAT entries include the following:

Value		
16-bit	*12-bit*	*Meaning*
00 00	000	Free space
00 01	001	Unused code
FF F0–FF F6	FF0–FF6	Reserved
FF F7	FF7	Bad block
FF F8–FF FF	FF8–FFFF	Last cluster in chain

Any other value is the number of the next sector in the chain. Because FATs can have 12-bit or 16-bit entries and certain values are reserved, the highest cluster number DOS can use is 4,079 (12-bit entries) or 65,519 (16-bit entries).

The FAT is the roadmap of the disk. Figure A.2 details the first 39 entries of a typical FAT from a hard disk. Each cluster has one entry in the FAT. Because each FAT entry shown is 16 bits, each 2-byte pair is a FAT entry. The number of clusters this entry represents is shown in hexadecimal and decimal above the entry.

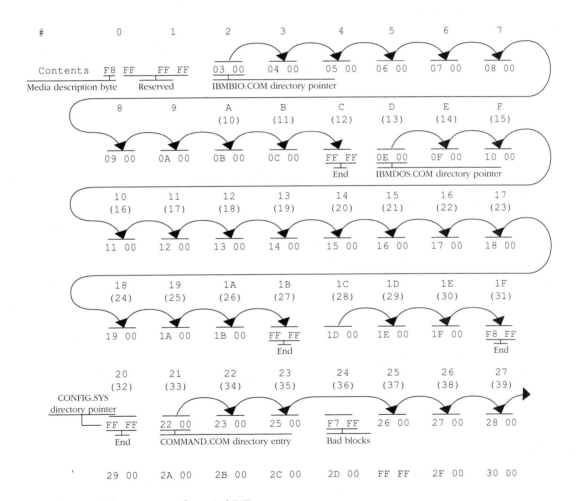

Fig. A.2. *The first 39 entries of a typical FAT.*

Notice the numbering of the entries. The entries are linear but start with 0. The third cluster of the disk (cluster 2) is the third FAT entry; the fourth cluster (cluster 3) is the fourth FAT entry; the fifth cluster (cluster 4) is the fifth FAT entry; and so on for all clusters of the disk.

The skewed numbers in the preceding paragraph are accurate. No cluster has a number of 0 or 1. The first 2 entries (entries 0 and 1) are reserved for use by DOS for housekeeping information. The first byte of the FAT holds the media description byte (which has the same meaning as the media description byte in the boot sector). The remaining bytes are filled with FFs hex. This means that the first usable cluster is the third cluster (cluster number 2).

Follow the way DOS tracks files in the FAT by using figure A.2. Notice that the directory entry for IBMBIO.COM states that the starting cluster used by the file is cluster 2. Move to FAT entry 2, and read the number. The number inside cluster entry 2 is the number 3; therefore, cluster 3 is the next cluster for the file. Move to the entry for cluster 3, and you find the number 4 inside, making cluster 4 the next cluster for the file.

The process continues. You look at the current cluster that names the next cluster. The process ends when you encounter one of the special values. In the case of IBMBIO.COM, the cluster numbered 0Ch (12 decimal) holds the value FFFF. This value designates the end of the cluster chain and the end of the chase. The file does not contain any more clusters. IBMBIO.COM uses clusters 2 through 0Ch.

Notice that IBMDOS.COM starts directly after IBMBIO.COM. IBMDOS.COM starts with cluster 0Dh (13d) and extends to cluster 1B (27d) where another FFFF is found. Notice that CONFIG.SYS (cluster 20 hex) is a short file that occupies only one cluster. CONFIG.SYS's single cluster simply contains the special end-of-chain value. The FAT entry for short files contains the end value rather than the number of a different cluster.

COMMAND.COM (starting at cluster 21 hex/33 decimal) shows a jump. Cluster number 24 contains the special value FF F7. (On the Intel CPUs, numbers are "reversed;" the number FF F7 is stored as F7 FF.) DOS uses this value to mark a bad sector.

When DOS stored COMMAND.COM, it encountered the special marker for cluster 24h (36d). DOS then looked for the next available cluster—cluster 25h (37d). DOS skipped the bad cluster and stored 25h in cluster 23h.

Understanding FAT Sizes

Because the FAT steals some disk space from user files, DOS uses different-sized FATs for different disks. The sizes of FAT entries do not vary on a particular disk but vary among types of disks (either 12 bits per entry or 16 bits per entry). Diskettes and hard disks under 18M use 12 bits per entry (1 1/2 bytes) for all DOS versions. Hard disk partitions over 18M use 16-bit entries (2 bytes) for DOS V3 and later.

Because DOS allocates disk space on the basis of a cluster, the number of sectors per cluster is important. If you have many short files, a smaller number of sectors per cluster helps you. If the cluster size is 8 sectors, a 1-byte file still uses 4K of disk space. Multiply the *slack* (space allocated to, but not used by a file) in each cluster by hundreds of files, and wasted disk space can run as high as 25 percent. The inverse is true; large files gain some modest benefits from larger cluster sizes.

The size of the FAT entry and, correspondingly, the size of the FAT are a compromise. Each FAT entry takes either 1 1/2 bytes or 2 bytes. Also, 2 copies of the FAT are stored for each disk. Under DOS pre-V3.31, each FAT was limited to 32K, a total of 64K. With COMPAQ DOS V3.31 or DOS V4, the FATs can double in size to 64K each or a total of 128K.

Cluster sizes reflect the compromises made in FAT size. To track many small clusters, the FAT grows. If the media is large (such as hard disks with capacities into the hundreds of megabytes), the FAT grows tremendously. Because larger FAT sizes require more disk accesses to read and more time for computations, the DOS implementation chooses a FAT entry and FAT size based on the compromise of wasted disk space versus total available disk space and speed of operations.

The final point to remember is that clusters are applicable only to the way disk space is allocated. Only DOS uses clusters; DOS shields programs from knowing about clusters. A program can request that DOS read or write a number of bytes or a number of sectors but not a number of clusters.

Tracing the FAT

Sometimes, you must repair the FAT manually—for example, when a FAT chain loops onto itself (see Chapter 14, "Troubleshooting Logical Damage). To handle this problem, you must find the starting cluster number from the directory entry and then trace each cluster until you spot the errant entry. The task is quick on disks with 16-bit FATs (disk partitions larger than 18M) but more difficult on 12-bit FATs (which is why I consider this trick with hard disks and not floppy diskettes).

For FAT tracing, find the starting cluster number from the file's directory entry. Determining the exact location within the FAT is somewhat laborious, but not difficult. Have on hand a calculator, preferably one that converts between decimal numbers and hexadecimal numbers. You also need a disk-sector editor.

To locate the first cluster, follow these steps:

Step 1: *Find the starting cluster number from the file's directory entry.*

Step 2: *Calculate the distance into the file the entry is located.*

Step 3: *Calculate the disk sector that holds the entry.*

Step 4: *Calculate the specific bytes that hold the entry.*

To find the starting FAT entry, you must find the FAT sector that holds the entry; then you must find the entry within the sector. After you have the entry, you can repeat the process to find the entire cluster chain for the file.

Calculations on 12-Bit FATs

The process for handling FAT entries differs for 12-bit and 16-bit entries. To find the cluster entry for 12-bit FATs, use the following formulas:

1. Starting cluster number (in decimal) x 1.5 = *file bytes*
2. INT (*file bytes* / 512) = *FAT sector number* that holds the entry
3. (*file bytes* MOD 512) − 1 = *byte offset* within the FAT sector
4. If *byte offset* is even (and a whole number), low 8 bits of following byte + *byte offset* = *entry bytes*.
   Or
   If *byte offset* is odd (and has a 0.5), next byte plus high 8 bits of *byte offset* = *entry bytes*.

Formula 1 takes the byte number of the start of the FAT entry. Because each FAT entry is 1.5 bytes long, multiplying the cluster number by 1.5 gives the entry's byte position with the FAT (called the *file bytes*).

Formula 2 determines which sector within the FAT holds the entry (the *FAT sector number*). Divide the number of file bytes by the size of a sector, 512 bytes per sector. The INT operation rounds down to a whole number (no sector has a fractional number). If the result is a fraction (such as 17.42), discard the fraction (.42), and use the whole number.

Formula 3 determines the byte within the sector that has the entry (*byte offset*). You divide the 2 numbers and use the remainder as the result. (For example, 33 MOD 4 is 1; 33.5 MOD 4 is 1.5.) You need the –1 because byte numbers within a sector start at 0, not 1. Because 0 is a counting number to computers, subtracting 1 results in the correct byte number.

Formula 4 gets the exact bytes used and calculates the value of the entry (the *entry bytes*). Because a 12-bit entry is 1 1/2 bytes, you need 1 byte plus 8 bits. The trick is getting the bit in the correct order; this part is complicated because the 8086 families store information from right-to-left (the first bytes are the low part of the value; the second bytes are the high part of the value). This "backward" storage is common but makes manually translating the number difficult.

If the *byte offset* is an even, whole number (without .5), add the low 8 bits from the following byte to the *byte offset*. If the *byte offset* is odd and has a .5, add the following byte to the high 8 bits from the *byte offset*. If you have any other combination of byte offset (even and a .5, or odd and no .5), your calculations are off.

For example, bytes 42 through 44 of the FAT sector contain the values 1D E0 01. If the byte offset is 42, add the second digit from byte 43 to the byte offset. The answer is 01Dh (29 in decimal).

If the byte offset is 43.5, add the next byte (byte 44) to the first digit from the original byte offset. In this case, the answer is 01Eh (30 in decimal).

Calculations on 16-Bit FATs

For 16-bit FATs, the calculations are easier. Because each entry takes 2 bytes, the formulas are simplified:

1. Starting cluster number (in decimal) **x** 1.5 = *file bytes*
2. INT (*file bytes* / 512) = *FAT sector number* that holds the entry
3. (*file bytes* MOD 512) – 1 = *byte offset* within the FAT sector
4. Next byte + *byte offset* = *entry bytes*

For example, bytes 42 through 45 of the FAT sector contain the values 15 00 16 00. If the byte offset is 42, add the byte offset to the next byte. The answer is 0015h (21 in decimal). If the byte offset is 44, the answer is 0016h (22 in decimal).

Repairing a Looping FAT Chain

If CHKDSK locks up while analyzing a disk, you probably have a looping FAT chain. To solve this problem, you should use a disk-sector editor to analyze the FAT chain for the suspect file. Usually, the last file listed by CHKDSK /V is the suspect file.

When you trace a FAT chain, the process is easier if the disk is unfragmented. Most of the chain will have only three types of numbers: contiguously ascending numbers, bad-sector indicators, or end-of-chain indicators. Contiguous files always ascend by one. The bad-sector marker is FF7 (12-bit FAT) or FFF7 (16-bit FAT). The end-of-file indicators are values from FF8 to FFF or FFF8 through FFFF.

After you find the starting cluster, keep looking for continuously ascending numbers. When a number violates the pattern, pause and examine the entry. If you encounter a bad-block marker, ignore the marker. If you see the end-of-chain marker, the file and FAT chain are intact. Scratch this file from the list and repeat the search on another suspect file.

When the number is out of order, however, you must jump to that entry to continue the trace. A forward jump is not unusual. Pull a mental trigger when you see a FAT entry that has a descending value. A FAT chain loops when one cluster entry points to the previous part of the chain. Note the current location within the FAT (the corresponding cluster number or the sector and byte in the FAT that holds the value) and the value held by the pointed-to cluster.

After you find the errant entry, change it to an end-of-chain indicator, save the change, and use the advice in Chapter 14 on troubleshooting to salvage the file.

Partitions

Partitions are the logical walls that DOS uses to subdivide hard disks. Partitions date back to DOS V2. Originally, partitions were used so that different operating systems could coexist on the same hard disk.

Inherent in the design of DOS was a magic disk storage barrier—32 megabytes. When hard disks started bumping against the magic 32M barrier, partitions became the way to subdivide a larger physical hard disk into multiple, apparent (logical) disk drives of 32M or less.

The use of multiple DOS partitions varies among implementations of DOS. COMPAQ started using more than one partition for DOS in its MS-DOS V2.1. IBM did not offer multiple DOS partitions until PC DOS V3.3. Most others started using two or more partitions for DOS sometime between COMPAQ V2.1 and IBM V3.3.

Understanding Partitioning Schemes

Partitioning schemes vary among implementations of DOS. Each scheme has a common use. Each partition has a starting and ending head, sector, and cylinder, and each partition holds a finite number of disk sectors. This information defines the logical wall between the partitions.

Each operating system recognizes and uses certain partitions and keeps its hands off partitions that the operating system does not recognize. (An errant program that bypasses the operating system can cause a program to violate the logical wall.)

With most DOS versions, you can subdivide the hard disk into four main partitions. The specifics of the partitions cloud from this point. Some implementations and versions of DOS treat partitions differently. For example, PC DOS pre-V3.3 uses only one DOS partition. Starting with PC DOS V3.3, DOS can use two partitions. The main partition is considered the primary partition; the second partition is the extended partition.

The primary partition is the only DOS startable partition. You can subdivide the extended partition further. For PC DOS V3.3 and later, you can subdivide the extended partition into additional areas called *logical volumes* or *logical disk drives*. By subdividing the extended partition, you can divide a single physical hard disk into as many as 24 logical disk drives with PC DOS. (More subdivisions of the extended partition are possible, but DOS allows only 26 disk drive names, and floppy drives take 2 drive names.)

This scheme allows PC DOS V3.3 to use a physical disk drive up to 768M (32M per logical disk drive x 24 logical disk drives). Under PC DOS V4, the scheme allows the use of a single physical disk up to 12 gigabytes (512M per logical drive x 24 logical drives).

Other manufacturers use different schemes. Before DOS V3.3, most implementations allowed 2 DOS partitions. One partition was the DOS partition; the second partition was a form of an extended partition. A device driver was provided by the manufacturer so that you could use the extended partition as a second logical disk drive. With this scheme, you could use disk drives up to 74M directly for DOS.

COMPAQ used a different scheme. In COMPAQ DOS V2.1 through V3.2, DOS could use each of the 4 main partitions. The provided ENHDISK.SYS driver allowed DOS to use each partition as a logical disk drive. The disk limit for COMPAQ DOS became 128M.

With DOS V3.3 and later, most implementors, including COMPAQ, followed IBM's lead in subdividing the extended partition into additional logical disk drives. The new approach meant that the largest disk drive directly usable by DOS V3.3 was 768M.

COMPAQ DOS V3.31 and DOS V4 use the same basic scheme as V3.30 (24 logical disk drives per physical disk drive). With DOS V3.31, however, each logical disk drive can be as large as 512M; with DOS V4, each logical disk drive can be as large as 1G (one gigabyte, 1,000M). The largest single physical disk drive that DOS can use is 12.2 gigabytes.

Because most personal computers do not use disk drives larger than 512M, the difference between COMPAQ V3.31 and DOS V4 is minimal.

Tracking Partitions

The computer starts loading the operating system by loading the first sector of the disk (track 0, side 0, sector 1). On a floppy diskette, the computer loads the DOS boot sector. On a hard disk, the computer loads the master boot record of the disk.

The *master boot record* is similar to the DOS boot record. The master boot record contains the master bootstrap loader, which starts the active partition (the partition that has an 80 hex as its active partition marker). This brings in the normal DOS boot sector, which continues the start-up of DOS.

The description of the media differs between hard disks and floppy diskettes. The master boot record holds the following disk partition information:

- Active partition marker
- Starting side, sector, and cylinder numbers of the partition
- Partition type
- Ending side, sector, and cylinder numbers of the partition
- Number of sectors before the start of the partition
- Number of sectors held by the partition

This information is a table that contains four 16-byte entries. Table A.3 shows the layout of partition information.

Table A.3
Partition Table Information

Location of Partition Table in Master or Extended Boot Records

Offset (hex)	Size (bytes)	PC DOS Use	MS-DOS Use
01BE	16	1st partition	4th partition
01CE	16	2nd partition	3rd partition
01DE	16	3rd partition	2nd partition
01FE	16	4th partition	1st partition
01FE	2	Signature:AA55h	

Contents of Partition Record

Offset (hex)	Size (bytes)	Use
00	1	Boot indicator
01	1	Beginning head (side)
02	2	Beginning sector/cylinder*
04	1	System indicator
05	1	Ending head (side)
06	2	Ending sector/cylinder*
08	4	Starting sector (relative to the beginning of the physical disk)
0C	4	Number of sectors in partition

System Indicator Meaning

00	An unused partition
01	DOS with a 12-bit FAT
02	XENIX
03	XENIX
04	DOS with a 16-bit FAT
05	Extended DOS partition
06	COMPAQ DOS V3.31 or DOS V4 "big" partition
75	PC/IX
DB	CP/M
FF	XENIX bad block table

* The sector number is contained in the low-order 6 bits of the first byte. The cylinder number, a 10-bit number, is contained in the second byte; and the upper 2 bits are contained in the high 2 bits of the first byte.

All DOS versions recognize partition type 01. All DOS versions 3 recognize type 04. DOS V3.3 universally recognizes type 05 (although some DOS V3.0 through V3.2 may recognize 05 also). COMPAQ DOS V3.31 and DOS V4 recognize type 06. DOS does not recognize any other value.

Because DOS does not start an extended partition, the extended partition has a different layout. The extended partition contains 1 to 24 subpartitions.

Each subpartition has an imitator of the master boot sector. The imitator holds only the subpartition information. Although the subpartition information is like the main disk partition information (both have 4 16-byte entries), only two entries are used.

The first partition entry defines the current subpartition (including partition type); the second partition entry defines where the next subpartition should be found. A 05 is used in the partition type for the second entry to inform DOS another subpartition exists. An 00 in the partition type tells DOS there are no more subpartitions.

Note one peculiarity about partitions between PC DOS and MS-DOS. PC DOS and MS-DOS store the partition information backwards from each other. PC DOS stores the first entry at the top and additional entries toward the end. MS-DOS stores its first entry at the end of the table and additional entries toward the beginning. Knowing this information can be helpful if you must reconstruct a partition record manually.

When creating the primary DOS partition, FDISK establishes the master boot record of the hard disk on side 0 of cylinder 0. The master boot record contains the start-up disk code and the master partition record. The master boot record's partition table lists the start, end, and type of each of the four possible partitions.

When creating the extended DOS partition, FDISK writes the information for the extended partition in the master boot record. When creating logical volumes, FDISK creates a boot record in each logical volume. The volume's boot record similar to the master boot record, holding another partition table.

However, the volume's partition record does not list the partitions of the drive. The logical volume's partition record gives the starting and ending point for the volume, and an entry to the boot record of the next volume. The boot record of each logical volume points to the boot record of the next logical volume.

To free the next volume, the "pointer" in the previous volume's record is filled with zeros (designating no further volumes). To delete the first logical volume, the table in the first boot record of the extended partition is zeroed.

ASCII Codes

This appendix presents the ASCII, extended ASCII, and extended function ASCII codes. In the tables, a circumflex (^) represents the Ctrl key. For example, ^C stands for Ctrl-C.

ASCII Codes

The standard codes for the American Standard Code for Information Interchange (ASCII) are presented in the following table.

Decimal	Hex	Octal	Binary	Graphic Character	ASCII Meaning
0	0	0	00000000		^@ NUL (null)
1	1	1	00000001	☺	^A SOH (start-of-header)
2	2	2	00000010	●	^B STX (start-of-transmission)
3	3	3	00000011	♥	^C ETX (end-of-transmission)
4	4	4	00000100	♦	^D EOT (end-of-text)
5	5	5	00000101	♣	^E ENQ (enquiry)
6	6	6	00000110	♠	^F ACK (acknowledge)
7	7	7	00000111	·	^G BEL (bell)
8	8	10	00001000	▫	^H BS (backspace)
9	9	11	00001001	○	^I HT (horizontal tab)
10	A	12	00001010	◙	^J LF (line feed - also ^Enter)
11	B	13	00001011	♂	^K VT (vertical tab)
12	C	14	00001100	♀	^L FF (form feed)
13	D	15	00001101	♪	^M CR (carriage return)
14	E	16	00001110	♫	^N SO
15	F	17	00001111	☼	^O SI
16	10	20	00010000	►	^P DLE
17	11	21	00010001	◄	^Q DC1
18	12	22	00010010	↕	^R DC2
19	13	23	00010011	‼	^S DC3
20	14	24	00010100	¶	^T DC4
21	15	25	00010101	§	^U NAK
22	16	26	00010110	▬	^V SYN
23	17	27	00010111	↨	^W ETB

Decimal	Hex	Octal	Binary	Graphic Character	ASCII Meaning
24	18	30	00011000	↑	^X CAN (cancel)
25	19	31	00011001	↓	^Y EM
26	1A	32	00011010	→	^Z SUB (also end-of-file)
27	1B	33	00011011	←	^[ESC (Escape)
28	1C	34	00011100	∟	^\ FS (field separator)
29	1D	35	00011101	↔	^] GS
30	1E	36	00011110	▲	^^ RS (record separator)
31	1F	37	00011111	▼	^_ US
32	20	40	00100000		Space
33	21	41	00100001	!	!
34	22	42	00100010	"	"
35	23	43	00100011	#	#
36	24	44	00100100	$	$
37	25	45	00100101	%	%
38	26	46	00100110	&	&
39	27	47	00100111	'	'
40	28	50	00101000	(	(
41	29	51	00101001	)	)
42	2A	52	00101010	*	*
43	2B	53	00101011	+	+
44	2C	54	00101100	,	,
45	2D	55	00101101	-	-
46	2E	56	00101110	.	.
47	2F	57	00101111	/	/
48	30	60	00110000	0	0
49	31	61	00110001	1	1
50	32	62	00110010	2	2
51	33	63	00110011	3	3
52	34	64	00110100	4	4
53	35	65	00110101	5	5
54	36	66	00110110	6	6
55	37	67	00110111	7	7
56	38	70	00111000	8	8
57	39	71	00111001	9	9
58	3A	72	00111010	:	:
59	3B	73	00111011	;	;
60	3C	74	00111100	<	<
61	3D	75	00111101	=	=
62	3E	76	00111110	>	>
63	3F	77	00111111	?	?
64	40	100	01000000	@	@
65	41	101	01000001	A	A
66	42	102	01000010	B	B
67	43	103	01000011	C	C
68	44	104	01000100	D	D
69	45	105	01000101	E	E
70	46	106	01000110	F	F
71	47	107	01000111	G	G
72	48	110	01001000	H	H
73	49	111	01001001	I	I
74	4A	112	01001010	J	J
75	4B	113	01001011	K	K

Decimal	Hex	Octal	Binary	Graphic Character	ASCII Meaning
76	4C	114	01001100	L	L
77	4D	115	01001101	M	M
78	4E	116	01001110	N	N
79	4F	117	01001111	O	O
80	50	120	01010000	P	P
81	51	121	01010001	Q	Q
82	52	122	01010010	R	R
83	53	123	01010011	S	S
84	54	124	01010100	T	T
85	55	125	01010101	U	U
86	56	126	01010110	V	V
87	57	127	01010111	W	W
88	58	130	01011000	X	X
89	59	131	01011001	Y	Y
90	5A	132	01011010	Z	Z
91	5B	133	01011011	[	[
92	5C	134	01011100	\	\
93	5D	135	01011101	]	]
94	5E	136	01011110	^	^
95	5F	137	01011111	_	_
96	60	140	01100000	`	`
97	61	141	01100001	a	a
98	62	142	01100010	b	b
99	63	143	01100011	c	c
100	64	144	01100100	d	d
101	65	145	01100101	e	e
102	66	146	01100110	f	f
103	67	147	01100111	g	g
104	68	150	01101000	h	h
105	69	151	01101001	i	i
106	6A	152	01101010	j	j
107	6B	153	01101011	k	k
108	6C	154	01101100	l	l
109	6D	155	01101101	m	m
110	6E	156	01101110	n	n
111	6F	157	01101111	o	o
112	70	160	01110000	p	p
113	71	161	01110001	q	q
114	72	162	01110010	r	r
115	73	163	01110011	s	s
116	74	164	01110100	t	t
117	75	165	01110101	u	u
118	76	166	01110110	v	v
119	77	167	01110111	w	w
120	78	170	01111000	x	x
121	79	171	01111001	y	y
122	7A	172	01111010	z	z
123	7B	173	01111011	{	{
124	7C	174	01111100	|	|
125	7D	175	01111101	}	}
126	7E	176	01111110	~	~
127	7F	177	01111111	Δ	Del

Decimal	Hex	Octal	Binary	Graphic Character
128	80	200	10000000	Ç
129	81	201	10000001	ü
130	82	202	10000010	é
131	83	203	10000011	â
132	84	204	10000100	ä
133	85	205	10000101	à
134	86	206	10000110	å
135	87	207	10000111	ç
136	88	210	10001000	ê
137	89	211	10001001	ë
138	8A	212	10001010	è
139	8B	213	10001011	ï
140	8C	214	10001100	î
141	8D	215	10001101	ì
142	8E	216	10001110	Ä
143	8F	217	10001111	Å
144	90	220	10010000	É
145	91	221	10010001	æ
146	92	222	10010010	Æ
147	93	223	10010011	ô
148	94	224	10010100	ö
149	95	225	10010101	ò
150	96	226	10010110	û
151	97	227	10010111	ù
152	98	230	10011000	ÿ
153	99	231	10011001	Ö
154	9A	232	10011010	Ü
155	9B	233	10011011	¢
156	9C	234	10011100	£
157	9D	235	10011101	¥
158	9E	236	10011110	₧
159	9F	237	10011111	ƒ
160	A0	240	10100000	á
161	A1	241	10100001	í
162	A2	242	10100010	ó
163	A3	243	10100011	ú
164	A4	244	10100100	ñ
165	A5	245	10100101	Ñ
166	A6	246	10100110	ª
167	A7	247	10100111	º
168	A8	250	10101000	¿
169	A9	251	10101001	⌐
170	AA	252	10101010	¬
171	AB	253	10101011	½
172	AC	254	10101100	¼
173	AD	255	10101101	¡
174	AE	256	10101110	«
175	AF	257	10101111	»
176	B0	260	10110000	▒
177	B1	261	10110001	▓
178	B2	262	10110010	█
179	B3	263	10110011	│

Decimal	Hex	Octal	Binary	Graphic Character
180	B4	264	10110100	┤
181	B5	265	10110101	╡
182	B6	266	10110110	╢
183	B7	267	10110111	╖
184	B8	270	10111000	╕
185	B9	271	10111001	╣
186	BA	272	10111010	║
187	BB	273	10111011	╗
188	BC	274	10111100	╝
189	BD	275	10111101	╜
190	BE	276	10111110	╛
191	BF	277	10111111	┐
192	C0	300	11000000	└
193	C1	301	11000001	┴
194	C2	302	11000010	┬
195	C3	303	11000011	├
196	C4	304	11000100	─
197	C5	305	11000101	┼
198	C6	306	11000110	╞
199	C7	307	11000111	╟
200	C8	310	11001000	╚
201	C9	311	11001001	╔
202	CA	312	11001010	╩
203	CB	313	11001011	╦
204	CC	314	11001100	╠
205	CD	315	11001101	═
206	CE	316	11001110	╬
207	CF	317	11001111	╧
208	D0	320	11010000	╨
209	D1	321	11010001	╤
210	D2	322	11010010	╥
211	D3	323	11010011	╙
212	D4	324	11010100	╘
213	D5	325	11010101	╒
214	D6	326	11010110	╓
215	D7	327	11010111	╫
216	D8	330	11011000	╪
217	D9	331	11011001	┘
218	DA	332	11011010	┌
219	DB	333	11011011	█
220	DC	334	11011100	▄
221	DD	335	11011101	▌
222	DE	336	11011110	▐
223	DF	337	11011111	▀
224	E0	340	11100000	∝
225	E1	341	11100001	β
226	E2	342	11100010	Γ
227	E3	343	11100011	π
228	E4	344	11100100	Σ
229	E5	345	11100101	σ
230	E6	346	11100110	μ
231	E7	347	11100111	τ

Decimal	Hex	Octal	Binary	Graphic Character
232	E8	350	11101000	◊
233	E9	351	11101001	θ
234	EA	352	11101010	Ω
235	EB	353	11101011	δ
236	EC	354	11101100	∞
237	ED	355	11101101	φ
238	EE	356	11101110	∈
239	EF	357	11101111	∩
240	F0	360	11110000	≡
241	F1	361	11110001	±
242	F2	362	11110010	≥
243	F3	363	11110011	≤
244	F4	364	11110100	⌠
245	F5	365	11110101	⌡
246	F6	366	11110110	÷
247	F7	367	11110111	≈
248	F8	370	11111000	°
249	F9	371	11111001	•
250	FA	372	11111010	·
251	FB	373	11111011	√
252	FC	374	11111100	ⁿ
253	FD	375	11111101	²
254	FE	376	11111110	∎
255	FF	377	11111111	

Extended ASCII Keyboard Codes

Certain keys cannot be represented by the standard ASCII codes. To represent the codes, a two-character sequence is used. The first character is always an ASCII NUL (0). The second character and its translation are listed in the following table. Some codes expand to multi-keystroke characters.

If an asterisk (*) appears in the *Enhance Only* column, the sequence is available only on the Enhanced Keyboards (101- and 102-key keyboards).

Enhance Only	Decimal Meaning	Hex	Octal	Binary	Extended ASCII
*	1	01	001	00000001	Alt-Esc
	3	03	003	00000011	Null (null character)
*	14	0E	016	00001110	Alt-Backspace
	15	0F	017	00001111	Shift-Tab (back-tab)
	16	10	020	00010000	Alt-Q
	17	11	021	00010001	Alt-W
	18	12	022	00010010	Alt-E
	19	13	023	00010011	Alt-R
	20	14	024	00010100	Alt-T

Enhance Only	Decimal Meaning	Hex	Octal	Binary	Extended ASCII
	21	15	025	00010101	Alt-Y
	22	16	026	00010110	Alt-U
	23	17	027	00010111	Alt-I
	24	18	030	00011000	Alt-O
	25	19	031	00011001	Alt-P
*	26	1A	032	00011010	Alt-[
*	27	1B	033	00011011	Alt-]
*	28	1C	034	00011100	Alt-Enter
	30	1E	036	00011110	Alt-A
	31	1F	037	00011111	Alt-S
	32	20	040	00100000	Alt-D
	33	21	041	00100001	Alt-F
	34	22	042	00100010	Alt-G
	35	23	043	00100011	Alt-H
	36	24	044	00100100	Alt-J
	37	25	045	00100101	Alt-K
	38	26	046	00100110	Alt-L
*	39	27	047	00100111	Alt-;
*	40	28	050	00101000	Alt-'
*	41	29	051	00101001	Alt-'
*	43	2B	053	00101011	Alt-\
	44	2C	054	00101100	Alt-Z
	45	2D	055	00101101	Alt-X
	46	2E	056	00101110	Alt-C
	47	2F	057	00101111	Alt-V
	48	30	060	00110000	Alt-B
	49	31	061	00110001	Alt-N
	50	32	062	00110010	Alt-M
*	51	33	063	00110011	Alt-,
*	52	34	064	00110100	Alt-.
*	53	35	065	00110101	Alt-/
*	55	37	067	00110111	Alt-* (keypad)
	57	39	071	00111001	Alt-space bar
	59	3B	073	00111011	F1
	60	3C	074	00111100	F2
	61	3D	075	00111101	F3
	62	3E	076	00111110	F4
	63	3F	077	00111111	F5
	64	40	100	01000000	F6
	65	41	101	01000001	F7
	66	42	102	01000010	F8
	67	43	103	01000011	F9
	68	44	104	01000100	F10
	71	47	107	01000111	Home
	72	48	110	01001000	↑
	73	49	111	01001001	PgUp
	74	4A	112	01001010	Alt- — (keypad)
	75	4B	113	01001011	←
	76	4C	114	01001100	Shift-5 (keypad)
	77	4D	115	01001101	→
	78	4E	116	01001110	Alt-+ (keypad)

Enhance Only	Decimal Meaning	Hex	Octal	Binary	Extended ASCII
	79	4F	117	01001111	End
*	80	50	120	01010000	↓
*	81	51	121	01010001	PgDn
*	82	52	122	01010010	Ins (Insert)
	83	53	123	01010011	Del (Delete)
	84	54	124	01010100	Shift-F1
	85	55	125	01010101	Shift-F2
	86	56	126	01010110	Shift-F3
	87	57	127	01010111	Shift-F4
	88	58	130	01011000	Shift-F5
	89	59	131	01011001	Shift-F6
	90	5A	132	01011010	Shift-F7
	91	5B	133	01011011	Shift-F8
	92	5C	134	01011100	Shift-F9
	93	5D	135	01011101	Shift-F10
	94	5E	136	01011110	Ctrl-F1
	95	5F	137	01011111	Ctrl-F2
	96	60	140	01100000	Ctrl-F3
	97	61	141	01100001	Ctrl-F4
	98	62	142	01100010	Ctrl-F5
	99	63	143	01100011	Ctrl-F6
	100	64	144	01100100	Ctrl-F7
	101	65	145	01100101	Ctrl-F8
	102	66	146	01100110	Ctrl-F9
	103	67	147	01100111	Ctrl-F10
	104	68	150	01101000	Alt-F1
	105	69	151	01101001	Alt-F2
	106	6A	152	01101010	Alt-F3
	107	6B	153	01101011	Alt-F4
	108	6C	154	01101100	Alt-F5
	109	6D	155	01101101	Alt-F6
	110	6E	156	01101110	Alt-F7
	111	6F	157	01101111	Alt-F8
	112	70	160	01110000	Alt-F9
	113	71	161	01110001	Alt-F10
	114	72	162	01110010	Ctrl-PrtSc
	115	73	163	01110011	Ctrl-←
	116	74	164	01110100	Ctrl-→
	117	75	165	01110101	Ctrl-End
	118	76	166	01110110	Ctrl-PgDn
	119	77	167	01110111	Ctrl-Home
	120	78	170	01111000	Alt-1 (keyboard)
	121	79	171	01111001	Alt-2 (keyboard)
	122	7A	172	01111010	Alt-3 (keyboard)
	123	7B	173	01111011	Alt-4 (keyboard)
	124	7C	174	01111100	Alt-5 (keyboard)
	125	7D	175	01111101	Alt-6 (keyboard)
	126	7E	176	01111110	Alt-7 (keyboard)
	127	7F	177	01111111	Alt-8 (keyboard)
	128	80	200	10000000	Alt-9 (keyboard)
	129	81	201	10000001	Alt-0 (keyboard)

Enhance Only	Decimal Meaning	Hex	Octal	Binary	Extended ASCII
	130	82	202	10000010	Alt-— (keyboard)
	131	83	203	10000011	Alt-= (keyboard)
	132	84	204	10000100	Ctrl-PgUp
*	133	85	205	10000101	F11
*	134	86	206	10000110	F12
*	135	87	207	10000111	Shift-F11
*	136	88	210	10001000	Shift-F12
*	137	89	211	10001001	Ctrl-F11
*	138	8A	212	10001010	Ctrl-F12
*	139	8B	213	10001011	Alt-F11
*	140	8C	214	10001100	Alt-F12
	141	8D	215	10001101	Ctrl-↑/8 (keypad)
	142	8E	216	10001110	Ctrl-— (keypad)
	143	8F	217	10001111	Ctrl-5 (keypad)
	144	90	220	10010000	Ctrl-+ (keypad)
	145	91	221	10010001	Ctrl-↓/2 (keypad)
	146	92	222	10010010	Ctrl-Ins/0 (keypad)
	147	93	223	10010011	Ctrl-Del/. (keypad)
	148	94	224	10010100	Ctrl-Tab
*	149	95	225	10010101	Ctrl-/ (keypad)
*	150	96	226	10010110	Ctrl-* (keypad)
*	151	97	227	10010111	Alt-Home
*	152	98	230	10011000	Alt-↑
*	153	99	231	10011001	Alt-Page Up
*	155	9B	233	10011011	Alt-←
*	157	9D	235	10011101	Alt-→
*	159	9F	237	10011111	Alt-End
*	160	A0	240	10100000	Alt-↓
*	161	A1	241	10100001	Alt-Page Down
*	162	A2	242	10100010	Alt-Insert
*	163	A3	243	10100011	Alt-Delete
*	164	A4	244	10100100	Alt-/ (keypad)
*	165	A5	245	10100101	Alt-Tab
*	166	A6	256	10100110	Alt-Enter (keypad)

Extended Function ASCII Codes

The following extended codes are available only with the Enhanced Keyboards (101/102-key keyboards); the codes are available for key reassignment only under DOS V4. The keys include the six-key editing pad and the four-key cursor-control pad. To reassign these keys, you must give the **DEVICE = ANSI.SYS /X** directive or the enable extended function codes escape sequence (**Esc[1q**). All extended codes are prefixed by 224 decimal (E0 hex).

Decimal	Hex	Octal	Binary	Extended ASCII Meaning
71	47	107	01000111	Home
72	48	110	01001000	↑
73	49	111	01001001	Page Up
75	4B	113	01001011	←
77	4D	115	01001101	→
79	4F	117	01001111	End
80	50	120	01010000	↓
81	51	121	01010001	Page Down
82	52	122	01010010	Insert
83	53	123	01010011	Delete
115	73	163	01110011	Ctrl-←
116	74	164	01110100	Ctrl-→
117	75	165	01110101	Ctrl-End
118	76	166	01110110	Ctrl-Page Down
119	77	167	01110111	Ctrl-Home
132	84	204	10000100	Ctrl-Page Up
141	8D	215	10001101	Ctrl-↑
145	91	221	10010001	Ctrl-↓
146	92	222	10010010	Ctrl-Insert
147	93	223	10010011	Ctrl-Delete

ANSI Terminal Codes

All ANSI terminal codes are preceded by an Escape (Esc) character and a left bracket ([). The Escape character is 27 decimal or 1b hexadecimal.

Cursor-Control Sequences

For the cursor-control sequences, if a value is omitted, the default value of 1 is used.

Cursor Position

Horizontal and Vertical Position

Esc[#;#H   The first **#** is the row (vertical coordinate);

Esc[#;#f   the second **#** is the column (horizontal coordinate). The starting value for either coordinate is 1 (also the default value).

Cursor Up

Esc[#A   **#** is the number of rows to move up.

Cursor Down

Esc[#B   **#** is the number of rows to move down.

Cursor Forward (Right)

Esc[#C   **#** is the number of columns to move forward (right).

Cursor Backward (Left)

Esc[#D   # is the number of columns to move backward (left).

Device Status Report

Esc[6n   Inputs through the keyboard a report on the current
cursor position.

Cursor Position Report

Esc[#;#R   Reports the current cursor position. The string is
returned by the ANSI console and is eight characters
long. The first **#** is the two-digit row number; the
second **#** is the two-digit column number.

Save Cursor Position

Esc[s   Saves the current cursor position within the
ANSI.SYS driver.

Restore Cursor Position

Esc[u   Sets the cursor to the horizontal and vertical position
that was saved by the **Esc[s** sequence.

Erasing

Erase Display

Esc[2J   Erases the display and also moves the cursor to the
Home position (the upper left corner of the screen).

Erase to End of Line

Esc[K   Erases from the current cursor position to the end of
the current line.

Modes of Operation

For all ANSI-operation-mode control codes, if a parameter is omitted, the
default value of 0 is used.

Set Graphics Rendition

Esc[#;...;#m   Sets the character attributes by the parameters listed in the following sections. The attributes remain in effect until the next graphics rendition command.

Set/Reset Mode Parameters

Parameter	Meaning
0	Cancel all attributes (normally white on black)
1	Bold on (high intensity)
4	Underscore on (monochrome display only)
5	Blink on
7	Reverse (inverse) video on
8	Cancel on (invisible characters—black on black)

Set Colors

Parameter   *Meaning*

Set Foreground

Parameter	Meaning
30	Black foreground
31	Red foreground
32	Green foreground
33	Yellow foreground
34	Blue foreground
35	Magenta foreground
36	Cyan foreground
37	White foreground

Set Background

Parameter	Meaning
40	Black background
41	Red background
42	Green background
43	Yellow background
44	Blue background
45	Magenta background
46	Cyan background
47	White background

Set Screen Mode

Esc[=#h   Sets the screen width or type based on **#**.

(for parameter 7 only)

Esc[=7h   Turns on the wrap at end-of-line;

Esc[?7   long lines automatically wrap onto subsequent lines.

Reset Screen Mode

Esc[=#1   Resets the screen width or type based on **#** (listed below).

(for parameter 7 only)

Esc[?71   Turns off wrap at end-of-line; long

Esc[=71   lines are truncated at the end-of-line.

Parameter	Meaning
0	40 x 25 monochrome
1	40 x 25 color
2	80 x 25 monochrome
3	80 x 25 color
4	320 x 200 color
5	320 x 200 monochrome
6	640 x 200 monochrome
7	Wrap at end-of-line (set mode), or do not wrap and discard characters past end of line (reset mode)
*14	640 x 200 color
*15	640 x 350 monochrome
*16	640 x 350 color
*17	640 x 480 monochrome
*18	640 x 480 color
*19	320 x 200 color

*Available with DOS V4.0 and later versions.

Keyboard Key Reassignment

Reassign Keyboard Keys

Esc[_sequence_**p**   Sets the sequence typed by the named key.

sequence can be in the form of _#;#;...#_ (where _#_ represents the one-, two-, or three-digit code for an ASCII character), or _"string"_ (a double-quoted string of characters), or any combination of the two provided that the _#_ and _"string"_ are separated by a semicolon.

Esc[#;#;...;p

or

Esc["string"p

or

Esc[#;"string";#;#;"string";#p

The first ASCII code (the first **#**) defines which key or keystrokes (such as a Ctrl-character combination) are being reassigned. However, if the first code in the sequence is 0 (ASCII Nul), the first and second codes designate an Extended ASCII key sequence. See Appendix B for the set of ASCII codes and the set of Extended ASCII codes.

The remaining numbers (**#**) or characters within the "string" are the replacement characters typed when that key or keystroke combination is pressed. Any nonnumeric characters used in the replacement must be placed within double quotation marks.

Enable/Disable Extended Keys on Enhanced Keyboards

Esc[1q   Enables assignment of the extended keys on the Enhanced keyboard. The sequence is the same as using the /X switch for the ANSI.SYS directive.

Esc[Oq   Disables assignment of the extended keys on the Enhanced keyboard.

ANSI.SYS Keyboard Scan Codes

Function Keys

Function keys	Alone	With Shift	With Ctrl	With Alt
F1	59	84	94	104
F2	60	85	95	105
F3	61	86	96	106
F4	62	87	97	107
F5	63	88	98	108
F6	64	89	99	109
F7	65	90	100	110
F8	66	91	101	111
F9	67	92	102	112
F10	68	93	103	113

Alphanumeric Keys with Alt Key Pressed

A	30	J	36	S	31	1	120
B	48	K	37	T	20	2	121
C	46	L	38	U	22	3	122
D	32	M	50	V	47	4	123
E	18	N	49	W	17	5	124
F	33	O	24	X	45	6	125
G	34	P	25	Y	21	7	126
H	35	Q	16	Z	44	8	127
I	23	R	19			9	128
						0	129

Note   The numerals are those on the top row of the typewriter area, not the numeric keypad or the function keys.

Cursor Pad Keys

Key	Alone	With Ctrl
Up arrow	72	
Down arrow	80	
Left arrow	75	115
Right arrow	77	116
Home	71	119
End	79	117
Page Up	73	132
Page Down	81	118
Insert	82	
Delete	83	

Other special code combinations include the following:

Key Combination	Code
Alt-hyphen (–)	130
Alt-equal sign (=)	131
Ctrl-asterisk (* on numeric keypad)	114
Shift-Tab	15
Ctrl-Alt-Num Lock	55
Ctrl-Alt-Scroll Lock	56

Product Resources

Following is a list of many of the products mentioned in or used during the research of this book. Although every effort has been made to provide a correct listing, Que Corporation cannot attest to the accuracy of this information.

386-to-the-max
386 control program

Qualitas, Inc.
8314 Thoreau Dr.
Bethesda, MD 20817
301/469-8848

All ChargeCard
286 memory
management board

All Computers
21 St. Clair Ave. East, #203
Toronto, Ontario, M4T 1L9
Canada
416/960-0111

BatKit
Batch file enhancer
(shareware)

Mississippi Date Equipment Company, Inc.
625C Lakeland East Dr.
Jacksonville, MS 39208
601/932-6332

BRIEF
Text editor

Solution Systems
335 Washington St.
Norwell, MA 02061
617/659-1571

**CompuServe
Information Services**
Time-sharing services and source
for shareware programs

CompuServe Incorporated
5000 Arlington Centre Blvd.
P.O. Box 20212
Columbus, OH 43220
800/848-8990
614/457-8650

CoreFast
Disk backup software

CORE International
7171 North Federal Highway
Boca Raton, FL 33431
305/997-6055

CPYAT2PC
1.2M format-copy for
360K diskettes

Microbridge Computers International, Inc.
655 Skyway, Suite 125
San Carlos, CA 94070
415/593-8777

CTRLALT Keyboard enhancer (shareware)	CTRLALT Associates, Inc. c/o The Support Group P.O. Box 1577 Baltimore, MD 21203 800/872-4768
DESQview Multitasking supervisor	Quarterdeck Office Systems, Inc. 150 Pico Blvd. Santa Monica, CA 90405 213/392-9851
Disk Optimizer Disk defragmenter	SoftLogic Solutions One Perimeter Rd. Manchester, NH 03103 603/627-9900
DS Backup Disk backup software	Design Software, Inc. 1275 W. Roosevelt West Chicago, IL 60185 312/231-4540
Excel Integrated spreadsheet, graphics	Microsoft Corporation 16011 Northeast 36th Way P.O. Box 97017 Redmond, WA 98073
FASTBACK/ **FASTBACK PLUS** Disk backup software	Fifth Generation Systems, Inc. 11200 Industriplex Blvd. Baton Rouge, LA 70809 504/291-7221
FastTrax Disk defragmenter	Bridgeway Publishing Corp. 2165 E. Franciso Blvd., Suite A1 San Rafael, CA 94912 415/485-0948
FilePaq PATH command for data files **FilePath** Disk sweep utilities	SDA Associates P.O. Box 36152 San Jose, CA 95158 408/281-7747
FLASH Disk cacher, RAM disk, print spooler	Software Masters, Inc. 6352 Guilford Ave. Indianapolis, IN 46220 317/253-8088
HTEST/HFORMAT (including HOPTIMUM) Low-lowel disk test-format package	Paul Mace Software, Inc. 400 Williamson Way Ashland, OR 97520 503/488-0224

Intelligent Backup Disk backup software	Sterling Software 16735 Saticoy St., Suite 111 Van Nuys, CA 91406 800/654-3790 800/225-9358 (CA)
Laserdrive 2000 CD-ROM player	Amdek Corporation 3471 North First St. San Jose, CA 95134 408/436-8570
Mace Utilities/ **Mace Gold** Disk utilities package	Paul Mace Software, Inc. 400 Williamson Way Ashland, OR 97520 503/488-0224
Norton Utilities/ **Advanced Utilities** Disk utilities package	Peter Norton Computing, Inc. 2210 Wilshire Blvd., Suite 186 Santa Monica, CA 90403 213/319-2000
PageMaker Desktop publishing software	Aldus Corp. 411 First Avenue South Seattle, WA 98104 206/622-5500
PCED/CED Command line editors (shareware/freeware)	Software Cove Group P.O. Box 1072 Columbia, MD 21044 301/992-9371
PC-Tools Disk utility package	Central Point Software, Inc. 15220 N.W. Greenbrier Pkwy., #200 Beaverton, OR 97006 503/690-8090
Periscope Memory-resident debugger	Periscope Company, Inc. 1197 Peachtree St. Altanta, GA 30361 404/875-8080
PKpak File archiver (sharware)	PKware, Inc. 7032 Ardara Ave. Glendale, WI 53209
PMAP DOS memory mapper	Software Cove Group P.O. Box 1072 Columbia, MD 21044 301/992-9371

PSFX
FX-85 emulation for
Postscript printers

Legend Communications, Inc.
54 Rosedale Ave.
Brampton, Ontario L6X 1K1
Canada
416/457-6289

ProKey
Keyboard macro package

RoseSoft, Inc.
P.O. Box 45880
Seattle, WA 98145
206/282-0454

QEMM/386
386 control program

Quarterdeck Office Systems, Inc.
150 Pico Blvd.
Santa Monica, CA 90405
213/392-9851

SideKick/
SideKick Plus
Desktop organizer

Borland International
4585 Scotts Valley Dr.
Scotts Valley, CA 95066
415/438-5300

SoftBytes
EMS simulator software
SoftBytes/386
386 control program

Vericomp Publishing
10951 Sorrento Valley Rd., Suite 1D-F
San Diego, CA 92121
619/535-0900

Software Carousel
Multitasking supervisor

SoftLogic Solutions
One Perimeter Rd.
Manchester, NH 03103
603/627-9900

Sourcer
Disassembler

V Communications
3031 Tisch Way, Suite 200
San Jose, CA 95128
408/296-4224

SpinRite
Disk tester, interleave setter

Gibson Research Corporation
22991 La Cadena
Laguna Hills, CA 92653
714/830-2200

STACKKEY
(including **BATUTIL**)
Keyboard enhancer, batch file
enhancer package (shareware)

CTRLALT Associates, Inc.
c/o The Support Group
P.O. Box 1577
Baltimore, MD 21203
800/872-4768

Super PC-Kwik
Disk cacher, RAM
disk, print spooler

Multisoft Corporation
18220 S.W. Monte Verdi Blvd.
Beaverton, OR 97007
503/642-7108

SuperKey Keyboard macro package	Borland International 4585 Scotts Valley Dr. Scotts Valley, CA 95066 415/438-5300
Tapcis Communications program for CompuServe (shareware)	Omni Information Services c/o The Support Group P.O. Box 1577 Baltimore, MD 21203 800/872-4768
The Source Time-share service and source for shareware programs	Source Telecomputing Corporation 1616 Anderson Rd. McLean, VA 22102 703/734-7578
Turbo Debugger Debugger **Turbo Lightning** Spelling checker, thesaurus	Borland International 4585 Scotts Valley Dr. Scotts Valley, CA 95066 415/438-5300
Vcache Disk cacher **Vopt** Disk defragmenter	Golden Bow Systems 2870 Fifth Ave., Suite 201 San Diego, CA 92103 619/298-9349
VEGA Deluxe EGA video board	Video-7 46335 Landing Parkway Fremont, CA 94538 415/656-7800
Ventura Publisher Desktop publishing software	Xerox-Ventura Software 9745 Business Park Ave. San Diego, CA 92131 800/832-6979
Windows/286 Windowing software **Windows/386** Windowing, multitasking supervisor **Word** Word processor	Microsoft Corporation 16011 Northeast 36th Way P.O. Box 97017 Redmond, WA 98073
WordStar Word processor	MicroPro International Corporation 33 San Pablo Ave. San Rafael, CA 94903 415/499-1200

Index

C

D

N

T

More Computer Knowledge from Que

For more information, call

1-800-428-5331

All prices subject to change without notice. Prices and charges are for domestic orders only. Non-U.S. prices might be higher.

MS-DOS User's Guide, Special Edition
Developed by Que Corporation

A special edition of Que's best-selling book on MS-DOS, updated to provide the most comprehensive DOS coverage available. Includes expanded EDLIN coverage, plus **Quick Start** tutorials and a complete **Command Reference** for DOS Versions 3 and 4. A **must** for MS-DOS users at all levels!

Order #1048
$29.95 USA
0-88022-505-X, 900 pp.

Using PC DOS, 3rd Edition
by Chris DeVoney

This classic text offers a complete overview of the new commands and user interface of DOS 4.0, and a useful **Command Reference** section.

Order #961
$23.95 USA
0-88022-419-3, 850 pp.

Managing Your Hard Disk, 2nd Edition
by Don Berliner

Learn the most efficient techniques for organizing the programs and data on your hard disk! This hard-working text includes management tips, essential DOS commands, an explanation of new application and utility software, and an introduction to PS/2 hardware.

$22.95 USA
Order #837
0-88022-348-0
600 pp.

Using DOS
Developed by Que Corporation

The most helpful DOS book available! Que's *Using DOS* teaches the essential commands and functions of DOS Versions 3 and 4—in an easy-to-understand format that helps users manage and organize their files effectively. Includes a handy **Command Reference**.

Order #1035
$22.95 USA
0-88022-497-5, 550 pp.

Que Order Line: **1-800-428-5331**

Free Catalog!

Mail us this registration form today, and we'll send you a free catalog featuring Que's complete line of best-selling books.

Name of Book _____

Name _____

Title _____

Phone (____) _____

Company _____

Address _____

City _____

State _____ ZIP _____

Please check the appropriate answers:

1. Where did you buy your Que book?
   - ☐ Bookstore (name: _____)
   - ☐ Computer store (name: _____)
   - ☐ Catalog (name: _____)
   - ☐ Direct from Que
   - ☐ Other: _____

2. How many computer books do you buy a year?
   - ☐ 1 or less
   - ☐ 2-5
   - ☐ 6-10
   - ☐ More than 10

3. How many Que books do you own?
   - ☐ 1
   - ☐ 2-5
   - ☐ 6-10
   - ☐ More than 10

4. How long have you been using this software?
   - ☐ Less than 6 months
   - ☐ 6 months to 1 year
   - ☐ 1-3 years
   - ☐ More than 3 years

5. What influenced your purchase of this Que book?
   - ☐ Personal recommendation
   - ☐ Advertisement
   - ☐ In-store display
   - ☐ Price
   - ☐ Que catalog
   - ☐ Que mailing
   - ☐ Que's reputation
   - ☐ Other:

6. How would you rate the overall content of the book?
   - ☐ Very good
   - ☐ Good
   - ☐ Satisfactory
   - ☐ Poor

7. What do you like *best* about this Que book?

   _____
   _____

8. What do you like *least* about this Que book?

   _____
   _____

9. Did you buy this book with your personal funds?
   - ☐ Yes   ☐ No

10. Please feel free to list any other comments you may have about this Que book.

   _____
   _____
   _____

Que

Order Your Que Books Today!

Name _____

Title _____

Company _____

City _____

State _____ ZIP _____

Phone No. (____) _____

Method of Payment:

Check ☐   (Please enclose in envelope.)

Charge My: VISA ☐   MasterCard ☐

American Express ☐

Charge # _____

Expiration Date _____

Order No.	Title	Qty.	Price	Total

You can **FAX** your order to **1-317-573-2583**. Or call **1-800-428-5331, ext. ORDR** to order direct.
Please add $2.50 per title for shipping and handling.

Subtotal _____

Shipping & Handling _____

Total _____

Que

BUSINESS REPLY MAIL
First Class Permit No. 9918   Indianapolis, IN

Postage will be paid by addressee

11711 N. College
Carmel, IN 46032

BUSINESS REPLY MAIL
First Class Permit No. 9918   Indianapolis, IN

Postage will be paid by addressee

11711 N. College
Carmel, IN 46032